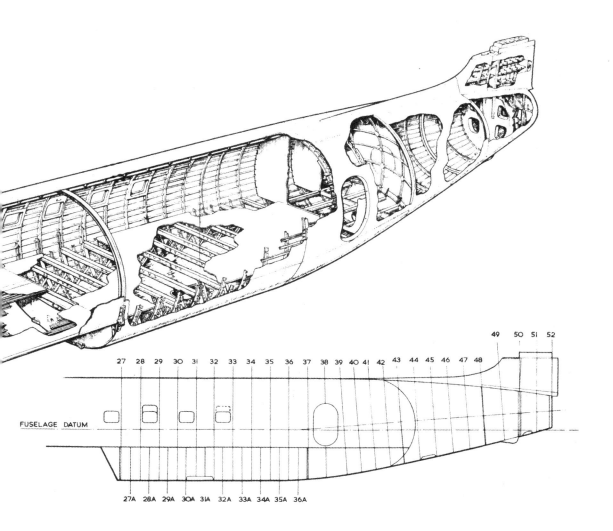

FUSELAGE DATUM

THE COMET THAT FELL TO EARTH

The story of the de Havilland DH 106 Comet 1

THE COMET THAT FELL TO EARTH

The story of the de Havilland DH 106 Comet 1

Robin Bray

HAYLOFT PUBLISHING LTD.

First published by Hayloft 2015

Hayloft Publishing Ltd, South Stainmore,
Kirkby Stephen, Westmorland, CA17 4DJ

tel: 07971 352473
email: books@hayloft.eu
web: www.hayloft.eu

ISBN 978-1-910237-01-4

A CIP catalogue record for this book is available
from the British Library

Papers used by Hayloft are natural, recyclable products made from wood grown in sustainable forests.
The manufacturing processes conform to the environmental regulations of the country of origin.

Designed, printed and bound in the EU

ENDPAPERS: The internal structure of the Comet 1 fuselage, © BAE SYSTEMS Heritage
FRONTISPIECE: BOAC Comets outside the erecting shop at Hatfield,
August 1951, © BAE SYSTEMS Heritage.

Acknowledgements

This is mainly a history book and is intended for the general reader who is interested in aeroplanes and the mishaps that occasionally befall them. But I am conscious that engineering, and even bits of medicine, have crept into it to provide some explanation of why things happened the way they did. I have been helped in this by Professors Bettess, Swift and Irving, mentioned below. Professor Bettess patiently explained to me the fundamentals of stress and strain, Professor Swift carefully read and commented on the manuscript and Professor Irving, to whom I owe an immense debt of gratitude, also read the whole manuscript and corrected my misconceptions about aircraft structures and cracks. Without them this would have been a much less accurate book.

I appreciate that the technical explanations may not be to everybody's taste so most of these parts are presented in footnotes and appendices and, if desired, can be avoided without destroying the story but I hope they will provide more interest for some readers. I am also very much aware that aeronautics is a complicated and highly mathematical subject and that I am not an engineer or a mathematician and this is not a textbook, so the explanations have been kept as simple as possible, perhaps, at times, to the point where they present an incomplete picture but not, I trust, too inaccurate a one. I hope that any aeronautical engineers who read these parts will forgive me.

Almost inevitably in a book such as this there will be errors of fact and opinions that irritate. So far as I can I have checked and re-checked the 'facts' and sought the views of others but the errors that remain and the opinions that follow are, of course, my responsibility and not those of my collaborators.

Every effort has been made to identify, locate and obtain the consent of the copyright holders of the material herein reproduced. However on one or two occasions this has not been possible and the author apologises for any inconvenience or distress so caused.

People and organisations I would especially like to thank are:

The staff of the National Archives, Kew, London.
The British Library at St. Pancras and Colingdale, London.
The library of the RAF Museum at Hendon, London.
Mr. Peter Bunting of the RAF Museum at Cosford, Shropshire.
Mr. Jim Davies and Mr. Barry Ballard of the British Airways Heritage Centre, Harmondsworth, London.
Ms. Christine Woodward of The National Aerospace Library, Farnborough.
The staff of Newcastle University Library, where most of this book was written.

The staff of Newcastle City Library.

The staff of the Library of the University of Northumbria at Newcastle.

Mr. Trevor Friend of the BAE SYSTEMS Archive, Farnborough, who found most of the photographs.

Professor P. Bettess of Durham University.

Professor P. E. Irving of Cranfield University, Bedfordshire.

Professor Tom Swift, of Cranfield University.

Mr. Mike Ramsden, originally of de Havillands.

Dawn Robertson of Hayloft Publishing who took the risk of publishing this book.

Dr. T. Clarke who read the manuscript and made many suggestions.

Dr. P. N. Cooper, Consultant Forensic Pathologist, Royal Victoria Infirmary, Newcastle upon Tyne.

and Dr. M. Bennet, also of the above, who both advised on pathology.

Dr. D. Finneron who read the manuscript and corrected my grammar.

Mr. Alan Brown and Mr. Brian Luff who discovered many of the original RAE photographs at FAST.

Mr. Paul Johnson of Newcastle University who carried out the finite element analysis.

Mr. Ian Sewell of The Design Unit, Newcastle University who supervised the above.

Dr. C. J. Vallis who provided computer advice.

And, of course, the wonderful Wikipedia, the first stop for any enquiry.

Robin Bray
March 2015

Contents

Chronology

23 12 1942	Brabazon Committee set up
02 09 1945	First test of the Ghost engine
04 09 1946	MoS orders 2 Comet prototypes
21 01 1947	MoS orders production of 8 Comets
28 06 1948	Ghost engine approved for civilian use
03 03 1949	First airframe completed
27 07 1949	First flight of the prototype
27 07 1950	First flight of the second prototype
09 01 1951	First flight of the first production Comet (G-ALYP)
13 03 1952	First production Comet delivered to BOAC
02 05 1952	First commercial jet flight
26 10 1952	YZ crashes on takeoff from Rome
03 03 1953	CF-CUN crashes on takeoff from Karachi
02 05 1953	YV crashes in a tropical storm near Calcutta
10 01 1954	YP breaks up in mid air off Elba
11 01 1954	All Comets grounded, Abell Committee set up
23 03 1954	BOAC Comets resume flying
08 04 1954	YY breaks up in mid air off Naples
12 04 1954	The Comet's Certificate of Airworthiness is withdrawn and the RAE investigation starts
24 06 1954	Comet fuselage fails in tank test
31 08 1954	Wreckage of central fuselage containing the ADF windows delivered to RAE
09 1954	RAE report completed
19 10 1954	Court of Inquiry starts
24 11 1954	Court of Inquiry finishes
12 02 1955	Report of the inquiry published
24 06 1956	More wreckage is found

Phonetic alphabet used before 1 March 1956

A	Able	N	Nan
B	Baker	O	Oboe
C	Charlie	P	Peter
D	Dog	Q	Queen
E	Easy	R	Roger
F	Fox	S	Sugar
G	George	T	Tare
H	How	U	Uncle
I	Item	V	Victor
J	Jig	W	William
K	King	X	X-ray
L	Love	Y	Yoke
M	Mike	Z	Zebra

Units of measurement

The units of measurement used in the text are from the Imperial system which was in use at the time of the events described and to a large extent still is in the United States. Below is an approximate conversion table to the metric system.

LENGTH:
1 inch	2.5 centimetres
1 foot	0.3 metres
1 yard	0.9 metres
1 mile	1.6 kilometres

MASS:
1 pound (mass)	0.45 kilograms
1 ton (UK)	1.02 tonnes (metric tons)
1 ton (US)	0.91 tonnes

FORCE:
1 pound (force)	4.45 newtons

PRESSURE:
1 pound/square inch	6,900 pascals (newtons/square metre)

POWER:
1 horsepower (mechanical)	0.75 kilowatts

Unless otherwise stated all times are Greenwich Mean Time, GMT, and are expressed as the 24 hour clock e.g. 13:45 means 45 minutes past 1 o'clock in the afternoon.

Abbreviations

A & A E E	Aeroplane and Armament Experimental Establishment
ADC	Aircraft Disposal Company
ADF	Automatic Direction Finding
AF	Air France
AIB	Accident Investigation Board
ARB	Air Registration Board
ARC	Aeronautical Research Committee (became Council in 1945)
ASB	Air Safety Board
BALPA	British Air Line Pilots Association
BCAR	British Civil Airworthiness Requirements
BEA	British European Airways
bhp	brake horsepower
BOAC	British Overseas Airways Corporation
BSA	Birmingham Small Arms
BSAA	British South America Airways
BTH	British Thomson-Houston
CPA	Canadian Pacific Airlines
DH	de Havilland
DTD	Directorate of Technical Development, part of the MoS
EAS	Equivalent Air Speed
FAST	Farnborough Air Sciences Trust
fps	feet per second
GEC	General Electric Company
GMT	Greenwich Mean Time
hp	horsepower
IATA	International Air Transport Association
IAS	Indicated Air Speed
IFALPA	International Federation of Air Line Pilots Associations
MAP	Ministry of Aircraft Production
MoS	Ministry of Supply
MPa	megapascal
psi	pounds per square inch
RAE	Royal Aircraft Establishment
RAF	Royal Air Force
RCAF	Royal Canadian Air Force
RFC	Royal Flying Corps
RNVR	Royal Naval Volunteer Reserve
rpm	revolutions per minute
SAA	South African Airways
SWG	Standard Wire Gauge
TAS	True Air Speed
TWA.	Trans World Airlines
UAT	Union Aéromaritime de Transport
UTS	Ultimate tensile strength
WU	Whittle Unit

To my father, Donald Dyer Bray,
a bank manager who would rather have been an engineer,
and to my mother, Doris Bray,
who made it all possible.

Preface

When I was a small boy growing up in a Manchester suburb in the early 1950s, one of the high spots of my life was a family trip to the Isle of Man. My parents and I flew from Ringway Airport in a de Havilland Dragon Rapide. This was a pre-war biplane and it was anything but 'rapide'. Even to my eyes it seemed small, quaint and old-fashioned. We returned in a Douglas DC-3 (Dakota) which I thought much more modern although it was still a pre-war design. Although I cannot remember it, I am sure that I would have gained status among my friends for having flown in an aeroplane, not as common an experience then as it is now. But I was completely eclipsed by another small boy, an American called John, who lived across the road from us and whose father was a businessman who used to give us rides on the running boards of his large American car. John had flown back from India in a Comet, the first jet airliner in commercial service, the summit of post-war civil aviation and the ultimate flying status symbol. This was when I heard of the Comet for the first time.

This is the story of the Comet 1, from its inception to its final grounding and the subsequent investigation into its fatal crashes. It does not include much about the later versions of the aircraft, when it had been transformed into a safe and efficient airliner but by then too late to regain a market which had been captured by Boeing and Douglas.

Robin Bray,
March 2014

Some things about aeroplanes

Before we start on the story of the Comet it would be useful to get some things straight about aeroplanes and how they fly. Like the law and medicine, aviation has its own vocabulary and it helps if you know the words. If you don't know your flaps from your fuselage or your ailerons from your elevators it might be a good idea to glance at Appendix 1. Aircraft buffs can safely skip it.

To avoid confusion the left and right of an aeroplane (looking down on it from above in the same direction as the aircraft is flying and assuming the aircraft is not flying inverted) are often referred to as the 'port' and 'starboard' and this convention will be used in this book. Continuing the nautical terminology the front end is sometimes called the 'fore end' and the tail the 'aft end' but in this text 'forward' and 'rear' are more often used. 'Top' and 'bottom' will be used as if the aeroplane is flying the usual way up.

The words aircraft and aeroplane will be used interchangeably in the text. Again to avoid confusion 'de Havilland' will be used as the name of the family or as an adjective referring to the company and 'de Havillands' as the name of the aircraft company. A capital 'D' will be used at the start of a sentence.

Individual aircraft are usually identified by their registration letters such as G-ALYY, the 'G' referring to Great Britain. Other national identification letters include CF for Canada (up to 1 January 1974) and F for France. In the text these letters are often abbreviated to YY or the words from the phonetic alphabet in use then, for example Yoke Yoke. For communication purposes the national identifier was also used and it became George Yoke Yoke. Airframes are also identified by their manufacture's number, such as 06012. On occasion registration letters were changed or transferred but the airframe numbers stayed the same. Some airframes were never registered and this number may be the only form of identification.

Introduction

Shortly before 10:00 GMT (Greenwich Mean Time) on the morning of 10 January 1954, several people on the southeast coast of the Island of Elba, off northwest Italy, heard a loud bang which seemed to come from somewhere overhead. About three minutes later some of them saw flames, smoke and wreckage descending towards the sea. What they were witnessing were the last moments of 'Yoke Peter', a BOAC (British Overseas Airways Corporation) Comet, which had exploded in mid-air about half an hour after taking off from Rome's Ciampino Airport heading for London. Six crew and 29 passengers died almost instantaneously. It was not the first fatal Comet crash, nor would it be the last. Less than three months later another Comet, flying from the same airport, but this time heading south towards Cairo, disappeared in similar circumstances.

The de Havilland DH106 Comet 1 was an all-metal, four-engined, jet-powered, passenger monoplane. Both its airframe and its engines were designed and manufactured by The de Havilland Aircraft Company based at Hatfield, to the north of London, and its associated engine company. The Comet was Britain's great hope of gaining for itself part of the civil aviation market in the face of almost overwhelming American competition at the end of the Second World War. In the event it was to prove a technological and human disaster that instead of winning much-needed exports would seriously damage Britain's aircraft industry. How had what seemed to be an engineering marvel, far in advance of all other airliners in the world, come to be in bits at the bottom of the Mediterranean?

The story of the Comet and its crashes is well known, at least to people of a certain age who take an interest in aviation history, but it is a fascinating story which will stand re-telling, if only to a new generation of people interested in aircraft and the people who fly them. Many of the files in the National Archives relating to the Comet were originally closed for extended periods, for example the transcripts of the public inquiry into the two Mediterranean crashes were originally closed until 2030. Fortunately these files have now been opened which has made the task of researching the history of the Comet 1 considerably easier.

The conventional story is that it was an heroic British failure in the spirit of the Light Brigade and Dunkirk. Plucky British pioneers, equipped with little more than empty toilet rolls and sticky-back plastic, leaped ahead of the lavishly-resourced Americans, to produce an aeroplane that was the envy of the world. Unfortunately, because of things that were unknown to science and engineering at the time, the aeroplane they produced had a series of accidents and an ungrateful world chose the Americans from whom to order their future airliners.

There is another version, however. This was related in a Channel Four documentary in its *Secret History* series made by Principal Films and broadcast on 13 June 2002. Although my boyhood interest in the Comet had never completely disappeared it was reawakened by watching this programme. The documentary implied that many of the faults in the Comet were known, or should have been known, to de Havillands, the manufacturer, BOAC, the main customer, and the British Government and were ignored for reasons of arrogance, ignorance, commercial gain, time pressures and national prestige and that this was then covered up after the crashes. Not surprisingly this was disputed by some of the surviving members of the team that had built the Comet. Some of them had taken part in the programme but felt that their words had been taken out of context and used to condemn a company that had done its best in an honest and decent way but had suffered for being first.[1] One of them, Mike Ramsden, published his objections in *General Aviation*[2] and subsequently a complaint to the broadcasting authority about the programme's accuracy was upheld.[3, 4] Understandably this made some of the people involved in the programme reluctant to talk about the Comet on future occasions, particularly as the story of this mythical cover-up was repeated in a more recent publication.[5] In fact there was a cover-up but it was about something quite different.

Two years after the crashes into the Mediterranean and the investigation and inquiry that sealed the Comet's fate more wreckage was trawled up by accident. The wreckage was examined at Farnborough and led to new ideas about where the Elba Comet's dis-integration had started and how aircraft structural failures could develop. The discovery of the wreckage itself was kept secret and remained so for many years. I first read about it in an article written by Mike Ramsden in 1989[6] but when I contacted him in 2011 he was unable to provide any more information. Requests to the Air Accident Investigation Branch, the Ministry of Defence (which inherited the Ministry of Supply archive), and the Civil Aviation Authority under the Freedom of Information Act failed to find any-thing. It was the chance discovery of a file compiled by Mr. A. J. Lucking, in the archive in the British Airways Heritage Centre at The Waterside, near Heathrow, that provided many of the answers.[7] It also gave the reference to a file at The National Archives in Kew in West London which he had helped to get opened. This contained the original letters about the discovery, the theory it helped to generate and the decision to keep it secret. It is described more fully in Chapter 28.

It is difficult now, more than 60 years after the Comet went into commercial service, to appreciate the blow to national pride that the Comet crashes produced. The death toll was on a different scale to that of the sinking of the Titanic, but its impact was similar and made all the worse for happening a second time shortly after the authorities had pronounced the aircraft safe.

This book will relate the history of the Comet 1, its development and its fall from grace, in some detail but more as a narrative than a technical account of the aircraft. There are already many excellent 'rivet counter' books about the Comet and this is not another of them. It will also look into the question of what was known about the

Comet's defects, when they were known and by whom and how their decisions were influenced. As always when looking back at mishaps of any kind it is important to judge events by the standards and knowledge of the time and not those of today.

The Comet 1 was made up of three groups: the Comet 1 came first and was equipped with Ghost 50 Mark 1 engines, the Comet 1A had Ghost Mark 2 engines and the 1XB had Mark 4s and a strengthened fuselage. The engines were progressively more powerful and the aircraft heavier but of the same external dimensions. There were other minor differences as well. The Comet 2 had Rolls-Royce Avon engines but in its original form it was otherwise almost the same as the 1s. The sole Comet 3 was an enlarged version with more powerful engines and different windows but in other respects the same type of fuselage. The Comet 4s were about the same size as the 3 but with redesigned, and much stronger, fuselages.

To my regret I never flew in a Comet, or even saw one fly, and the closest I have managed to get is in various museums. Most of these aircraft are Comet 4s and the nearest thing to a complete example of a Comet 1 is the 1XB in the museum at RAF Cosford. The only remaining, unaltered, Comet 1 fuselage is in the de Havilland Aircraft Museum at London Colney, near Hatfield.

Chapter 1

THE PEOPLE WHO MADE THE COMET

The de Havilland Aircraft Company was one of several British aircraft manufacturing concerns that started in the early 20th century and bore the names of their founders. Geoffrey de Havilland was born in 1882 in a village near High Wycombe of a difficult and impecunious father,[1] at that time a curate, and an harassed mother.[2] Shortly afterwards the family moved to Nuneaton where his father became vicar and in 1896 to the living at Crux Easton, a village on the north Hampshire Downs. Geoffrey had an older brother, Ivon and a much younger one called Hereward as well as two sisters. Both Geoffrey and Ivon were fascinated by mechanical things and had their own workshop in one of the outbuildings where, to the admiration of their younger brother, they investigated model steam engines and later on petrol engines. Geoffrey and Ivon even installed an electrical generator and wired the house for lighting.[3] Ivon went on to enter the motor manufacturing business and became the chief designer of the Iris Motor Company but, never strong, he died of influenza in his early twenties.

After school in Rugby and Oxford, Geoffrey declined a career in the Church and in 1900 started a three year course in mechanical engineering at the Crystal Palace Engineering School. While he was there he made a petrol engine from published drawings and fitted it to a cycle frame so that he could travel to and from Crux Eaton. When he finished the course he returned to Rugby to become an apprentice at a company that made steam engines where he built another motor cycle engine, this time to his own design. In 1905 he left to join the Wolseley Tool and Motor-Car Company as a draughtsman but found the work boring and the management regime harsh.[4] After a year he moved on to a bus manufacturing company in London where he became interested in the new flying machines that were being talked about in engineering circles.

At the bus company Geoffrey fell in with another worker called Frank Hearle, who later became Geoffrey's brother-in-law, and they talked endlessly about flying machines. Through Ivon, Geoffrey had got to know the owners of the Iris Motor Company at Willesden, one of whom, Guy Knowles, offered to invest £500 to build an aeroplane if Geoffrey would do the same. There was no prospect of Geoffrey being able to do this by himself but his maternal grandfather, Jason Saunders, a successful businessman who lived near Oxford, had been sufficiently impressed by his grandson's achievements and enthusiasm to put up the money. In fact he did better than that and offered Geoffrey £1,000 as a premature legacy. Geoffrey later described him as "the most important figure in my life"[5] and the indirect founder of the de Havilland enterprise.

Geoffrey promptly resigned from the bus company and three weeks later visited Knowles to tell him the news only to discover that he had changed his mind. Geoffrey left but after talking it over with Hearle returned to Knowles to explain his predicament. Knowles sympathised and agreed to pay him the same amount he had been earning, for a limited period, until he could find another source of finance.[6]

The first step was to design an engine. The need was for an engine that delivered around 45hp (horsepower) but weighed as little as possible. The design work took about four months and the Iris Motor Company agreed to build it for £220,* rather less than de Havilland and Hearle had expected.[7] This took another six months and the rest of the legacy from Geoffrey's grandfather. It turned out to have about three times the power-to-weight ratio of the first of the Wright brothers' engines.** In the meantime de Havilland and Hearle found a workshop in Fulham to build the aeroplane that their engine was to power.

Their design was for a biplane with a rudder but no fin, a fixed tailplane and an elevator at the front. There were two 'pusher' propellers, made of steel tubing with adjustable aluminium blades, driven by shafts and bevel gears from the single, transverse engine. The airframe was built from wooden struts braced with piano wire. The wings, rudder, tailplane and elevator were covered with thin, doped cotton sheeting. Bicycle wheels and bicycle steel tubing were used for the undercarriage.[8, 9]

Around this time Geoffrey got married and Louie, his new wife, joined him in the Kensington flat in which he was already living. Building the aeroplane was a family affair with Louie making all of the fabric covering on her hand-operated sewing machine.

By the spring of 1909 the aeroplane was almost ready for its first flight. It still had to be assembled somewhere as the workshop was too small and, of course, they had little idea of how well it would fly, or even whether it would fly at all. With another stroke of luck de Havilland had been able to buy a shed at Seven Barrows on the Hampshire Downs, conveniently near to Crux Eaton. The two sheds there had been built by another aviation pioneer, J. T. C. Moore-Brabazon, for his own aeroplane but he had decided to house it elsewhere and no longer needed them. Not surprisingly the aeroplane took them longer to get ready than anticipated but in December that year de Havilland took off for the first time.

Unfortunately he had little idea of how to fly, a deficiency that might have occurred to at least one of them at an earlier stage, but in any case the complicated design they had devised probably made controlled flight impossible. After several trial runs

---

* According to de Havilland. Sharpe, the historian of de Havillands says £250.[10]

** de Havilland's engine developed 45hp and weighed around two hundredweight – about 224 pounds – giving a power to weight ratio of 1:5.[8] The engine used for the first of the Wright Brothers' aeroplanes developed about 12hp and weighed about 170 pounds, giving a power to weight ratio of about 1:14.[11] On the other hand their first aeroplane flew rather better than Geoffrey's and it was six years earlier.

Geoffrey finally managed to leave the ground and pulled back hard on the stick. The machine responded by rising almost vertically for a short distance. This over-stressed the spars (the main structural members) on one wing, which fractured, and then the same thing happened on the other side. Both wings then folded upwards and Geoffrey and the aeroplane fell about fifteen feet back to the ground. Had the spars not failed first the aircraft would surely have stalled* with the same end result. The airframe was completely wrecked but fortunately the engine and de Havilland survived. He was lucky that the aeroplane had flown (or been flown) so badly that it had not gained much height or speed as many aviation pioneers met their ends in similar circumstances.

Within a few days they had moved the remains back to the workshop at Fulham and de Havilland had written to his grandfather saying that "it had flown but crashed" adding, "but better that than never to have flown at all."[12] When he was asked later what was wrong with the aircraft de Havilland replied that there was hardly anything right.[12] It was a (literally) painful learning experience, but learn they did. For their next try they selected better and stronger wood and changed the controls to a foot bar for the rudder and a universal control stick for the ailerons and elevator. The twin propellers were changed to a single (pusher) propeller and the engine turned 90 degrees so that it could be driven more directly from the crankshaft. The original crude propellers were changed for a shaped wooden one. After flight tests the front elevator was abandoned which improved the longitudinal stability of the aeroplane.[13] The whole machine had become more conventional and it flew far better. After some practice de Havilland was able to fly figure-of-eights and to stay in the air for about 20 minutes and reach a maximum speed of 38mph (miles per hour), a vast improvement. It was even possible to take passengers, Hearle first and then Mrs. de Havilland, possibly unwisely, holding Geoffrey junior.

De Havilland had achieved what he had set out to achieve but more money would be needed for any further advances. He was bemoaning his lack of money to an old colleague, Major Fred Green, who now worked at the Government Balloon Factory at Farnborough. He suggested that de Havilland write to Mervyn O'Gorman who was the superintendent there. At this time Farnborough made balloons and kites but had not got as far as aeroplanes. De Havilland was interviewed at O'Gorman's house in Chelsea and in January 1911 he, Hearle and their aeroplane were taken on by the government, the machine being valued at £400.

The de Havilland aeroplane was gradually improved and became known as the FE1** and he used it to become an official pilot on 7 February 1911, being awarded certificate number 53. He provided flights for several of the people at Farnborough and on 31 July reached an altitude of 1,000 feet in the same aeroplane. The assistant superintendent, Lieutenant J. T. Ridge, suffered a minor crash in it on his second lesson and

---

* A stall is the inability of the wings to generate sufficient lift to maintain the aircraft's altitude. In this case any stall was most likely to have been caused by too steep a climb.

** At that time Farnborough had a peculiar nomenclature for different types based on French aeroplanes: FE, Farman Experimental, for pusher (rear) propellers, BE, Bleriot Experimental, for tractor (front) propellers and SE, Santos Dumont Experimental, for canard types (see later).

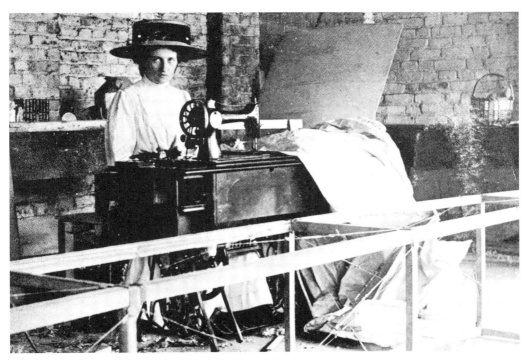

Fig. 1.1 Louie stitching the fabric on Geoffrey's first aeroplane.

a comprehensive engine failure on his third, following which the aircraft was retired. Ridge survived only to die in a crash in an experimental aeroplane the following August. The FE2 followed but suffered an engine failure on its first outing when a piston broke up, its fragments being ejected through an exhaust port. De Havilland successfully flew it for the first time two days later on 18 August. It lasted until 23 February 1914 when it spun* into the ground killing E. T. Haynes, a civilian scientist at Farnborough.[14]

Experimental work continued, leading to the use of the tractor propeller, the abandonment of the forward elevator and the move towards modern ailerons rather than the wing warping the Wright brothers had used. This eventually produced a more stable aeroplane (the BE2C) that did not need constant adjustments by the pilot and much longer flights became possible. On 12 August 1912 de Havilland used an earlier version the BE2, which retained wing warping, to reach a new altitude record of 10,560 feet. Two of the scientists who were involved in this work, Edward Busk and Keith Lucas were both killed in flying accidents shortly afterwards, Busk from an engine fire which then engulfed the whole aeroplane, and Lucas from a collision over

---

* A spin is a complication of a stall causing the aircraft to descend in a corkscrew path. It occurs when one wing is stalled more than the other and consequently has more drag. The aircraft then yaws towards the more-stalled wing and the spin starts. Spins were often fatal in the early days of aviation before methods of recovery were developed. The first recovery was said to be that of Lieutenant Wilfred Parke in 1912. The aerodynamics were finally understood after a series of experiments by Frederick Lindemann in 1917.

Salisbury Plain.*[15] As an illustration of Busk's success in making the BE2C stable the aeroplane landed itself although he was probably already dead.[16] Another problem at this time was the high frequency of crashes involving monoplanes, in retrospect probably from flutter** and their production was banned by the government.

It is something of a tribute to de Havilland's flying skill that he survived this period in spite of being Farnborough's only qualified pilot for over a year and having had several close calls and one serious crash. This happened when de Havilland was flying the small, single-seat, BS1, which amounted to a scaled-down BE2, at Farnborough in March 1913. He had thought that its rudder looked too small and so it proved. The aircraft went into a flat spin (a spin in which the nose of the aircraft is less elevated) which the small rudder was unable to correct and he hit the ground hard, breaking his jaw among other things. Several of his teeth were collected from the wreckage and returned to him in an envelope by a helpful mechanic.[17]

In January 1914, after he had recovered, de Havilland joined the Inspection Department at Farnborough. This was not much to his liking but he did meet a young engineer called Frank Halford who was to become one of the great figures of British aero-engine design, playing an important part in the evolution of the piston engine and then the turbojet. Halford had been in the engineering school at Felstead School and went on to Nottingham University to do engineering but left in 1913 without a degree. He learned to fly at Brooklands and then became an instructor on Boxkites at the Bristol School of Flying. At the start of the Great War he worked as an engine examiner and a lifetime interest began. Halford joined the Royal Flying Corps (RFC) in 1914 but was recalled from France in 1915 to improve the design of an existing Beardmore engine to increase its power output. This was when he met de Havilland. The engine became the Puma which was used in the DH4, one of the most successful of the First World War bombers.

In May 1914 de Havilland left to join the Aircraft Manufacturing Company, later known as Airco. His job description said that he should "design and supervise the construction of such aeroplanes as the company may require and will pilot any such aeroplanes designed by him."[18] No doubt the second provision had the effect of encouraging care in the first. The company was run by George Holt Thomas whom de Havilland had got to know from his many visits to Farnborough. There de Havilland would meet Francis St. Barbe and Wilfred Nixon, two people who would play significant roles in the future de Havilland company. Hearle had left Farnborough in November 1912 to work for another aircraft company but their paths were to cross again later.

The future Airco had just moved into new premises, an old bus depot on the Edgware Road in north London, and de Havilland was considered a bit of a catch for them. Up to now they had just assembled other people's aircraft but they planned to

---

* Sharpe says (probably) from elevator flutter (see below).[19]

** Aeroelastic flutter is the oscillation of a non-rigid structure produced by air flowing rapidly over its surfaces. If the energy input from the air flow is greater than the damping of the system the oscillation can increase to destructive levels. It was a potent cause of wings falling off aeroplanes when the fairly rigid truss of the biplane was replaced by the more flexible, wire-braced cantilever of the early monoplanes. It still causes anxiety to the designers of suspension bridges and tall chimneys.

design and build their own. Holt Thomas was something of a visionary. In 1906, while working in his father's newspaper publishing business, he had set up a prize for the first straight flight of a mile by an aircraft. In 1911 he had arranged to assemble Farman biplanes and started what became the Aircraft Manufacturing Company in Hendon in 1912. St. Barbe had joined at the start and having lived in France proved useful in deciphering the French instructions for assembling the Farmans.

The new factory was less than palatial but de Havilland managed to find space to set up his design office over what had been the commissionaire's office. It was a propitious time to start an aircraft company as Europe was moving inexorably towards war. Although by this time de Havilland was convinced that tractor propellers were better than pushers they had a significant disadvantage if you wanted to fire a machine gun from the front of the aeroplane. De Havilland's first project was to design a two-seater pusher biplane, designated the DH1, and considerable progress had been made when war with Germany broke out that August. De Havilland's involvement with the DH1 was interrupted by his being called up for service as a captain in the RFC. He was bundled off to Scotland to patrol off the east coast looking for German warships, a process somewhat hampered by his having no idea how to distinguish them from British vessels. After a month or so he was returned to Farnborough and a few months later back to the factory at Hendon on condition that he stayed in uniform and on RFC pay. In fact Holt Thomas made up the difference.

Another person who would later become involved with the Comet wrote to de Havilland in early 1915 offering his services as a structural engineer. Charles Walker had trained as a civil engineer at University College London and served his apprenticeship in Gateshead. He knew little about aircraft but offered to work for six months for nothing, which made the decision to employ him easier, and he started almost at once working on the stresses in airframes. With his intelligence and sense of humour he became more than just a colleague to de Havilland.

Meanwhile the DH1 had been completed and de Havilland flew it for the first time at Hendon in January 1915. It flew well but was underpowered for the weight of military equipment that had been added to it. As soon as possible the 70 bhp (brake horsepower*) Renault V-8 engine was changed for a 120 bhp Beardmore which increased the maximum speed from 80 to 90 mph. Only about 100 were built as the competing FE2, was preferred for manufacturing reasons and received most of the Beardmore engines. In the meantime de Havilland started work on a single-seat derivative called the DH2. This was the first time the company had done any serious static strength** tests with Walker using a simple Dennison machine to estimate the tensile, compressive and bending strengths of various components. Completed sections of the aircraft were not tested although Farnborough had already pioneered this in 1912 by suspending a BE1 upside down and weighting the wings to three times the normal load.

In those days aircraft were comparatively simple and it did not take long to develop a new type. The DH2 was flying by July 1915 and performed well. About 400 were

---

* Brake horsepower, the power measured at the engine's crankshaft.
** Static strength is the capacity to withstand a load applied once over a period of a few seconds.

built and used extensively in France. Manufacturing such a large number meant that the factory had to be enlarged and subcontractors engaged to make components such as wing spars and ribs. The war accelerated development and pretty soon de Havilland was working on the DH3, the first of their twin-engined aircraft, intended to be a fast bomber. Although it was almost as fast as current fighters and theoretically capable of bombing Berlin the view of the War Office was that fighters, rather than bombers, were needed and only one DH3 and one much-modified DH3A prototype were built.

The DH3 was a disappointment for de Havilland and the company but success was about to follow. The DH4 was another fast bomber but this time with a more-powerful engine and the more-efficient tractor propeller. It received a wide variety of engines starting with the 230 hp BHP (Beardmore Halford Pullinger) and ending with a 525 hp Packhard. Also a way of firing the machine gun through the propeller arc using an inter-rupter gear had been invented. The DH4 first flew in August 1916 and almost 1,500 were built in the UK and more in America although Trenchard, the head of the RFC, wrote in a letter to de Havilland, "I do not think it is entirely suitable for bomb drop-ping" but he did agree that, "it is extremely handy to fly."[20] In practice almost all of them had the Rolls-Royce Eagle, a more powerful engine than Halford's Beardmore.

In order to cope Airco was subcontracting more and more and about 90 firms were making parts for the DH4. By 1918 they were producing almost 300 aircraft a month.

In early June 1917 Frank Hearle joined Airco at the peak of DH4 production and took charge of the experimental shop. Nixon joined the next year and started to take over the financial running of the company. St. Barbe was already in charge of sales before de Havilland arrived. The DH5, a single-seat fighter, followed and was built in reasonable numbers (550) but the next big success was the DH6, a two-seat trainer. Many young pilots had lost their lives in training accidents, particularly with the pres-sures caused by the war, and for this reason the DH6 was designed to be easy to fly. It had a heavily cambered* aerofoil** so that it could stay in the air at less than 30 mph which helped to reduce the appalling attrition. An added attraction was a lever for the instructor to disengage the pupil's controls in an emergency. It was also easy to make, something that was becoming more important as raw materials became harder to find as the U-boat war continued. It was affectionately known by the Australians as the 'Dung Hunter' but the British called it the 'Sky Hook' or the 'Clutching Hand'. Over 2,200 DH6s were produced, a number that would have seemed inconceivable before the war, but even this figure was exceeded by the DH9.

The DH9 was another single-engined bomber; an evolved version of the DH4. It first flew in June 1917 but started life with an inadequate engine and consequently a feeble performance. In spite of its engine the DH9 was put into mass production, reach-ing a maximum of 370 per month in the summer of 1918 and by the end of 1918 3,200 had been built in Britain. It was much improved by fitting the more-powerful (430 hp)

---

* The camber is the bulge on the upper surface of the aerofoil, providing some of the lift. It is usually at a maximum about a quarter the way along the chord line – the shortest distance between the leading and trail-ing edges.

** The aerofoil is the cross-sectional shape of the wing.

Fig. 2/1 Captain Geoffrey de Havilland and a DH9A, copyright BAE SYSTEMS Heritage.

Napier Lion but this came too late for wartime use. The DH9 was also adapted to be fitted with the excellent American Liberty engine to become the more competent 9A but the end of the war pretty much stopped production after about 885 had been built. The next bomber, the twin-engined DH10, just made it into production before the war ended; apart from the prototypes only ten were produced.

During the course of the war de Havilland came into contact with two of the great figures in British aviation, Henry Tizard and Frederick Lindemann. De Havilland thought well of Tizard, who had changed test flying from a matter of opinion to a science, but thought less well of Lindemann who later, as Lord Cherwell, had Churchill's ear and eclipsed Tizard after the latter discounted the possibility of German directional beacons in the Second World War.[21] In fact de Havilland's judgement was prescient. Cherwell, as well as being notoriously waspish,* had somewhat uneven scientific judgement whereas Tizard was usually proved right. Among other things Tizard played a large part in setting up the wartime radar system and encouraging the development of the jet engine.

De Havilland had had 'a good war', as had Airco, but he was exhausted and disappeared into a nursing home for an enforced rest shortly after the Armistice was declared. Something similar happened to the aircraft industry. No doubt after medieval wars the makers of bows and arrows faced the same difficulties as demand for their

---

* It was said of him that "...he rarely committed the sin of being rude by accident."[22]

products collapsed, but the Great War had been the first of the big industrial wars and the problems would accordingly be bigger. Massive industrial capacity had been built up, not just in aviation but in steel, ship building, munitions and many other industries, but now the contracts were being cancelled and the workers dismissed.

Before 1914 there had hardly been a civilian aircraft industry but the war had forced development to the point where there might be some prospect of carrying high-value cargo, such as mail, and some high-value passengers. A few DH4s had already been converted to carry two passengers facing each other in the body of the fuselage, getting in and out via a hinged lid, and Airco set about adapting the DH9 for commercial use as well. Small airlines were being set up and the first scheduled international service was started between London and Paris on 25 August 1919. It used de Havilland-designed aircraft, a DH4 and a DH16 – an adapted DH9 able to carry four passengers. Airco started production of the DH18, the first of their aircraft designed from the start to carry passengers. But the new airlines were struggling to fill the few seats they had; orders for new aircraft were few and only six DH18s were built. In 1920 Holt Thomas reluctantly sold Airco to the Birmingham Small Arms Company (BSA) who promptly announced that they would stop all work on aircraft.

This may not have come as a surprise to de Havilland who negotiated a release from his contract which had passed to BSA. He also managed to obtain the design rights, contracts and parts for the aircraft currently under construction but then had to find the money to set up a new company. This was not an easy time to attract investment but de Havilland wrote to people he thought might have money and be willing to risk it manufacturing aeroplanes. Several people put up small sums, including an air-minded parson in Farnborough who invested £1,000, and de Havilland himself provided £3,000. But the biggest amount came from Holt Thomas who agreed to provide £10,000 over a period of time as some of his other investments would have to be disposed of. This was the beginning of The de Havilland Aircraft Company which was formally incorporated on 25 September 1920.

On Monday 5 October 1920 two almost-complete airframes and some machine tools were moved into the two sheds on Stag Lane Aerodrome, Edgware, that were to be the company's new home. The machine tools were driven by an ancient gas engine which provided endless challenges to its two minders and eventually exploded. The aerodrome had been the site of a commercial flying school, the London and Provincial Aviation Company, which had ceased operations in July 1919 after a dispute with the Civil Aviation Authority which refused them a licence. After trying their hand at chocolate-making, and only succeeding in making a sticky mess in one of the sheds, the owners were anxious to rent out their property. As well as the two large sheds there were two smaller huts; one was to become the drawing office and the other the administrative centre.

The accommodation was fairly basic and for the first year an enterprising gipsy lady provided food from her caravan parked near the sheds. Nixon was to be the company secretary, Hearle the works manager, St. Barbe would deal with the commercial side, Walker would provide the science and de Havilland and Arthur Hagg the design skills.

Between 50 and 60 other people had also come with them from Airco. They had some work to be going on with, both repairs and making new DH18s for sale. The problem was that there were many war-surplus aircraft available which inhibited sales of new aircraft but at least produced a need for spares.

In order to make ends meet the company started to provide aircraft on a variety of contracts. Alan Cobham, later to start an in-flight refuelling company, was employed as a jobbing pilot and also took part in air races. Even a flying school was opened. Early in 1921 the company's prospects started to look brighter. The Air Ministry ordered two prototypes each of two new designs: one was an advanced monoplane the other a biplane bomber. The latter was produced without much difficulty but did not result in any further orders but the former caused them much trouble with its poor longitudinal stability (pitch) and eventually had to be abandoned as the problem seemed insoluble. The next project, the DH34, was more successful. It was a ten-passenger biplane which proved easy to develop and gave years of reliable service to the airlines that bought it.

About this time the owners of the airfield suddenly demanded that de Havillands either get out or buy the airfield and buildings. Unfortunately they wanted £20,000 for the freehold which was way beyond the company's means but once again salvation was at hand. A young man who was apparently not without funds got in touch about buying a bespoke aeroplane for himself and one passenger. The cost of such a one-off project would be enormous but Mr. Butler seemed undeterred by the estimate of around £3,500. Not only that but he enquired about investing in the company and wondered whether £50,000 would be a suitable sum. Although all this sounded too good to be true Mr. Butler proved to be reliable and the company was able to complete the purchase of the aerodrome, a process they had already started without any idea of how they could finish. Mr. Butler's DH37 had its maiden flight in June 1922 and went on to be a great success.

Frank Halford, now a major, whose career was to be inextricably linked with de Havilland's, had also had an interesting war. In 1916 he met Harry Ricardo, a talented engine designer and another pioneer in the aviation world who was to have a big influence on Halford's career. At the end of the war Halford spent more than two years in the United States negotiating licensing agreements for Ricardo's patents, after which he returned to work with him on motorcycle engines at his London company. In 1923 Halford left Ricardo's firm and started his own company where he acted as a consultant to the ADC (Aircraft Disposal Company). This had been set up to make what use it could of the large number of aero-engines left over from the war. It was here that Halford came into contact with de Havilland again. He was to become de Havillands' chief engine designer until his death in 1955.

The real breakthrough for de Havillands came with the realisation that there was a potential market for a small, inexpensive aeroplane that could be used as a private run-about or a trainer. They had already produced a small monoplane, the DH53, with a 698cc (cubic centimetre) engine producing 26 hp but it was so underpowered that it had suffered the indignity of being overtaken by a train while Cobham was flying it over Belgium.[23] De Havilland and Halford were discussing this one day in early 1924 and in between laughing about Cobham's humiliation de Havilland suggested to Halford that he should produce a 60 hp engine weighing about 350 pounds.[24] Rather than designing a whole new engine, which would take some time, Halford managed to do it by halving an existing eight-cylinder Airdisco engine left over from the war and it became the ADC Cirrus, a remarkably quiet engine. The two-seat light aeroplane became the DH60 (Cirrus) Moth, the first of an extensive family. It was flown by de Havilland for the first time on 22 February 1925.

Their timing was excellent as the government were trying to encourage flying by subsidising flying clubs up and down the country and the Moth was ideal. The aircraft was easy to make, particularly after Harry Povey, later to be in charge of constructing the Comet, made their first manufacturing jig which cut the assembly time from one week to one day. As they were finished, the Moths were colour-coded according to the club they were going to: red for Newcastle, blue for Lancashire. To demonstrate the Moth's stamina Cobham flew the first one from Croydon to Zurich non-stop and then back again after lunch with an average speed of 71 mph. Altogether 60 of the first type of Moth were produced.

By now Mr. Butler, the financial saviour of the company, had been elected chairman and R. M. Clarkson, later the principle aerodynamicist of the Comet, had joined the technical staff. Another recruit, who joined the company from Oxford as a mathematician and aerodynamicist, was Neville Shute Norway who later became a well-known novelist. He moved on to work with Vickers at Howden in Yorkshire on the R100 airship which he described in his autobiography.* After the Second World War he wrote a novel about metal fatigue destroying an airliner which was considered by many to predict what befell the Comet although there were, in fact, important differences.**

The Cirrus engine came from the Aircraft Disposal Company and de Havillands were therefore dependent on them for a continued supply at whatever price they chose to ask. New engines take time to develop and get right but de Havilland hankered after an engine of his own. Halford was already improving the Cirrus so that it would produce 85 hp but de Havilland asked him to design one that would give 100 hp. In the meantime de Havillands went on making a modified Moth (the 60X) with the Cirrus 2 and the later Cirrus 3 engines, producing 394 of them.

Halford started work on the new engine, to be called the Gipsy, on 29 October 1926 and the first production example was delivered on 20 June 1928. A souped up version of it had already been used for a racing Moth (called the DH71 Tiger Moth) which set a world record for a light aeroplane for the 100 kilometre closed circuit at 186 mph on 24 August that year. The DH60G Gipsy Moth proved to be a highly successful combination and 1,162 were made, some with the more powerful (120 hp) Gipsy Two engine. In 1931 an even-more-powerful version was flown with the 130 hp Gipsy Major. This was just the beginning and the Moth family kept the firm going through the lean years of the Great Depression. De Havillands made 146 DH60 Moth Majors but went on to build 261 Puss Moths, a high-winged monoplane, and an amazing 5,055 DH82s,

---

* *Slide Rule*, 1954, Heinemann.
** *No Highway*, 1948, Heinemann.

confusingly also called the Tiger Moth. The reason for the Tiger's enormous success was that it became the basic trainer for the RAF before and then during the Second World War. There was even a radio-controlled version, called the Queen Bee, used for target practice. The Gipsy acquired more fame during the war as the power behind the coils slung under Wellington bombers to explode magnetic mines.

There were some other Moths, one a four-seater passenger plane, but they sold in much smaller numbers. One of the later types, a Moth Minor, nearly accounted for Geoffrey junior and John Cunningham, both test pilots for the company. In the summer of 1938 they were carrying out tests to see how far back the centre of gravity could be safely located by inducing a spin and seeing whether it could be corrected. They found the answer all right but had to parachute out in the process. Fortunately neither was hurt. The Moth family evolved into the post-war, Canadian-designed, Chipmunk with a developed Gipsy Major 10 engine, an astonishing life span for an aero-engine.

Although the Moths kept de Havillands going during the 1930s they did produce other aircraft as well. The best known were the twin-engine DH84 Dragon and the DH89 Dragon Rapide, both passenger biplanes and both powered by Gipsy engines. One of the stimuli for producing the Dragon was a Romford bus-driver-and-proprietor-turned-airline-owner called Edward Hillman. He was an early believer in low-cost airlines and wanted to undercut Imperial Airways on the London to Paris route. It took de Havillands four months to build the first Dragon, largely from Moth parts. It sold for £2,800, unfurnished. By December 1932 the first Dragon had been delivered to Hillman and another five followed. In all 115 were built, some of them mark 2s and

Fig. 3/1 DH82 Tiger Moth 9 (L6923), copyright BAE SYSTEMS Heritage.

Fig. 4/1 DH84 Dragon, copyright BAE SYSTEMS Heritage.

some seaplanes. They were sold all over the world, some of the first going to the Iraqi Airforce, and proved reliable and very economical. Another 87 were built in Australia during the war.

The Dragon was followed by the four-engined, ten-seater version (the DH86) built for the Australian Government to connect with the Imperial Airways route to Singapore. These used Halford's new six-cylinder Gipsy engine and flew for the first time on 14 January 1934 starting service with the Australians later that year. Among many other airlines it was used by Imperial Airways on the continent and by Railway Air Services within the UK. The Gipsy Six was a good engine and soon replaced the Gipsy Major on the Dragon to turn it into the DH89 Dragon Rapide, increasing its cruising speed from 114 to 132 mph. This became another triumph for de Havillands which made 685 of them and sold them all over the world. It stayed in production until 1945 and continued in service many years after that.

The Moths and the Dragons were commercial successes for de Havillands and they allowed the company to grow on a sound financial basis, but they were hardly cutting-edge aeroplanes. They were wooden biplanes, in many ways not much more sophisticated than things that were flying around in 1918. Compared with contemporary American passenger aircraft such as the Douglas DC-2 and the Boeing 247, which were fast, all-metal* monoplanes, they belonged to a previous generation. De Havillands were capable of doing better and they showed this when they made the DH88 Comet

---

* The 'metal' referred to here was the aluminium alloy used to make the fuselage skin. In this context the word was used to distinguish it from the wood or wood-and-canvas construction of an earlier age (but see below, the wooden Mosquito and Chapter 4, aluminium alloy.)

racer. Admittedly it was still made from wood but it was a monoplane with variable-pitch propellers,* wing flaps and a retractable undercarriage.

The DH88 was constructed to take part in a race from England to Australia for a £10,000 prize put up in March 1933 by Sir Macpherson Robertson, a Melbourne industrialist, to celebrate the centenary of the foundation of the State of Victoria. The actual race would start on 20 October 1934. De Havilland himself felt that they could not stand by and let the race take place with no British entries and they made the decision to take part. They had nothing on the stocks that would have any hope of winning so the company would have to design and construct a special aeroplane over a very short period of time as well as dealing with all the other orders they had on their books. From the company's point of view as well as diverting resources it would not be much of a commercial prospect either as it would be expensive to make and there would be little market for an aircraft constructed specifically for the race. On the other hand it would be good publicity if they won and they would pick up some new technology in the

Fig. 5/1 DH88 Comet Racer (CS-AAJ) 03 1935, copyright BAE SYSTEMS Heritage.

---

* The pitch of a propeller is the distance the propeller would move forward during one complete revolution assuming that there is no slippage relative to the air it is moving through. It is proportional to the twist of the propeller blades. A propeller blade acts as a small wing and as such has an angle of attack (see Chapter 4). Among other variables this determines the mass of air displaced backwards and therefore the thrust of the propeller. As the aircraft moves forward this angle of attack is decreased by the air the blades meet and the thrust decreases. This can be compensated for by increasing the pitch of the propeller using a mechanism at the hub of the propeller. Fine pitch is used during take off and landing when the aircraft is moving slowly and coarse pitch when the aircraft is cruising. A fixed-pitch propeller is a compromise for all speeds.

process so they decided to do it. It had to be fast, obviously, but also able to fly 2,600 mile stages which meant taking off with a heavy fuel load and then cruising as economically as possible, leading to the need for variable-pitch propellers. Fast, but economic, cruising needed a thin wing monoplane which would limit its lift, hence the trailing-edge flaps.

Hearle and his colleague Arthur Hagg were dispatched to America to look at variable-pitch propellers. The best choice seemed to be Hamilton propellers, from a company (Hamilton Standard) based at Hartford Connecticut, but they would need considerable adapting and time was limited. Less sophisticated, but easier to adapt, was a French system made by a company near Paris called Ratier. In the end Ratier propellers were used. At the same time as the propellers were being investigated, Halford was working on upgrading the Gipsy Six engine by increasing its compression ratio and maximum revolutions. Five Comets were built and three were entered for the race. The first one flew on 8 September and it was a desperate rush to correct the inevitable problems and get them ready for the race.

There were 64 entries: 21 American and by now sixteen of them British. In de Havilland's view the two most formidable competitors were a KLM Douglas DC-2 and a Boeing 247. The race began at RAF Mildenhall and all three Comets started. One of them came first in a time of 70 hours, 54 minutes and 18 seconds, another came fourth but the third had to retire with engine trouble. Black and Scott, the crew of the winning Comet, also had had a problem with one of their engines when it started to lose oil pressure. Fortunately a de Havilland mechanic had cured this at Darwin by cleaning its oil filter.* Overall not a bad result for the company. The DC-2 was second and the Boeing third; not bad results for them either, particularly as they were standard airliners and not a specially-designed racer like the Comet. The real lesson of the race was that the current American passenger aircraft were streets ahead of anything the British were producing and if de Havillands were going to compete they would have to do better than wooden biplanes with fixed-pitch propellers.

For de Havillands one of biggest, if not the biggest, gain from taking part in the race to Australia had been appreciating the need for variable-pitch propellers. Although the Ratier propeller had been used for the race de Havillands preferred the Hamilton design and in June 1934 they obtained a licence to manufacture them. This involved a considerable investment in machine tools, many times the cost of the licence, and formed the basis of what would become 'The de Havilland Propeller Company.' The first of the new propellers was delivered to The Bristol Aeroplane Company in July 1935 and a considerable business, which included exports to several European countries, was rapidly built

---

* Halford was on a bus in Regent Street on the way to have lunch with his daughter at the Café Royal when the conductor pointed out a newspaper placard which said that Black and Scott had retired from the race. Halford rushed back to his office in Golden Square where a journalist was waiting to speak to him. By great good fortune the Press Association had a telephone line open to Darwin and Halford was able to speak directly to the mechanic involved. Halford was worried about its pistons but the mechanic had sorted out the problem himself. In the heat of the moment Halford forgot about meeting his daughter but he managed to retrieve the situation by contacting her and they both had a late lunch.[25]

up, justifying the heavy investment outlay. In 1937, with war looming, the government encouraged de Havillands to set up a 'shadow'* propeller-manufacturing site and a factory was started near Bolton. By this time the Stag Lane site was probably the largest manufacturer of variable-pitch propellers in the world. It remained the site for the engine division but the aircraft division had moved to Hatfield Aerodrome, in Hertfordshire, north of London, in 1934 as Stag Lane was becoming hemmed in by the London suburb of Edgware and was less and less suitable as a location for an airfield.

The other lesson from the race, that they needed a better airframe and probably bigger engines, was also learned and acted upon. In November 1934, only days after the race had finished, a letter was sent from the company to the Air Ministry pointing out the fine performance of the American aircraft and the need for Britain to make more advanced airliners if they were to compete. It also emphasised that de Havillands had incurred considerable costs in making and preparing the Comets for the race and enquired whether any financial assistance might be forthcoming to produce a new passenger aircraft.

Eventually, after prompting, the Air Ministry replied in March the following year saying that, "...it will not be possible for the department to place a non-competitive order with a single firm for the construction of a prototype, and that your particular proposal cannot, therefore, be entertained."[26] De Havillands did not give up, however, and talks continued and the following January their efforts were rewarded with a contract for two DH91 Albatrosses but with the understanding that more than half their costs would be borne by the company.

Designed by Arthur Hagg, the prototype Albatross was rapidly produced and flew for the first time on 20 May 1937. It was a four-engined monoplane of an exceptionally clean design able to carry 22 passengers and using the new Gipsy twelve-cylinder engines made from two sixes joined in an inverted V. It cruised at 210 mph and did 2½ miles to the gallon. The fuselage was made of two plywood skins glued to a layer of balsa wood between them. The wing was made in one piece from a thick skin of wooden planking, reducing the need for much of an internal structure. The first two were intended to be transatlantic mail carriers but five were ordered by Imperial Airways as passenger aircraft and started on the London to Paris and Brussels routes in December 1938 although they were really designed for longer trips. Unfortunately only these seven were made as the war intervened and the government lost interest in passenger aircraft. The ones that had been made were pressed into RAF service and four subsequently crashed, one was destroyed by enemy action and the remaining two, with little prospect of spares being available, were scrapped in 1943.

The Albatross was a far more advanced aircraft than the Dragons but it is a moot point how successful it would have been in an open competition with American aircraft

---

* The 'shadow' system was a government-sponsored scheme to increase and disperse the manufacture of aviation products by setting up new factories usually managed by motor car companies. It was started by Lord Swinton, the Secretary of State for Air, in 1935 and continued by Sir Kingsley Wood, his successor, as part of the rearmament programme. The original idea came from George Bulman, the civilian head of engine development in the Air Ministry.[27]

Fig. 6/1 DH91 Albatross E2, copyright BAE SYSTEMS Heritage.

such as the Douglas DC-3 which had only two engines but could carry more passengers and had appeared two years earlier. Although still carrying fewer passengers than the DC-3 a better prospect might have been the DH95 Flamingo, the first aircraft designed by R. E. Bishop, the future designer of the Comet. This was the first stressed-skin, all-metal aircraft built by the de Havilland company. It was a high-wing monoplane powered by two Bristol Perseus XIIC radial engines and could carry between twelve and sixteen passengers depending on the range required. It flew for the first time on 22 December 1938. The production aircraft had a maximum speed of 243 mph and a range of 1,345 miles, better in both respects than the Albatross and but for the war might well have had a rosy future. In the event only fifteen were completed. Some were used by BOAC, others by the RAF and the Royal Navy. One conveyed Churchill on his several trips to France during the Battle of France. Five survived the war. This aircraft provided some of the structural experience for building the Comet although by that time de Havillands had produced the Vampire jet fighter, which was mainly metal but had some wooden parts, and the all-metal Dove.

As 1938 progressed another war with Germany began to look inevitable and those in charge at de Havillands, principally de Havilland himself, Hearle, Nixon, St. Barbe and sometimes Butler, Bishop and Clarkson, began to discuss what contribution they might make. They were unused to working with the military but realised they would have to get over this. The first plan was for a bomber version of the Albatross but when the sums were done it became apparent that a smaller aircraft could do the job better, also a much more powerful engine, the Rolls-Royce Merlin, had became available. By the time of Munich the proposal had become more definite. This was to be the Mosquito, a twin-engined, fast, clean monoplane rather in the style of the Albatross and like the Albatross made of wood. By this time most airframe constructors had moved away from wood as being old-fashioned although the spruce providing most of the Mosquito's structural strength had, weight for weight, rather greater tensile strength along the grain than aluminium alloy.[28] There were at least four other reasons for using wood: they had the experience of working with it, carpenters would be more available than metal workers, it would save time and the stocks of aluminium alloy were all allocated. The Mosquito would also be unarmed, relying on its speed to survive, in many ways a reincarnation of the DH4 concept. It was to become de Havillands' great contribution to the war effort.

Fig. 7/1 DH95 Flamingo (RN BT 312), copyright BAE SYSTEMS Heritage.

In October 1938 de Havilland and Walker presented their case at the Air Ministry without eliciting much interest, indeed they were told to 'forget it' and to turn their attention to something they could cope with, such as designing a wing for somebody else's aeroplane.[29] This delayed events but other ministry work was taken on in the meantime and they tried again the following September. Perhaps minds were more concentrated by then and the idea was picked up by Air Marshall Wilfrid Freeman, the Air Member for Development and Production and the organisational genius behind much of the British wartime aircraft production. In spite of considerable opposition to the idea of its being unarmed the company was authorised to proceed at the end of December.

By this time the technical offices had been moved to Salisbury Hall, a moated manor house at London Colney, about five miles from Hatfield, and Bishop and his team of about 30 were given the job of designing the new aeroplane there. The team now included C. T. Wilkins as the assistant designer and Robert Harper as the head of the stress section, both of whom would later be involved in designing the Comet, all products of The de Havilland Technical School. Bishop later said that the outline of the Mosquito's fuselage had come from the shape of a stuffed pike in a glass case on the wall of a lavatory there. The pike had been caught by Winston Churchill in the hall's moat before the 1914-18 war.*

Ronald Bishop had joined the company in 1921 at the age of eighteen as its second premium apprentice (i.e. he, or more likely his parents, had to pay a sum of money up front) after Portsmouth Grammar School and starting at London University which he left because, as he often recalled, he had 'failed Part One.'[30] He worked his way through the sheet metal shop, the fitting shop, the wood shop and the engine shop before reaching the drawing office in 1923. His first job was to design parts for the DH51 biplane, a forerunner of the famous Moth family. These were hard times in the aircraft industry and in 1931 the young Bishop was laid off by de Havillands and almost took a job with Junkers in Germany. In the end he found work with a French aircraft company but after a few weeks de Havillands retrieved him and he stayed with them for the rest of his career. In 1936 he took over the leadership of the drawing office after Hagg left and designed the elegant Flamingo. He became a director of the company in 1946.

Bishop was a quiet, modest, frugal and unassuming man but he also had drive and determination, almost to the point of ruthlessness. Nevertheless he was loyal to his staff and treated them very fairly. He was described by John Wilson, a de Havilland test pilot, in the Principal Films documentary about the Comet, as "An austere man. Not totally without humour but it didn't often show and he was very, very strong minded." And by Ralph Hare, who worked in the de Havilland design department, as "Quite a bit of a chaser... a brilliant designer but as a man, a man of some moods. Sometimes he would be happy, other times the reverse." He distrusted academics and theorists who had never actually made anything. "The man's a fool," he would say of them dismissively. He preferred mechanical simplicity, rejecting electrical for mechanical devices even at the expense of adding weight, and was known as "Bishop, Bellcrank and Lever" by the engineers at BOAC.[31, 32, 33] He was, by all accounts, an authoritarian figure in a more authoritarian age and not someone who would welcome views that differed from his own. Perhaps this was a result of having had to get things done during a war for survival but it probably did stifle debate. He retired in 1964 and died in 1989.

Of all his creations Bishop was most proud of the Mosquito. The prototype was built in a shed** at the back of the hall in less than eleven months after the design work was

---

* Churchill's mother, Jenny, had bought the hall in 1905.
** The site of this shed is now part of the de Havilland Aircraft Museum. The shed itself no longer exists.

started. Beaverbrook,* had issued instructions for it to be abandoned on at least three occasions and work had been stopped in May 1940 but they managed to get it restarted in July. It had been protected by Freeman and became known as 'Freeman's Folly'. The fuselage was constructed in two longitudinal halves of the same thin plywood skins with interposed balsa that had been used for the Albatross. The two halves meant that the internal equipment could be easily installed before they were fitted together. The undercarriage legs were just columns of rubber blocks in compression, avoiding a considerable amount of engineering. When it was finished it had to be taken to bits and then reassembled at Hatfield and was flown for the first time on 25 November 1940, painted yellow in the hope that the local anti-aircraft gunners would spare it.

Following the bomber a fighter version was produced and, after a certain amount of thought on Geoffrey junior's part, it was flown off from the small field next to the 'barn' where it had been built. Alarmingly two days before this a German man in plain clothes and equipped with a radio had been dropped into a nearby field.**[34]

For some two and a half years the Mosquito was the fastest aeroplane in the war on either side and de Havillands and various other companies went on to manufacture almost 8,000 of them which absorbed most of the company's resources during the war. After the Mosquito, Bishop and his team designed the twin-engined Hornet, a fast, long-range, piston-engined fighter that looked like a slightly-smaller Mosquito. It did have internal differences though. The fuselage was similar to the Mosquito's but the wings had a double upper skin of plywood and an under skin of light alloy with composite wood-metal spars. The wood and metal parts were glued together using a system developed by Dr. Norman de Bruyne and Malcolm Gordon who had been working with de Havillands since 1936. This was the first use of their Redux*** process in a production aircraft. It was later used in the Dove and the Heron and more extensively in the Comet. The Hornet was intended for the Pacific but was too late to see active service. It was one of the fastest piston-engined fighters with a maximum speed of 472 mph at

---

* Lord Beaverbrook, 1879-1964. A volatile Canadian newspaper magnate who was one of Churchill's chums. He published his first newspaper at the age of thirteen but made his fortune from the questionable buying and selling of shares in cement plants in Canada. He moved to England in 1910, became an MP and started to build a newspaper empire, eventually owning the *Daily* and *Sunday Express* and the *London Evening Standard*. In 1940 Churchill made him Minister of Aircraft Production and later Minister of Supply. After a visit to Moscow in 1941 he became a champion of the 'Second Front' to relieve the pressure on the Soviet Union and was something of an embarrassment to the government. Attlee was reputed to have said that Churchill often listened to Beaverbrook's advice but was too sensible to take it.

** The man was Karel Richter who had arrived in the early hours of 13 May. After burying his equipment he went into hiding for three days and then walked into London Colney where he asked a policeman to take him to the nearest hospital. Instead he was taken to the nearest police station. His mission was nothing to do with the Mosquito but to check up on another German agent, code named Tate, about whom the Germans had become suspicious.They were right to have become suspicious as Tate was working for the British. This made it difficult to make use of Richter and he was tried in camera, sentenced to death and hanged at Wandsworth on 10 December 1941, aged 29.[35]

*** From REsearch and DUXford where the work was done. The adhesive consisted of a liquid and a powder hardener. The joint surfaces were coated, allowed to stand for at least 30 minutes and then brought together under pressure and raised temperature for about half an hour.

22,000 feet and in its Mark 3 version was the last one to see active service (in Malaya) with the RAF.*

Halford remained de Havillands' chief engine designer although he was not directly employed by them. As well as being associated with de Havillands, Halford worked with the London firm of Napier to produce the 350 hp, 16-cylinder Rapier, which was used to power the upper half of the Short Mayo Composite which first flew in 1937 (see Chapter 7). The Rapier evolved into the 24-cylinder Dagger, but Halford's *tour de force* with Napier was the Sabre. This monster was one of the most powerful piston engines ever produced with 24 cylinders in an H configuration producing 3,500 hp in its later versions.[36] It used sleeve rather than poppet valves, a device invented in the early 1900s but never widely adopted because of manufacturing difficulties and its high oil usage. Halford had picked up the idea from Ricardo but it was also being used by Fedden at Bristol's. The Sabre first ran in 1938 and by 1940 it was producing more than twice as much power as the contemporary version of the Rolls-Royce Merlin, the most famous of the wartime engines. The Sabre was a complicated and, at least initially, a temperamental engine. It was difficult to manufacture and suffered frequent failures of lubrication of its sleeve valves leading to piston seizures and several crashes.** This was eventually cured when pressure was brought to bear on Bristol's to share their sleeve-valve manufacturing technology and it went on to power the Hawker Typhoon. The future for fighters lay with the jet engine.

The Vampire was de Havillands' first jet-propelled aircraft. It was not a research aircraft like the Gloster Whittle (see Chapter 3) but was intended from the start to go into service. It was a small fighter designed by Bishop around Halford's new jet engine, the H1, later called the Goblin. It consisted of a central pod, containing the cockpit and engine, to which the tapered wings were attached. From the rear of the wings two narrow booms projected backwards with a fin at the end of each of them. The fins were joined by a single horizontal tailplane raised above the line of the jet exhaust. This unusual layout was driven by the need to keep the jet pipe as short as possible to minimise power loss from the engine. It was not quite all-metal as the cockpit section was made from plywood and balsa. The Vampire was the first British or American aircraft to exceed 500 mph. It came too late for the war but nevertheless was highly successful commercially and sold to more than a dozen countries which were anxious to replace their now-obsolete, piston-propeller fighters with relatively-cheap jet ones. It was also produced in a naval version and was used for the first jet-landing on an aircraft carrier. On 23 March 1948 John Cunningham flew a specially-prepared Vampire with four feet long wing extensions and a strengthened hood to achieve a new high-altitude record of 59,446 feet. This particular one had the later, more-powerful, Ghost engine which would be used in the Comet as well as the Vampire's successor, the Venom.

De Havillands, like other aircraft manufacturers, had grown enormously during the

---

* Unsurprisingly the actual fastest is disputed but other candidates include the Dornier Do 335 which had two engines, a tractor at the front and a pusher at the rear, and the Supermarine Spiteful which was a Griffon-engined Spitfire derivative with a new wing.

** Postan says it '...provided one of the Second World War's most melancholy stories.'[37]

war. The company had a large propeller-manufacturing concern as well as overseas subsidiaries in Australia, Canada and New Zealand but its greatest achievement had been the superlative Mosquito, unquestionably one of the greatest aircraft produced by either side during the war. By the end of hostilities the company was in the forefront of the new jet engine technology both in terms of making the engines and one aircraft (the Vampire) for them. It was also starting to produce a relatively-straightforward civilian aircraft, the DH 104 Dove. This was an all-metal, low-wing monoplane with two Gipsy Queen engines driving three-bladed propellers. It was the first British transport aircraft to have reversible-pitch propellers to provide braking after landing and flew for the first time on 25 September 1945. The Dove carried between five and eleven passengers in an unpressurised cabin with large square windows. It proved to be robust and reliable and was a great commercial success as airlines all over the world rebuilt their fleets. In its various forms it sold 542 examples. Although both of these aircraft were commercial successes the Vampire was beginning to look dated with its unswept wings and the Dove was hardly at the forefront of aviation technology. Even with their later versions, such as the Venom and the four-engined Heron, it was unlikely they would stretch the designers or fill the company's workshops.

De Havilland himself was always very conscious of the collapse of the British aviation industry after the First World War. At that time there was little in the way of a civilian, passenger-carrying market to turn to but it had developed considerably before the Second World War and there was every prospect that it would pick up again after hostilities finished. Clearly the war had brought considerable technical advances, some of which could be used in a new generation of passenger aircraft. The Brabazon Committee would be the official response to this and the Comet would be de Havillands' main effort and the best prospect to fill its factories.

Chapter 2

THE BRABAZON COMMITTEE

The idea of using jet engines to propel a large passenger-carrying aircraft emerged within de Havillands sometime between May and June 1941.[1] This was not long after the existence of internal combustion gas turbines (turbojets) had become known outside the small group of people developing them. De Havillands was unusual, although not unique, in having an engine as well as an airframe division which may have helped to keep them well informed and they were among the first to design and build a turbojet (see Chapter 3). During the early discussions in the company the idea of fitting two of their new jet engines to the pre-war Flamingo airliner was considered and then rapidly dismissed. Calculations by Clarkson, the chief aerodynamicist, and some of his colleagues showed that except for very short stages all its carrying capacity would be taken up by the fuel for its inefficient engines. It was apparent that an aircraft using jet engines would have to travel very fast and very high (see Chapter 3) to have any chance of commercial success and would therefore need to be an entirely new design. At this stage of the war such a project was clearly out of the question and any exploration of it, other than a theoretical one, would have to wait for hostilities to end.

In November 1942 Air Vice Marshall Sorley, then the Assistant Chief of the Air Staff (Technical Requirements), was dispatched to the United States to examine the American aircraft industry. Sorley had made his name by taking part in the air attack on the German warships *Goeben* and *Breslau* in January 1918 when they emerged from having been blockaded in Istanbul's harbour for most of the war. He had managed to stay in the RAF between the wars and played an important part in making sure that the new Hurricane and Spitfire fighters were equipped with eight Browning machine guns and not the four Vickers ones originally specified. He went on to command the Aeroplane and Armament Experimental Establishment (A&AEE) at Boscombe Down and from 1943 to 1945 worked in the Ministry of Aircraft Production (MAP).[2]

On his return from America Sorley strongly recommended that some British design capacity be allocated to future transport aircraft. During the war, of necessity, virtually no civilian passenger aircraft were produced in Britain and almost all the transport aircraft used by the Allies were of American design and manufacture. Sorley's report made it clear that by the end of the war the American civil aircraft industry was going to be in a much stronger position than the British. The government responded to this in late 1942 by setting up a committee to look into the future of British civil aircraft manufacture after the war. This was surprisingly far-sighted, not to say optimistic, on the part of the government considering that up to then the only significant British victory had been the Second Battle of El Alamein and the end of the war still seemed depressingly far away.

J. T. C. Moore-Brabazon, who was to be the chairman of the committee, was a well-known aviation pioneer. He was born in 1884, educated at Harrow and showed an early interest in aviation by launching model gliders from boxes into the still air of the Albert Hall with his friend Charlie Rolls.*[3] He started, but did not finish, an engineering degree at Cambridge. He was the first Englishman to fly a powered aeroplane after having learned to fly in France in 1908. The following year he proved that pigs really could fly by taking a small one squeezed into a waste-paper bin attached to one of the wings of his aeroplane for a short hop. He was the first person to qualify as a pilot in Britain and received the Royal Aero Club's certificate Number One. Inevitably his car had the registration FLY 1.**

After serving in the RFC during the Great War, where he pioneered aerial photography, Brabazon emerged with the rank of lieutenant-colonel and became a Conservative Member of Parliament. He was a junior minister in the 1920s and supported Churchill's pleas for more energetic rearmament in the 1930s. Perhaps because of this, at the time, unpopular view, he did not progress much politically but his loyalty was eventually rewarded in October 1940 when Churchill appointed him Minister of Transport. One of his achievements during this appointment was to open the London underground stations during air raids for the people to take shelter. In retrospect this seems an obvious step but it was taken against the advice of his civil servants who warned him that as a consequence he would be personally responsible if any disasters ensued.[4]

Brabazon succeeded Lord Beaverbrook as Minister of Aircraft Production in May 1941 after one of the latter's frequent resignations (allegedly a total of fourteen) was finally accepted. Beaverbrook had suggested Brabazon as his successor but the latter recorded that when he took over the ministry that "The Air Ministry and the MAP were scarcely on speaking terms, so to speak, and as our sole reason for existing was to supply the Royal Air Force with planes, this stuck me as rather ridiculous."[5] It seems that Brabazon was a more conventional minister than his predecessor, which would not have been difficult. Air Chief Marshall Freeman at the MAP wrote in a paper to the Permanent Under Secretary at the Air Ministry that "On Lord Beaverbrook's arrival planning ceased... the manufacturers... were bullied to produce aircraft without being given the raw materials to enable them to fulfil their job."[6]

In turn Brabazon was also to resign, although not voluntarily. In February 1942 he

---

* Rolls was killed in a flying accident in 1910. He was the first British person to be killed as a result of powered flight. He was introduced to Henry Royce in the Midland Hotel in Manchester in 1904 and provided the finance and business acumen to complement Royce's technical expertise in the firm they founded together in 1906. By the time he was killed he was losing interest in the business and had become a non-executive director. Rolls-Royce has remained a permanent feature of the British aero-engine scene although it no longer makes cars and in 1971 had to be rescued from financial collapse by the British Government.

** Brabazon was determined to get this when FLY appeared as a new registration but was beaten to it by a keen fly-fisherman. It cost him a new Rover in exchange for the owner's Vauxhall.[7]

Fig. 1/2 Avro York 685 (FAMA LV-XGO), copyright BAE SYSTEMS Heritage.

gave a speech at a private lunch in Manchester after which he expressed the view that the fighting between Germany and the Soviet Union would relieve the pressure on Britain.[8] Although this was an opinion frequently expressed in private among members of the Conservative Party it was thought to be unhelpful to have it expressed publicly at a time when the Soviet Union was an important, if somewhat suspect, ally.* Churchill asked for his resignation but as consolation he was elevated to the Lords that year and became Lord Brabazon of Tara. The Tara part came from the ancestral home, Tara Hall, in Ireland. His successor as minister for a short time was Colonel J. J. Llewellyn and then the ascetic Sir Stafford Cripps but Brabazon's influence in the aviation world was not over.

The first meeting of the committee which came to bear Brabazon's name was held on 23 December 1942. The seven members of the committee, drawn from the MAP and the Air Ministry, but not from the industry, were asked to outline the various types of civilian aircraft they thought would be needed after the war and to suggest firms that could prepare designs for them. The idea was to find aircraft with which Britain could compete successfully with America, which was regarded as the only country that would pose much of a threat. As an interim measure they were also to consider which military aircraft could be converted for civilian use and to identify any spare design and production capacity within the industry that could be used when the changeover took place.[9] The Brabazon Committee was by no means the only one that considered the post-war

---

* John Colville, one of Churchill's private secretaries and a diarist, recorded that it was "a sentiment widely felt." Apparently "a snooper" at the lunch reported it and Jack Tanner of the Amalgamated Engineering Union announced it, Colville says maliciously, at a meeting of the Trades Union Council.[10]

future of civil aviation, the Shelmerdine and Lamplugh Committees covered similar ground and Lord Beaverbrook continued to be an influential figure[11] but the Brabazon Committee was the most relevant to the genesis of the Comet.

After their tenth meeting on 9 February the following year the committee recommended the adaptation of four military types for civilian use: the Avro Lancaster, which was given a new fuselage with a square cross section and became the York, the Vickers Warwick, an unsuccessful bomber derived from the Wellington, which nobody knew what to do with, and two other bomber conversions – the Lancastrian, again from the Lancaster but much less reworked than the York, and the Halton from the Halifax. None was to be a great success although the York was perhaps the least bad. There were also two derivatives of the Short Sunderland flying boat – the Hythe, with fairings covering where the gun turrets had been, and the more-comprehensively-converted Sandringham. Both were reasonably successful but the days of the flying boat were nearly over.

The committee also suggested five new types, designated Brabazon I to V: I, a large land-based passenger aircraft capable of crossing the North Atlantic; II, a smaller twin-engined passenger aircraft for European routes which would be a replacement for the ubiquitous DC-3; III, a four-engined medium-range aircraft for Empire routes; IV, a jet-propelled mail plane for the North Atlantic and V, a small feeder airliner.[12] The suggestion of the jet-propelled type IV appears to have come from the committee rather than the de Havilland company although around this time (January to June 1943) de Havillands were independently looking at the idea of a short-range civil transport powered by four of its jet engines. From now on there were two strands to the development of the jet transport: the Brabazon Committee producing its reports and recommendations and de Havillands doing design studies.[1]

Sorley's report was followed by an even more comprehensive survey of the American aircraft industry, this time carried out by Sir Roy Fedden. Fedden was one of of the giants of the aero-engine world and had produced a family of radial* piston engines for The Bristol Aeroplane Company ending with the mighty Hercules and the even mightier Centaurus, both of which used the sleeve valve which he had developed. He had become the chief engineer of the company but was sacked on 1 October 1942 after a disagreement with the board. This falling out had had the unusual distinction of reaching the House of Lords when Lord Brabazon had to be reassured by a government spokesman that all possible steps had been taken to repair the rift but that in the end it had proved to be irreparable.[13]

Fedden had upset the board by sending them a letter suggesting that the company should be reorganised. The board did not reply and had never made Fedden a member although his engine division was bigger and more profitable than the airframe division.

---

* A radial engine is one in which air-cooled cylinders radiate out from the centre rather like the petals in a daisy. Their piston rods combine in the centre to drive a shaft attached to the propellor. They have a bigger frontal area than a water-cooled engine, and therefore produce more (parasitic) drag but are not vulnerable to the loss of coolant. The relative merits of radial and water-cooled engines are about even and they were produced in similar numbers during the war.

There was also a disagreement about the royalties that Fedden received on each engine sold which the board had originally agreed to but now felt were excessive. An irresistible force, Fedden, had met an immovable object, the board of The Bristol Aeroplane Company and Fedden had been forced to leave, the only surprise was that it had taken as long as it had.*[14] As far as the members of the board were concerned the last straw was Fedden's knighthood in January 1942 which they thought would make him even more impossible to deal with. Fedden lost his life's work and Bristol's lost their gifted engine designer and took more than a decade to recover.**[15]

Fedden's talents, however, did not go entirely to waste and shortly after his dismissal he became a special adviser to Colonel Llewellyn. Fedden was energetic, well-informed and well-known to the Americans and was an excellent choice to lead what became known as the 'Mission to America'.

Fedden's team set sail for New York on 20 December 1942, just before the first meeting of the Brabazon Committee, and arrived on Boxing Day with Fedden having kept them hard at work during the voyage. The mission lasted just over two months and the report was finished and circulated by June that year. 'Mission to America' was an impressive document, running to some 670 pages, and painted a picture of an enormous, and still growing, aviation industry with technical resources that the British had probably never even dreamt of.[16] It was clear that the British aviation industry would have a hard, perhaps even an impossible job, to compete with the Americans after the war, particularly as far as passenger aircraft were concerned.

'Mission to America' was circulated on a secret basis to the industry and the relevant politicians and civil servants, the more senior receiving bound and numbered volumes,*** but it received a mixed reception. Some of the diehards of the industry referred to it as 'Fedden's Folly'; one undercarriage manufacturer produced a written rebuttal of the newfangled idea that a steerable nose wheel would ever replace the current tail-down arrangement and nearly all the companies either refused to believe much of its content or thought they knew better.[17] One part singled out for particular ridicule was the numbers of trained technical staff that Fedden had said were working for companies such as Boeing. These were between eight and fifteen times greater than those employed in comparable British companies. Wellwood Beall, the vice-president of

---

* Sir Roy Fedden and Air Chief Marshall Freeman were not the best of friends. Fedden considered that Freeman was prejudiced against radial engines and Freeman found Fedden impossible to deal with. When Major Bulman, who worked with Freeman at the MAP, was appointed Director of Construction of Research Facilities (DCRF) Freeman roared with laughter and told him that he had been appointed as Director for Coping with Roy Fedden.[18]

** According to Sir Peter Masefield, little had changed by 1956 when he moved from British European Airways (BEA) to Bristols as managing director. He was not invited to join the board or allowed to make any significant decisions by himself. On arrival he was given to understand that Bristol's was "a place for gentlemen, who were above such things as balance sheets."[19] Their talented chief designer, Leslie Frise, inventor of the Frise aileron, had left in 1948. The board had thought he was "getting too big for his boots."[20]

*** The copy in the National Archives is number 1 and was allocated to Sir Stafford Cripps who by now had replaced Colonel Llewellyn as the Minister for Aircraft Production.

Boeing, visiting Britain in October 1944 was told by a famous figure in the British aviation industry that Fedden had ridiculously stated that Boeing had 3,200 technical staff. Beal confirmed that it was incorrect; it had been correct when Fedden had visited but it was now 3,880.[20] It is difficult to say whether Fedden's report had much beneficial effect on the British industry but almost certainly it had less effect than it ought to have had.*

The Cabinet responded to the Brabazon Committee's report, in the way of governments, by setting up another committee, unoriginally called the Second Brabazon Committee. This had an expanded membership which included Geoffrey de Havilland, and Alan Campbell-Orde from BOAC

The Second Brabazon Committee held a total of 62 meetings starting on 25 May 1943 and ending in November 1945, after which it produced its fifth and final report. At this distance it is difficult to say how much it was influenced by Fedden's report but it must at least have added a sense of urgency. De Havilland was able to show the committee the results of the work done at Hatfield on the jet transport. At the fifteenth meeting on 25 August 1943 the Type IV was discussed and Dr. Harold Roxbee Cox (later Lord Kings Norton), the Director of Special Projects at the Royal Aircraft Establishment (RAE) at Farnborough, was asked to do a study on a jet transport with ranges from 1,000 to 2,000 miles. Brabazon suggested that he consult de Havilland who was not present at this meeting.

During the wait for Cox's paper de Havillands put in a considerable amount of work looking at various designs using pure jets. In November 1943 they looked at a short range (700 miles), 20 seater, civil transport with three of their Goblin turbojets at the rear of a central pod and twin fuselage booms, rather like the Vampire fighter they were working on. Various sizes were examined between November 1943 and April 1944 as well as using three of the larger Ghost engines which had not yet run. Overlapping with this, between December 1943 and February 1944, they also made a fairly extensive study of the pros and cons of a canard design** (see next page).

Roxbee Cox presented the results of his calculations at the 34th meeting of the com-

---

* This was not the only report that Fedden produced. At the end of the war he was sent to Germany to find out what he could about the German aircraft industry.[21] He discovered they were years ahead of the Allies in the design of fast aircraft and had lavish research facilities which had been largely unknown to the Allies. Some of these were dismantled and removed to the UK. In Fedden's view the Allies had been fighting the air war with aircraft at the end of their development potential (such as the piston-engined, propellor-driven Mustang) whereas the Germans were turning out jet and rocket-propelled fighters, in other words the first of the next generation, by the hundreds, to say nothing of the V1 and the V2. Fedden's report on this was received with little official interest, after all the Allies had won the war. He was also horrified to discover that one of the German technicians he talked to (Bruno Bruckmann of BMW) had read a copy of 'Mission to America' on Christmas Day 1943. Ironically its content had been believed by the Germans because Fedden's name was on it and they knew him and his reputation. As well as revealing some of the secrets of the American aviation industry to the Germans it had had, probably more importantly, the effect of completely demoralising them when they saw the enormity of what they faced. Fedden was unable to find out whose copy had found its way to Germany but it may well have been deliberately leaked, possibly by Allen Dulles of the Office of Strategic Services, to produce the effect that it did.[22]

mittee on 2 February 1944. He recommended the use of propellors driven by gas turbines (turboprops) rather than a pure jet. There was considerable support, even within de Havillands, for the view that the pure jet in its present state of development would be uneconomic over long distances but the turboprop was a more complex engine and so far none was available. It was decided to refer the matter to BOAC for a study into the economics of the different engines.

The de Havilland company's studies formed the basis of Brabazon Paper No. 92 presented by de Havilland (now Sir Geoffrey) at the 41st meeting on 19 April 1944. This was discussed together with Roxbee Cox's paper (No. 90) and it was decided to recommend an immediate start for de Havilland's proposal for a pure jet with a range of 600 to 700 miles followed as soon as possible by a turboprop aircraft with a longer range. At the 43rd meeting on 3 May the committee thought it impractical to specify the requirements for the type IV in detail, as it had with the other types, and just set out broadly what was required.[1]

In May 1944 David Newman, one of de Havillands' aerodynamicists, was visiting the United States where he became aware that the Americans were also looking into the possibilities of a pure-jet transport. While in Los Angeles Newman met Major Heenan, who was shortly to be appointed to BOAC as an adviser on future projects. He was keenly interested in the idea of the jet transport and visited Hatfield the following August to follow it up. Campbell-Orde, also from BOAC, was another who was supportive of the jet transport. He had been converted when watching a Vampire on test and Charles Walker, de Havillands' Chief Engineer, had turned to him and said "You can have that performance in an airliner."[23]

Although the idea of a short-range, pure jet was incorporated into the interim report of the Second Brabazon Committee on 18 May 1944 there was a niggling feeling within de Havillands that they could do better, at least in terms of range. Even increasing the takeoff run could increase the range considerably and various alternatives, such as just carrying mail, were suggested to allow the Atlantic to be crossed. Provided that it could be obtained, the company felt that long range was the correct niche for the pure jet and the emphasis changed to this. In August 1944 de Havillands produced a design for the three-Ghost Vampire-type aircraft carrying six passengers and 2,000 pounds of mail and presented it to the committee on 13 October (Fig. 2/2). A model of it was sent to the RAE for wind tunnel tests on 28 February but by March the following year the layout had changed into a more conventional fuselage with four Ghosts. Depending on the diameter of the fuselage it could carry 24 passengers seated three abreast (8 feet 6 inches) or 24 to 36 passengers seated four abreast (10 feet).[1]

** A canard is an airframe layout in which the horizontal tail surfaces are replaced by small wings, called canards, in front of the main wings. The angle of attack of the canards produces a variable amount of lift to control the aircraft's longitudinal attitude and stability. The conventional tail generates a download that has to be counteracted by a greater upload generated by the wing. The canards generate an upload which in theory reduces the amount of power needed to keep the aircraft in the air. In practice though the two sets of wings interfere and any advantage may well disappear. Some modern aircraft, such as the Eurofighter Typhoon, use the canard as a control device.

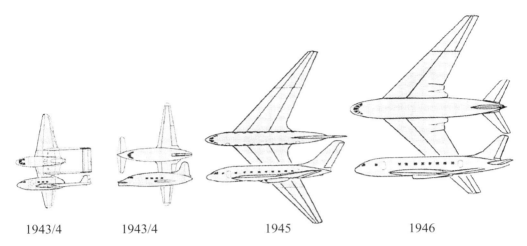

1943/4   1943/4   1945   1946

Fig. 2/2 Design studies for the Comet (Courtesy Bzuk, Wikimedia Commons, recaptioned)

De Havillands finally got the contract to start design work on the jet transport from the MAP in February 1945 (Specification 20/44) and gave it the designation DH 106. It was later called the Comet, reusing the name of de Havilland's elegant 1930s racer. The requirement to be able to cross the North Atlantic was dropped in July 1945.

At the end of the war in Europe Bishop and Clarkson travelled to Germany and saw the advances they had made in designs for high-speed flight, particularly in swept-back wings.[24] This caused a radical design rethink and the studies with unswept wings were abandoned and replaced in July 1945 by a swept-wing design with no tailplane and four engines buried in the wing roots. This was an unusual configuration which had been pioneered by the Messerschmitt Me 163 rocket-propelled fighter, co-incidentally called the Komet, although it had only a single engine at the rear of the short fuselage. The Komet first flew in 1941 and entered active service in 1944. The attraction of not having a tailplane was that the aircraft's drag was reduced, an important advantage at a time when jet engines had limited power and high fuel consumption. The potential disadvantage was that it might cause problems of controlling the aircraft in flight.

Perhaps surprisingly the Ministry of Supply (MoS), which by now had replaced the MAP, accepted the tailless design but they agreed with de Havillands that they should produce an experimental aircraft of the same shape to prove its validity. Design work for this, headed by J. C. M. Frost, started on 20 August 1945. This ultimately emerged as the DH108, called the Swallow by the ministry but not by the company. Three of them were built.

The DH108 consisted of a wooden-framed fuselage covered with aluminium alloy sheeting. To save time the fuselage design was based on that of the Vampire and two were removed from the English Electric production line at Preston for conversion. The metal wings of the first one had a sweepback of 43 degrees which was increased to 45 in the second two. At the rear of the fuselage was a fin and rudder but no horizontal tailplane. In a conventional aircraft the trailing edges of the outer parts of the wings

Fig. 3/2 DH108 Swallow (VW120) and the second prototype Comet fuselage (G-ALZK) on 3 March 1949, copyright BAE SYSTEMS Heritage.

have moving surfaces called ailerons, which cause the aircraft to roll and turn. Similar devices on the tailplane, called elevators, make the aircraft pitch up or down (see Appendix 1). To control the Swallow these functions were combined as movable sections, called elevons, on the trailing edge of the wings that served as elevators or ailerons depending on whether they moved in the same or different directions. The RAE at Farnborough had expressed some reservations about the stability of the Swallow, suggesting that it might develop a 'Dutch roll' (uncommanded yaws and rolls) accompanied by wingtip stall at slow speeds possibly leading to an unrecoverable spin. Because of this de Havillands had attached Handley Page leading edge slats* locked in the open position and anti-spin parachutes in containers at both wing tips.[25]

The first Swallow (TG 283) was completed in August 1945 and made its maiden flight on 15 May 1946, piloted by Geoffrey junior. It had a maximum speed of only 280 mph and was used for slow-speed stability trials. In spite of the reservations expressed by the RAE, it proved to be reasonably controllable and the test programme was successfully completed. It was transferred to Farnborough in 1948 for further testing but crashed after developing an inverted spin on 1 May 1950, killing its pilot Squadron Leader Genders. His parachute failed to open in time after he had abandoned the aircraft at low altitude.

The second Swallow (TG 306) was destined for high-speed trials and received the more powerful Goblin 3 engine. Its first flight was in August 1946. It was certainly fast

---

* A slat is a thin, flap-like device attached to the leading edge of a wing to increase lift at slow speeds by allowing the wing to operate at a greater angle of attack without stalling. Like flaps they are retracted at higher speeds.

for its time, being thought capable of well over 600 mph and, as such, suitable for an attempt on the World Air Speed Record, at that time held by a Gloster Meteor at 614 mph. TG 306 had initial stability problems which seemed to have been largely cured but disaster struck on 27 September when it broke up while flying fast at low level over the Thames Estuary, piloted by Geoffrey junior.

This particular flight was one of a series in which the aircraft had been flown level at different speeds at high altitudes and then dived at high speed. This time the tests would be at high speed and at low level, therefore mixing a high Mach* number with a high EAS** (equivalent air speed), a combination in which the aircraft's stability was unknown. The plan was to dive to Mach 0.87, or less if a problem was encountered, at an altitude of less than 10,000 feet and then to make a level run at low altitude over the sea at maximum rpm (revolutions per minute). The intention was to do the test in this sequence as it was anticipated that some nose-down pitch might develop at speed at these lower altitudes.[26]

Geoffrey took off from Hatfield at 17:26 in good weather with a full load of fuel and headed for the Thames Estuary. The witness statements were inconsistent but it seems likely that TG 306 was flying at high speed from west to east at 'medium' height, probably around 7,000 feet, and broke up suddenly when it was over the Thames near Egypt Bay. An observer on Canvey Island on the north bank of the Thames estuary, Lieutenant H. W. A. Godfrey, himself a pilot, described hearing a loud bang. When he caught sight of the aircraft one wing had already detached and the fuselage with the other wing still attached was spinning. Other witnesses described a loud bang and one or both wings separating from the fuselage and spinning slowly down to earth. In the air, presumably where the explosion had taken place, was a ball of pale orange smoke slowly dispersing. Some accounts said both wings came off at about the same time and then fell 'like leaves' as well as recording a second, double, explosion. According to a Mr. Mudge, who followed the events from Rochester on the south side of the estuary, the time of the accident was 17:38, only twelve minutes after takeoff.[27]

The wreckage was scattered over an area measuring 4,000 feet west to east and 2,000 feet north to south confirming the direction of flight. The wreckage fell onto the

---

* Ernst Mach – pronounced mark – was an Austrian physicist and mathematician (1836 to 1916). He did much of the pioneering work into supersonic air flow in the 1870s. The Mach number is the ratio of a particular speed to the local speed of sound. So Mach 0.5 is half the speed of sound, Mach 2 is twice the speed of sound etc. Mach numbers less than 0.8 are referred to as subsonic, between 0.8 and 1.2 transonic and from 1.2 to 5.0 supersonic.

** When an aeroplane is flying, its speed through the air is estimated using a Pitot tube. This consists of a tube, blocked at one end, with its open end facing the direction in which the aircraft is flying. The pressure that builds up in this tube, the stagnation pressure, is compared with the pressure measured at a side orifice, the atmospheric or static pressure. The difference between these two readings is called the dynamic pressure. This generates the indicated airspeed (IAS) displayed in the cockpit. For various reasons this may not be the true airspeed, particularly in high-speed flight where the air becomes compressed in the Pitot tube generating an erroneously high pressure and therefore an erroneously high speed reading. Using charts the IAS can be corrected to the speed at sea level that would produce the same dynamic pressure as that of the true airspeed at the altitude at which the aeroplane is flying. This is called the equivalent air speed. It is a concept more used in test flying than everyday flying.

mud of the tidal bed of the Thames which caused some difficulty in its retrieval. Accurate plotting of the places where individual pieces had fallen was impractical due to possible movement by the water. From the distribution of the wreckage the RAE investigation tentatively suggested that the starboard wing detached first, followed by the disintegration of the front fuselage at about 6,000 feet and the remainder of the air-craft at about 2,000 feet.

Examination of the wreckage showed that both wings had failed in download (i.e. they had been pushed or pulled down relative to the fuselage when the aircraft was fly-ing the normal way up). The disintegration of the fuselage was secondary to the wings falling off. There was no evidence of any structural, mechanical or material defect. Neither was there any evidence of flutter being the cause of the wing failures and cal-culations showed that the speed necessary to induce flutter, about 1,230 mph, was much higher than any likely to have been reached.[26]

The aeroplane carried a primitive flight data recorder which was found and revealed that the breakup had probably occurred in a shallow dive at about 7,000 feet at a speed of 581 mph EAS (Mach 0.872).

Geoffrey's body was not found until 7 October when it was washed ashore at Whitstable. An autopsy showed that he had suffered a massive head injury and a broken neck. His harness had failed in upload, suggesting that the aircraft had pitched down violently but the cockpit canopy showed no sign of impact. It had become detached although it had not been deliberately jettisoned.

Even with all this information it was not clear why the aeroplane had broken up when it did and it took some high-speed wind tunnel tests at Farnborough to work out what had happened. These revealed that at Mach numbers over 0.86 there was a loss of elevon effect in the pitching plane which at speeds greater than Mach 0.9 changed to a reversal of control caused by the wings becoming distorted by the air passing over them. Accompanying this was a nose-down change of trim and reduced longitudinal stability resulting in the aircraft pitching nose down into a steep dive with no possibility of recovery. This produced massive stresses on the airframe resulting in the starboard wing being torn off followed by the general disintegration of the whole structure.

It seems probable that TG 306 suddenly developed high frequency longitudinal oscillations which overstressed the starboard wing attachments and caused the wing to separate in down load.[26] The rest of the disintegration then followed and Geoffrey was flung upwards out of the aeroplane when it was in a down pitch sometime after the canopy had separated. Geoffrey was the second of de Havilland's sons to have died in a flying accident; in 1943 John had been killed in a mid-air collision while flying a Mosquito. It was a double tragedy from which their mother never fully recovered.

Before his death Geoffrey junior had formed the opinion that it was a bad idea to do away with the tailplane. Nevertheless a third Swallow (VW 120) was constructed, mainly to continue the research into high-speed flight with swept-back wings. It had a more pointed nose, a slightly extended fuselage and a smaller and a more aerodynamic canopy, It was first flown on 24 July 1947 by John Cunningham who had become the chief test pilot after Geoffrey's death. In the light of recent events it was equipped with an ejector

Fig. 4/2 Geoffrey de Havilland, Jnr., copyright BAE SYSTEMS Heritage.

seat. This aircraft later became the first in Britain to exceed the speed of sound in a dive from 40,000 to 30,000 feet, on 6 September 1948, with John Derry at the controls.[28]

On 19 August 19 VW120 was transferred to the MoS and based at Farnborough where it was flown by another test pilot, Eric Brown,* who described the experience in his book *Wings on my Sleeve*:[29]

> The first object was to get the plane going as fast as possible, as high up as possible and then gradually step down the height just as Geoffrey de Havilland (Jnr.) had been doing when the aeroplane broke up at 10,000 feet. Our first series of tests were made at 35,000 feet, and I reached Mach 0.985 after a dive from 45,000 feet.
>
> ...Then we repeated the tests at a medium height level of 25,000 feet. But this time I reached only 0.94. This time I was deliberately jerking the stick backwards and forwards to simulate the effect of the bumpy air which would have been met with at low altitudes such as that at which the world record run would have taken place and Geoffrey de Havilland had been flying when he was killed. Even with the slightest sharp movement fore and aft the aircraft began to oscillate to an extent that was becoming dangerous at this

* Eric 'Winkle' Brown was a renowned test pilot. Among his many other achievements he flew a total of 52 different captured German aircraft, including ten flights in the rocket-propelled Messerschmitt 163, albeit only as a glider. He was also one of the few people, quite possibly the only person, to fly two of the fastest piston-engined propeller fighters, the de Havilland Sea Hornet and the Dornier 335.[30, 31] In 2014, at the age of 95, he bought a new sports car and appeared on *Desert Islands Discs*.

speed.

I had had no trouble of this kind at 30,000 feet, but here was a warning signal that the Swallow lacked longitudinal damping at the higher indicated airspeeds met at lower heights. A long plank will always balance better than a short one, and in a conventional aircraft with a normal tail unit the inherent stability usually damps the oscillating motion before it becomes really dangerous. But it had long been suspected that a tailless aircraft would lack this steadying feature. It is rather like cutting off the tail of an ordinary machine and trying to re-balance it at a point much farther forward.

With this very much in mind I descended to 10,000 feet, knowing all the time that it was at this stage that Geoffrey de Havilland had met disaster.

At Mach 0.88 it happened. The ride was smooth, then suddenly went all to pieces. As the plane porpoised wildly my chin hit my chest, jerked hard back, slammed forward again, repeated it over and over, flogged by the awful whipping of the plane. My thoughts were grim.

This was how it happened. This was how he had died. In the same second his head had cracked the canopy top and broken his neck,* the wings had gone, the plane broken up.

He was a big man, I was short. And I had had my seat lowered as far as it would go, with this in mind. I wouldn't break my neck yet. This was the moment of truth. But I was going under fast, I couldn't keep this up. The whole plane was oscillating as fast as a hand can wave goodbye. The G was murderous and getting worse.

Like another hand guiding me, the drill we had practised so hard took over. Both hands went out, both hauled hard back, one on the throttle, one on the stick. The motion ceased as quickly as it had started. I sat, head bowed, shaking. If this hadn't worked I would have been finished.

As with the first two Swallows, VW 120 duly crashed, killing its pilot Squadron Leader Muller-Rowland on 15 February 1950 near Brickhill in Buckinghamshire. The Board of Inquiry blamed the crash on a failure of the pilot's oxygen delivery system. All in all the Swallow had a short but consistently lethal career.

Fortunately Bishop's ideas had already changed before the first 108 had flown. By March 1946 the Comet's wings were still swept but the tail had reappeared. This allowed larger flaps on the wings and so lower landing and takeoff speeds. In turn this meant a smaller and lighter wing and hence a bigger payload. The possibilities of using an axial jet engine were also being discussed although, like the turboprop, none was commercially available yet. At this time the design for the transport had 40° swept wings with four Ghosts and a swept tail but by July the leading-edge sweep had been reduced to 25°, more for centre-of-gravity reasons than for high-speed flight, with the trailing edge much less swept. The tailplane was tapered with slightly swept leading edges. The fin was symmetrically tapered. By August the design had pretty much been finalised and on 27 September Sir Geoffrey telephoned BOAC to agree the final points of the design so the detailed design work could start. That evening young Geoffrey was killed.

By November 1946 a complete specification for the DH 106 was ready. At an all up weight of 100,000 pounds it was estimated that it could carry a payload of 7,000 pounds

---

* The RAE report said there was no evidence of an impact on the cockpit canopy.

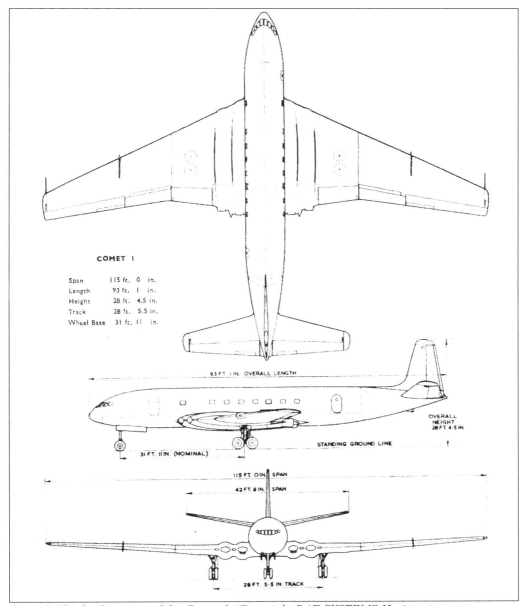

Fig. 5/2 The final version of the Comet 1 (Copyright BAE SYSTEMS Heritage)

(24 passengers) from London to Gander in Newfoundland, while for Empire routes an all up weight of 96,000 pounds and a stage length of 2,200 miles would give a payload of 10,000 pounds (32 passengers). On 21 January 1947 the MoS issued a contract to the company for the construction of eight Comets at an approximate cost of £250,000 each. These aircraft were intended to be operated by BOAC but British South American Airlines (BSAA) then ordered another six only to have five of them cancelled when it

was subsumed within BOAC. These nine were in addition to the two prototypes. The projected unit cost of £250,000 proved, as might be expected, to be a gross underestimate.

In their final report in November 1945 the Brabazon Committee decided that no fewer than nine new types were needed. There were to be two type I large transatlantic passenger aircraft. The first became the enormous Bristol Brabazon which flew for the first time in 1949. The second was intended to be a developed version of the first, with turboprops rather than piston engines.* Both were products of the pre-war view that long-distance flying was for the rich, or important, few, travelling in relatively slow aircraft in spacious luxury because of the length of time they had to spend cooped up. Occupying almost the same niche, but slightly later, was the equally enormous Princess flying boat.

In retrospect it is amazing to think that a virtually-bankrupt nation, at the end of an exhausting war, could devote so many of its scarce resources into building two of the largest aircraft the world has ever seen. Even today their statistics are staggering. The Brabazon had eight, 18-cylinder, Bristol Centaurus radial engines grouped in pairs, each pair driving large, contra-rotating, propellers. Its wingspan was 230 feet, larger than a Boeing 747-400 and only eclipsed in 2005 by the Airbus A380's at 261 feet and the immense Hughes Spruce Goose, another white elephant, at 320 feet. The Princess flying boat, had an amazing ten Bristol Proteus turboprop engines, eight coupled in pairs and two outboard singles. It had a slightly smaller wingspan of almost 220 feet, still larger than the 747's 211 feet.**

The type II European transport divided into three types, one of which became the commercial success story of the Brabazon Committee – the Vickers Viscount. The other two were the now largely-forgotten Ambassador and the Apollo. The Brabazon III, the medium-range Empire airliner, never came to anything although the Britannia perhaps came closest to it. The type V, the small feeder airliner, became two aircraft, both made by de Havillands and both reasonably successful: the two-engined Dove and the four-engined Heron, although the Dove had been started in 1943 before the committee had started to meet. The Comet was to be the most ambitious of the Brabazon designs to survive as far as commercial service.

---

* Lord Hives, a shrewd businessman and the head of Rolls-Royce, was once told that it was such a pity that the Brabazon had not had his marvellous engines which would have made the outcome so different. He thought for a moment and replied, "You have no idea how hard I had to work to make sure that the business went to a competitor."[32]

** Whitney Straight of BOAC said that "...the Princess was likely to be the largest and the most criticism-worthy white elephant ever produced in the history of aviation."[33]

Chapter 3

THE ENGINE

The great bugbear of long-distance air travel was how long it took; less time than going by sea certainly but there were many other distractions to help in passing the time on an ocean liner. Passenger aircraft of the immediate post-war era cruised at little more than 300 mph at about 20,000 feet and crossing from London to New York took around 20 hours if the time spent at refuelling stops was included.[1] Flying any distance was time-consuming, expensive, boring, unreliable and uncomfortable although the airlines tried their best to provide a luxury service. The answer to some of these problems was speed and most of the design features of the Comet sprang from this need to be faster.

Before the Comet all passenger aircraft in commercial service were powered by internal combustion piston engines using petrol and driving propellers. These were just larger versions of the engine that drives most cars. The propeller was the means of using this engine to move the aircraft forward. The blades of the propellor act like small wings and as they rotate they push large volumes of air behind them. The aircraft obeys Newton's Third Law* and 'reacts' to this rearward movement of air by moving forward itself. The problem was that the piston-engine-propeller combination had intrinsic limitations and had been developed about as far as it reasonably could be by the end of the war.

The internal combustion piston engine is a heat engine; it combines an oil-based fuel with air, compresses the mixture and then ignites it. This produces a massive rise in pressure which pushes a tightly-fitting piston along a cylinder which is closed at one end and open at the other. Just beyond the open end the linear movement of the piston is converted to rotation by a rod attached at one end to the base of the piston and at the other eccentrically to a shaft – the crankshaft. In turn the crankshaft is connected via a gearbox to the propeller. Although this might sound simple in principle there is a considerable amount of engineering to make sure that it all functions.

There is a practical limit to the amount of power that can be delivered by a piston engine. The hottest part of the engine is within the cylinders which can only be cooled at their walls and the larger the cylinder the smaller its surface-to-volume ratio and the less efficient the cooling. So more power means more cylinders and thus more complication and less reliability. Doctor, later Sir, Stanley Hooker, one of the giants of gas

---

* For every action there is an equal and opposite reaction.

Fig. 1/3 Sir Stanley Hooker (copyright Rolls-Royce/courtesy of Rolls-Royce Heritage Trust)

turbine development, once calculated that to produce 4,000 hp a piston engine would need 36 cylinders.[2] In fact Halford's Sabre VII engine and the Rolls Eagle almost managed it with 24,[3] and the Sabre may even have exceeded it in a special version, but the principle was correct. It reached its apotheosis in the 71.5 litre, radial, Pratt and Whitney Wasp Major that had four rows of seven cylinders and drove the Boeing Stratocruiser.* The Brabazon coped by having coupled engines. The most powerful piston engines had become very big and very complicated.

There were other problems too. In order to fly faster it is necessary to fly higher where the atmospheric pressure, and hence the air density, is lower, which causes less parasitic drag (see Chapter 4). Lower air density also means that a smaller mass of air is entrained into the cylinders of the engine and its power decreases accordingly. To maintain their power output, high-flying piston engines need to have air pumped into them by compressors (superchargers) but even these have limitations.** High altitude also reduces the efficiency of propellers as a smaller mass of air is pushed backwards reducing the thrust. Using larger and faster-rotating propellers with more and better-shaped blades and even contra-rotating propellers is only a partial solution as the blades interfere with each other and as their tips approach supersonic speeds their efficiency decreases considerably.[4] Taken together these constraints mean that the speed and altitude of aircraft powered by piston engines driving propellers was limited.

The obvious solution was to use the new turbojet engine and it became the defining technology of the Comet. The jet engine was not constrained by having to use a propeller and could provide greater speeds by delivering more power. This was the principal

* There was an even larger, 36 cylinder, 127 litre, 5,000 hp Lycoming XR-7755 which was designed in 1944 but only two were built and neither flew.
** Hooker, started his career as a fluid-dynamics mathematician and made his name by redesigning, and much improving, the supercharger for the Spitfire's Merlin engine. He repeated the trick later on by providing two superchargers in series for the Merlin 61 which enabled the Spitfire IX to hold its own with its German opponents.[5]

advantage of the turbojet. Although in many ways it was less efficient than the piston engine it could generate more power from the same mass and volume of engine, although this improvement was relatively small for the Ghost and the real benefits would only be seen with later engines.*

Among the victors of the Second World War Britain held the lead in jet engine technology and the hope was that the Brabazon type IV would be able to use this expertise to leapfrog the Americans and seize the market for advanced airliners. To some extent it might be said that the Comet was an engine looking for an airframe but it is probably truer to say that it was the result of several things coming together at the same time: a commercial need to find a saleable product, a new engine technology becoming available and an awareness of new aerodynamics.

De Havillands had got into the jet engine business early by producing their own engines and the Vampire fighter but, in common with other British manufacturers, they had no recent experience of making large passenger aircraft. They had some pre-war experience with the Flamingo but it was limited. Knowing that the company would be facing a collapse in military orders at the end of the war it was not surprising that de Havilland and his company showed considerable interest in the type IV. De Havillands was as good a choice to make it as any of the British aircraft companies of the time and probably better than most.

There are several types of internal-combustion jet engine. All entrain a large volume of air, compress it and then use an oil-based fuel to heat and expand it so that it is expelled at high speed from the rear of the engine. The fundamental reason for the greater power intensity of the jet engine is that it can admit vastly more air over a given time period than an equivalent-sized piston engine can.

The simplest jet engine is the ramjet. This is little more than a tube open at both ends with fuel squirted in half way along and ignited. Unfortunately to make it work it has to be moving forward at around 300 or 400 mph, both to get enough air in, to compress it sufficiently, and to make sure the expanded gas emerges from the right end. It has found a role in guided missiles which are launched with solid-fuel boosters to get them up to speed. The pulse jet used in the German V1 is a variation of the ramjet. It, too, is a simple tube but with a mechanism for intermittently closing off the front end when the tube has been charged with air and fuel and then ignited. Like the ramjet it needs a push start.

The turbojet is a more practical engine. As its name suggests it is a combination of a jet engine and a turbine. The turbine extracts energy from the jet efflux and uses it to drive a compressor at the front of the engine to suck in and compress large volumes of

---

* D. P. Davies, the author of a standard textbook on flying jet transports, says that at best a piston engine produces about two pounds of thrust for each pound weight and a turbojet at worst about four.[6]   The Comet's Ghost 50 Mark 1 engines weighed 2,011 pounds and had a maximum thrust of 5,000 pounds giving a power to weight ratio of about 2.5, only a slight improvement over a piston engine. The larger Rolls-Royce Trents have a ratio of over 7. As an illustration of the incredible intensity of power of a modern jet engine Bill Gunston, a British aviation writer, points out that a turbine (but not the rest of the engine) that would fit into a suitcase could generate as much power as 50 diesel locomotives.[7]

air. This air, at very high pressure, is then fed into the combustion chambers where it is mixed with fuel and ignited. The resulting, much-larger, volume of hot gas leaves through the rear of the engine and provides the thrust as well as driving the turbine. This turbine-compressor combination was the most important feature of the turbojet and it removed the need for an external source of gas such as the air compressed by the forward motion of the ramjet. Hence a turbojet can run when the aircraft is stationary or building up to cruising speed, although it still needs an external power input to start.

Like the ramjet the turbojet amounts to a tube open at both ends although its contents are rather more complicated. Starting from the inlet at the front end, the first moving part is the compressor. The purpose of the compressor is to convert the energy in its rotating parts into an increase in the temperature and pressure of the air flowing through it. There are two types of compressor, centrifugal and axial. A centrifugal compressor is a rapidly-spinning disc, also called an impeller, with walls, or vanes, radiating outwards from its centre. A large volume of air enters at the centre and is flung outwards, being accelerated and compressed at the same time. From the periphery the air passes into a circumferential diffuser which also contains vanes which slow the flow and continue the process of converting it into pressure. About half the increase in pressure takes place in the impeller and the other half in the diffuser. The diffuser also reduces the chance of the airflow extinguishing the flames when it enters the combustion chambers, the next section of the engine.

An axial compressor consists of a series of discs with blades radiating out from their perimeters. It is called axial because the entrained air moves along the axis of the engine. Each blade has the shape of an aerofoil, rather like a propeller blade. The discs are attached to a central, longitudinal shaft which rotates at high speed when the engine

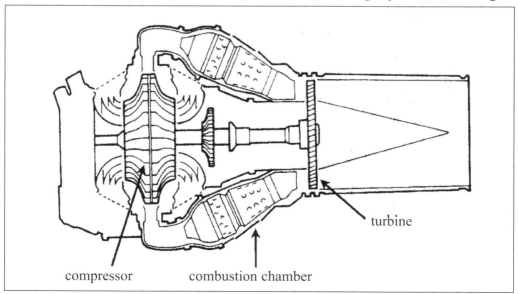

compressor   combustion chamber   turbine

Fig. 2/3 A double-entry, single-stage, centrifugal turbojet (Copyright Rolls-Royce plc/courtesy of Rolls-Royce Heritage Trust)

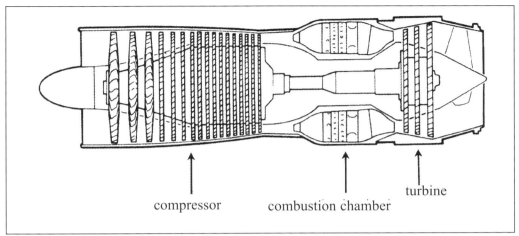

Fig. 3/3 A single-spool axial flow turbojet (copyright Rolls-Royce plc/courtesy of Rolls-Royce Heritage Trust)

is running. Each rotating disc with its blades has a similar, but stationary, set of blades downstream of it called a stator (not shown in the above diagram) which converts the rotational kinetic energy of the air into static pressure. Each pair of compressor disc and stator is called a stage. The whole set of stages is contained within the cylindrical body of the engine with little clearance between the tips of the rotating blades and the wall to keep reverse air flow to a minimum. The air is progressively moved along the engine and compressed by successive stages. The gradual decrease in the cross-sectional area of the annular gas pathway keeps the axial velocity of the gas nearly constant. Several stages are needed and in modern engines the stages may be grouped into two or three sets each rotating at different speeds, the high pressure section just before the combustion chambers rotating the fastest. As well as being compressed the air is also warmed by the process of compression. The greater the overall compression ratio the greater the thrust and the greater the efficiency of the engine. This is the main advantage of the axial compressor over the centrifugal, it can work in a series of stages and produce much more overall compression than a centrifugal compressor as well as being able to entrain more air. At the end of the compressor stages the air is fed into the combustion chambers.

The combustion chambers are multiple cylinders, grouped around the periphery of the central rotating shaft, into which the fuel is pumped, added to the hot high-pressure air from the compressor and ignited. The resulting extremely hot air with a small amount of burned fuel, still at very high pressure, leaves the rear of the chambers at high speed and enters a single, central, hollow cylinder containing the turbine. More modern engines use a single, annular combustion chamber.

A turbine is a mechanism for extracting energy from fluid flow, in this case the hot gas emerging from the combustion chambers, to convert it into rotary motion, in this case the turbine disc or discs, in order to do work. These discs are similar to the compressor discs with multiple peripheral blades closely surrounded by the engine casing. Each turbine disc is attached to the central shaft connected to the compressor. There are three types of turbine: impulse, reaction and a combination of the two. Impulse turbines project high velocity fluid through fixed nozzles onto roughly bucket-shaped blades attached to a rotating shaft. The blades move away producing the rotation (Newton's Second Law*). Reaction turbines alter the direction of flow of the driving fluid and accelerate it through a nozzle which then moves in the opposite direction to the jet (Newton's Third Law). In practice modern turbines are a combination of impulse and reaction types in proportions that may vary even along the length of an individual blade.

Early turbojets had a single turbine disc but modern turbines have several discs which may be rotating at different speeds on different concentric shafts (multi-spool) driving different stages of the compressor. The first part of a multi-stage, multi-spool turbine is the hottest and rotates the fastest, driving the high-pressure section of the compressor. In a similar way to the stator plates in the compressor there are multiple stationary plates, called nozzle guide vanes, in front of each rotating turbine disc which direct the flow of gas and increase its velocity. As the gas passes through the turbine and its temperature and pressure decrease and the turbine discs increase in diameter and in multi-spool engines rotate more slowly. The pressure drop in the turbine is less than the build-up in the compressor so the excess can be used to accelerate the jet exhaust rearwards.[8]

The turbine, or the first of multiple turbine discs, is usually the limiting part of the engine. It receives high velocity gas which produces a large lateral load on the blades forcing the disc to rotate. The discs rotate at high speed producing a massive centrifugal load on the blades and all of this takes place at a very high temperature. This causes the blades to suffer from metal fatigue, thermal fatigue (cracking caused by temperature gradients developing during heat cycles), creep (a gradual elongation) and corrosion. The high pressure turbine discs operate in an extremely hostile environment at the very edge of what is possible. This 'edge' is continually being advanced as the higher the temperature the more efficient the engine, prompting the use of ever-more-exotic alloys and blades with complex cooling mechanisms to slow their deterioration.

The internal shape of a multiple-disc turbine chamber is usually a diverging annulus, formed by the casing and the base of a central cone, to accommodate the increasing size and exposure of the turbine discs. The apex of the cone points in the direction of the gas flow and extends into the nozzle area which in civil aircraft engines usually has a convergent shape to increase the velocity of the escaping gas. The internal shape of the early, single-disc, turbine chamber shown on page 58 (Fig. 2/3) was parallel-sided but the Ghost's was convergent.

The jet engine works by accelerating a large mass of air through the engine and ejecting it at high speed out of a rear-facing nozzle, an example of Newton's Second Law. The reaction to this force, the thrust, pushes the aircraft forward, giving about as good a demonstration of Newton's Third Law as you are likely to get.** ***

---

* Force = mass x acceleration.

The early turbojets had an enormous fuel consumption which limited the range of the aircraft they powered. One senior RAF pilot who was allowed to fly the Gloster Whittle was reputed to have said that it was the only aircraft he had ever flown where you could see the fuel gauge pointer move as the engine was running.[9] There were several reasons for this. One of the most important was the way the turbojet produced its thrust. It turns out that greatly accelerating a smaller mass of gas, like the early engines did, uses far more fuel than accelerating a larger mass of gas rather less, like a modern fan jet does.****

There are other reasons for the turbojet's high fuel consumption. One measure of an engine's efficiency is its propulsive efficiency. This is the work done to propel the aircraft divided by the work done by the engine to accelerate the air passing through it. It can be shown that the faster the aircraft moves forward, or the slower the jet efflux, the greater the propulsive efficiency of its engine* (see next page). Hence the engine in a turbojet-powered aircraft, unlike that in a propeller aircraft, becomes more efficient the faster it flies and a turbojet only becomes really efficient at speeds more like those of Concorde than the Comet. Against this is the increased drag of high-speed flight, particularly as supersonic speeds are approached.

** In the early days of the jet engine when Hooker had to explain the principle of how it worked, by no means as well known then as it is now, he used to release the neck of an inflated balloon and allow it to fly about the lecture theatre. On one occasion he forgot to prepare the balloon in advance and at the last minute retreated to the Gents. to inflate it. Perhaps a little apprehensive at the forthcoming lecture he overdid the blowing and the balloon exploded loudly. This was followed by an anxious cry from a nearby cubicle asking whether everything was all right. It is interesting to speculate about what was going through the mind of the gentleman in the cubicle.[10]

*** $T = Mt^{-1}(Vj - Va)$ where T = thrust

Mt^{-1} = mass of air passing through the engine per unit time

Vj = velocity of the jet efflux

Va = forward velocity of the aircraft

(This ignores the gas produced by burning the fuel, which is about 2% of the mass of air taken into the engine, and the nozzle becoming choked when Vj reaches the speed of sound at the temperature of the jet efflux. Vj for the Ghost was subsonic).

**** The kinetic (or moving) energy (K.E.) of the jet exhaust depends on the product of the mass of gas in the jet efflux and the square of its velocity.

$K.E. = \frac{1}{2} M.V^2$ where M = mass

V = velocity

The power of the engine is the rate at which this energy has been converted from the energy in its fuel.

$P = \frac{1}{2} Mt^{-1}.Vj^2$ where P = power of engine

When an engine has reached a steady state its fuel consumption is directly proportional to its power output. Power output, and therefore fuel consumption, depends on V^2 but thrust is a function of velocity change i.e. V. Thrust can be increased by raising the air flow though the engine (Mt^{-1}) or by increasing the jet velocity (Vj). Other parameters remaining constant, thrust and fuel consumption will increase linearly with increases of M; doubling M doubles the thrust and doubles the fuel consumption. But increasing the thrust by increasing Vj increases fuel consumption in proportion to Vj^2. So doubling the thrust by doubling Vj increases fuel consumption by (approximately) a factor of four, as well as making the engine much noisier. So for the same thrust it requires less fuel to accelerate a large mass of gas a little than accelerating a small mass of gas a lot, hence the greater fuel efficiency of the high-bypass-ratio fan jet.)

Another measure is the thermal efficiency of the engine. This is a measure of how much of the heat produced by the burning fuel is used to accelerate the gas passing through the engine. Much of this heat is inevitably lost to the atmosphere in the jet efflux and even modern engines can only manage a thermal efficiency of about 45%. The higher the turbine inlet temperature compared with the compressor inlet temperature the greater the thermal efficiency of the engine and the greater the velocity of the jet efflux. Hence the struggle to get higher and higher turbine temperatures.

Other factors include the rate of rotation of the turbine and compressor. This is generally designed to be most efficient at the aircraft's cruising speed and is usually about 90% of the maximum. If run at this rate at low level the aircraft's speed would generate considerable drag and it is much more economical for jet-powered aircraft only to fly fast at high altitude. There was also a general lack of refinement of the early turbojets with inefficient centrifugal compressors and a single-stage, relatively low-temperature turbine with inefficient blade shapes.

Like the piston engine the turbojet's power output is reduced by increasing altitude as it entrains less dense air but it is much less affected. Also its loss of power is offset to some extent by the low air temperature, making the engine more efficient,[11] as well as the higher speed at which the aircraft moves at altitude and the lower ambient pressure which produces less back pressure on the jet exhaust giving it a higher velocity. Other advantages are a far simpler and more efficient cooling system and vastly less vibration than with a piston engine.[6]

Given the work they were expected to do the power output from the early turbojets was limited, particularly compared with what came later. Nevertheless they were the only way that aircraft could fly faster, higher and more comfortably and it is easy to see why a jet airliner was such an attractive proposition.

The history of turbojet development

Turbines have a history stretching back to antiquity but the first practical ones of any size and power were produced by Charles Parsons in the early 1880s. These were axial turbines with the driving gas, steam, coming from a boiler heated by coal. This separate supply of driving gas was one of the main differences between Parson's turbines and the new internal-combustion turbines which burned the fuel within the engine itself making the entrained air into the driving gas. By 1889 Parsons had set up a company in Newcastle upon Tyne to manufacture steam turbines for driving electricity generators and later on ships. They were hugely successful and are still extensively used today.

The turbojet started life in several different places at about the same time, as is so

---

* (note from page 61)

$$Pe = 2Va / (Va + Vj)$$ where Pe = propulsive efficiency

It can be seen from this that the closer Va is to Vj then the greater the propulsive efficiency – the Froude effect. However the net thrust (the thrust available in flight) is generated by the difference between Va and Vj and as Va becomes closer to Vj the net thrust decreases. The modern fan jet achieves high propulsive efficiency by lowering Vj and compensating for the reduced thrust by having a greater mass flow through the engine.

often the case with inventions. The two main places were Germany and Britain but there were also contemporary developments in America, Italy, France, Switzerland and Sweden. In 1919 the Air Ministry, prompted by the Aeronautical Research Committee (ARC), asked the director of its South Kensington Laboratory, Dr. W. J. Stern, to look into the prospects of using turbines to drive aircraft propellors. Unfortunately Dr. Stern took no account of developing an engine suitable for aircraft and just considered the statistics of a current industrial turbine and concluded that it would be too heavy and too inefficient to be of any use. His prediction was that the aircraft turbine, "will not be rendered practical by a revolutionary design of some lucky inventor. The steam turbine engineer and the metallurgist... are the people with whom future development must rest."[12] He was at least right about the metallurgist. Stern's negative view was to blight British official opinion for some years to come.

Fig. 4/3 Dr. A. A. Griffith (copyright Rolls-Royce plc/ courtesy of Rolls-Royce Heritage Trust)

Another major figure in British turbine history was Dr. A. A. Griffith who worked at the RAE in Farnborough. In the 1920s he developed a theoretical basis for the design of axial turbines which was published in 1926.[13] Griffith pointed out that current gas turbines were hopelessly inefficient because insufficient thought had been given to the design of their blades which consequently usually operated in a stalled condition. Their efficiency would be much improved by designing them as aerofoils, reducing their angles of attack* and placing them further apart to reduce interference. His paper also contained the essentials of what would now be called a turboprop, with a compressor and turbine connected by the same shaft with an interposed combustion chamber or chambers. With the blessing of the ARC he proceeded to build a test rig which did

---

* This is the angle between the chord line of the blade and the oncoming gas. See Chapter 4 for a description of aerofoils and how they function.

appear to work satisfactorily. This led to a proposal to build an engine of a particularly complicated design, only part of which was ever completed. As an illustration of the sophistication of Griffith's ideas he proposed having a series of high, medium and low-pressure turbines driving a similar series of axial compressors in order to obtain optimum gas flow,[14] an arrangement that was only realised in the Rolls-Royce RB 203 Trent in 1967.[15] Griffith's paper was reviewed by the ARC in 1930 which concluded that "...the superiority of the gas turbine over the reciprocating engine cannot be predicted."[16]   Shortly after this Griffith was moved to South Kensington which had no manufacturing facilities. Not long after he arrived there he was asked to assess a proposal for a turbojet from an unexpected source.

Flying Officer Frank Whittle, then aged 22, had realised that a jet engine could be used to propel an aeroplane faster and higher than had previously been thought possible. The story of Whittle's struggle with officialdom and the recalcitrant technology of the turbojet is well known,[17, 18] but it is perhaps not entirely the story that has sometimes been portrayed of a lone genius struggling against an obstructive and devious bureaucracy.[19, 20, 21] The turbojet turned out to be an example of a device which is easy of concept and difficult of execution and as a consequence it suffered a long and tortuous gestation. Even Whittle said, "The invention was nothing. The real achievement was making the thing work."[22] It is therefore not surprising that its development would test his patience and that of the officials and industrialists with whom he came into contact.

Whittle started with the idea of a piston engine driving a compressor to provide air for combustion chambers but he soon realised that a turbine downstream of the combustion chambers could do the job more efficiently. This was not an original idea, Charles Parsons had patented the idea in 1884[23] and Griffith, unknown to Whittle,[24] had already suggested it for an aero-engine but it was Whittle who was to turn it into a practical proposition. It was also a lot simpler to use the excess energy in the exhaust to propel the aeroplane than getting the turbine to drive a propeller.

In 1929 Whittle submitted his ideas to the Air Ministry who were unconvinced and referred him to Dr. Griffith who similarly dismissed it, perhaps because Whittle had suggested a centrifugal compressor rather than Griffith's axial compressor but also because he was able to find a mistake in Whittle's calculations. Griffith and W. L. Tweedie, an official at the Air Ministry, could also foresee problems finding materials able to withstand the turbine's hostile environment. The advantage of the centrifugal over the axial compressor was that it was simpler to design and manufacture and there was much more experience of making them as they were already used in superchargers. The disadvantage was that they produced less compression and they also meant a wider engine causing more drag. Nevertheless at this stage centrifugal compressors were a more practical proposition than axial compressors and were to be so for several years. The materials problem was real enough though.

In spite of the lack of official support Whittle took out a patent for a single-shaft turbojet in January 1930. This was not put on the Secret List and was thus free for all interested parties to read and it almost certainly was read by his competitors in Germany.[25]

Discouraged, but not defeated, Whittle continued with his ideas and was thought well enough of within the RAF to be sent on their engineering course at Henlow and in 1934 to Cambridge where he got a first after doing the three year engineering tripos in two years.*

Whittle's turbojet patent came up for renewal in 1935 but the Air Ministry refused the £5 fee and Whittle felt he could not afford to pay it himself, but things were about to change. A firm of investment bankers, O. T. Falk and Partners, took an interest and provided enough money in March 1936 to set up a small company called Power Jets, with Whittle as the engineer in charge. Although he was still a serving RAF officer Whittle was allowed a year's

Fig. 5/3 Air Commodore Frank Whittle (copyright Rolls-Royce plc/courtesy of Rolls-Royce Heritage Trust)

leave of absence to do a postgraduate year at Cambridge, provided he did not spend more than six hours a week working for Power Jets. It is uncertain whether this was a strict requirement or just a means of justifying to the Treasury the secondment of a serving RAF officer to work on a project that was thought not to have much of a future. It is, though, a demonstration that Whittle was not being treated with the official indifference that is sometimes portrayed.

---

* As well as being an inventive engineer the younger Whittle was an accomplished pilot who became known for his dare-devil flying at the Hendon air displays. He was also involved in early experiments in catapulting aircraft, replacing a large sheep which was said to have had an "intrepid and professional attitude," at least until the catapult was activated.[26] Whittle survived 47 sea-plane catapult launches, including one with a passenger, Flight Lieutenant Kirk. Immediately after this launch Whittle was alarmed to discover that it was very difficult to stop the nose of the aeroplane from pushing upwards. After a few seconds he glanced back to find his passenger seemingly impaled on the tail fin but nevertheless able to give a nonchalant 'thumbs up'. Understandably steering was not improved by this event, a deficiency rendered more immediate by a large German liner at that moment passing directly across the path of the aircraft. Fortunately Whittle was able to alight on the sea short of the liner, Kirk clambered back into the rear cockpit, and disaster was averted.[27]

While at Cambridge, and with the help of Arnold Hall who will reappear later in the Comet story, Whittle designed the compressor for a new engine called the WU (Whittle Unit). This was to be a bench engine with a double-sided centrifugal compressor,* a single-stage axial turbine and a single large combustion chamber wrapped around the outside of the engine. The combustion chamber had been a problem. Whittle needed one that would burn much more fuel and produce much more heat than any currently in use, about 24 times as much in fact. After being turned down by several companies he managed to find the Edinburgh firm of Laidlaw, Drew and Co. that was willing to have a go. The other problem, and one that was to stay with gas turbines, was finding metals that would withstand the very high temperatures that the turbine blades would be exposed to.

In June 1936 a contract was awarded by Power Jets to the British Thomson-Houston Company (BTH) of Rugby to make the WU engine. This was an understandable choice, as BTH made turbines, but it proved to be less than totally satisfactory as they never seemed very committed. An alternative might have been one of the established aero-engine companies and Whittle had approached Bristols in 1930 but had been turned down.[28] Whittle later became determined not to use any of them because he feared they would take over and then exclude him.[29]

BTH did the work on a cost plus an agreed percentage profit but funds were hard to come by. The work was classified and private investors were reluctant to put money into something that they could be told little about. The Air Ministry refused a research contract, with their Deputy Director of Research, Dr. D. R. Pye, telling Whittle that, "It's hardly likely you will succeed where so many better-equipped people have failed."[30] Nevertheless Whittle had found a friend in Henry Tizard, now Rector of Imperial College and the Chairman of the ARC, who was able to persuade the Air Ministry of the need to set up a programme of tests for the new machine.[31] At this time Tizard was developing the idea of the air defence of Great Britain being based on a radar warning system with fighters being guided to incoming hostile aircraft rather than using standing air patrols. The idea of a fast fighter able to do this was clearly of interest to him.[32]

Battling against the odds, financial and otherwise, Whittle managed to complete the WU in March 1937 and after a couple of false beginnings it was ready to run on 12 April 1937. It was started using a large electric motor and once the fuel was introduced and ignited in the combustion chamber the turbine took over with a loud shriek and rapidly increased in speed with the combustion chamber glowing red hot. Most of the BTH workers ran for cover as the machine was clearly out of control but Whittle stayed to cut off the fuel supply only to find that the turbine continued to accelerate. Fortunately this was short lived and it slowly wound down. The same thing happened the following day. This was a puzzle but eventually the reason was found – fuel had been pooling on the floor of the combustion chamber before ignition had been started. Draining the

---

* It was a single stage, (i.e. the pressure was raised in one continuous process) double-entry (the air was admitted to both sides of the impeller) compressor.[33] See Fig. 2/3.

Fig. 6/3 Lord Brabazon (right) and Frank Whittle (copyright Rolls-Royce plc/courtesy of Rolls-Royce Heritage Trust)

chamber cured this but, to their continuing discomfort, the turbine still ran away on the third test, only stopping when the compressor seized in its casing. This time the problem was found to be a spring in the fuel burner that had been weakened by the heat.

Whittle continued his work, not helped much by BTH obliging him, for safety reasons, to move to a disused foundry they owned at Lutterworth, where sand literally 'got in the works'. The WU engine was rebuilt with new turbine blades and different burners and testing resumed in April 1938. In May some of the turbine blades fouled the casing causing considerable damage and the engine had to be rebuilt again. The Air Ministry must have been having second thoughts by now as they overcame their doubts about financing a new and inexperienced company of limited engineering competence, particularly one involving private investors,[34] and paid £1,000 for the rebuild. Testing resumed in October 1938 and on 30 June the following year the unbelieving Dr. Pye, by now the Director of Research at the Air Ministry,* revisited, saw the engine running and had something of a conversion experience. During the drive back to the station at Rugby, Whittle had the curious experience of Pye reciting to him all the advantages of

---

* His place as Deputy Director had been taken by William Farren, later the Director of the RAE at Farnborough and one of the assessors at the Comet Inquiry. Whittle felt that Farren did not trust him and at first he was rather lukewarm in his support of Whittle's work.[35]

the gas turbine as if he were trying to convert a sceptic.[36] Pye arranged for another engine to be built, this time suitable to be installed in an aeroplane, and even set about getting one to put it in. This marked a turning point in the official attitude towards the Whittle engine.

The new engine, called the W1, was much lighter, had better burners, and an

Fig. 7/3 The Gloster Whittle (copyright Rolls-Royce plc/courtesy of Rolls-Royce Heritage Trust)

improved compressor and turbine. A second engine, the W1X, which was not intended to fly, was also built and was first run on 14 December 1940. This engine was fitted in the first of the two Gloster E28/39s (W4041/G), the first British jet aircraft, later called the Whittle. The W1X engine was used for taxiing trials, some with Whittle himself at the controls, and then for short hops on 8 April 1941. The W1 first ran on 12 April and then replaced W1X which was sent to General Electric at Lynn, Massachusetts, for demonstration purposes. On 15 May the W1 was used for the maiden flight of W4041/G.*[37] This was the final proof that Whittle had produced a practical engine that would enable fighters to fly faster and higher than ever before and in all probability within the duration of the current war. A contract was signed to manufacture 80 Gloster F9/40s a month. This was a practical fighter, later called the Meteor. Bearing in mind the limited thrust of the W1 these were to have two engines each.

The next engine that Whittle and Power Jets produced was the W2 which was intended to power the production Meteors. The engine turned out to have an unexpectedly

---

* Not unlike what was to happen at the Comet's first flight, no professional film record was made. The Air Ministry had refused to provide an official unit to record the event so the only film of the event is an amateur one.[38]

difficult development period and went through several iterations. There were three types of problem: surging, reliability and the performance of the rotating parts and the introduction of the fuel and air into the combustion chambers.[39] All would become well known as inherent problems in turbojet design. Surging was an intermittent reversal of airflow though the compressor caused by the inability of the turbine to deal with the flow of gas it was presented with. It proved difficult to cure but was so, eventually, by extensive redesigning of nearly every major component. Turbine troubles were almost all related to the high working temperatures involved and were solved by the metallurgists in the form of an alloy called 'Nimonic 80'. The firm of Joseph Lucas solved the combustion problems by replacing Whittle's 'swirl vanes' with a 'colander' design.

As well as the technical problems there were significant organisational ones. It had

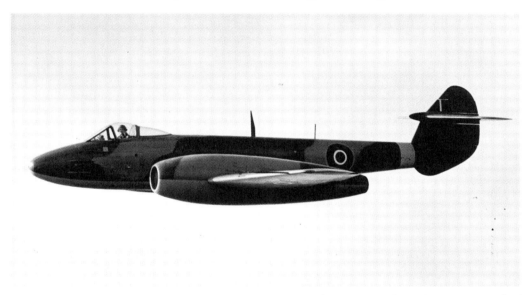

Fig. 8/3 RAF Gloster Meteor F Mk IV, EE360-6, (copyright Ministry of Supply, image supplied by BAE SYSTEMS Heritage)

been decided by the Air Ministry that the W2B version was to be manufactured by BTH, Rover and Vauxhall with Power Jets, as Whittle saw it, sidelined as a research and development organisation. Rovers were handed an incompletely developed engine and being an engineering company themselves were unable to resist introducing their own design ideas. Some of these were sensible, such as straight-through combustion chambers and several complex production jigs, but inevitably some were less successful and as a result relations between Rover and Power Jets deteriorated steadily. This situation persisted into late 1942 until, according to Hooker, Ernest Hives, the Works Manager of Rolls-Royce, took Spencer Wilks, the Chairman of Rover, out to dinner and swapped Rolls-Royce's tank factory in Nottingham for Rover's jet engine factory at Barnoldswick.[40] This turned out to be one of those deals, perhaps not done quite as

Fig. 9/3 Lord Hives* (copyright Rolls-Royce plc/
courtesy of Rolls-Royce Heritage Trust)

casually as it might seem, that altered history.** By this time Wilks had become both sickened and irritated by his dealings with Power Jets[41] and was probably relieved to see the back of the whole project. Significantly the Rover engineer-in-charge at Barnoldswick, Adrian Lombard, was kept on by Rolls and became a major figure in their gas turbine business.

In fact Rolls already had a stake in the turbojet business. In 1939 Hives had employed Griffith and installed him in the company's guest house, Duffield Bank, and told him "to go on thinking," which was exactly what Griffith was good at doing. His designs, which included a contra-rotating, contra-flow ducted fan engine,[42] were far in advance of anything else at that time, but also far in advance of anything that could be made. Nevertheless it must have given Hives the idea that the gas turbine was the engine of the future. Even before the meeting with Wilks, Hives had arranged for Rolls to make parts for Whittle's engines. From the moment Rolls took

---

* Hives was a remarkable man who will be remembered, among other things, for his remarks. Stanley Hooker joined the company from Oxford to be told by Hives, on short acquaintance, that he was, "not much of an engineer."[43] Hooker, who later had a big falling out with Hives, used this as the title of his autobiography.

** By this stage Air Chief Marshall Freeman had returned to the MAP and could see there was a problem between Whittle's Power Jets and Rover and he told Air Vice-Marshall Linnell, the Controller of Research and Development, to find a solution. Linnell suggested that Rolls-Royce and Power Jets should merge but Freeman failed to persuade Whittle, who was more than a little unhinged at this time by a combination of stress, exhaustion and, long-term, inadvertent, amphetamine dependancy,[44] and had to settle for Rolls-Royce taking over Rover's factory at Barnoldswick. According to Furse, (Freeman's biographer) Freeman and Linnell were the people behind the meeting but Bulman says Stafford Cripps, the minister, was the one who persuaded Wilks. [45, 46, 47]

over in January 1943 development of the W2B surged ahead. In December under Rover it had been run for 24 hours; in January under Rolls this increased to 400. The W2B evolved into the Welland 1 which entered service in the Meteor in May 1944. Quite soon it was replaced by the Derwent 1, which used Rovers' idea of straight-through burners, which powered the later versions. The Meteor saw active service chasing flying bombs over southern England and later flew over parts of liberated Europe although it was said to have been kept in the western parts to avoid it falling into German or, according to Hooker, Soviet hands.[48] If true the latter was particularly ironic as after the war the Derwent was sold to the Russians who then manufactured it in large numbers and used it in Korea among other places. Rolls went on to produce another, more powerful, centrifugal engine from the Derwent called the Nene.*

In the meantime, in April 1944, after a suggestion by Whittle, who by this time was in poor health, what was seen by the MAP as the anomalous position of Power Jets was resolved by nationalising the company. This was partly because of the large amount of government money that had flowed into Power Jets and partly to consolidate gas turbine research into one establishment.[49] There was also pressure from the established engine manufacturers, particularly Hives and Halford, who feared competition. Power Jets were banned from making any more jet engines and as a result the company gradually withered, taking with it Whittle's ideas for thrust augmentation and what would later become the turbofan and the afterburner.** [50]

In January 1946 the government announced that Power Jets would be amalgamated with the turbine research part of the RAE to become the Gas Turbine Research Establishment at Pyestock, about two miles from Farnborough.*** Whittle resigned the same day and within two months most of the team of engineers he had built up followed. No doubt Whittle had not been the easiest person to get along with; it is doubtful whether he could have achieved all that he did had he been. He had the understandable protectiveness of a father towards an only daughter and the endless struggles with officialdom and, as he saw it, wayward companies, had taken their toll of his mental health. He was no longer to play a significant part in engine development. Once the technology was proved, Whittle had it taken away from him although he came to be acclaimed as the 'Father of the Turbojet'. This may seem ungrateful – and in many ways it was – but it was probably inevitable that big companies like Rolls and de Havillands, with their vastly greater resources, would take over production and development rather than having to set up a whole new mass-engineering business almost from scratch, particularly in time of war and particularly with Power Jets' history of patchy development

---

* Hooker left out Power Jets' intake guide vanes from the Nene's compressor and then found it worked better with them restored. As he put it, "Rolls-Royce got a medal for throwing away all the 'gubbins' that Power Jets had put into the intakes, and then got another medal for putting it all back again."[51]

** Towards the end of the war the idea emerged of designing a long-range bomber (the LR1) for the Pacific theatre. The engines were to be axial turboprops, turbojets or turbofans. The cessation of hostilities turned the bomber into a transport but the MAP considered there would be no use for such an aircraft and in any case developing the pressurised cabin would be too difficult.[52]

*** Like Farnborough, and the rest of the RAE, this is now defunct. It was closed in 2000.

Fig. 10/3 Frank Halford and G-ALVG, 17 July 1949, (copyright Rolls-Royce plc/courtesy of Rolls-Royce Heritage Trust)

progress. In due course a Darwinian process of natural (or commercial) selection took place from which a single, large, gas-turbine company – Rolls-Royce – emerged in the UK. In 1976 Whittle, by now rather more appreciated, went to live in the United States. He died in 1996.

At the same time as Whittle's engines were evolving there were several other parallel lines of development, one of which eventually resulted in the engines for the Comet. Halford and de Havillands had become aware of the existence of gas turbines at an early stage. In 1938 Dr. Eric Moult, one of Halford's associates, had come across part of a jet engine. He had been visiting Vauxhall's plant in Luton and had spotted the impeller from a centrifugal compressor but was told to keep it secret.[53] It transpired that Vauxhalls had been asked by the Air Ministry to make parts for Whittle because of their expertise with large magnesium castings. Shortly afterwards Halford's group was included in the secret and were also asked for advice about making large castings in magnesium alloy. Tizard (now Sir Henry), as the chairman of the ARC, asked Halford to look into the prospects of using Whittle's engine in an aeroplane and Halford arranged to meet Whittle at Power Jets and also visited BTH. Halford reported positively to Tizard but said that a much greater effort would be needed to get the engine into service before the war ended.

By the spring of 1941 Tizard, "harassed with the vicissitudes of Whittle,"[54] decided to ask Halford to produce a useable jet engine. A set of drawings of Whittle's engine was sent to him and a contract awarded by the MAP to design and produce a turbojet suitable to propel a de Havilland fighter. The contract specified a thrust of 3,000 pounds and a maximum diameter of 50 inches, just large enough to squeeze a pilot in the fuselage accommodating it.

Halford's engine was a simplified version of Whittle's.* It had a single-sided impeller and, like one of the Rover engines, straight-through combustion chambers whereas Whittle's had a double-sided impeller and combustion chambers that doubled back on themselves. The reason for this seemingly perverse arrangement was that Whittle wished to make the shaft between the impeller and the turbine as short as possible to avoid whirling.** Halford made the shaft much wider which stiffened it and allowed it to be longer. The straight-through chambers also provided more thrust and reduced complication. The single-sided impeller was able to make use of the ram effect when the aircraft was flying at speed as well as avoiding the plenum chamber that had to surround the double-sided one. The disadvantage was that the impeller had to be bigger making the engine wider than the equivalent Rolls-Royce Derwent (50 inches compared with 41.5). Whittle did not approve of the changes but they went ahead anyway.

One of the problems Halford's team experienced was designing the combustion chambers, just as Whittle had. A major difficulty was providing, for test purposes, the massive flow of air they would be exposed to when the engine was working. They were able to borrow a large compressor from Napier that had been used to supercharge the Lion engine used in the Schneider Trophy Races. Even this proved insufficient for some of the tests and the combustion chamber had to be taken to the site of the Dartford Tunnel whose construction had been halted by the war but whose massive air pumps were still in situ and proved ideal.***[55] The Bosch and Lucas companies were also involved in designing and making parts for the combustion chambers.

The drawings for Halford's engine (the H1) were delivered to the factory floor on 8 August 1941 and construction began. The prototype engine had its first run on a test bed at Hatfield on 13 April 1942, just 248 days later, an incredibly short time to produce a new engine[56] and was an example of what an experienced and properly-resourced aero-engine company could do. As with all new engines there were problems: difficulty with starting, an inadequate fuel pump and the intake being sucked flat by the compressor. It had its first full-speed run on 13 June 1942 and delivered its design thrust of 3,000 pounds, albeit with an unexpected noise that was later traced to resonance in the impeller vanes. This was cured by cutting back the tips of the vanes.

On 8 December 1942 a specification for a single-seat, jet-powered fighter that was

---

* In engineering terms the turbojet was much simpler than a piston engine of equivalent power. Hives, on being told of this (by Whittle) said that they (Rolls) would "soon design the bloody simplicity out of it."[57] He was right. Taking into account the metallurgy, the design of the various blades and the control systems, a modern axial fanjet is about as complicated as anybody could wish for.
** A rapidly rotating and even slightly unbalanced shaft will tend to vibrate with the material furthest from the axis of rotation and half way along the length of the shaft tending to pull outwards the most. This is called whirling. The amplitude of the vibrations will increase considerably if the frequency of the vibration coincides with the natural frequency of the shaft and may reach the point where it becomes destructive.
*** Whittle also mentions doing this in his account of the development of his engines.[58] Bulman says the MAP arranged it.[59]

to become the DH100 Vampire was issued to de Havillands. It detailed a maximum speed of at least 490 mph and a service ceiling of over 48,000 feet but the engine needed another 2½ years of development before it could be put into service use. The Vampire made its first flight on 20 September 1943 with Geoffrey de Havilland Jnr. as the pilot. Although it was intended for the Vampire, the H1 also provided the engines for the maiden flight of the Meteor on 5 March 1943. The aircraft had been built but Whittle's engines had been delayed and de Havillands and Halford were asked if they could provide engines for it. This involved modifying the engines slightly as they were designed with their air intakes side by side to suit the Vampire whereas the Meteor needed them to be one above the other. Turning the engine through 90 degrees solved most of the problems.

At this time jet engines were very much a novelty and their properties were not entirely appreciated by everyone concerned. Before the first flight of the Meteor the pilot, Michael Daunt, walked across the front of the aircraft while its engines were running, not realising the volume of air that was moving into them. He was promptly sucked into the orifice of one of them, his head and shoulders disappearing inside. Fortunately he was pulled out before anything disastrous happened and suffered nothing worse than bruising.* Thereafter guards, named Daunt Stoppers, were provided to cover the intakes during ground running.[60]

The Meteor went on to use Rolls-Royce engines as de Havillands were thought to have enough on their plate providing engines for the Vampire. By this time, 1944, Halford's firm had been taken over by de Havillands to form The de Havilland Engine Company and Halford became their chairman and technical director. The H1 was rechristened the Goblin and was developed to give progressively more and more thrust for the Vampire and the experimental DH108 Swallow and ultimately evolved into the more-powerful, but still centrifugal, Ghost (the H2) which was designed to deliver 5,000 pounds of thrust. This was intended to be used in the DH112 Venom, a more sophisticated version of the Vampire, but was also used for the Comet.

The Ghost was basically a beefed-up version of the Goblin and kept the latter's robust simplicity with a single-sided impeller and a single stage turbine. The new engine first ran on the test bed on 2 September 1945,[61] reaching its designed maximum thrust early in 1946. It originally had fourteen combustion chambers but these were cut to ten to reduce its diameter. Airborne testing began in July 1947 using a pair of converted Lancastrians, the Ghosts replacing the two outboard engines. The Lancastrians took off with the Merlins which were then stopped when a safe height had been reached and just the jets used. The engine was also tested at altitude in Cunningham's record-breaking Vampire with the extended wings.

The Ghost had originally been designed as a military engine but to be used in a civil airliner it had to be considerably modified to make it safer, more reliable and longer-lasting. Testing continued on the bench and in the Lancastrians and finally (the Ghost

---

* Whittle says that Daunt was 'no feather-weight.' Had he been he might have disappeared even further into the engine.[62]

50 Mk.1) in the Comet prototype. Halford said that it had taken him 22 years to produce a piston aero-engine that would achieve 1,000 hours between overhauls but it took only eight years to manage the same with the Goblin and Ghost.[63] The Ghost's 5,000 pound thrust, was roughly equivalent to a propeller engine of 12,000 horsepower.* Later versions of the Ghost developed up to 5,500 pounds of thrust.

Figs 11/3, 12/3 Ghost engines (Copyright Rolls-Royce/courtesy of Rolls-Royce Heritage Trust)

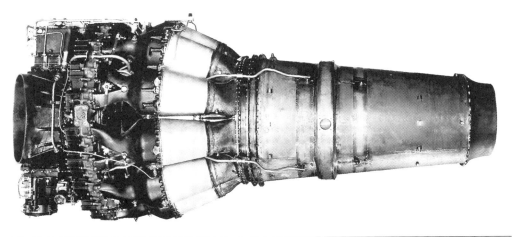

---

* Converting the pounds of thrust of a jet engine – a force – to the familiar horsepower – a rate of doing work – of a piston engine was not an intuitive thing. Hives was unimpressed by the 800 pounds thrust of the early Whittle engine, remarking to Hooker that, "It would not pull the skin off a rice pudding." Hooker was prepared for this and explained that the current Merlin-propeller combination generated the equivalent of about 840 pounds thrust (see Appendix 2).[64, 65] The remark about rice pudding was also attributed to Frank Owner reporting about gas turbines to Roy Fedden.[66]

Fig. 13/3 Avro Lancastrian (VM703) used as Ghost test bed, 8 August 1947 (Copyright BAE SYSTEMS Heritage)

It may seem almost inconceivable now but at that time there were several manufacturers, or near-manufacturers, of jet engines in the UK: Rolls-Royce, de Havillands, Bristols, Armstrong Siddeley, Metropolitan Vickers and Napier.* Rolls-Royce was certainly the dominant maker of piston engines with the Merlin and the Griffin, but it was by no means certain they would take the lead in jet engines as well. Hives had shown considerable foresight in employing Griffith to 'go on thinking' in 1939 and Rolls had

---

* Bristols became interested in turbojets in July 1941 but decided to develop a turboprop which became the axial Theseus and ran for the first time in May 1945. A series of engines followed, some were turboprops such as the Proteus, and some pure jets such as the Olympus. Their final triumph was the Pegasus for the Harrier. The company, by now merged with Armstrong Siddeley, was purchased by Rolls-Royce in 1966.[67]

Armstrong Siddeley had an axial turbojet running in April 1943 which eventually matured into the Python turboprop. A series of snakes followed, including the Mamba, Adder and Viper as well as the series they inherited from Metropolitan-Vickers. They had moderate success but the company was taken over by Bristols in 1959.[68]

Metropolitan-Vickers was an experienced turbine-manufacturing company that collaborated with the RAE to produce a turbojet with a nine-stage axial compressor which first ran in December 1940. A later version (the F2) flew in a Lancaster on 29 June 1943, the first British axial turbojet to do so. It evolved into the Beryl which powered the world's first jet-propelled flying boat (the SR A/1). They even began work on a turbofan in 1941. Under government pressure they withdrew from making aero-engines in 1947 leaving their final engine, the highly-successful Sapphire, to Armstrong Siddeley.[69]

Napier had been taken over by English Electric in 1942 after struggling to get the Sabre right. After the war the company produced the Nomad which was a combination of a two-stroke diesel and a gas turbine. Napiers later went on to produce axial turboprops which saw some use in helicopters as well as fixed-wing aircraft.[70] Their aero-engine business was eventually taken over by Rolls in 1962.

gradually become more and more involved in jet engine production and development during the war. Nevertheless at the end of the war they were still very much a producer of piston engines and nearly all their expertise and tooling lay with them. On 30 May 1946 Hives told the board of Rolls-Royce that, "Our future lies on the turbine engine side. There are no new aircraft contemplated or being built that will take the Merlin or Griffon engines, or any other piston engine."[71] Hives had to change Rolls from the dominant manufacturer of piston engines to the dominant manufacturer of jet engines, a difficult thing to do which required remarkable courage and conviction and once again demonstrated Hives's leadership qualities. Many companies in similar dominant positions have either failed to see the future or failed to have the courage to change and have consequently been eclipsed by new technology.

Rolls, of course, had stuck to engines and had not become involved in airframes but de Havillands and Bristols were trying for both. The alternative engine for the Comet was an axial turbine, the AJ65, being developed by Rolls-Royce. This had greater scope for future development in the sense that it could provide more thrust and greater fuel efficiency because it was possible to use a series of axial compressor stages whereas more than two centrifugal compressors produced little improvement. But designing efficient axial compressors and turbines is difficult and Rolls were having considerable trouble getting them right and it took about five years for the engine to evolve into the successful Avon which powered the later Comets. It was not an option for the first Comets because it was not available as a practical engine. Metropolitan Vickers and Armstrong Siddeley had also developed axial jets but neither had a suitable engine available at the time. Although it remained to be seen which would emerge as the dominant engine manufacturer de Havillands, particularly with Halford, seemed to have as good a chance as any.

To reduce drag the Comet's four engines were buried within the wing roots with individual elliptical air intakes and long jet pipes that extended just beyond the wing's trailing edge. This position also had the advantage of reducing the effects of asymmetric thrust if an engine failed and consequently allowed a smaller fin and rudder, again reducing drag. The high air intake position made the ingestion of foreign objects into the engines less likely but it made accessibility more difficult and posed safety concerns if an engine caught fire and weakened the wing. Any engine fire would also be alarmingly close to the fuel tanks. There was the additional risk that a separated turbine blade could escape the engine containment and slice into the fuselage. To guard against both of these eventualities steel bulkheads were placed between the engine and vulnerable parts of the airframe and the jet pipes were surrounded by a steel tube cooled by external ram air, both adding weight to the aircraft.[72] The air intakes to the engines had to pass through large openings in the front spar and similarly the jet exhaust passed through openings in the rear spar, both causing structural problems and adding weight to the wing roots. Having the engines so close together could also allow parts from a disintegrating turbine to enter the adjoining engine with unfortunate consequences. This engine position caused considerable cabin noise as well as the risk of damage to the fuselage skin from the jet exhaust.

In the long term the buried configuration would have become untenable with the much-wider turbofans and Boeing's (later) choice of underwing engine pods proved prescient, particularly as the increase in drag they produced was less than expected. Pods had other advantages and disadvantages. They allowed a slimmer and less-complicated wing root as well as a lighter wing, easier access to the engines, less exhaust damage to the fuselage and the pylons reduce span-wise air flow (see Chapter 4, the wings). Their down side was that an engine failure would produce greater asymmetric thrust and would need a larger rudder to compensate for it. They were also more vulnerable to foreign body ingestion and more likely to get damaged if the aircraft rolled when close to the ground.[73]

Perhaps as an expression of anxiety about the power of the Ghosts the outlets of the jet pipes were separated enough to allow the installation of a small rocket engine fuelled by hydrogen peroxide, the de Havilland Sprite, to assist take off at hot and high airfields. Each rocket provided about as much thrust as each Ghost but only for around twelve seconds. They were later found to be unnecessary and were abandoned.[74]

As things turned out the Comet's engines performed reliably and to specification and none of the future catastrophes could be blamed directly on them. On the other hand their lack of power and high fuel consumption exerted a constraining influence on the whole design of the Comet with the need to minimise weight. The future would lie with axial engines but when the first Comets were built the Ghosts were as powerful and as reliable as any engine available and they were the obvious choice.

Chapter 4

DESIGNING THE AIRFRAME AND ITS SYSTEMS

The two big things that an aeroplane has to battle against to get into the air, stay there and make progress through it, are its weight and the resistance of the air that it is flying through. These are parcelled together as 'drag'. The drag produced by getting the aeroplane into the air is called induced drag (from lift-induced drag) and is overcome by the lift generated by the wings. The drag produced by the aeroplane moving through the air is called parasitic drag (strictly speaking zero-lift drag which includes form or profile drag) and is overcome by the engines pushing the aircraft forwards. The faster the aeroplane flies the greater the parasitic drag and this is generally what limits the maximum speed of a particular aeroplane. It is useful to express these two types of drag as the power needed to overcome them as power output is directly related to fuel consumption. The power needed to overcome induced drag depends on the weight of the aircraft, the efficiency of its wings in producing lift and its forward speed. If the first two remain constant the faster the aircraft moves forward the more lift it generates and less power is needed to overcome induced drag. The power needed to overcome parasitic drag depends on the size and shape of the aeroplane and the density of the air it is flying through and increases as the cube of its speed. This means that to double the speed of an aeroplane in level flight, other things being equal, the engines need to provide eight times as much power.

To the passengers speed was the whole point of the Comet. From the airlines' perspective greater speed meant greater utilisation of the aircraft and the crew, and less need for space in the aircraft for leg room and for bored passengers to walk around. It also removed or reduced the need for sleeping accommodation or overnight hotel stays on long trips. Flying fast meant flying high where the air was less dense and provided less resistance, and so less parasitic drag, as the aircraft moved through it. Flying high also meant that a pressurised cabin was necessary. As the Comet flew higher than its predecessors, so the pressure differential across the cabin wall would be greater and the cabin would have to be stronger. Flying fast also meant reducing parasitic drag as much as possible by having a narrow, streamlined fuselage, thin wings with buried engines, a small tail fin and a retractable undercarriage. Thin wings with a symmetrical aerofoil (see below), that would be perfectly adequate at high speeds, produce limited lift at low speeds so flaps were necessary to increase lift and reduce landing and take off speeds. The limited power and low fuel-efficiency of the engines required as light an airframe as possible to minimise induced drag and to increase the payload and fuel capacity. The weight of the fuel necessary to give the aircraft a usable stage length was one of the main constraints on the Comet's performance. Even with a light airframe frequent refuelling stops would be necessary with a rapid refuelling system so that its speed advantage was not wiped out.

The remainder of this chapter discusses these design features in more detail.

The wings

If the Comet's engines came from Britain the shape of its wings owed a lot to the Germans. Their prewar research into the sweptback wing, and their use of it towards the end of the war, revolutionised wing design for aircraft approaching the speed of sound.

Wings are what makes an aeroplane fly. They are, in effect, specially-shaped cantilevered beams projecting out from each side of the fuselage which carry the weight of the aircraft when it is in the air and depending on the arrangement of the undercarriage, much of it when it is on the ground. The wings produce lift as air flows past them. The engines just serve to push the wings forward to generate this airflow.

Perhaps surprisingly, as they have been around for some time, there are still different views about how wings generate lift. What follows presents one (simplified) explanation. People interested in alternatives and more rigorous explanations should consult books on aerodynamics.

As a wing moves forward its leading edge divides the mass of stationary air it meets so that it moves in a complex fashion above and below the wing. As it leaves the wing's trailing edge the air moves downwards. Most of this air comes from the flow over the top of the wing. The mass of this air and the speed at which it moves are considerable and for a large aircraft amount to many tons per second. The wing reacts to this downward air movement by moving upwards, in other words it experiences lift, another example of Newton's Third Law. The magnitude of the lift (a force) is equal to the product of the mass of air diverted and its vertical acceleration (Newton's second law).

Two features of the wing produce this downward air movement: the more important is the upward angulation of the wing so that its leading edge is higher than its trailing edge – the positive angles of incidence and attack* – the other is the shape of the wing in cross-section, the aerofoil. This is usually an elongated droplet-shape with the widest part about a quarter of the way back from the leading edge. Most wings have an asymmetrical aerofoil with a bigger bulge on the upper surface, the camber, which in itself generates some lift even with a zero, or slightly negative, angle of attack. The Comet had a thin, symmetrical aerofoil designed for high speed, so the only mechanism providing lift was its positive angle of attack.

Lift can be increased by making an aeroplane fly faster or increasing its angle of attack but there is a limit to how far this angle can be increased and the aeroplane still be able to fly. As the angle of attack increases it reaches a threshold, generally some-

---

* The angle of incidence is the fixed angle between the chord line of the wing and a reference line on the fuselage which runs parallel to the longitudinal axis of the fuselage and usually represents the direction of minimum drag. The angle of attack is the (variable) angle the chord line presents to the air when the aircraft is flying. These are the American rather than the British definitions.

where between 8 and 20°, at which the airflow over the rear of the upper wing surface begins to separate from it and no longer moves downwards from the trailing edge, causing the wing to lose lift. If the angle of attack continues to increase, this area of separation enlarges and at some point the wing loses so much lift that the aeroplane falls to earth – it stalls. However the conditions in which stalling most often occurs is when the speed of the aeroplane has been progressively reduced and the angle of attack has been increased in stages to maintain lift until the critical angle is reached. The separated flow and the increasing angle of attack also increase the drag of the wing and slow the aeroplane even more. These circumstances are most likely to be met during landing and taking off and it is easy to see why these are vulnerable moments in any flight. Aircraft flying at very great altitudes also have to use a large angle of attack to maintain lift in the thin air and are therefore vulnerable to stalling in spite of their high speed although their height should allow time for control to be regained.*

The shape of the aerofoil is also significant for stall characteristics. Wings with a large camber allow a greater angle of attack before a stall develops and a thick and rounded leading edge makes the onset of the stall less abrupt althought both increase parasitic drag. The Comet's thin, relatively sharp and symmetrical aerofoil was therefore more vulnerable to stalling and the onset of any stall would be more abrupt.

The shape of the wing in plan form also affects its characteristics. Increasing the area of the wing increases the mass of air diverted downwards and increases lift. The Comet's wing area was large compared with modern jet transports as well as being tapered. The tapering allowed the wings to be made structurally lighter because more of the lift, and therefore the bending moment, is generated towards the root than towards the tip. Also the root has a longer chord and can therefore be built deeper without affecting the thickness/chord ratio, an important feature for high speed performance. Greater thickness allowed fuel and the undercarriage to be accommodated more easily. The disadvantage of the tapered wing is that it is more difficult, i.e. more expensive, to make. Also the area most likely to stall first is about two thirds along the wing. As any stall is likely to be asymmetric it may lead to the end of the most affected wing dropping and the aircraft rolling. The ailerons are on the outer third of the wing so this type of stall can lead to the loss of aileron function which is unfortunate as they would be the means of correcting the roll.

As well as having a positive angle of incidence, most wings, and the Comet's were no exception, are tilted slightly upwards from their roots – the dihedral. This increases the aircraft's tendency to return to normal flight when it experiences a yaw, in other words it increases the aircraft's stability, a useful feature for passenger aircraft but not

---

* This did not appear to have worked for Air France flight 447, an Airbus A330, flying at high altitude through a storm over the South Atlantic from Rio de Janeiro to Paris on 1 June 2009. According to the final report issued on 5 July 2012 the pilots appear to have been confused by initial false instrument readings and not realised they were stalling and continued to pull the nose up in spite of the stall warning sounding for 54 seconds. The false reading may have been caused by the pitot tube becoming blocked with ice. The aircraft was stalled throughout its 3½ minutes of descent and crashed into the sea, breaking up on impact and killing all 228 people on board.[1]

necessarily so for fighters which have to be able to change direction easily.

The wings are attached to the fuselage at one of three positions. The most common for passenger aircraft is at the bottom of the fuselage, as they were in the Comet. This allows the spars, the main structural beams inside the wing, to continue across from one wing to the other without obstructing the cabin, a notorious problem with the Lancastrian which inherited its mid-fuselage spar from the Lancaster bomber. They were moved to the roof in the more-developed York. Lower wings allow the undercarriage to be shorter and lighter but places the engine intakes closer to the ground and more vulnerable to ingesting foreign objects. The mid-fuselage position is often used in fighter aircraft and the high position (on the roof of the fuselage) is used mainly for cargo aircraft which need to be close to the ground for loading. This generally means that the undercarriage has to be in pods attached to the fuselage. The wing roots are shaped to minimise drag and stress concentrations by being curved on the upper and lower surfaces to join the circumference of the fuselage more smoothly.

It will have become apparent that like a lot of things in an aeroplane the shape of the wing is a compromise. A wing shape like the Comet's that is optimised for high subsonic speeds with low parasitic drag does not need to generate much lift coefficient * because its speed gives it enough to stay in the air. A wing designed for slow-speed flight, where air resistance is less of an issue, needs to generate more lift from its shape but can tolerate more drag. As even the fastest aircraft moves more slowly during landing and takeoff, the best solution is for the wing to have different shapes for different speeds. The wing does this for slow speeds by using flaps on the trailing edges. Plain flaps are controllable strips of trailing-edge aerofoil, inboard of the ailerons, whose own trailing edges can be rotated down to give that part of the wing more curvature and generate more lift. As aircraft designs have evolved, flaps have become more complicated and modern aircraft often have extending flaps, sometimes with gaps between multiple sections, increasing the wing area as well as its curvature. Lift at low speeds can also be increased by having fixed, down-facing bulges called droops, or movable slats, on the leading edge of the wing which, like flaps, also increase wing area and camber.

The Comet had two plain flaps outboard of the engines, the centre flap extended from rib three to rib seven and the outer from ribs seven to twelve. Beneath the engines there was a split flap which consisted of a corrugated panel that rotated down without affecting the shape of the wing above it which meant that it was less effective. There was a leading edge slat on the wing of the first prototype Comet but it was found to have little effect and was locked in the 'up' position and then eliminated in subsequent aircraft. A mistake as it turned out.

In the early part of the Second World War pilots began to notice that aircraft moving at high speed, particularly at high altitude, sometimes developed violent buffeting and controls that were difficult to move, or even needed to be moved in the opposite direction. The aircraft also tended either to pitch up, with the risk of the wings parting com-

---

* Lift coefficient, C_L, is a dimensionless number that relates (for example) the lift of a wing to its area and the density and relative velocity of the air through which it is moving.

$C_L = 2 L / p V^2 A$ where L = lift, p = air density, V = velocity of the air and A = area of the wing.

pany with the fuselage, or, more usually, pitch down to enter an increasingly steep and uncontrollable dive. If the pilot was lucky the aircraft became responsive at lower altitudes and he was able to pull out of the dive, albeit with some effort.

Different aircraft developed this problem at different speeds and in different ways: the Spitfire was particularly good in this respect but the more-recently-designed Typhoon and the American Lockheed Lightning were badly affected. The Typhoon came from the same designer (Sydney Camm) and manufacturer (Hawker) as the successful Hurricane and was intended to take over from it as a fast, high-altitude interceptor and was given the powerful, but problematic, Sabre engine. When it was tested it was found that its high-altitude performance was dire and it had to be relegated to low-level ground attack and V1 chasing, in which roles it was very successful.* Fortunately this was just what was needed at this stage of the war and Hawker's efforts and the taxpayers' money were not wasted. The Lightning's performance was gradually tweaked by altering its aerodynamics and by providing it with a dive-recovery flap under the wing and it ultimately became a successful fighter.

These pilots were experiencing the early signs of what came to be called the 'sound barrier'. Sound is what we hear. It is produced by a sinusoidal compression wave moving through a fluid medium, generally air, reaching our ears. An aircraft flying at less than about 500 mph continuously generates compression waves which move away from it in all directions at the speed of sound. At speeds greater than this the air flow in places, typically the middle to rear half of the wing, can accelerate to the speed of sound and even exceed it.** In these areas the sound waves cannot move away upstream and they become compressed. These areas of supersonic airflow are terminated by shock waves moving away almost perpendicularly from the wing surface. The shock wave is of much greater amplitude and has a much steeper rise in amplitude than the usual compression wave and contains much more energy. This considerably increases the drag of the wing as well as creating the sonic boom (if there is someone there to hear it). The area of subsonic air flow behind the shock wave tends to be turbulent and to separate from the wing producing the buffeting as well as adding to the drag. The aircraft speed at which sonic flow first happens is called the critical Mach number.

The speed of sound varies almost entirely with the temperature (the square root of the absolute temperature to be precise) of the air in the atmosphere, the hotter the air the faster sound travels. Hence the speed of sound is lower in the cold air at high altitude (about 660 mph at 40,000 feet) than it is at sea level (about 760 mph). This is why a pilot in trouble at high altitude could find his problems resolving at low altitude when the areas of supersonic airflow on the wings became subsonic although the air might well be moving faster in terms of mph

---

* This was not the only problem with the Typhoon. It had a structural weakness towards the rear of the fuselage which sometimes caused the tailplane to break off.[2] The tail was strengthened but it was never completely cured. As if this were not enough it was also subject to carbon monoxide ingress into the cockpit.[3] Altogether an alarming aeroplane.

** The speed here is the air speed relative to the wing. Outside the wind tunnel it is the wing that moves forward through air which, at first, is stationary.

The phenomenon of high speed buffeting was investigated by deliberately diving aircraft at high speed from high altitude, which must have been an alarming experience for the pilots involved. It became apparent that an important factor for developing problems at high speed was the thickness of the wing. To make it strong and able to accommodate the fuel, guns and undercarriage Camm had made the Typhoon's wing very thick. Its thickness/chord ratio was 19.5% at the root reducing to 12% at the wing tip with its maximum thickness at 30% of chord[4] whereas the Spitfire's was 13% and 6%[5] with maximum thickness at 30%. The solution for the Typhoon was a thinner wing with the point of maximum thickness further back from the leading edge. This became the successful Tempest, the younger sibling of the Typhoon, with a thickness/chord ratio of 14.5% at the root tapering to 10% at the tip with its maximum thickness at 37.5% of chord.[4] The thinner the wing (i.e. the smaller the thickness/chord ration) the less the acceleration of the air over it and the faster the aeroplane can fly before it reaches its critical Mach number. Curiously Camm seemed to be in denial about the consequences of high speed flight and even after the war he continued to scorn all this "new fangled Mach nonsense."[6]

Other things were also happening at these high speeds: aeroelastic effects caused control reversal as well as flutter of the wings and control surfaces and the rearward movement of the centre of lift of the wing produced the downward nose pitch. It would be some time before all these phenomena were fully understood and dealt with.[7]

All this the British and the Americans eventually managed to work out for themselves but they missed another trick. In the early 1930s a German academic aerodynamicist called Adolf Busemann developed a theory that if a wing were to be angled back from the fuselage this would be an advantage in high-speed flight.* This was made public at the 5th Volta Conference in Rome in 1935 but seemed to be ignored by the rest of the world.**[8] Busemann's theory was translated into practice by the Germans in the early part of the war but only became apparent to the Allies when aircraft such as the rocket-powered Me 163 Komet and the twin jet Me 262 were first seen in 1944.*** Neither the British Meteor, the first Allied jet fighter, nor the later Vampire, had swept wings which limited their high subsonic performance. The Me 262 had engines not much more powerful than those of the early Meteors but the maximum speed of the Messerschmitt in level flight was about 536 mph at 23,000 feet whereas that of the early Meteors was 415 mph at 10,000 feet, mainly because the Messerschmitt was aerodynamically cleaner. Towards the end of the war Meteors flew over parts of liberated Europe but by this time the Luftwaffe had largely disappeared and it never entered combat with any of the several German jet aircraft that had emerged by this time. In retro-

---

* The angle of sweepback is the angle between a line at 90⁰ to the long axis of the fuselage and the quarter chord line of the wing.

** But not entirely. In his book about the Miles M.52 projected supersonic aircraft, Eric Brown says that Busemann's work was discussed when he visited the National Physical Laboratory in 1943.[9] Busemann (1901-86) was brought to Britain by the Farren Mission and later worked at the Langley Research Center in the United States.

spect it was probably as well.

For structural reasons there is a limit to how thin a wing can be made, particularly if it is to accommodate wheels and fuel tanks, and sweepback is a way of achieving 'apparent' thinness. Compared with the same, but unswept, wing a sweptback wing presents a longer 'chord' to the air passing over it parallel to the fuselage. As the thickness of the wing stays the same its thickness/chord ratio appears to be reduced and the point of maximum thickness is further back, hence its higher critical Mach number.*

As always there is a price to be paid. At very slow speeds some of the airflow migrates along the top of the swept wing towards the tip, does not contribute to lift and may cause the wing tips to stall with the loss of aileron control. Using flaps to increase lift and adding wing fences to reduce outward flow can compensate for this and the Comet 1 had both. On balance more is gained than lost by a sweep back appropriate for the maximum speed of the aircraft.

Interestingly the Germans also experimented with forward-swept wings which had the advantage of converting this lateral airflow to a less-disadvantageous inward flow and even flew a four-engined jet bomber (the Ju 287) with this configuration.[10] It proved to have structural problems with the wings twisting and flexing and only one was completed. It, and an unfinished second example, fell into the hands of the Russians at the end of the war. This second aircraft was fitted with swept-back wings and was said to have reached a speed of 621 mph. Since then forward-swept wings have occasionally re-emerged in new aircraft designs but have never acquired much of a following. In the same way that backward sweep tends to correct yaw, forward sweep tends to exacerbate it. Modern computer-controlled, fly-by-wire systems can deal with this but the German pilots must have found it something of a trial.

In normal service little of this would have applied to the Comet. The Comet 1's

---

*** According to Bill Gunston their sweptback wings may have been fortuitous.[11] He recounts that Willy Messerchmitt told him that the designs had nothing to do with increasing critical Mach numbers. It may have had more to do with increasing the stability of the aircraft – swept wings resist the tendency to yaw – and the position of its centre of gravity. For whatever reason it was done it no doubt helped their high-speed performance. Both aircraft reached remarkable speeds in test conditions, the Me 163 managed 623 mph at 13,000 feet and the Me 262 the same speed at 30,000 feet, about Mach 0.92. Amazingly a Spitfire reached the same Mach number in April 1944 but this was in a dive and it lost its propeller and gearbox in the process and converted itself into a glider.[12] Nevertheless it was quite an achievement for what was a pre-war, old-technology aeroplane. There have been suggestions that the first manned aircraft to exceed the speed of sound were these German aircraft and not the generally-credited American Bell X 1 in October 1947 but it is more likely that they were flying at high subsonic speeds and had artifactual instrument readings. Bullets, of course, had long exceeded Mach 1 and unmanned vehicles such as the V2 rocket reached Mach 4 during the final part of descent. The German four-stage, solid-fuelled, surface-to-surface rocket called the Rhine Messenger (Rheinbote) was said to have reached an impressive Mach 5.5.[13]

* Busemann's explanation was that the relevant airflow for compression problems was moving at right angles to the wing's leading edge, i.e. along the true chord. Its velocity vector was consequently reduced by a factor of Cos Ø where Ø is the angle of sweepback. Its numerical effect is the same as the above where the 'chord' length has been increased by 1/Cos Ø.

cruising speed was about 450 mph (Mach 0.68 at 40,000 feet). Its critical Mach number was 0.82, equivalent to just over 540 mph at 40,000 feet.[14] It was a speed a Comet was unlikely to reach except in an emergency dive.

The Comet's wing had a moderate leading edge sweep back of 25⁰ but a mean sweep-back of about 20⁰.* Like the Me 262, this may have been more for reasons of stability than reducing its critical Mach number but using the above criteria, the critical Mach number would have reduced to about 0.77 without any sweepback.** The design proved satisfactory at cruising speed and altitude but could be problematical at takeoffs and possibly also at landings (see Chapters 10 and 11).

The wing consisted of four parts: the centre section within the base of the fuselage, the stub wing out to rib twelve, the extension wing from rib twelve to rib twenty and the wing tip. The centre section and the inner part of the stub wing to rib seven had front and rear spars which were continuous from one wing to the other. Near the wing roots the spars had large cutouts to accommodate the engines intakes and exhausts. A secondary spar was incorporated into the leading edge of the wing.[15] Along the span of the wing, parallel to the chords, was a series of equally-spaced ribs which were bolted to the skin. The top and bottom skins were Reduxed to thin, closely-placed beams called stringers running between the ribs. In cross section the stringers were shaped like a witch's hat with a tall rounded crown and a wide brim, the 'brim' being the part attached to the skin. The ribs, spars and stringers defined the size and shape of the wing and were covered with aluminium alloy sheeting to make the wing impermeable to air. The skin varied in thickness from 10 SWG (standard wire gauge, 0.128 inches) at the fuselage end to 14 gauge (0.08 inches) towards the tip. Similarly along the leading edge it varied from 12 (0.104 inches) to 14 gauge.[16]

---

* The Comet's wing was not a simple sweep back with parallel leading and trailing edges. It had a leading edge sweepback of 25⁰. Just outboard of the engines the trailing edge swept forward at 8½⁰ for over 10 feet (to rib 7) and the remainder had a sweep back of about 8⁰.[16] The quarter chord sweepback, the most important part for compressibility effects, was more like 20⁰. Cos 20⁰ is 0.9397.

** Inboard of rib 7 the aerofoil was an N.P.L. Section N.A.N. - 414-011, outboard of rib 12, a DH Section with large leading edge radius EMQ 11½/40. From rib 7 to rib 12 was a fairing between the two aerofoils. It had a span of 115 feet, a chord at the root of 29 feet 6 inches, chord at the wing joint of 17 feet 9 inches and a chord at the tip of 6 feet 9 inches. It had a thickness chord ratio of 11.5% and a dihedral from the wing joint to the tip of 4⁰. Its angle of incidence was 2⁰. The area of the wing, with ailerons, was 2,015 square feet and the aspect ratio worked out at about 6.5. The ailerons were 21 feet 6 inches long. Each aileron had a control tab 7 feet 3½ inches long.[16]

***(see next page), Stress, an important concept in the story of the Comet, is the force per unit area acting on a solid object or structure and tending to deform it. For an object being stretched the stress is referred to as tensile, for an object being squeezed, compressive, and for an object being twisted, shear. It is possible for stress distributions within a body to be either uniform or to vary greatly with location in the body. Together with the strength of the material, the size and distribution of stresses in a structure will determine the loads and forces it can sustain without failure. The stresses are critical to the performance of engineering structures such as bridges and aircraft. Strain is the change in size or shape (the deformation) that the stress produces. Other things being equal the bigger the stress the bigger the strain. Small stresses produce strains that return to their original size or shape and are referred to as being within the elastic range. Larger stresses cause a permanent change and are said to be in the plastic range. If the stress goes on increasing it ultimately leads to some sort of break, (See Appendix 5 for more detail).

The internal wing structure amounted to a series of connected boxes in which the skin was stressed*** and provided a considerable part of its strength and rigidity. When an aircraft is on the ground the wing bends down under its own weight outboard of the undercarriage leg. The upper surface of the outer wing is therefore in tension and the lower surface in compression. The situation is reversed when the aircraft takes to the air when the whole wing is bent up as it generates lift and supports the weight of the fuselage. Now the upper surface is in compression and the lower in tension. The wing is also pushed rearwards by the air that it meets in flight and tends to rotate in the same direction as its angle of attack leading to shear stresses in the skin. Buffeting produces other stresses which may be repeated many times during the course of one flight. A stressed skin means that is is pulled tight and fixed to the internal structure, generally some form of frame which ultimately makes up part of a box. This structure is an efficient means of resisting these forces for the minimum structural weight. The usual mode of static failure of a stressed-skin box is the buckling of a sheet in compression or shear although this does not usually lead to a catastrophic failure in the air.* Smaller structural boxes allow higher stresses to be tolerated but weigh more.

To make the structure of a wing so strong that it would never break would also make it so heavy it would never fly and some compromise has to be reached. The usual standard is to make the wing strong enough to withstand 150% of the largest load likely to be placed upon it. This is assessed first by calculation and then by progressively bending the wing, using weights or hydraulic rams, until it reaches its ultimate static load.** The wing also needs to be able to withstand reasonable torsional (twisting) stress.

As well as making the wing, and the rest of the aircraft, strong enough to cope with large immediate (static) stresses and strains it also needs to be able to deal with the insidious effects of smaller loads repeated over a long period producing metal fatigue.*** Being long cantilevers and exposed to large forces, wings are particularly prone to fatigue problems. At the time of the Comet's design quite a lot was known about metal fatigue but rather less emphasis was placed on it then than it was later. The

---

* This was investigated by an Austrian, Dr. Herbert Wagner (1900-82) in Germany in the 1920s who developed a theory to explain the behaviour of metal sheets fixed at their edges and exposed to various stresses and consequent strains.[17] At the end of the war he was removed to the United States under the auspices of Operation Paperclip, arriving with seven large suitcases of blueprints and other data. He worked for the U.S. Navy for several years and then returned to Germany.

** The ultimate static load (see also ultimate strength, Chapter 18) is the maximum load expected in service multiplied by a safety factor, in this case 150%. Testing involves holding the ultimate load for three seconds without a fracture occurring. The structure in question would be expected to fail soon after the ultimate load had been exceeded.

*** Metal fatigue, a great nuisance to engineers, is the process by which cracks start and then grow in a metal structure under the influence of repeated applications of stress. The maximum value of these stresses is significantly less than the ultimate static strength of the material. After a sufficient number of cycles the largest crack will achieve a critical size and the structure will fail completely on the next stress application. Fatigue was to play a significant role in the story of the Comet, (see Appendix 5 for a more complete account.)

idea of testing the wing for its fatigue life, by exposing it to smaller stresses repeated many times, developed during the early lifetime of the Comet 1 after cracks had been discovered in the wings of RAF transports and some civilian aircraft.* One quite large American passenger aircraft, the Martin 202, had crashed in 1948 killing 37 people when a wing spar failed.

The Comet wing was tested by repeated loadings of 10% to 40% of its ultimate load applied 5,000 times. At that time there were no reliable data about gusts at the Comet's cruising height and these loads were just estimates.[18] The tests revealed three main areas of weakness which would have led to a fatigue life of about 1,100 hours,[19] "between one-fortieth and one-twentieth of what we normally require and usually obtain", according to a letter written by Dr. P. B. Walker of the RAE** to the Ministry of Supply.[20] In other words the wing was completely inadequate. The relevant parts were redesigned and then tested as separate items although not all were in agreement that this was a satisfactory process.[19] The same wing was then tested for static strength and in May 1951 it failed at 80% of ultimate load. The failure was in a part which had already been weakened by the fatigue tests and because of this the RAE decided that the modified wing would be acceptable.[19] Dr. Walker, often to be a dissenting voice in what followed, continued in his letter that "in no circumstances could we agree to static and fatigue tests being planned for the same specimen."***[21] Fatigue testing by the company continued as the Comets were introduced into service with the idea that as long as the testing was well ahead of the hours currently flown the wings should be safe. The RAE still wanted to test a complete wing with repeated loadings and this eventually took place with a wing from the prototype in June to August 1954.[22]

Along the length of the stub wing the internal spaces between the ribs and spars were used as fuel tanks, to accommodate the mechanisms that move the control surfaces of the wing and for housing the undercarriage while in flight. As the wing is where lift is generated it is the most supported part of the aircraft in flight and is therefore the most efficient place for the heavy fuel load to be carried. In the Comet the wing roots also contained dinghies in case of a water landing. Modern passenger aircraft wings often have a box beam and thicker skins which make them structurally stronger than those of the Comet's era as well as having podded engines forward of the wings which have a damping effect on wing vibrations by increasing their flutter speeds.

---

* The Dove, another de Havilland product, suffered a fatigue problem with its wings causing a fatal crash in Australia in 1951. The crash investigators, perhaps unwisely, travelled to the scene in another Dove. They discovered the cause of the crash was a fatigue fracture in the main spar. When they checked the main spar on their own aircraft they discovered to their discomfort that it, too, had a significant fatigue fracture.[23]
** Dr. Percy Walker (1903-79) was the Head of the Structures Department at Farnborough and played a significant part in the Comet investigations and inquiry, see Chapters 16, 19, 23 and 29. He went from Cambridge to work on the design of the ill-fated airship R101 at Cardington in Bedfordshire. Walker started at Farnborough before the war, moved to the MAP at the outbreak of war but returned in 1945.
*** In this context Walker meant doing fatigue and then static testing[24] but, as will become apparent, doing the tests in reverse order was just as deceptive, see Chapter 21.

The fin and tailplane

One of the early designs for the Comet omitted the tailplane and another substituted a canard. As the design of the Comet matured a more conventional tailplane appeared although at first both the fin and tailplane were markedly swept back. In the end a more conventional tapered fin and a tapered tailplane with slightly swept leading edges were adopted.

The fin and tailplane were made in a similar way to the wings with front and rear spars along their lengths, a series of ribs at right angles to the spars and stringers between the ribs with the skin stretched over them. The tailplane had a leading edge sweep back of 15^0, a dihedral of 10^0 and an incidence of 1^0.[25] The tailplanes were symmetrical and could be interchanged. The tips of the fin and tailplane incorporated various radio aerials. Apart from the tips, the trailing edges of the fin and tailplane were made up of the rudder and elevator control surfaces which rotated about a series of hinges. All the control surfaces incorporated mass balances at their outboard ends to reduce the strain on their operating mechanisms. The elevators had small balance tabs near the inboard end of their trailing edges to allow fine tuning. Towards the base of the fin was a wooden insulating box that electrically isolated the upper fin so that it could be used as a high frequency radio aerial.[26]

No particular problems emerged from the design of the tailplane apart from the insulating box in the fin which appeared to be a structurally weak point and was strengthened after the Elba crash.[27] Apart from this the design was more or less repeated in the later models until the Nimrod* appeared.

The fuselage

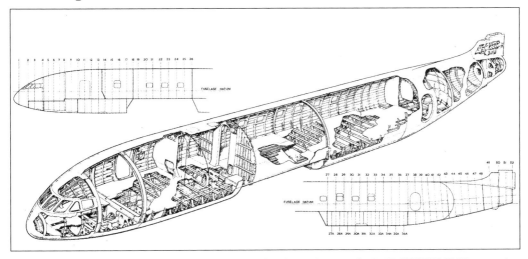

Fig. 1/4 The internal structure of the Comet 1 fuselage, (copyright BAE SYSTEMS Heritage)

---

* An RAF maritime reconnaissance aircraft based on the later Comets.

For a jet airliner's fuel consumption to be as little as possible the aircraft had to cruise at a higher altitude than the contemporary piston-engined aircraft. High altitude means a low ambient air pressure, which is uncomfortable in itself for the passengers and crew, and a low partial pressure of oxygen in the air. This, in turn, produces a low partial pressure of oxygen in the blood (hypoxaemia) causing cerebral impairment progressing to unconsciousness and ultimately death. Up to a point the hypoxaemia can be relieved by breathing oxygen, which sometimes had to be used by passengers flying over mountain ranges in unpressurised aircraft. Professor Gordon recalls that one of the skills now lost to mankind is the ability to eat one's lunch while wearing an oxygen mask.[28] A far better solution is to have a pressurised cabin which provides an atmosphere equivalent to about 8,000 feet above sea level. This is an altitude that can be easily tolerated by most people although it produces mild hypoxaemia and sometimes a little discomfort from pressure effects. To provide a pressurised environment air of the correct temperature has to be pumped into the fuselage producing a pressure differential between the inside and the outside of the cabin. The higher the altitude the greater the differential required. There also has to be a sufficient change of air to avoid carbon dioxide build up.

The first passenger aircraft to have a pressurised cabin was the Boeing B307 Stratoliner which flew for the first time on the last day of 1938. It had a maximum pressure differential of 2.5 pounds per square inch (psi). The Stratoliner was followed by the Lockheed Constellation in 1943, the British Avro Tudor in 1945 and the DC-6 in 1946, but the Comet could fly almost twice as high as its predecessors and required a pressure differential about 50% greater.

The Comet's normal cruising altitude was about 35,000 feet at which the ambient pressure (under standard conditions) is around 3.46 psi. The ambient pressure at 8,000 feet is 10.92 psi, hence the transmural pressure difference at cruising altitude is about 7.5 psi. To allow for higher altitudes being reached and to include a safety margin the Comet's pressure differential could reach 8.25 psi, referred to as P or 1P, which kept the same cabin pressure at 40,000 feet. In case the cabin pressure became too high there were two discharge valves set to open at 8.25 psi and an independent safety valve set at 8.5 psi.[29] The cabin air was originally intended to come from compressors driven by the engines but this proved difficult and the equipment heavy. A better solution was found that bled air off the engines and then cooled and filtered it to remove any oil.

A differential of 8.25 psi does not seem much compared with that in many pressure vessels such as steam locomotive boilers which were usually run with internal pressures around 250 psi,*[30] but a fuselage is much larger and lighter than anything in a steam locomotive. The most efficient shape for a pressure vessel is a sphere. This is clearly impractical for an aircraft fuselage which is generally a hollow cylinder blocked at both ends. These ends are stronger if they are more or less dome-shaped, rather like the sealed end of a cigar tube. Although it is not apparent from the outside of an aircraft the rear bulkhead of the pressurised cabin projects rearwards as a dome-shape, leaving the interior of the tail section at ambient pressure. The front end is usually an approximation

---

* The transmural pressure differential at sea level is the internal pressure minus 14.7 psi.

to a dome, the Comet's more so than most. This tube is then inflated when it is flying at altitude, rather like a sausage-shaped balloon, producing circumferential (hoop) and longitudinal stresses and hence strains. It can be shown mathematically that the hoop stress has twice the magnitude of the longitudinal stress (see Appendix 5) which, as Professor Gordon points out, is why sausages being cooked generally split lengthwise and not crosswise.[31] It is therefore doubly unfortunate that windows and doors, which significantly weaken the structure, are cut into the sides in more or less straight lines, providing, as it were, the 'tear here' perforations.

In addition to the pressure-generated stresses, the fuselage is subjected to other stresses and strains even when it is standing on the ground but even more when taking off, flying and landing. Different parts of the fuselage experience longitudinal tension, compression and torsion, often in different directions at different times. Rather like a beam bridge the centre section of the fuselage experiences these stresses the most. In practice the dominant mode of failure from these loads is local compressive buckling.

It is not surprising that designing such a structure to be both strong and light is something of a challenge. The Comet fuselage was made by attaching thin aluminium alloy* sheeting to long stringers which are themselves attached to transverse frames. Some aircraft, but not the Comet, have fewer but stronger beams called longerons running the length of the fuselage. In the case of the Comet the alloy skin was glued to the stringers by the Redux gluing process. In the centre section of the fuselage over the wings, near windows 2, 3 and 4, the skin was also riveted to the frames. The stringers were spaced at intervals of about 5½ inches and braced by frames 21 inches apart. The 'witch's hat' stringers were similar, but not identical, to the ones in the wings, 1¼ inches deep with their 'brims' attached to the skin. The frames had a Z-shaped cross section 2¾ inches high and were notched where they were crossed by the stringers. At these points the flanges of the stringers were attached to the frames by 2 BA** countersunk-head bolts. Except in the centre section the frames were not otherwise attached to the skin.[32]

The thickness of the metal skin varied according to the stresses to which it was likely to be exposed, thicker skin reducing the stress. In the Comet the skin was slightly thicker along the line of windows. The various cutouts for windows and doors had reinforced edges and the passenger door opened inwards[33] and the crew door slid upwards[34] so that they were unlikely to burst outwards with the pressure differential.

The aluminium alloy used for the Comet skin was a new one called DTD 546B (Directorate of Technical Development) which contained between 3.5 and 4.8% copper

---

* Aluminium itself is too weak for structural use in aircraft and alloys must be used, the first being a copper, manganese, magnesium, aluminium alloy called Duralumin (from Durener Metallwerke), invented by Dr. Alfred Wilm in 1909. Although much stronger, Duralumin corrodes readily, a problem that was cured by covering it with a thin sheet of pure aluminium. After heat treatment the aluminium bonds with the alloy.[35, 36] The alloy sheets used in the Comet were similarly clad. The first all-metal aircraft, a monoplane made of steel, was produced by Hugo Junkers in 1915 (the J1 or 'Tin Donkey'). Not surprisingly it was too heavy to perform well. He later pioneered the use of Duralumin.
** British Association, a definition of small screw threads, now largely obsolete.

Fig. 2/4 Inside the forward cabin before fitting out, (Ministry of Supply, image suppied by BAE SYSTEMS Heritage)

with traces of iron, silicon, magnesium, manganese and titanium. Its minimum thickness was 22 gauge (0.028 inches) and its maximum was the 20 gauge (0.036 inches) sheet at the side of the fuselage where the windows were. The stringers were made from 20 gauge DTD 687A sheeting (an aluminium alloy with zinc and magnesium and traces of copper and manganese). The frames were made from DTD 610 sheeting which had a similar chemical composition to DTD 546B. The window frames had a Z cross section 2.85 inches deep, made from thicker 16 gauge (0.064 inches) DTD 610 alloy and covered, where it was attached to the skin, by a sealing strip of the same thickness and material (see Chapter 30). The window frame was Reduxed to the skin and the sealing strip then Reduxed over it. In addition there was a double line of ⅛ inches rivets, countersunk at each end, through all the layers at the corners of the windows. Some of the windows, 1, 6 and 8 on each side, were slightly larger and doubled as escape hatches. These had similar frames. The shape of all the cutouts was rectangular with rounded corners of radius 3 inches for the windows and 4 inches for the escape hatches. The windows were 16.6 inches wide and 14 inches high and the escape hatches 19 and 21.5 inches. The two forward escape hatches interrupted a circumferential frame but the remaining windows and escape hatches were positioned between frames.[37]

The two ADF (automatic direction finding) windows in the centre line of the roof of the forward cabin were similarly constructed with internal Z-shaped frames but the surrounding skin was doubled to 0.056 inches. The reinforcing plate was added after the window failed in a water tank test at a pressure of 12.75 psi in December 1948.[38] The plate was attached to the underlying skin with a double row of rivets around its whole circumference.

Fig. 3/4 Nose test section after ultimate strength test, 2 December 1948, (copyright Ministry of Supply, image supplied by BAE SYSTEMS Heritage)

The structure of the fuselage has been covered in some detail because it has relevance for the events that befell the Comet. For its time it was relatively conventional except, perhaps, for the Reduxing. Also the skin was significantly thinner than the later Boeing 707 (0.04 to 0.07 inches compared with the Comet's, 0.028 to 0.036 inches)*[39]

Although the design of the fuselage and pressure cabin was relatively conventional its wall would be exposed to greater pressure gradients and temperature differentials than usual. The British Civil Airworthiness Requirements (BCAR) called for a 'proof' pressure of 1.33P in which there was no permanent deformity of the structure and a

---

* As part of his training to join the Comet fleet, Peter Duffey, a first officer, spent some time on the factory floor at de Havillands. He commented that he pushed the side of a fuselage and "it popped out at me again and I thought 'My God, it's very, very thin.'" Pete Follerby, another Comet First Officer, recalled that they used to joke that it was "made of silver paper."[40] In the summer of 2011 the author travelled to the de Havilland Aircraft Museum at London Colney to investigate this on the sole remaining Comet 1 fuselage. The authorial finger was applied to the skin at the level of the windows to see whether it felt like silver paper. It didn't.

'design' pressure of 2P (the maximum pressure the structure could be expected to withstand).[41] These standards were the same as those for the RAF and the International Civil
Aviation Organisation. De Havillands elected to exceed these standards and specified a
design pressure of 2.5P and tested the cabin to 2P. The reasoning behind this was that
a cabin that would survive undamaged to a pressure differential of 2P would not fail in
service when exposed repeatedly to pressure of just P even when combined with all the
other stresses that flight would impose upon it.*

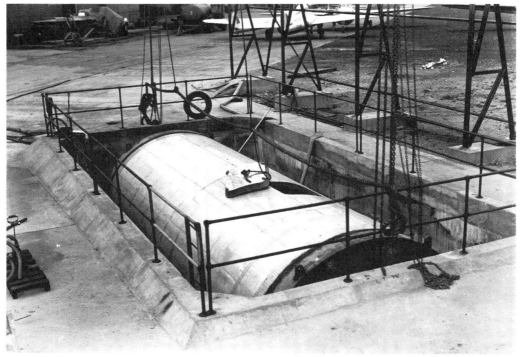

*Fig. 4/4 Fuselage test section in the water tank (copyright Ministry of Supply, image supplied
by BAE SYSTEMS Heritage)*

De Havillands built two sections of cabin for testing. The front part was 26 feet long
and stretched from the nose to nearly the front spar and eventually included the cockpit
windows, a cabin window, an ADF window and a door. The centre part was 24 feet long
and extended from a few feet in front of the forward spar to a few feet aft of the rear
spar and included the large cut-out for the wing and later a window. The sections were
pressure-tested at first using compressed air from the factory's supply and then in a
sunken, concrete water tank built specially for the purpose and just large enough to
accommodate the sections. The front section was exposed some 30 times to pressures
of between P and 2P and 2,000 times to a pressure just over P to prove that it was
satisfactory as a pressure vessel. These were not intended as fatigue tests but, as Lord

---

* In other words it was using a static test as a fatigue test. This was based on a 1946 paper by D. Williams.[42]

Fig. 5/4 Nose test section being removed from the water tank, 2 December 1948, (Ministry of Supply, image supplied by BAE SYSTEMS Heritage)

Cohen later said in his report on the Comet crashes, they no doubt added to the confidence of the designers that they had produced a strong aeroplane.[41] In addition a panel with a window in its frame was tested to 19.75 psi at which point it developed a tensile crack starting at the riveting of two of the corners of the reinforcing plate and spreading linearly along the whole panel. As this had happened at 2.25P it was considered that the structure was sufficiently strong.[43] The window itself was separately pressure-tested to 85 psi while it was supported in a rigid frame as well as being exposed to - 60°C (Celsius). Five windows were pressurised to 8.5 psi daily and exposed to weathering on the roof of a building, all without sustaining significant damage.[44]

Between 1949 and 1951, as construction work on the Comets was proceeding, there was a growing awareness among designers of the dangers of fatigue in aircraft structures, particularly in wings. About the middle of 1952 these thoughts about fatigue failures were extended to pressure cabins.[45] The testing requirements for RAF pressure cabins were altered to include a static test of 2P, a proof test to 1.33P and repeated loading tests of 1.25P applied 10,000 times.[41] At about the same time the technical staff of the Air Registration Board (ARB), the body responsible for issuing Certificates of Airworthiness, were reviewing the situation for civil aircraft and in due course went one better and required applications of 1.25P 15,000 times and suggested that certain vulnerable parts, such as riveted joints and window frames, might have to be designed to cope with 3P.[41]

De Havillands were keeping up with these changing standards. By July 1953 no Comet had exceeded 2,500 flying hours (about 800 flights) and the front part of the test cabins had experienced 16,000 P cycles (equivalent to 48,000 hours at three hours flying time per pressure cycle) in the water tank, well ahead of the aircraft in service. By September this number had increased to 17,900 as well as the 30 earlier applications of between P and 2P. The front section then failed by developing a fatigue fracture at the corner of the ADF window, originating at a small defect in the skin.[46] As the number of cycles was so far in excess of those any Comet was likely to experience in its service life it was thought that this represented an adequate safety margin. In the meantime, on 2nd May, a BOAC Comet had fallen apart in a storm near Calcutta.

Fig. 6/4 Testing a passenger cabin window, 22 June 1949, (copyright BAE SYSTEMS Heritage)

The powered controls and other systems

Most aircraft before the Comet had manual controls that worked using levers and wheels moving cables that ran the length of the aircraft to reach ailerons, rudders and elevators. The advantage of this system was that it provided 'feel' to the pilot. If there was a lot of air pressure on an elevator the control was proportionately harder to move and the pilot knew about it straight away, in other words there was a built-in, negative feed-back loop. But as aircraft got bigger and flew faster they became more difficult, and ultimately impossible, to control using just the muscle power of the pilot. The solution to this was to provide power-operated controls. In the Comet these were in the form of hydraulic boosters. There were three main hydraulic systems all pressurised by engine-driven pumps and two auxiliary systems, one of which could be hand-pumped if necessary. All were colour-coded and for safety reasons had a degree of cross-over redundancy. The hydraulic system provided power for units called Servodynes. These were dedicated aircraft power-control devices, manufactured by the British Lockheed Company of Leamington Spa. They were controlled by cables run from the flight deck, the Servodynes, in effect, adding power to the pilot's cable movements. These, augmented, movements were then transmitted by more cables to the ailerons and by push-pull rods to the elevators and rudder. The Servodynes were all located in a single bay in the rear fuselage which was convenient for maintenance but generated a considerable amount of heat which had to be dealt with by extra ventilation.[47] The power controls were tested in a Mosquito and a Hornet as well as in the later Swallows.

These were the pioneering days of powered controls. One of the problems experienced in the early Comets was the lack of 'feel' in the controls. They did the job of moving the control surfaces but gave the pilot an inadequate sense of how hard they were having to work. They also had a high 'break out' force which meant that the pilot had to push or pull quite forcefully before the control would activate which could lead to rather jerky progression or 'over control.' Ultimately, but not for the Comet 1s, this system was changed to a more sophisticated one which had more 'feel' and a lower break out force.

The design of the instrument panel and much of the flight deck was based on the Lockheed Constellation. In Cunningham's view this was the best airliner of the time and Campbell Orde of BOAC had sent him to Dorval in Canada to train on it and then to fly scheduled services as a crew member so that he was completely familiar with it. He recalled that the captains, "…flew very well but often thumped their aircraft down rather than making a smooth landing," possibly, he thought, a legacy of their prewar experience with heavy aircraft and flying boats.[48] This led to the Comet having a substantial undercarriage.

Power fuelling

The unique selling point of the Comet was its speed and therefore the time it saved on long journeys. Its potential downfall was its short range and frequent refuelling stops and so everything that could be done to reduce the time spent refuelling was vital. Up to now the usual method of refuelling had been a gravity process via a fuel port on top of the wing but the Comet was designed to have a pressure-refuelling system that would be quicker and would use a port on the much-more-convenient underside of the wing. The Comet 1 had two integral tanks in each stub wing, the inner and outer, and four bag tanks in the section of the wings under the fuselage.[49] Using pressure refuelling it took about half an hour to load the fuel.

Other systems

There were other, perhaps lesser, problems for the designers. The nose section of the Comet, not much removed from a simple domed end to the fuselage cylinder, was a rad-

Fig. 7/4 Comet 1 control cabin repica on a Horsa glider fuselage (TL348) with Sir Geoffrey watching, 19 December 1946, (copyright BAE SYSTEMS Heritage)

Fig. 8/4 Nose test section and Ghost engine during noise and vibration tests, 18 October 1948, (copyright BAE SYSTEMS Heritage)

ical departure from most contemporary designs which usually had a cockpit shaped like a bubble, on top and somewhat behind the the nose. The design was tested by replacing the front end of a Horsa glider with a wooden mock up of the Comet's nose. This was to see whether the pilots' view was adequate and also to check the clearance of rain water from the windows. The glider was towed by a Halifax bomber around the skies of southern England with John Cunningham at the controls of the glider looking for rain showers, which proved surprisingly hard to find.

Cabin noise from the new jet engines was another worry. Cunningham's record-breaking Vampire was partly dismantled and its jet exhaust pointed close to the test nose section while the noise it generated was monitored inside.[50]

One innovation was the rig used to prepare the test pilots for manoeuvring with a double nose wheel, a relative rarity in those days. It consisted of a lorry chassis whose front suspension consisted of the two Comet nose wheels with a large Mosquito under-carriage wheel on either side, not touching the ground but acting rather like bicycle sta-bilisers to prevent the rig overturning. This was driven around the apron at Hatfield with a flag on the top of the cab to warn people to keep their distance. Looking at the photographs it appears that Sir Geoffrey had at least one ride on the rig. The undercar-riage of the Comet prototype had the above conventional nose wheels with a single large wheel below each wing rather in the manner of a wartime bomber. These were replaced by four-wheel bogies in the production aircraft which spread the load over a bigger area. Edward Heath, later Prime Minister, claimed the credit for suggesting this when he was a junior minister at the Civil Aviation Authority.[51]

Fig. 9/4 Nose wheel test vehicle with Charles Wilkins driving and Sir Geoffrey present, 30 January 1948, (copyright BAE SYSTEMS Heritage)

The DH 111, the Comet bomber

At the end of the war the government was giving some thought towards the weapons that would be used in the future. Clearly one of these would be the atomic bomb and it would be of little use to have a bomb without a method of delivering it. Early versions of the 'special bomb' were likely to be heavy and bulky and as well as being able to accommodate such a load any carrier would have to fly fast enough and high enough to deal with the jet-propelled interceptors that were already coming into service, indeed it would have to deal with the second generation of jet fighters by the time it came into service.

In 1945 de Havillands were made aware of an Air Ministry requirement (OR 199) for a fast, unarmed, jet-propelled, high-altitude bomber to replace the Mosquito. This would eventually become the twin-engined, English Electric Canberra but in 1946 OR 229 specified a four-engined bomber with a cruising speed of 500 knots and a ceiling of at least 55,000 feet which would ultimately bring into being the three V-bombers. De Havillands were clearly interested in producing some derivative of the Comet to meet this requirement and with their experience of turbojets were well placed to be a successful bidder.

Their first thoughts involved a photo-reconnaissance version of the Comet but Bishop submitted a proposal for a bomber to the Air Ministry on 27 May 1948. One account of this aeroplane, the DH 111, describes a narrower fuselage than the Comet's, around 9 feet high and 6 feet wide, with a length of about 95 feet. It had a bulbous nose to accommodate the radar, the same wing-root location for the engines as the Comet and a bubble-type cockpit canopy. A drawing shows a clean, mid-wing aircraft with a tail fin very like the Comet's and a fuselage that tapered upwards to the tail from the rear wing spar.[52] It was just able to carry the proposed British atomic bomb whose estimated weight was then around 10,000 pounds. However this weapon steadily increased in size and weight eventually reaching an impressive 21,000 pounds which was thought too much for the aircraft and the proposal was dropped in October 1948.

As things turned out the weight of the first usable atomic bomb (Blue Danube) was 10,000 pounds and its successor (Red Beard 1) was 2,000 pounds.[53] Had the bomb not grown so much during its development phase it is possible that because of commonality with the Comet the RAF would have had its atomic bomber before the Vickers Valiant which came into service in 1955. On the other hand de Havillands probably had their hands full producing the Comet.

Chapter 5

THE COMET PROTOTYPE TAKES SHAPE

After the Ministry of Supply contract was awarded on 4 September 1946 for two prototypes to specification 20/44 the final drawings were produced and construction of the first prototype could begin early the following year.[1] This took place in the experimental hanger at de Havillands' main factory at Hatfield in some secrecy. It was said that Bishop kept a model of the early, tailless, airliner design on his desk to put visitors off the scent.[1] Mike Ramsden, at that time a de Havilland apprentice, said that they "were not allowed in the experimental department, but if you put your overalls on and put some drawings under your arm, and walked through the doors with self assurance, nobody said 'Hey what are you doing?' and I used to go in regularly to see how it was getting on."[2]

Fig. 1/5 The first prototype (G-ALVG) with its engines not yet installed, 22 March 1949, (copyright BAE SYSTEMS Heritage)

The aeroplane taking shape was like nothing the shop floor workers had seen before. Mike Ramsden again, "...I can't tell you how thrilling it was to see this almost alien machine. It was really comparable to (the) space shuttles and space stations of today's technology."[2] It is difficult to appreciate this excitement now in an age when jet airliners are commonplace and most people in the western world have travelled in one. It is only when photographs of contemporary aircraft are compared with what was taking shape on the factory floor at Hatfield that it is possible to get an idea of the awe that young apprentices such as Ramsden must have felt.

De Havillands were also aware that they had to get on with things. Ralph Hare, who worked in the design department, said that "...a lot of pressure was put on us at that time to produce an aeroplane quickly. We were aware that the Americans would soon catch up if we allowed them to and so we were working very long hours, as we were previously on the Mosquito during the war."[2]

In fact the Americans were not in the race. Vickers flew an experimental Viking with two Rolls-Royce Nenes, on 6 April 1948[3] and Avro followed in September with a Tudor 1 using four Nenes. Vickers decided to use turboprops and built the Viscount with four Rolls-Royce Darts which first flew in 1950. Avro stayed with the Nene to develop the Ashton from the Tudor 2 only to be eclipsed by the Comet, the first airliner designed from the start to be jet propelled, which flew for the first time on 27 July 1949. Close behind were the Canadians with the Avro Canada C-102 with four Rolls-Royce Derwents which had its maiden flight on 10 August 1949.[4] Avro Canada eventually

Fig. 2/5 The first prototype with two test sections, 13 July 1949, (copyright BAE SYSTEMS Heritage)

Fig. 3/5 The first prototype being weighed, 19 July 1949, (copyright BAE SYSTEMS Heritage)

gave up on their aircraft and only built a prototype, mainly because a jet fighter they were developing took most of the company's resources. The Boeing prototype that developed into the 707, the Boeing 360-80 or Dash 80, flew for the first time on 15 July 1954. This project started in early 1952 after Bill Allen, Boeing's president, saw the Comet flying at the 1950 Farnborough Show and later visited Hatfield.*

The prototype Comet was completed and shown to the press for the first time on 3 March 1949 at Hatfield. Over the following four weeks its systems were subjected to extensive tests and then, on 2 April, the four Ghost engines were started for the first time in situ. Engine tests were completed by 25 July and the prototype, later registered as G-ALVG, was prepared for its first flight.[1]

John 'Cats-Eyes' Cunningham, as de Havillands' chief test pilot, was naturally going to fly the prototype on its first outing. Cunningham was a genuine British hero who disliked his nick-name. A quiet, unassuming gentleman who had started with de Havillands as an apprentice but developed a love of flying after joining the Royal Auxiliary Air Force. As a result of this he became a test pilot for de Havillands but was

* On one of the visits to Hatfield the Boeing delegation apparently considered that, compared to their B-47 production line, the Comet assembly was more like a "small town auto-repair shop." [5]

called up by the RAF at the beginning of the war. He became famous, and acquired his nick-name, as a night fighter pilot. His successes, of course, were due to airborne radar rather than any ability to see in the dark and he had been fortunate to have been teamed up with an able radar operator called Cecil Rawnsley who later wrote a book about their escapades.[6] Nevertheless Cunningham was a gifted pilot and was to do most of the Comet test flying and proving trips. He retired in 1980 having tested the later marks of the Comet as well as the DH121 Trident. He died not long after taking part in the Principal Films documentary in which he made a dignified appearance.

On 27 July the press and various government and BOAC officials were invited to meet the flight crew after two short hops had been carried out during the morning. Victor George was then returned to its hanger for some final checks and, rather unfortunately in the light of subsequent events, the press departed on mass, thinking that nothing of any great importance was going to happen that day. As the aircraft had passed all its checks and the weather was good Cunningham took the decision to make the first flight. This showed a certain lack of media savvy. This was, after all, the maiden flight of a new, ground-breaking aircraft that represented all the hopes and aspirations for the commercial success, survival even, of a major British aircraft company, perhaps an entire industry. Had the press been there it would have represented a major 'photo. opportunity' and

Fig. 4/5 Control cabin, (ZK), 10 February 1950, (copyright BAE SYSTEMS Heritage)

an enormous amount of free publicity. Perhaps it was an expression of an honest and decent, engineering-led company in an earlier age just not thinking about publicity but it was a lost opportunity. It made no difference to the flight but there would certainly have been more film and photographs if they had been present. As a result of this some members of the media were furious and the aviation correspondent of *The Times*, it was said, vowed never to mention their name again.[7] He may not have done, but his newspaper certainly did. They reported the flight the next day and there was a subsequent report on 1st August.

Fig. 5/5 Charles Wilkins and Ronald Bishop, 27 July 1949, (copyright BAE SYSTEMS Heritage)

The engines were started at 18:17 and the maiden flight lasted 31 minutes. As well as John Cunningham the crew consisted of John Wilson as co-pilot, Tony Fairbrother as flight engineer and 'Tubby' Walters and Frank Reynolds as observers. The flight did little more than allow Cunningham to test its basic flight characteristics and controls but before landing he did a low fly past to show off the aircraft to the workers who had made it. Cunningham pronounced it as being "very promising so far."[8]

After the first flight a major programme of flight testing began on 5 August with five flights that week and the performance envelope was progressively explored. The aircraft appeared to have few vices and was quieter inside the cabin than had been expected. During the second week of trials the prototype reached 400 mph at 38,500 feet. The aircraft's pressurisation system was used for the first time on 27 August but only at a pressure differential of 2 psi. Over the first eleven months of trials the average flight time per day was about one hour. This may not seem a great deal but much time was spent between flights doing maintenance and making adjustments and alterations.

The Comet was shown to the public at large for the first time at the Farnborough Air Show from 5 to 12 September. John Wilson recalled of this occasion:

Our fly-past speed was 340 knots, very fast for an aircraft which had only been flying for three weeks... We had Chris Beaumont (the Chief Test Pilot of the D. H. Engine Company) with us, and he stood at the entrance to the cockpit – every time we pulled 2½-3g to go around the corner Chris found that the floor on which he was standing was

Fig. 6/5, above, Frank Halford, Frank Whittle, Sir Geoffrey de Havilland and Charles Walker.
Fig. 7/5, below, John Cunningham, John Wilson and others on the day of the first flight of the
first prototype. (Both images taken on 27 July 1949 and copyright of BAE SYSTEMS Heritage)

Fig. 8/5 The first prototype Comet 1 (G-ALVG), 3 August 1949, (copyright BAE SYSTEMS Heritage)

bulging up.* And there was a loud bang at that speed from the nose of the aircraft where the skin panted, so when we heard this bang we knew, without checking the airspeed indicator, that we were doing 340 knots. In later years we realised that these were indications of how flimsy the structure really was.[9]

The story of the bang was also related by Wilson in the Principal Films documentary when he commented that at first they thought they had hit something but when they got on the ground they could not find anything except that on the nose skin there was a dished panel which appeared to have been caused just by air pressure.

After Farnborough the Comet flew into London Airport (now Heathrow) on 22 October to try out approach and landing patterns. These were found not to interfere with the slower, propellor-driven, aircraft movements. The aircraft then flew to Tripoli for 'hot and high' trials and to assess fuel consumption. It covered the almost 3,000 miles round trip in a little over 6¾ hours of flying time.[8]

---

* For the floor to do this the width of the fuselage must have been reduced. At 340 knots in a 3g turn the aircraft is banking at an angle of 70⁰ and describing a circle more than four miles in circumference. It is likely that the 3g load on the wings bent them upwards significantly and as the entrance to the flight deck was above the main spar this put the floor plate into compression from side to side. The bulging could be up or down depending on the the floor's attachment to the fuselage. There might also have been some bending produced by the forces on the tailplane generated by the turn.

Fig. 9/5, above, the first prototype, side view, 3 August 1949.
Fig. 10/5, below, photographed from below on 4 August 1949.
(Both images copyright BAE SYSTEMS Heritage)

Fig. 11/5, John Cunningham being interviewed by the BBC (copyright BAE SYSTEMS Heritage)

So far the prototype had operated with a single large wheel under each wing but in December these were changed for four-wheel bogies. It was decided not to change the wing undercarriage cavities so these wheels had to remain in the locked-down position for some 56 flights. In February 1950 the single wheels were restored and the trials resumed. Also in February the cabin was fully pressurised for the first time.[10]

As the trials had progressed relatively uneventfully it was decided that flights with passengers could start, albeit not with the paying public. On 16 March Victor George carried sixteen passengers drawn from the de Havilland company, the MoS and the press, to Rome, an airport that would become very significant in the Comet story. Five days later the Comet flew to Copenhagen, again with members of the press on board, and reached a maximum speed of 490 mph at 34,000 feet.[10] Tropical and arctic trials followed and then some three months of maintenance during which the prototype received a BOAC paint finish.[11] This replaced the polished metal finish that the Principal Films documentary alleged was used to save weight. If this had been true, and as the engines were unchanged, it is not clear how the prototype suddenly became able to carry the extra weight.

Towards the end of 1950 the prototype was fitted with a dummy refuelling probe and trials were carried out with an Avro Lancaster playing the part of the tanker.[11] This

Fig. 12/5 Sir Geoffrey de Havilland (copyright BAE SYSTEMS Heritage)

was at the behest of Alan Cobham who had pioneered in-flight refuelling and could see a new opportunity here. Slip stream problems were encountered and, probably fortunately, it was concluded that in-flight refuelling was not a practical proposition for large aircraft like the Comet in regular airline service. Work with the prototype continued through 1951. Starting in May it included 30 flights during which the de Havilland Sprite rocket engines were fired about 500 times.[11] By this time the first production aircraft were coming into service with BOAC. During most of 1952 Victor George was used for development work with the Ghost engines. New wings intended for the Mark 3 Comet were tried out, complete with pinion tanks and leading edge droops. After these tests the original wings were replaced.[12]

Victor George ended its days in Farnborough having been flown there in July 1953 for structural testing, mainly repeated up and down stressing of the tailplane and wing as well as fuel tank pressure testing.[12] As a result of these tests cracks appeared in the wing after the equivalent of 6,000 hours of flying and in August the following year it suffered a major structural failure.[13] What remained of the aircraft was then moved to the 'Comet storage area' on the airfield. It was finally scrapped, probably in the late 1950s, thus removing the opportunity to preserve a significant aircraft in the history of aviation.[14]

In the meantime a second prototype had been built. G-ALZK made its first flight on

Fig. 13/5 VG in BOAC colours, 7 July 1952 (copyright Vauxhall Motors, image supplied by BAE SYSTEMS Heritage)

27 July 1950, exactly a year after the maiden flight of the first prototype, piloted, as might be expected, by John Cunningham and it underwent the usual manufacturer's trials. It was then painted in BOAC colours and handed over to them for training and route-proving flights starting in March 1951. These flights covered South Africa, the Middle East, India, Indonesia and Singapore with a variety of BOAC captains and crews. Only minor problems showed up, such as the air-

Fig. 14/5 The nose of the second prototype (G-ALZK) emerging from the fuselage shop for pressure testing, 4 February 1949, (copyright BAE SYSTEMS Heritage)

craft sinking into the tarmac in the midday heat at Basra, in Iraq. This was solved by taxiing the aircraft around until steel reinforcing mats could be provided.

Later on another, potentially more serious, incident occurred. On 16 October the aircraft had considerable trouble getting airborne from Kallang airport in Singapore. All had seemed normal but the aircraft failed to accelerate normally during its takeoff run and only just managed to clear the radio masts at the perimeter. It appeared that the perforated steel planking which made up the runway was pressed down by the large main wheels of the undercarriage setting up a 'bow wave' of planking which created resistance to forward movement. It was decided that in future only hardened runways should be used for large aircraft such as the Comet. A total of 470 flying hours were accumulated with BOAC and 31 countries visited after which ZK was returned to Hatfield for an overhaul.[15]

ZK was then cleared to carry passengers, mainly potential customers and VIPs, the latter including Prince Philip on 13 March 1952. De-icing and anti-icing trials followed and four-wheel bogies were fitted in April, again fixed in the down position, and used to test the anti-skid braking system. In due course the original wheels were reinstated. The aircraft was officially owned by the Ministry of Supply but continued to be lent to de Havillands for the remainder of 1952 and into 1953 and then 1954 by which time it was being used to investigate the Comet crashes. Like its predecessor ZK ended its days at Farnborough having been moved there, minus its engines, in 1957. It was used for radio trials and ultimately for Nimrod development before being scrapped in the mid-1970s.[15]

Chapter 6

THE PRODUCTION AIRCRAFT

D e Havillands started production of the BOAC Comets before testing of the prototypes was complete. While this undoubtedly saved time it also entailed some risk. It would be expensive and time-consuming to change jigs and completed parts of a production aircraft when a defect was belatedly discovered in one of the prototypes. This might have led to a reluctance to change something that ought to have been changed and this was certainly alleged in the Principal Films documentary and brought up at the inquiry but there is no evidence that this happened. Sir Geoffrey, in his autobiography, says that it was his decision and that he took it to stop the designers trying out too many new ideas on the prototypes knowing that problems could be sorted out before production started.[1] Judging from the fairly outlandish designs that were first put out for the Comet this seems a reasonable concern.

A production line was set up at Hatfield and arrangements were made for the manufacture of the first nine aircraft. The first two Comets had been almost hand-made by the experimental department but the production aircraft were constructed from modules. These included the nose, the front cabin, the centre section, the rear cabin, the tail cone with the base of the tail fin, the stub wing and the extension wing.[2] It was not surprising that some problems became apparent when more mass-production methods were employed. An early difficulty was that the workers found the alloy sheeting used for the aircraft's skin stiff and hard to roll into the shape of the fuselage. Not only that but they complained that it showed signs of cracking as it was stressed.[3] The design was very much that of the prototypes although the nose probe was omitted.

The person in charge of production at Hatfield was Harry Povey. His career had started at the Royal Aircraft Factory at Farnborough in 1914 and his first association with de Havilland began during the 1914-1918 war. He joined the company formally in 1924 and became the production manager of the aircraft division shortly before the start of the Second World War. During the war he spent three years in Canada organising production of the Mosquito. He became a director of the de Havilland company in January 1951. In April 1951 he gave a highly-illustrated talk on making the Comet to the Royal Aeronautical Society on which this account is based. This was later published in the *de Havilland Gazette*. He was a well-respected practical man but, like many in the industry in that era, he was without an academic background, indeed in a reply to a question at the end of his presentation to the society Povey explained that he was "not a scientist or a designer – he merely produced bits and pieces." [4]

Povey had the task of designing and making the tools and jigs for a totally new airframe and had to do it within strict time and money constraints. The original plan had been to fly the first production aircraft six months after the prototype's maiden flight but as things turned out this slipped to twelve months, which still seems an amazingly short time, particularly as the prototypes underwent considerable changes in the design of their flying control systems. Povey and his team were in at the start with the designers which meant that they could design and make production tools that would be ready in time for the experimental department to use making the prototypes. As well as entailing some risk, as ideas were bound to change and evolve, it also altered the order in which some of the design work was done.[5]

An early decision had been to make extensive use of Reduxing to make the joints between the stringers and the sheets of alloy used to form the fuselage and wing coverings. De Havillands already had considerable experience of this, having used Redux on the Dove, but the Comet presented a much bigger challenge. Two 25-feet-long presses had to be designed and made, in house, to Redux the fuselage sections and one 35-feet-long one for the wings. Extensive use was made of plaster models to define the three-dimensional shape of the airframe. The loft department produced loft plates which were used to draw the shapes onto sheet metal which was then cut to size and shape.* These were assembled into three-dimensional structures which were then filled with plaster to provide accurate solid models from which most of the tooling was made. One model of the forward part of the fuselage was used to make no fewer than 64 pairs of tools for Reduxing the stringers to the skin. The plaster model was accurate to $\frac{1}{32}$ inches and had a complete replica of the position and shape of all the stringers and panels on its surface, the stringers being represented by grooves in the plaster.[6]

Reduxing was an efficient method of joining metal and turned out to be a reliable one but it was a fiddly business. It involved coating the two, ultra-clean, perfectly-fitting surfaces to be joined with the adhesive and then applying heat (140° C) and pressure for around half an hour until bonding was complete. The pressure had to be completely uniform and was applied to both sides by a series of loose metal cappings. In turn pressure was applied to these by master pressure bars which were hollow and heated by steam passing along them. The cappings were long metal bars accurately shaped from the plaster cast of the fuselage, each one forming a separate tool for a particular length of curvature and, as if this were not complicated enough, allowance had to be made for any change in shape and size at their working temperature. The master bars also took their shape from the plaster model but were not specific to a particular stringer. Clearly setting up the tools was a time-consuming process but once done the process of attaching the stringers to the fuselage skin was accurate and relatively quick and straight forward.[7]

A different technique was used for the nose cone. This was formed from a sheet of alloy (DTD 610) which was shaped by a drop hammer using a series of three punches

---

* Lofting is the transfer of lines from a drawing to a full-scale outline on a sheet of material in order to make the part concerned. It was a technique borrowed from boat building.

to form the inside of what became an asymmetric cone.[7] The transverse fuselage frames were manufactured in presses as straight lengths which were then stretched and bent around formers of various radii in a Hufford machine to suit their positions in the airframe. Keeping the frames in tension as they were bent avoided producing wrinkles on the surface of the frame.[8]

The window frames were also made as drop-hammer pressings and were Reduxed to the fuselage skin while it was being formed on the jig. This involved two castings, one located accurately inside the fuselage jig, which determined the posi-

Fig. 1/6 Harry Povey next to ZK's fuselage, 27 July 1949
(copyright BAE SYSTEMS Heritage)

tion of the window frame, the other on the outside which provided the steam heating and was pushed against the inner frame by two (recycled) Mosquito hydraulic flap jacks powered by a hand pump from the same source. The whole apparatus was mounted on a trolley and the process took about 25 minutes.[9] Curiously there was no mention of rivets in Povey's account although by the date of this account (April 1951) drawings in the type description showed that they were being used.[10] Povey had found it difficult to fix the windows using just Redux and had asked Bishop whether he could rivet the corners (see Chapter 31).

The fuselage side panels consisted of four skins, 30 inches wide and 22 feet long onto which all the stringers were Reduxed. The panels were then joined into one large skin by lap joints made by two rows of countersunk rivets inserted by a large automatic riveting machine. The finished sheet measured 10 feet 2 inches by 22 feet.[11]

The fuselage components were made separately on static jigs and then, as they got bigger and more unwieldy, they were moved onto trolley jigs to avoid further manhandling. Anticipating a large number of orders de Havillands had laid out a track system on the shop floor. This consisted of five longitudinal tracks (A to E) and several shorter tracks at right angles forming a matrix. Although the floor might not have been completely level the tracks were made level to an accuracy of $\frac{1}{32}$ inches and were used to move the trolley jigs carrying the various components and to position them accurately as the pieces were joined. As the fuselage became more complete it moved from track A to track E. When it was finished a preliminary pressure test to 2 psi was carried out. The fuselage was then wheeled out of the shop for the 11 psi 'proof' pressure test to take place more safely in the open air.[12]

The wing was built in a similar manner. It was made up of the stub wing with a separate leading edge and flap, the extension wing, again with a separate leading edge and flap, and the wing tip. The stub wing, with the engine compartments and their corrugated coverings, made up the most substantial part and was assembled on a static jig but all the later operations were carried out on trolley jigs at different stations.

The stub wing jigs were built over pits to allow easy access to the underside. The spars, ribs and wheel-well walls were positioned first and the lower skin attached. This skin, made of DTD 687, was shaped accurately using clamps to push it onto contour boards. When the bottom surface was complete the wing was turned over and transferred to a similar jig for the top surface to be worked. Perhaps surprisingly this involved removing the skin already fitted to allow access.[13]

The corrugated shapes around the engines were among the most difficult parts to produce. A plaster cast of the shape was made and concrete stretcher-press tools cast directly onto it. The alloy sheets, which were twenty feet long and four feet wide, were shaped by being stretched over the concrete former, a process that took about ten minutes. Some other wing members were made using the same technique which proved to be accurate and reliable. The wing leading edges also presented a problem as they had to be accurate to a tolerance of 0.01 inches. They were made from sheets of DTD 546 in a stretcher press over carefully-milled metal formers.

When the top skin was complete the stub wing was moved to the drilling rig. Here the stub wings were moved up against the centre section of the fuselage and their sweep back, dihedral and angle of incidence carefully checked. Holes were then drilled through the steel fish-plates and spar boom for the bolts that would fix the wing to the centre section. This drilling involved accurately placing 252 holes to allow the complete interchangeability of the wings. Povey was particularly proud of the radially-mounted drill head that could be moved to drill at any angle within reach of its radial arm. The bottom skin was reattached at the same time.

The tanks, which were an integral part of the stub wings, were sealed with Bostik and a rubber solution, the person doing it being provided with protective clothing and an air supply for the occasion as well as a communication system to call for help. The stub wings were then moved outside the shop to be filled with 2,000 gallons of paraffin and any leaks dealt with.

The extension wings consisted of two skins with Reduxed stringers and were made in an orthodox jig. Like the stubs the extension wings were also fully interchangeable.[14]

The fuselages and wing parts were ultimately moved to the final assembly area where there were two lines of fuselages served by a single line of wings. The stub wings were attached at each side of the fuselage to the centre section, then the fin and the horizontal tailplane and finally the extension wings. The fitting of the engines and the var-

Fig. 2/6 YP, VG and ZK in publicity shot, 28 March 1951 (copyright BAE SYSTEMS Heritage)

ious systems took place at the same time as the airframes grew on the track.[12]

The many photographs (129 in 39 pages) that illustrate Povey's article show a rather spartan factory environment with young men, often in a sports jacket and tie, operating machines and checking alignments. There are no women visible. There is a bewildering variety of jigs and some machine tools. The impression given is that everything, or almost everything, in the aircraft was built on site rather than being bought in from outside specialist manufacturers and just put together as it would be in a modern aircraft-assembly plant. The machines were hand-operated and there was an air of craftsmanship that has departed from factories using computer-operated machine tools. Some of the tools are clearly adapted from equipment lying around the factory, such as the Mosquito hydraulic flap jacks used in Reduxing the window frames to the fuselage skin. The comment from the Boeing visitors that the Hatfield factory resembled a "small town auto-repair shop" (see Chapter 5) was unjustified, unless American auto-repair shops had enormous presses and a multitude of jigs, but it probably was much less sophisticated than a contemporary Boeing or Douglas plant.

Chapter 7

THE AIRLINE THE COMETS WOULD JOIN

The airline that took the first Comets into service was the British Overseas Airways Corporation (BOAC). Among the British airlines it was the obvious, indeed the only, choice. BOAC was a publicly-owned (nationalised) company formed at the beginning of the war by the amalgamation of the two main British airlines, Imperial Airways and British Airways, themselves having been formed earlier by the amalgamation of several smaller companies, Imperial in 1924 and British Airways in 1935.

In February 1938 Lord Swinton, the Secretary of State for Air, received the report of the Cadman Committee which had been set up in 1937 to look into the future of British civil aviation.[1] The report was critical of the management of Imperial Airways and of its poor relations with its employees, particularly the pilots. It also accused the company of not co-operating fully with the Air Ministry. In May, before any of the Cadman findings had been acted upon, Lord Swinton resigned and Sir Kingsley Wood took over.[2] Swinton was a competent and knowledgeable minister but in November 1935, after having been appointed the previous June, he accepted a peerage and his absence in the Lords meant that he was unable to defend himself against criticism in the Commons. This became an increasing handicap, although much of the criticism was unfair, and eventually Chamberlain, after defending him several times, felt he could no longer do so and Swinton 'stepped aside'.[3]

Kingsley Wood had previously been the Minister of Health and before that the Postmaster General. He was admirably equipped in the best British political tradition of the educated amateur to be the Secretary of State for Air in that he knew nothing about aeroplanes.* He was known in the Air Ministry as 'Little Sir Echo', a reflection of his lack of height and lack of his own opinions on aeronautical matters.[4] In the circumstances the latter might be considered more of a virtue than a vice as long as his advisors were well chosen and their advice taken and both of which, by and large, seemed to have been the case although he caused the then Air Marshall Freeman some frustration at times.[5] He later achieved fame, of a sort, by his answer to a suggestion from Leo Amery on 5 September 1939 that in view of Germany's shortage of timber

---

* He had apparently freely admitted that he "did not know one end of an aircraft from another."[4] Bulman said he was a kindly man who liked to be photographed. When they visited Napiers to see the Sabre several photographs were taken of him bending over the engine, spanner in hand as if he were about to tighten the last nut.[6]

the RAF should try to set fire to the Black Forest. Wood responded that there was no question of even bombing the munition works at Essen, which were private property, or lines of communication, and that doing so would alienate American opinion;[7] a bizarre exchange on both sides. In spite of this he became the Chancellor of the Exchequer in the Churchill Government in 1940, gradually raising tax until the top marginal rate reached 19s 6d (97.5p) in the pound. He died unexpectedly in 1943 on the morning that he was due to announce the introduction of PAYE (pay as you earn). In spite of his appearance and humble background he became respected as a competent, if not charismatic, administrator.[8]

In view of the findings of the Cadman Committee, Kingsley Wood decided that he had to change the leadership of Imperial Airways. In June he told Parliament that he had appointed another non-aviator, Sir John Reith, the Director General of the BBC, to be the chairman of Imperial Airways, prompting the resignation of its general manager, Woods Humphrey, who had been a pilot and engineer and, with some of the pilots, probably the cause of most of the unrest in the company.[9, 10] He was also accused of being too commercial, something that BOAC could not be accused of again for some time. However Woods Humphrey was not universally disliked and many were unhappy with his abrupt departure.[10] Reith and Kingsley Wood had frequently clashed when the latter had been the Postmaster General with responsibility for the BBC. Reith was a (very) strong personality and it says something for Kingsley Wood that he was able to stand up to him, also that in spite of their previous differences he chose him for this appointment.[8]

Reith thought little of the company he was about to join. He described its accommodation as:

> ...an old furniture depository behind Victoria Station... inside were counters, luggage on the floor, a few people standing about... I went along a dark passage between wooden partitions, peering at the doors wondering which to try first. Here it was – a bit of paper with 'Managing Director' written thereon. From Broadcasting House to this![10]

The Cadman Report had concluded that there should be two main British airlines but in spite of this Kingsley Wood announced in the Commons that the government would favour the amalgamation of Imperial Airways and British Airways into a single public corporation. The bill to create BOAC was presented to Parliament on 12 June 1939 but Imperial Airways and British Airways were not taken over until 1 April 1940.[11, 12]

Imperial was by far the bigger of the two companies and had the more extensive route network through Europe, Africa, India, Australia and even China. It was the recipient of government subsidies and as a consequence was expected to buy British and serve the Empire but in July 1937 the first trial crossings of the Atlantic had started in co-operation with Pan American. The British half of the route used the new C-class flying boats that were also to be used for the Empire Air Mail Scheme in Africa and the Far East. The Americans used their slightly-older Sikorsky 42 flying boats. Compared with the Americans, whose competent Douglas DC-3 had entered service in 1936, much of Imperial's equipment was slow and old-fashioned. Even the new British air-craft, such as the Armstrong Whitworth Ensign and the unfortunately-named de Havilland Albatross, were having problems* but the Short flying boats were a success and the de Havilland Flamingo looked hopeful.

British Airways was rather less subsidised and flew from its new base at Heston, west of London, mainly to northern Europe, using largely foreign-made aircraft. They had flown Neville Chamberlain to Germany three times in 1938 for his 'Peace for our time' meetings using American Lockheeds.

Reith was appointed as the chairman of the new corporation and even claimed to have invented its name.[13] Clive Pearson, the chairman of British Airways, was made deputy chairman. Agreement was reached between the government and the sharehold-ers and the two companies were taken into public ownership, partly at the insistence of Reith who said he would resign if this did not happen. The corporation was to receive a government subsidy as necessary, which it frequently proved to be. The subsidy was capped at £3,900,000 a year until 1953, which seems a considerable sum for the time; £100,000 was reserved for helping internal airlines.[11] Reith saw BOAC as a public cor-poration, rather like the BBC, with service to the public rather than profit and dividend to be the driving force.[14] It was not an amalgamation that the original companies had either wanted or sought but they were obliged to make it work, a task that would not be made any easier by the onset of war.

At the start of the war BOAC had 69 aircraft made up of thirteen different types of aircraft and twelve types of engine.[15] Inevitably the war restricted the activities of the new corporation and some of their aircraft, particularly the flying boats, were promptly commandeered by the RAF. The remaining aircraft suffered an increased attrition rate having to fly under wartime conditions with little chance of their replacement. Croydon Airport, Imperial's old base, and Heston were closed to civilian traffic and the land planes had to move to Whitchurch, near Bristol, and Exeter and the flying boats moved from Southampton to Poole. BOAC's headquarters were transferred from London to the Grand Spa Hotel in Bristol.[16] The outlook looked grim. All the activities of the cor-poration "were completely subordinated to the military" and Reith was warned by Harold Balfour, the Under Secretary of State for Air, that "there would be no civil avi-ation left."[17]

Reith soon felt that his talents would be better employed elsewhere and, to his delight, in January 1940 Chamberlain appointed him Minister of Information. He resigned from BOAC the following March and was replaced by Clive Pearson.[18] Reith did not last long in his new job however as Churchill replaced Chamberlain and he and Churchill had never got on. He was moved to the Ministry of Transport, then the Ministry of Works, but was eventually sacked and became a lieutenant-commander in

---

* The Ensign was difficult to control and the engines tended to cutout at takeoff because of oiled-up spark-ing plugs. The fuselage of the second Albatross had suddenly sagged just to the rear of the wings when in flight during overload trials. It had then broken in two on landing.[13]

the RNVR (Royal Naval Volunteer Reserve) at a salary one thirtieth of that he had been receiving two years before.[19] His career had something of a revival after the war but he never regained the influence he had had when he was in charge of the BBC.[20]

BOAC aircraft were used extensively for transporting troops and equipment and two of the C-class flying boats (Cabot and Caribou)* were lost in Norway in early 1940 doing this[18] but most of the activity was to and from France after that country was invaded by Germany. Longer routes to Africa, India and beyond were re-established but the great need was to be able to cross the Atlantic. This route had already been explored before the war using Caledonia and Cambria fitted with extra fuel tanks but had been constrained by the aircrafts' lack of range carrying any sort of payload.[21] One option that had been tried in July 1938 was the piggy-back arrangement of the smaller Mercury sitting on top of the larger Maia flying boat (the Short-Mayo Composite**). The Mercury carried mail and enough fuel to cross the Atlantic which made it too heavy to takeoff just under its own power. Once airborne, and at the appointed speed and altitude, the aircraft separated and the carrier aircraft returned to base while the Mercury headed off.[22, 23]

Another option was inflight refuelling promoted by Sir Alan Cobham using elderly-looking Handley Page Harrow tankers stationed at Shannon in Ireland and at Hattie's Camp, which later became Gander Airport, in Newfoundland. Unlike the modern arrangement the recipient aircraft attached the hose to its tail end, no doubt to avoid the nasty complications that its propellors might have produced. The procedure was that a grapple was wound out of the flying boat's tail and the tanker fired another cable by rocket to catch the grapple and pull it up to the tanker. The tanker's hose was then attached to it, winched down to the flying boat and connected to its fuel system so that about 800 gallons of petrol could be transferred over about twelve minutes.[11, 24] It sounds a tortuous affair but amazingly fifteen successful refuelling flights took place; one failed because the two aircraft could not find each other and the refuelling was prematurely abandoned on several other occasions.

Thankfully neither of these arrangements achieved acceptance into regular airline practice. Several Mayo Composite separations were carried out successfully but it proved to be an evolutionary blind alley, eclipsed by more powerful engines that allowed more fuel to be carried. Further in-flight refuelling trials were carried out in 1948 using Lancastrian tankers serving Liberators. David Beaty, a pilot-turned-author, describes carrying out eight of them and found them "easy and efficient", but others did not. In the end the economics of maintaining the tankers at Gander and Shannon finished it.[25] The idea reappeared with the Comet in 1951 (see Chapter 5) only to meet the same fate. It has, of course, since become commonplace with military aircraft.

The Americans had introduced a scheduled transatlantic service on 24 June 1939

---

* They were both armed with seven Vickers .303 machine guns and one dummy machine gun, said to be a broom stick painted matt black, which was installed in the refuelling cup in the tail.[26]

** Short (Brothers) was the name of the manufacturer and Mayo referred to Major R. H. Mayo, the Technical Manager of Imperial Airways whose idea it was. He later became a designer with Shorts.

using their enormous Boeing 314 flying boats.[27] These could manage the trip with various intermediate stops carrying a useful payload of up to 35 passengers but, in one respect at least, the Germans were ahead of them. In August 1938 they had flown a fast land plane, the four-engined Focke-Wulf Condor, non-stop from Berlin to New York and then back again three days later. Admittedly it had been full to the brim with fuel and carried no passengers or cargo but it showed what could be done.[28] The British started their flying boat service to New York in August 1939 but it survived the outbreak of war by only a few weeks. In August 1940 this service was reopened with C-class flying boats equipped with long-range tanks. The first flight carried only three passengers and some mail and even that needed one in-flight refuelling over Foynes in western Ireland and stops at Botwood (Newfoundland) and Montreal, reaching Port Washington 36¼ hours after leaving Ireland.[29]

One of the more exciting flying boat routes was what became known as the 'Horseshoe Route' from Durban up the east coast of Africa to Cairo and then across India to Singapore and ultimately onto Australia and New Zealand. In 1936 Imperial had started a route across Africa from Lagos to Khartoum and to avoid the fighting in the Mediterranean and North Africa this route was resurrected by flying south from England, along the west coast of Africa to Lagos, then the Congo and across Africa joining the Horseshoe route at Juba on the White Nile in southern Sudan or Kisumu on Lake Victoria.*[30, 31]

BOAC also became involved in ferrying new American aircraft across the Atlantic from Canada to Britain. Although this was not without hazard it proved safer than sending them by sea. These flights were started on 10 November 1940 by Donald Bennet, an accomplished navigator and pilot who had made the first trans-Atlantic crossing of the Mercury part of the Mayo Composite.[32] Bennet led the way for the other aircraft to follow, a precursor of the role he was to play later when he started the Pathfinder Force of Bomber Command. He also started the Return Ferry Service to get the ferry pilots back to Canada to pick up the next tranche of aircraft.[33]

Another route that BOAC was instructed to start was the service to Stockholm, mainly to pick up ball bearings which British industry seemed to find difficult to make in sufficient quantities. A fast ex-Polish Lockheed was used for this;[34] later in the war the even-faster Mosquito was substituted. The flying boats re-instituted the route to Malta via Lisbon and Gibraltar and two of them, disguised as Sunderlands, helped to evacuate soldiers from Crete. In 1941 the government purchased three of the enormous Boeing 314A flying boats at $1 million (£259,250) each to increase capacity on the Poole, Lisbon, Lagos route. They were bought without prior authority by Harold Balfour while he was on a visit to America. On his return to London he was rebuked by

---

* One of these flying boats, Corsair, survived after 'landing' on the River Dungu, some 200 miles from its intended destination. In the process it hit a rock and started to sink but the crew managed to beach the aircraft and the passengers escaped though a hole in the roof. It was the subject of an epic salvage operation which involved building a dam to provide enough depth of water for it to takeoff. In the style of Leopoldville and Stanleyville, the village constructed by the African workers was called Corsairville. The story of Corsair's rescue was later turned into a book.[35]

Kingsley Wood and Churchill, and Beaverbrook refused to see him.[36] In fact they were a good buy and proved reliable and very useful. One of these leviathans, Berwick, was used by Churchill to return from America in some comfort in January 1942, after which Balfour was forgiven.* They had to be serviced in Baltimore which was therefore incorporated into their routing (Baltimore, Botwood, Foynes – where their loads were transferred to Poole or Whitchurch – Lisbon, Bathurst, Lagos, then back to Foynes and Baltimore or, when the winter made Botwood unusable, Baltimore, Bermuda, the Azores, Lisbon, Foynes, Lisbon, Bathurst, Lagos, Belem (in Brazil), Trinidad, Bermuda and Baltimore).[37, 38]

The Horseshoe Route was severed when Japan took Singapore, the last of the flying boats leaving the island on 4 February 1942 carrying a fortunate 40 passengers. Two more of them left Java on the 28th of that month just ahead of the Japanese but one of them was never heard from again. Other flying boats were destroyed at their moorings by Japanese fighters and one crashed at Darwin and another at Sabang.[39] Altogether the C-class flying boats had an exciting war.[40]

There were also three larger and more modern G-class (S 26) flying boats that had been taken over by the RAF at the beginning of the war. One, the Golden Fleece, had already been lost but the other two were returned to the corporation and used for the West African route. The American Consolidated Liberators started to become available in 1941 and with their long range were mainly used on the North Atlantic route. Their first east-bound flight from Montreal was on 4 May 1941 flown, as might be expected, by Donald Bennet.[41] They were cold, uncomfortable and had an alarmingly long takeoff run when fully laden with fuel but they were also reliable, which was more important. Their long range suggested that a regular transatlantic passenger service would become a practical proposition after the war and Pearson was already wondering about the sort of aircraft that would be needed. This was one of the prompts for the setting up of the Brabazon Committee.[42]

The attrition of BOAC aircraft continued throughout 1942 and into 1943 with more of the flying boats being lost including the second of the G-class, the Golden Horn, which crashed into the River Tagus at Lisbon on 9 January 1943; only the radio officer survived. Later that January President Roosevelt crossed the Atlantic in a comfortable Pan Am Boeing 314 for the Casablanca conference. Churchill had to make do with a decidedly uncomfortable Liberator.[43]

During 1942 friction had developed between BOAC and the Air Ministry and in particular with Air Marshall Tedder in North Africa, who accused the corporation of inefficiency.[44] One of the problems was that BOAC was neither a fully independent business with complete freedom of action within the law, nor a public service with the

---

* Churchill in his account of the Second World War recalls that because of a navigation error on the way to Plymouth, Berwick was within five or six minutes of crossing over the German guns at Brest.[45] It was also mentioned in Lord Moran's diary of his meetings with Churchill[46] although it was not a diary entry and he said he learnt about it afterwards. Beaty doubts whether it was true and feels that it may have been added to the text for dramatic effect.[47] It might just have been a 'false memory' on Churchill's part but if so it seems an extraordinarily detailed one.

authority that that entailed and as a result it often seemed to come at the end of the queue for staff and equipment. This situation festered on into 1943 and after a meeting with Sir Archibald Sinclair, the Secretary of State for Air, on 1 March, Pearson was told that all BOAC operations were to be subservient to the newly-formed RAF Transport Command. As a consequence, later that month, Pearson resigned together with three other members of the board. Sinclair responded by appointing Sir Harold Howitt, a financial expert, as temporary chairman, and Simon Marks, of the Marks and Spencer family, and John Marchbank, a former general secretary of the National Union of Railwaymen as members of the board.[48] It was unclear what their qualifications were for running an airline, particularly in time of war. Within two months Viscount Knollys had replaced Howitt who became his deputy. Knollys had at least been a pilot in the RAF but was currently the managing director of the Employers Liability Assurance Corporation. Marks and Marchbank continued as members of the board. *The Aeroplane*, a British aviation magazine, was critical of the arrangement and commented that, "The difficulties which led to the resignation of the former directors still remain to be resolved."[49]

BOAC's routes slowly increased with the Horseshoe Route being reconnected using four Catalina flying boats equipped with extra tanks flying non-stop from Ceylon (Sri Lanka) to Perth. The first flight took place on 10 July 1943 and lasted 27 hours and 50 minutes. It could only manage one passenger and some mail but at least the air link to Australia had been re-established.[50] The more-direct route to Cairo across north Africa reopened as the area was cleared of enemy troops, removing the need for the route across central Africa. The northern route to Russia which had started earlier in 1943 was changed to a safer one via Cairo and Teheran. Even in the midst of the yet far-from-won war thought was being given to the future. Croydon Airport was considered too small and plans were made to improve and extend Gatwick Airport as well as buying an area of 2,800 acres, which contained a village called Heathrow, adjacent to Hounslow Heath. The management of BOAC were hoping that the pre-war policy of only buying British would be abandoned and that they could set about acquiring a fleet of the new DC-4s and Constellations.[51]

In early 1944 BOAC received the first of the Lancastrians, albeit without much enthusiasm as the nine passengers they could carry was not much more than their crew of five. Things looked up a bit when the more-satisfactory York, able to carry twelve passengers, appeared soon after but the corporation would be condemned to operate several thinly-disguised bombers for many years, mainly to save dollars.[51]

As the war drew to a close the management and employees of BOAC must have looked with envy at the wealth of modern and efficient passenger aircraft that the Americans already possessed. They were soon to be joined by the Boeing 377 Stratocruiser which had two spacious decks, a cruising speed of 310 mph and a range of 4,000 miles. It was, of course, fully pressurised and offered a level of comfort that the passengers on BOAC's Lancastrians and Haltons could only imagine.

Meanwhile, in October 1944, Viscount Swinton reappeared on the scene as the first

Minister of Civil Aviation, with the authority to control BOAC and the other civilian airlines which were beginning to re-emerge.[52] On 13 March 1945 a government White Paper was issued which defined three national airlines all with different areas of operation. BOAC would operate the routes to North America and the Commonwealth, as well as China and the Far East. The European routes would be operated by a new group which became the British European Airways Corporation (usually shortened to BEA) and South America would be allocated to an airline set up the previous year by some shipping interests called British Latin-American Airlines Limited,[53] later to become British South American Airways (BSAA). Spelled out in the paper was the government's intention that they should use British aircraft. This was confirmed by the incoming Labour Government which also removed the possibility of the shipping interests being involved in the South American routes.[54]

BOAC was by far the biggest and had the advantage of having an organisation-in-being over most of the world.[55] Even so it would have to change from being a war-time service, where money was not the first consideration, to developing a more commercial outlook. In truth it never really managed this until it was completely privatised in the 1980s but it did move in that direction. Ahead lay endless meetings about route agreements between different countries starting with a Commonwealth conference in London in July 1945. Swinton left office again in 1945 with the change of government.

The end of the war saw BOAC possessing a fleet of about 207 aircraft of seventeen different types, seven of which were flying boats, as well as very dispersed ground facilities.[56] In November 1945 the corporation opened its first Empire route to Johannesburg and agreements were reached for other routes including New Zealand and Canada but it was only at the beginning of 1946 that the ban on civilians flying was lifted. London Airport had its first runway but apart from that it was not much more than a large muddy field. The European division of BOAC (what would become BEA) operated from the nearby RAF airfield at Northolt and the Atlantic and Empire routes were based at Hurn, near Bournemouth. Meanwhile the flying boat services to Singapore reopened from Poole using civilianised Sunderlands. These later moved back to the old base at Hythe, near Folkestone. The European routes were well provided for with ex-RAF DC-3s with the prospect of the new Vickers Viking to replace them in due course but BOAC lacked an aircraft to compete with the American DC-4s and Constellations on the route to New York. The only solution was to buy American until new British aircraft, such as the Avro Tudor, became available. The Treasury was persuaded to relax its grip and precious dollars were found to purchase five Constellations.[57]

Other routes, such as those to South America, had to make do with Lancastrians and Yorks. London Airport, still in a rather unfinished state, opened for business on 31 May 1946. The BOAC service to New York using the Constellations and offering seats for 42 passengers started on 1 July. The east to west flights took 19¾ hours which included stops at Rineanne in western Ireland and Gander; the flying time was 17½ hours. One way cost £87 and return £156.[58] Unfortunately this service had to be stopped almost immediately because the Americans grounded all Constellations for 30 days after a fatal crash of one of TWA's following an engine fire. The Americans substituted DC-4s but BOAC could only resort to Lancastrians.[59]

At the beginning of September the Constellation service to New York resumed at three times a week and shortly afterwards the first of twenty Tudor 1s were received by BOAC, the Vikings appeared for BEA and BSAA had the first of its disasters when a York crashed soon after taking off from Bathurst in Gambia. The Tudor proved to be a failure, the Viking a modest success and BSAA continued to have crashes.

Like the York, the Tudor was derived from a bomber, in this case the Avro Lincoln rather than the Lancaster. Again like the York it was more removed from the bomber design than the Lancastrian and the Halton and formed part of the second phase of British post-war passenger aircraft. It had the wings and the four Merlin engines of the Lincoln but a single tail fin. It also had a new pressurised cabin of circular cross-section, the first on a British passenger aircraft, with a few round windows and was intended to carry 24 passengers across the Atlantic. The prototype flew for the first time on 14 June 1945 and the first production Tudor flew in January 1946 but showed directional and longitudinal instability, was overweight, had pressurisation problems and a much reduced range. As a result in February 1946 BOAC specified 343 modifications before they would accept them.[60]

The Tudor II was also being developed by Avro. This had a longer fuselage, with many large square windows, to accommodate 60 passengers over a shorter range. It flew for the first time in March 1946 but showed the same directional problems as the Mark 1 and as a consequence both developed the largest tail fins in the business. BOAC were reluctant to have anything to do with it but BSAA seemed to take to them. More setbacks occurred and on 23 August 1947 the Tudor II prototype crashed during takeoff, killing its designer Roy Chadwick who had also designed the Lancaster. It was later found that the cables to its ailerons had been crossed. This did not make BOAC any keener to accept the Tudor in any form and a certain amount of acrimony developed between the corporation and the manufacturer. Undeterred Air Vice-Marshall Bennet, the Chief Executive of BSAA, continued to use the Tudor in its various marks and showed his confidence in it by piloting it himself on a number of occasions for long flights. A committee was set up to look into the problems with the Tudor and in its report was critical of BOAC for insisting on so many non-essential modifications which had delayed its introduction into service. It found that "...there is no suggestion of any unsoundness in the basic design."[61] In fact its design was unsound and BOAC were right to be wary of it.

As well as having concerns about the Tudor, BOAC was having doubts about the Bristol Brabazon which they felt was too big and too expensive.[62] The corporation still believed there was a need for a Brabazon Type III and remained keenly interested in the Brabazon IV.

In the six months from July to December 1947 the corporation provided about one tenth the number of Atlantic crossings as the American carriers. Even this meagre

Fig. 1/7 Avro Tudor Mk 1 (BOAC G-AGRE), copyright BAE SYSTEMS Heritage.

proportion decreased over the next six months. BOAC continued to lose money, over £8 million in 1946-7, the *Daily Telegraph* commenting that "...we should have been in pocket if all the passengers travelling by air had been paid £50 (each) not to go."[63] BOAC blamed the Tudors and the high cost of running the flying boat service. No doubt some of this was true but the corporation was also showing the financial incontinence of a nationalised company that was subject to political interference and bureaucratic delay and prevented from making its own commercial decisions. Irritatingly for BOAC, BSAA made a profit in spite of using Tudors as well as the uneconomic Lancastrians and Yorks.[63]

BSAA's fortunes were about to change, however. On 30 January 1948 one of BSAA's Tudor IVs vanished after leaving the Azores for Bermuda and the Ministry of Civil Aviation grounded all Tudors. Unwisely Bennet challenged this through an interview in the *Daily Express* and was sacked as a result.[64] After an investigation by the Air Safety Board it was agreed that the Tudors could resume flying but only carrying cargo. Air crashes were much more common in those days but the flying public did not seem much deterred, perhaps as a result of having become accustomed to them during the war. Over the period 1 January 1946 to 30 April 1948 BOAC had two fatal crashes, BEA three and BSAA four. BSAA was much smaller than the other two and carried not much more than 10% of BOAC's number of passengers. In spite of this BSAA's Tudors were allowed to resume carrying passengers but for the time being not between the Azores and Bermuda. This was not because of superstition about the Bermuda triangle but because it was a long stage with a small island to find at the end of it with no alternative airfields within easy range if the weather turned bad.[65]

By this time the limit of the £3 million annual subsidy was largely ignored and was supplemented by a 'deficiency grant'. Government restrictions on buying long-range American aircraft, in BOAC's view the only ones worth buying for the Atlantic routes, were relaxed further and six Boeing Stratocruisers and 22 Canadian-built DC-4s, called Argonauts by BOAC, were ordered. BSAA stayed British and put into service eleven Tudor IVs and Vs. Twenty five of another British aircraft, the Handley Page Hermes, were ordered for BOAC. The Hermes prototype had crashed on its first flight in December 1945 causing its development to be delayed until its directional instability was corrected. The first production Hermes flew on 5 September 1948. It appeared suitable for the African services but had insufficient range for the Atlantic. As things turned out BOAC preferred its Argonauts and refused the first four Hermes as overweight, eventually cocooning them at London Airport. In due course they were sold on to secondary airlines, most ending up being used for trooping.[66]

The Berlin Airlift, lasting from June 1948 to May 1949, caused a sudden infusion of public money into many airlines, including BEA and BSAA, but in spite of this the nationalised airlines continued to haemorrhage money. In early 1949 BSAA lost two more aircraft, a York and a Tudor and in March the government announced that BOAC and BSAA were to merge. Fortunately BOAC were able to fly Stratocruisers earlier than they had anticipated, having bought four from Scandinavian Air Lines, and used them for the first time on the London to New York route on 6 December. This was originally billed as 'non-stop', which was rather stretching the truth, and the advertising manager had to write to the chairman confirming that it had been changed to 'direct'.[67]

On 27 July 1949 the Comet prototype made its first flight and the ponderous Brabazon followed in September. As well as the Brabazon, the Bristol company was also working on a less ambitious airliner which became the turboprop Britannia. It offered a longer range than a pure jet and would therefore be a prospect for crossing the Atlantic. This was something for the future, however, and it flew for the first time on 16 August 1952. For various reasons, many to do with its engines, its entry into service was much delayed and BOAC only managed to get it into service in February 1957, by which time the technology had moved on. In 1949 it was difficult to know whether the future lay with small, fast, jet airliners such as the Comet, large, slow, piston-engined ones, such as the Brabazon, offering more comfort but a longer incarceration, or turboprop aircraft like the Britannia providing something in between.

BOAC was now beginning to reach the stage where it had at least some of the aircraft it needed to be competitive. It had a competent chairman in Sir Miles Thomas, who had taken over from Sir Harold Hartley in July 1949, and in Whitney Straight an able chief executive.

BOAC soon increased its New York Stratocruiser service via Prestwick or Gander from three to five times a week and ultimately, with the Constellations, to daily.[68] London Airport was still a work-in-progress and none of the central terminal buildings had yet appeared although several hangers had been built on the periphery. The Comet prototype was making proving flights to North Africa and the Brabazon was continuing its test flights. The Hermes IV was introduced on the service to South Africa but the corporation still refused to accept the overweight early ones and another Tudor had crashed. The Viscount prototype was flying and performing well and BEA used it to start the world's first turboprop service for an experimental two weeks in July and August 1950 between London and Paris.[69]

There were other signs of things to come. Until now passenger aircraft had carried a single class providing relatively luxurious accommodation and this was enforced by IATA (the International Air Transport Association). The airlines were beginning to break with this and start economy-class flights using smaller seat pitches. At first these were on different aircraft but it was only a matter of time before the wealthy would have to share their aircraft, if not their cabins, with the less well off.[70]

The days of the slow but elegant and comfortable flying boats were also drawing to a close and BOAC stopped operating them in November 1950.[71] Although loved by their passengers they were expensive to run and vulnerable to sea and river conditions when 'landing' or taking off, to say nothing of submerged tree trunks and other floating debris. The need for their special talents was rapidly disappearing as more runways were built and aircraft ranges increased. This meant that the future for the enormous Princess flying boats was bleak. The prototype flew for the first time in 1952 but its two sisters were cocooned and all three were eventually scrapped in 1967. Less obviously the niche for the giant Brabazon was also looking less secure. It had a long way to go before it could enter airline service and promised to be expensive to run and BOAC were rapidly losing interest. Two were started but again only one ever flew and it ended up being scrapped in 1953. It seemed likely that smaller, faster aircraft, such as the Comet, would reduce journey times to the point where sleeping berths and excessive comfort were not needed, or at least the travelling public would be less willing to pay for them.

BOAC had now made most of the transition from being a wartime service to a quasi-commercial one and under the leadership of Sir Miles Thomas the corporation made an operating profit for the first time in 1951-2.[72]

This was the world that the Comet was joining. The flying boats had gone and piston-engined aircraft, mainly American, were dominant on all the routes. In 1956 one of them, the DC-7C, would provide the first truly non-stop London to New York service but they were at the end of their development potential and the turboprop Viscount showed the way propeller aircraft would go. The long-range British aircraft produced for BOAC had proved lamentable and the airline's hopes for a home-grown future were focused on the Comet and perhaps the Britannia. The Comet was a bigger leap of faith than the Viscount, or even the Britannia, but compared with piston-engined aircraft it offered much shorter journey times and greater reliability albeit at the price of multiple stops with no possibility of crossing the Atlantic. It would also be an elite service with no prospect of accommodating economy-class seats in its present form and it seemed likely in the future that more people would want to travel but would not be willing, or able, to pay for the luxury that had hitherto been the norm.

Chapter 8

INTRODUCTION INTO SERVICE

The first of the production Comets, the aircraft destined for airline service, was completed at the end of 1950 and registered as G-ALYP.[1] It made its maiden flight on 9 January the following year and after extensive tests received its Certificate of Registration on 18 September. The only problem was a leaking rear door which had to be replaced. Test flying continued and it eventually received a Certificate of Airworthiness on 22 March 1952. Yoke Peter (YP) was formally handed over to BOAC on 13 March although they had already used it to start flights in February. Its first long, route-proving flight was to Johannesburg and lasted from 15 to 22 April. The aircraft landed at Palmietfontein Airport and the idea was to fly it over to the new Jan Smuts Airport so that it could be the first to land there. Unfortunately Yoke Peter was beaten to it by a local pilot who touched down in a small aircraft earlier the same day but at least it was the first jet to land there.

Fig. 1/8, G-ALYP at London Airport, 15 March 1952, (copyright BAE SYSTEMS Heritage)

After a total of 339 hours of tests and training flights YP was used for the first BOAC jet flight carrying fare-paying passengers on 2 May 1952 from London to Johannesburg via Rome, Beirut, Khartoum, Entebbe and Livingstone; six stages. This was the first commercial jet flight in the world. It lasted 23 hours and the aircraft arrived 25 minutes early and had to circle overhead to use up some time and ultimately arrived about three minutes ahead of schedule. It was greeted by about 20,000 people who were at the airport to get a glimpse of the future. The return flight on 5 May took 22 hours and 48 minutes. Later scheduled services took a shorter route to Johannesburg by substituting Cairo for Beirut[2, 3] and, in 1953, cost £175 single or £315 return,[4] equivalent to about £4,100 and £7,400 in 2012, rather less than the current (June 2014) British Airways first class return fare of £10,140.

Yoke Peter became a regular on this route although some of its flights were not without incident. A heavy landing at Khartoum required a de Havilland engineering team to be flown out to repair its undercarriage and flaps. More attention was needed after it returned to Britain. In December 1952, when taking off from Bahrain, there was an explosion at the trailing edge of one of the wings followed by an engine fire. The take-off was successfully aborted but the engine and parts of the fuel system were seriously damaged and had to be replaced. Its Certificate of Airworthiness was renewed on 11 March 1953. In November, after 3,207 flying hours, a new door was fitted and the fuselage was successfully pressure-tested to 11psi. Yoke Peter continued relatively uneventfully on regular route flying until 10 January 1954 when it disintegrated while flying

Fig. 2/8 First BOAC Comet service (YP) departing from London Airport, 2 May 1952, (copyright BAE SYSTEMS Heritage)

Fig. 3/8 First Comet service returns to London Airport, 6 May 1952, (copyright BAE SYSTEMS Heritage)

over the Mediterranean near the island of Elba with the loss of all on board (see Chapter 12).

The second production Comet 1 was registered as G-ALYR and flew for the first time on 28 July 1951, receiving its Certificate of Airworthiness on 16 October.[5] This aircraft was used for a Royal joyride on 23 May 1952, taking the Queen Mother and Princess Margaret for a flight over Europe. Yoke Romeo's career later took a turn for the worse after it taxied off the perimeter track at Calcutta's Dum Dum Airport and its undercarriage sank into the soft ground. Captain Willerton tried to retrieve the situation by increasing engine power but unfortunately only succeeded in driving the starboard undercarriage up into the wing.

The reason for the incident was that the Comet's taxiing lights were too weak and the crew had to use the more-powerful landing lights. These overheated quickly and therefore had to be alternated. The switches to do this were inconveniently located low down on the left side of the cockpit wall behind the captain's seat, close to the switches for the taxiing lights. It therefore took a certain amount of contortion to operate them and in the process the captain took his hands off the nose steering wheel which self-centred, causing the aircraft to turn and the right-hand bogie ran off the paved area. As a consequence of this event the switches were later relocated to the upper front panel. The aircraft was considered beyond local repair and was dismantled and transported back to the UK by sea. It was stored by BOAC for some time at London Airport but events overtook it and it was ultimately moved to Farnborough for pressure testing. It was scrapped in 1963.

The third production Comet 1, G-ALYS, first flew on 8 September and was handed over to BOAC on 4 February.[6] After being used for crew training it entered scheduled service but this ceased after the final grounding of all the Comets on 24 April 1954. It was then flown to Farnborough for testing and was extensively damaged after its fuel system was (deliberately) over filled. Further fuel tests were carried out to see whether the tank vents were vulnerable to blockage in icing conditions. It was finally used for tests on its ailerons and rudder and was scrapped in the early 1960s.

The next aircraft (manufacturer's number 06006, registered as G-ALYT) became the Comet 2 prototype.[7] It had a fuselage extended by three feet and larger air intakes for the more powerful, axial, Avon 502 engines producing 6,600 pounds of thrust. YT was used by de Havillands for test work and then by BOAC for route proving but after April 1954 was only flown unpressurised. It continued to be used for various tests, some of them involving work for the forthcoming Comet 4, and ended its days being used for training apprentices at RAF Halton. It was scrapped in 1967.

The fifth Comet 1 (06007, G-ALYU) was, in fact, the second to enter service with BOAC.[8] It was damaged in a landing accident in Khartoum during route-proving but was repaired and entered regular service on 2 May 1952. It inaugurated the second Comet route to Columbo on 11 August and to Singapore on 4 October. In 1953 it suffered a failure of all its electrical systems after taking off from Beirut. As the fuel pumps had stopped, and fully expecting that the engines would soon stop, the captain broadcast a Mayday. In the event the engines continued to function and the aircraft, heavily loaded with fuel, made a safe landing with the help of a torch directed over the captain's shoulder and aimed at the instrument panel. YU continued in service until the final grounding of all the Comets in April 1954. It was flown to Hatfield where the static load-bearing capability of its tail unit was tested as part of the investigation into the Calcutta crash (see Chapter 11) which had thrown doubt on its strength. It had a total of 3,539 flying hours. Yoke Uncle was then transferred by road to Farnborough to be pressure tested. This started on 19 May and continued until mid-1955. Its remains ended up being used for fire training at Stansted and were finally destroyed in 1961.

The next Comet (06008) was originally registered as G-ALYU but this was changed by BOAC to G-ALYV and it started regular services in late April 1952.[9] On June 8 Captain Harry Foote, who would feature again in the Comet story, clipped a wattle hedge with it while landing at Beirut. He had landed in the approved fashion, which involved cutting the engines at several hundred feet because of their slow wind down and just aiming the aircraft at the start of the runway.* The crew only became aware of the incident when the ground staff pointed out the dent in the flaps. Foote was subsequently exonerated as the hedge, used to keep out goats, was above the regulation

---

* This is taken from the account in Painter[9] but it may refer to reducing the reolutions on two of the engines rather than all four (see Chapter 9). He adds that this technique had been developed by de Havillands but was later changed.

height. Scheduled fights continued until 2 May 1953 when Yoke Victor disintegrated after running into a violent tropical storm soon after taking off from Calcutta airport.

The seventh Comet 1, G-ALYW, flew for the first time on 25 February 1952 and was delivered to BOAC on 14 June and entered scheduled service soon after.[10] It was used to transport the Queen Mother and Princess Margaret to Southern Rhodesia (now Zimbabwe) in June 1953. Apart from a malfunctioning autopilot on one occasion YW had an uneventful service career. The aircraft was at Columbo when all the Comets were grounded on 9 April 1954 and was flown back empty to London Airport on 27 April and cocooned. About a year later YW was dismantled and moved to Farnborough. It was finally acquired by the RAF, cut into two sections and fitted out as a Nimrod. The sections were mounted on road trailers and used for exhibition purposes. The front section is the oldest known surviving fragment of a Comet airframe although converted to look like a Nimrod nose. With the demise of the Nimrod it has now passed out of RAF hands.

The eighth airframe, G-ALYX, first flew in July 1952 and subsequently started scheduled services with BOAC.[11] It suffered two problems during its short career. The first was a spurious fire warning which caused a hasty return to Columbo airport and the second was a serious malfunctioning of its autopilot which caused the aircraft to swing off course. The pilot found that he could not disengage the autopilot without switching off all the electrics. This prompted a diversion to Malta where the problem was thought to have been fixed only for the same thing to happen again when the journey to London was resumed. It was later found to have been caused by a lose screw which had shorted out a circuit. YX was at Cairo when the final grounding occurred later that month. After three weeks it was flown back to Hatfield for checks on fuel tank leaks and to see whether the engine exhaust was damaging the airframe. Like most of the other Comet 1s, it was moved to Farnborough and cocooned. The fuselage was later moved to to the RAE's aerial and communication facility at Lasham in Hampshire where it was used for aerial tests after having been mounted on a turntable. It was scrapped in 1996.

The ninth aircraft, G-ALYY, had a somewhat chequered career ultimately ending in disaster (see Chapter 14). It first flew on 10 September 1952 and started regular services within a month or two.[12] In January 1953, while flying from London to Johannesburg, it landed short of the runway at Entebbe killing a local man who was working on the approach lights. The subsequent inquiry (see Chapter 11) blamed the pilot for an error of judgement. In July 1953 Yoke Yoke landed by mistake on the runway of the Bombay Flying Club rather than at the main Santa Cruz airport. The weather was reported to be bad with severe winds blowing straight down the runway. The mistake was compounded by the aircraft landing some 500 yards from the threshold of the runway, having to brake strongly as a consequence and veering to the right, bursting all the tyres on the right bogie and causing considerable structural damage. Fortunately no one was hurt. After repairs it was flown back, empty, to London after making an impressive takeoff run of only 650 yards, no doubt with an attentive audience. Later that year it was used for training by South African Airways (SAA) but, together with the other Comets, it was temporarily grounded in January 1954 after the crash of Yoke Peter near Elba. The opportunity was taken to carry out an extensive service and inspection and a full cabin pressure test and it returned to service with BOAC on 24 February. On 7 April SAA used YY for a flight to Johannesburg which ended in its mid-air disintegration off the Mediterranean island of Stromboli the following day.

The final Comet 1 was G-ALYZ (06012) which made its maiden flight on 23 September 1952.[13] It had an extremely short career of just 81 flying hours in BOAC service, crashing on takeoff from Rome's Ciampino airport (see Chapter 10). No lives were lost but the airframe was considered to be irreparable and was scrapped in situ.

BOAC was the only airline to buy Comet 1s but a more advanced version, the Comet 1A, was bought by Canadian Pacific Airlines (CPA), Union Aéromaritime de Transport (UAT), Air France (AF) and the Royal Canadian Airforce (RCAF).

The 1A had the more powerful Ghost Mark 2 engine with a static thrust of 5,000 pounds. It also had a fuel capacity 906 gallons greater which increased the maximum stage length from 1,500 miles to 1,770 miles. Its maximum weight consequently increased to 115,000 pounds which reduced its payload by 700 pounds.[14]

The first example (06013)[15] was bought by CPA, registered as CF-CUM and named 'Empress of Vancouver'. It made its first flight on 11 August 1952 and was set out to carry 48 passengers. As things turned out the aircraft was never delivered because its sister aircraft, CF-CUN, was destroyed on takeoff at Karachi on 3 March 1953 and Canadian Pacific cancelled the order. CF-CUM was used by de Havillands to explore different wing shapes. It was then bought by BOAC as its sole 1A, becoming G-ANAV. It spent only a short time with BOAC because of the 1954 crashes and was moved to Farnborough in May 1954 for flight testing by the RAE. It made some 50 unpressurised flights from Farnborough with an RAF crew and its ceiling limited to 38,000 feet accompanied by an RAF Canberra which filmed it during each flight.[16] The flights were without incident except for one occasion when a tanker was driven across the runway as the Comet was taking off. The aeroplane just managed to stop in time.

Tests on the long-suffering Able Victor continued on the ground. Cranes were attached to each horizontal tailplane and increasing up and down loads were applied to them. This continued until mid-1955 when the fuselage was moved to the water tank for pressure testing. Eventually the fuselage was dumped on the airfield at Farnborough but its nose acquired a kind of immortality when it was purchased by the Science Museum and put on display. The internals of the flight deck had to be recreated by the museum staff, mainly in wood, as they had been removed for the tank tests. In 1994 it was moved to the Science Museum store at Wroughton.

Its sister, CF-CUN, (06014) the 'Empress of Hawaii', first flew on 24 December 1952 but crashed after a failed takeoff in Karachi on its delivery flight[17] (see Chapter 10). Its flying career lasted 44 hours.

The third Comet 1A (06015) was purchased by UAT and was registered as F-BGSA after making its first flight on 13 November 1952.[18] It began scheduled services to West

Africa the following February. These were extended to South Africa in October. Its Certificate of Airworthiness was withdrawn on 15 March 1954 following the Elba crash having flown for 1,991 hours, F-BGSA was stored at Le Bourget for several years before being scrapped. The second UAT Comet 1A, F-BGSB, (06016) had a similar career and was grounded after 2,022 flying hours and, like its sister, subsequently scrapped.[19] There are unconfirmed reports that either SA or SB was used a model for the Caravelle's nose.

The third UAT Comet, F-BGSC, (06019) had a somewhat shorter career. It first flew on 15 April 1953 and was accepted by the airline later that month and started scheduled services on 7 May.[20] On 25 June the aircraft failed to stop after landing at Dakar and ran beyond the end of the runway and over a ditch which ripped off its undercarriage. The aircraft was scrapped at Dakar after the 1954 crashes.

The other French airline to buy 1As was Air France. It was slower than UAT in placing its orders and its first aircraft, F-BGNX, (06020) made its maiden flight on 6 May 1953 and started earning revenue on 19 August 1953.[21] It was grounded in January 1954 after the Elba crash and purchased by the MoS, re-registered as G-AOJT and flown to Farnborough for structural tests and ultimately dismantled. The tail was used for explosive firing tests at the Ball Hill Range in 1957 and the fuselage cocooned and kept at Farnborough. The fuselage was turned down by the Science Museum owing to its poor condition but was rescued by the de Havilland Aircraft Museum at London Colney in March 1985 where it remains.

The second Air France aircraft, F-BGNY, (06021) had only 420 flying hours before it too was grounded on 11 January 1954 and, like its older sister, was purchased by the MoS.[22] It was re-registered as G-AOJU and flown to de Havillands' Chester factory for conversion to 1XB standards. This involved installing the more-powerful Ghost 50 Mark 4 engines, strengthening the fuselage and fitting new windows. It was then converted to a high-altitude navigation trials aircraft by Marshalls of Cambridge and used by the A&AEE at Boscombe Down for the next five years. In February 1964 JU was flown to Stansted for use by the fire school and its engines transplanted to G-APAS. It was also used for air bag lifting trials but by 1970 the aircraft had been burned and disposed of.

The third and final of Air France's 1As, F-BGNZ, (02022) was delivered in July 1953 and began service in September only to be grounded the following January after 373 flying hours.[23] It was flown back to Hatfield and was ultimately purchased by the MoS and flown to Chester to be converted to a 1XB. This was used for a programme of extensive flight testing as G-APAS until April 1968 and then moved to the museum at RAF Cosford. For some reason it has acquired a BOAC paint finish. It is the only largely-intact Comet 1, albeit in 1XB form. It remains on display there although there is currently (2015) no access to its interior because of radioactivity from the paint on the cockpit instrument dials.

The only other purchaser of the Comet 1A was the Royal Canadian Air Force. Their two aircraft (airframes 06017 and 06018, RCAF designations 5301 and 5302) were slightly different from the others as they had the Ghost 50 Mark 4 engines, which were rated at 5,500 pounds, and an increase in all-up weight to 117,000 pounds. [24, 25] Both were delivered in early 1953 and formed the world's first jet transport squadron. Both were grounded after the 1954 crashes. 5301 was flown, unpressurised, to Chester and rebuilt as a 1XB. After tests it was returned to Canada in September 1957. It continued in RCAF service until 1963. In 1965 most of it was scrapped apart from the nose section which was sold to the National Aviation Museum at Rockville, Ottawa, but cockpit radioactivity precluded public display.

Its sister, 5302, was stored for two years after the 1954 grounding and then flown by John Cunningham in 1956 to Chester to be converted to 1XB standard. It was returned in 1957 and retired in 1963. After various changes in ownership it was broken up at Miami airport in 1975.

Chapter 9

PASSENGERS AND CREW

The pilot experience

The men, and they were all men, who flew the Comet formed an elite group within BOAC. Most had learned to fly in the RAF and few would have flown a jet aircraft before. Certainly their time in BOAC would have been spent flying piston-engined, propeller transports and with the Comet they had to learn a new way of flying. This was a problem as there were significant differences between propellers and jets and it is known that in times of extreme stress pilots tend to revert back to earlier, well-learned behaviour patterns.[1]

The pilots selected for the Comet had to undergo a seven-week conversion course. At first this was at the de Havilland Servicing School but later moved to the BOAC Central Training Unit at Cranford, near London Airport.[2] The course started by familiarising the pilots with equipment that they might not have seen before such as power-boosted controls, bogie undercarriages and air brakes as well as the more obviously new features such as the Ghost engine. They were also able to visit the Comet production line at Hatfield where Peter Duffey had doubts about the thickness of the aircraft's skin (see Chapter 4).[3]

The course ended with an Air Registration Examination which lasted a day and contained about 100 questions. Once this was completed the flying part of the conversion course started. This had four 1½ hour periods of circuits and landings, two at night and two by day, and an instrument flying period in the London Control Zone. There was a flight to demonstrate the onset of compressibility effects and an opportunity to experience an emergency descent using the air brakes. The technique of relighting an engine in the air was shown to them as well as carrying out practice flights with one or two engines throttled back to simulate engine failures.[2] There were also opportunities to become familiar with the new items of electronic equipment such as the Marconi ADF sets. The course ended with a check flight during which the pilot's newly-acquired skills had to be demonstrated to a training captain. Even when the course had been completed satisfactorily a captain had to carry out two full familiarisation trips under supervision before he could be in charge on a particular route.

The differences between the Comet and the aircraft these pilots had been flying previously could all be traced back to their engines. Jet engines had quite different characteristics to the piston-propeller combinations the pilots were used to, as well as making the aircraft fly faster and higher, both of which also changed the pilot's job. Most of these differences were known by the time the new crews were being trained but the difficulty of overlaying new skills on old and well-practised skills was perhaps not as well appreciated. In due course this would lead to the crashes of two, possibly three, Comets.

The thrust of a piston-propeller combination depends on the engine r.p.m., the pitch of the propeller blades and the manifold pressure (i.e. the mass of air being pushed into the cylinders). In practice the thrust increases directly with the r.p.m. which, in turn, is dependent on the position of the throttle lever. As the throttle lever is pushed forwards the thrust rapidly increases in proportion. This is not true of a turbojet where the thrust takes longer to build up. An inch of lever movement at the lower end of the r.p.m. range in a turbojet will produce a much smaller increase of thrust than an inch towards the upper end of the r.p.m. range; in other words the throttle-thrust relationship is non-linear. If more thrust is needed in a hurry and the engine is idling then a heavy hand has to be used on the throttle levers. The effects of throttle movement in the opposite direction are also different. An idling propeller produces drag and therefore a braking effect but an idling jet still produces some thrust, hence propellers are better at slowing an aircraft on the runway after landing even without using reverse pitch.[4] The Comet's engines did not have reverse thrust and the pilot had to rely heavily on its brakes, a potential problem compounded by its superior streamlining, thin wings and tricycle undercarriage all producing less parasitic drag.

These different characteristics make a jet engine slower to build up thrust if it is idling, say six to eight seconds compared to three or four with a piston-propeller combination. This may require an element of forward thinking on the part of the pilot in some landing and takeoff emergencies, exactly the circumstances in which he might regress to his earlier training. The solution was to keep the engine r.p.m. at a fairly healthy level until any possible need for a sudden increase in thrust had completely disappeared.

There is another advantage to having propellers when flying at slow speed – they generate lift by pushing a large mass of air over the wings, hence reducing the stalling speed. The jet engine has a similar, but much smaller, effect as the jet efflux entrains air over the wing. These three consequences of jet engines, lack of instant power, slow acceleration and higher stall speeds can make landing and taking off rather more fraught than when there were propellers at the front.

There are other differences for the pilot to bear in mind. The high fuel consumption of the early jets was one of the determining features of Comet flight plans and everything possible was done to maximise fuel economy by flying high and fast. The ideal flight plan for the Comet was to get to the end of the runway with the least delay and to start the takeoff run as soon as possible using full power. The aircraft should then climb to a cruising altitude of about 36,000 feet as quickly as possible* at which point the engine revolutions should be reduced to the most economical rate. The power should then be kept constant and the aircraft allowed to climb slowly to about 38,000

---

* In practice full power causes rapid engine deterioration and is therefore only used for a short time. Most of the climb is carried out with less power than for takeoff but more than for cruise-climb.

Fig. 1/9 Control cabin with a BOAC crew, 24 April 1952, (copyright BAE SYSTEMS Heritage)

feet as its fuel was used up and it became lighter, the so-called 'cruise-climb' where the angle of attack stays more or less constant. The descent should start as late as possible to reduce the time spent at low altitude.[5] One economy measure sometimes used during the descent was to reduce the rpm of the two inner engines to idle while keeping the outer ones turning at a more economic rate rather than throttling back all the engines. Clearly air traffic considerations would constrain this at times but when the Comet started its service life the airways were considerably less congested than they are now. Nevertheless running out of fuel was a constant worry and the stages were all of a conservative length for this reason.

Another consequence of high fuel consumption was that the fuel load made up a larger proportion of the aircraft's weight at takeoff. Therefore the change of weight from the time of takeoff to the time of landing was greater, producing a larger change of flying characteristics than had been usual in propeller aircraft. It also caused a greater rate of climb when cruising as the fuel was used up more rapidly as well as more fuel dumping being necessary if the aircraft had to return soon after takeoff.

Flying fast and high has its own consequences.[6] Greater momentum means it is more difficult to change direction and if the aircraft had deviated from the intended course it will have gone further and the correction needed would be greater. Flying faster also poses problems when flying through violent weather as more stresses will be applied to the airframe and with power-operated controls there is a risk of over correction, particularly if the feed-back to the pilot is deficient and the breakout force high as they were in the Comet.

Flying high means having to provide a viable environment for the aircraft's passengers and crew with a pressure cabin. Apart from monitoring the cabin pressure this should provide little difficulty for the crew in normal circumstances. Should the cabin pressure drop suddenly the pilot must bring the aircraft down to a level at which the ambient pressure is sufficient to keep the passengers alive, around 15,000 feet, although this may be impossible in mountainous regions. The emergency descent is carried out at the maximum permitted speed allowed for the aircraft and some forethought is needed to plan for flattening out at the bottom of the dive and using air brakes and even deploying the landing gear may be necessary. Above about 14,000 feet oxygen should be immediately available to the pilots as their mental functions deteriorate rapidly with sudden decompression. At the Comet's cruising altitude of 35,000 feet consciousness is lost in less than one minute.[7] An added complication is that the aircraft's interior will fill with condensation and flying debris which will not add to the passengers' equanimity, particularly if they have just witnessed one of their fellow passengers being blown through a window.

A more subtle danger is a slow pressurisation failure that for some reason is not detected by the crew. This leads to progressive hypoxaemia of the passengers and crew with the loss of higher brain functions and ultimately unconsciousness and death. At least one passenger aircraft flew on autopilot at 34,000 feet for three hours with the pilots either unconscious or dead, presumably from hypoxaemia, and crashed when its fuel was exhausted.[8]

High altitude also produces problems of reduced stability, reduced aerodynamic damping, a restricted operating speed range and reduced manoeuvrability. In other words the aeroplane is operating in a much smaller flying envelope, for example the maximum operating speed may not be much more than the stalling speed.[9]

The differences produced by the jet engines leading to the need for high speed and high altitude are well known now but were much less so when the Comet came into service. Some of them, in particular the wing shape and the pressure cabin, would cause major problems in the Comet. Others, such as the engines, performed almost faultlessly to specification. Even with all the problems of being first it was quite clear to the crews from the outset that jet transports were the future and even in the light of subsequent events nobody seriously considered going back to pistons and propellers. Flying the Comets was a popular and prestigious job but one ex-RAF radio operator told his son that he was just glad that nobody was trying to shoot him down.[10]

The passenger experience

The Comet 1A was economically best suited to stage lengths of between 1,000 and 1,700 miles[11] but the Comet 1 was only able to manage a maximum of 1,500 miles. Within these limits the 1A costs per passenger mile were between 1.3 and 1.15d (old pence – 1952 figures, equivalent to about 13p when corrected for inflation), similar to the DC-6, DC-7 and the Constellation and rather better than the Hermes at 1.5d, which could only manage shorter stages anyway. The Britannia offered better figures (around 0.9d) but was not yet available and, as things turned out, would not be for some time. These figures assumed the maximum number of seats that could be fitted into the aircraft at a minimum seat pitch, 66 in the case of the Comet 1A, and that they were all occupied. In practice BOAC used 36 seats in the shorter-range Comet 1, which alters the figures somewhat. The comparisons are also affected as the seat numbers for the other aircraft appear to be fairly representative of airline practice at that time. The Comet 1 was therefore more expensive to operate than the aircraft mentioned above but was usually able to obtain higher load factors (percentage of seats occupied) because of its speed and comfort.

Although BOAC did not charge a premium over the first class fare for travelling on the Comet any flying in those days was an expensive experience. This meant that the Comet would be best utilised travelling between two relatively affluent cities whose populations had good reasons to want to travel from one to the other, as well as there being enough airfields along the way to accommodate the short stages. The long-standing 'Empire' route from London to Johannesburg filled most of these criteria and was the first route flown by the BOAC Comets. A typical timetable shows a departure from the Victoria terminal at 12:30 to leave Heathrow at 14:00, and arrive at Rome at 17:30. After refuelling the departure from Rome was at 18:30 to arrive at Cairo at 22:30, leaving Cairo at 23:30 to arrive at Khartoum at 02:40 and leaving again at 03:20. Entebbe was reached at 07:20 and left again at 08:20 to land at Livingstone at 10:50 and depart at 11:50. Johannesburg was finally reached at 13:40, almost 24 hours after leaving London.[12] Five hours of the journey had been spent on the ground refuelling, no doubt waking up any passengers who had managed to get to sleep. It must have been an exhausting experience but was certainly quicker than what had come before.

More routes were added as more aircraft became available, eventually reaching Tokyo via an impressive ten stages and 48 hours of incarceration unless the journey was broken.[13] Unfortunately the important route to New York was impractical and this remained the domain of the longer-ranged, piston-engined aircraft for several years to come. Nevertheless the Comet was commercially viable over long, multi-staged routes as long as the fares and the occupancies stayed high.

There are some contemporary accounts of flying as a passenger on BOAC's Comets. The following is taken from an account by an aviation journalist (M.A.S.) of a flight to Rome as the first stage of a trip to Johannesburg.[14] He (presumably) had already flown to Rome in the bare Comet prototype with John Cunningham at the controls and was anxious to see what the production version was like. This particular flight was a BOAC training flight intended to be as close to a service flight as possible. The captain this time was Philip Brentnall DFC and he had with him a complete second crew for training purposes. There were two stewards and a stewardess looking after the passengers which was one more steward than would be on the service routes.

The correspondent's first impression was that the Comet was ahead of its passenger organisation in that it took as long to get to the airport and to emerge from the formalities as it took to cover the first 1,000 miles. In those days BOAC had a terminal at Victoria where luggage could be deposited and transport by coach would then be provided to the airport. He describes rushing to the terminal due to imagined lateness, sitting down for ten minutes, weighing and checking in luggage and having his ticket verified, drinking coffee for fifteen minutes and then being herded into the coach. The coach then sat there for five minutes awaiting 'mislaid list, bag or child'. There was then a 'rapid' drive to the airport, something that certainly would not happen now. Following a ten minute sit in the lounge there was a bustle through immigration and customs which took about fifteen minutes, part of which he spent wondering what the American lady ahead of him could have in her nine "different-shaped, matching-in-colour suitcases". Finally there was a coach trip in the rain from the gate to the aircraft. No mention of queues for security checks, x-ray machines, having to take off belts and empty pockets to go through metal-detectors and remove shoes in case they are loaded with explosive. Although he seemed a little irritated by the process, to a present day traveller it all sounds remarkably quick and civilised.

The Comet finally started its engines on the apron and moved towards the runway, the correspondent sounding a little surprised that it did this rather than being towed to the runway in order to save fuel. He mentioned that there were still mounds of earth and building material beside the taxi-way – the airport was still far from being finished. There was a pause at the threshold of the runway as an aircraft flying on three engines came into land, not an uncommon sight in the age of piston engines. He comments that apart from the lack of vibration and the different noise of the engines he could have been in any comfortable four-engined airliner. Even in those days of much less congestion at Heathrow, it still took fifteen minutes from starting the engines to starting the takeoff run.

For the passenger used to piston engines, even starting the four Ghosts was a new experience as the turbines increased in power with a rising whine but noticeably more slowly than with a piston engine. At little more than halfway down the runway the tail went down and a few seconds later the Comet left the ground, climbed quite steeply and then throttled back and levelled off at about 3,000 feet, presumably to reduce the noise for people living below. When it was over more open countryside the Comet climbed and had reached about 30,000 feet by the time the sea was visible below. Now the light coming through the large windows was uncomfortably bright and the correspondent, in retrospect, thought about the pressure difference across the cabin wall that was making his trip so comfortable. This was another relic of having flown on non-pressurised aircraft with uncomfortable ambient pressure changes; it would not occur to a modern traveller, even in retrospect.

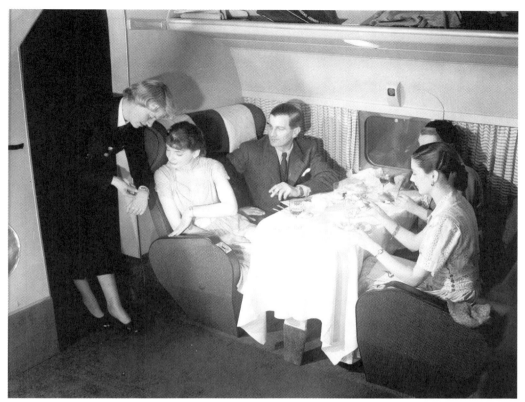

Fig. 2/9 Forward passenger cabin (mock up) 9 January 1951, (copyright BAE SYSTEMS Heritage)

As they flew towards Paris aperitifs were offered and shortly afterwards lunch trays appeared, red or white wine was poured out and the meal began. By the time Paris passed below their altitude had reached about 35,000 feet and, fed and watered by now, the *Flight* correspondent explored the cabin. In the eight-seat front cabin the level of noise allowed a normal conversation but he thought it more noisy than he had expected from his earlier flight in the prototype. He moved forward into the cockpit and found the reason why. It was almost completely silent and this was where he had spent most of his earlier flight. Moving back to the main cabin he noticed a higher noise level, a high, penetrating whine which increased the further back he walked and was at its worst in the rear toilets. But it was not so loud as to be a problem and he soon became accustomed to it. He postulated that this was produced by the effect of the four jet exhausts impinging on the sides of the fuselage. There was little vibration except a 'tickle under the sole of the foot' when standing over the front spar.

The view from the windows was 'quite good' without propeller discs or engines getting in the way. The view from the front cabin allowed him to see down and forward and those in the rear cabin, behind the wing, just downward. From a height of 40,000 feet, before beginning the descent to Rome, he was able to see Corsica, but Elba, a

Fig. 3/9 Main passenger cabin (G-ALZK) 29 March 1951, (copyright BAE SYSTEMS Heritage)

significant place in the Comet story, was invisible somewhere beneath the aircraft's nose. By this time they had been flying for 1 hour and 35 minutes and had reached a speed of 470 mph. While in the cockpit the captain had shown the correspondent the periscopic sextant mounting ring in the roof. This was iced up and useless but was soon to be replaced with an electrically heated one. It was useful, the captain told him, for navigating over Africa where radio aids were sparse.

Soon there was a change in note from the engines as the descent into Rome started, later the dive brakes were extended on the upper surface of the wings. The angle of descent seemed no different than normal although the g-force on the turns in the circuit seemed a little more than usual. The flight had taken 2 hours and 15 minutes and had seemed much less tiring than covering 1,000 miles in a propeller aeroplane, which anyway would have taken about 4 hours. After an hour spent refuelling it would be off again for Beirut, on the way to Johannesburg.

Another correspondent (C.B.B-W.), this time travelling on the third Comet built, the first production Comet for BOAC, (i.e. the ill-fated YP) described himself as somewhat jaded when it came to flying after having to do so much of it in the course of his duties.[15] Nevertheless he was impressed by his trip on the Comet. It was a demonstration flight put on by de Havillands for the benefit of some potential customers from France and, appropriately enough, was over France. He sat in the front row, i.e. in the front cabin and facing the rear. The pilot was John Cunningham. An added bonus was watching John Derry takeoff in one of the two prototype DH-110 all-weather fighters. One of these was later to kill him.

The take-off was unremarkable but height gain seemed rapid and the front cabin was noticeably quiet. After a visit to the cockpit the main cabin was sampled. In contrast with the previous correspondent he found that the noisiest seats were in the first two rows and the most quiet were those at the rear but all were less noisy than in other current aeroplanes. Again the lack of vibration was noticeable.

The passengers' seats were 'delightfully comfortable and easily adjusted' although they left an uncomfortable gap between the top of the head and the neck which, he thought, could have been bridged with a small pillow. The conclusion was that the "Comet will put existing airliners in the shade; but truly one has to fly in it to realise how wholly dissatisfied passengers will be with other types once they have experienced Comet travel."

A correspondent from *The Aeroplane*, who was on the same flight as M.A.S. over France,[16] also felt that the flight deck was the quietest part of the aircraft. He, too, remarked on the general smoothness of the engines, particularly when compared with the 'lumpy' vibrations produced by piston engines when they are being started. He felt that while the intensity of the cabin noise in flight may be the same as in a conventional airliner the higher-frequency sound might be less tiring. When the two inner turbines were throttled back for the descent the aircraft was "almost dead-quiet and vibration-less, the aircraft might be poised motionless under the blue of the sky." As they neared the cloud layer "a gently-sudden (sic) deceleration and a steepening of angle gave the clue, before looking out over the wing, to the fact that the air brakes were 'out'." These were opened and closed several times during the descent to avoid exceeding the maximum permissible speed and to keep the rpm of the outer turbines at a level that would maintain cabin pressure. He also seemed impressed with the air conditioning system which coped with the pollution from twenty cigarettes simultaneously alight, a problem that has disappeared from most modern passenger aircraft.

Travelling on the Comet was considered very glamorous and the rich and famous were eager to try it. There is a light-hearted account of Comet travel from Joan Brooks who was a stewardess on the early Comets. She recalled that there was usually somebody famous on every sector: Frank Sinatra, Trevor Howard, Lady Mountbatten. On one night sector from Entebbe, Grace Kelly and Clark Gable had the front cabin to themselves and, according to the steward, who was keeping a discrete eye on things, availed themselves of the opportunity to join (or rejoin) the Mile High Club.[3]

Chapter 10

THE CRASHES BEGIN

Setting aside minor incidents the first significant Comet 1 crash occurred on 26 October 1952. It resulted in the loss of an aeroplane which had 81 hours and 33 minutes of flying time but caused only a minor injury to one of the occupants. Unusually for a serious crash in the days before flight data and cockpit voice recorders, the details of what happened on the flight deck are known because both pilots survived.

The aircraft, G-ALYZ, was on route from London to Johannesburg and had landed at Rome's Ciampino airport at 16:37 GMT for its first refuelling stop. This leg of the trip had been uneventful and Captain Harry Foote had made an entry of 'No defects' in the log. The aircraft was refuelled to a total of 38,091 pounds, four passengers disembarked and five joined, making the aircraft slightly heavier, at 100,370 pounds, than it had been on takeoff from London; the maximum permitted all-up weight was 105,000 pounds. Its centre of gravity was calculated and found to be within the safe range. The intended destination was Cairo.[1]

All seemed well as Captain Foote taxied YZ to the threshold of runway 16, moved over to the centre line, completed the pre-takeoff checks and set the flying controls to neutral. It was dark and raining and the horizon was invisible to the pilots although First Officer Josling said that he could see to the end of the runway.[2] The temperature was 19°C and the altitude of the airport was 400 feet, neither hot nor high, and the wind speed was 10 knots, coming from about 45° to the right of the direction of takeoff.

The flaps were lowered to 15°, the engines set to full power, the readings on the instruments noted to be within normal limits and the brakes released. Yoke Zebra began to accelerate down the runway. At an indicated air speed of 75 to 80 knots (86 to 92 mph) the nose wheel was lifted off the runway and Captain Foote, who was conducting the takeoff, corrected a slight swing to the right. At 112 knots (129 mph) Foote pulled the control column back and the aircraft left the ground. Shortly after this, when he felt the aircraft had reached a safe height, Captain Foote called for the undercarriage to be moved up. At this moment the left wing dropped violently and the aircraft swung to the left. Foote managed to correct this and level flight was regained but it became apparent to him that the aircraft was accelerating less quickly than normal. This was without reference to the air speed indicator and was probably an impression gained from visual cues, such as the runway lights, as he looked out of the cockpit window.

At about this time the pilots felt a pronounced judder which Foote interpreted as the onset of a stall. In spite of twice moving the control column forward the judder contin-

Fig. 1/10 Captain Foote's crashed aeroplane at Rome with 'Comet', 'BOAC' and its registration letters painted out, (copyright British Airways Heritage)

ued and the aircraft came down onto its main wheels, which had not yet been raised, and bounced. At this point Captain Foote felt that there had been a loss of engine power and that this was the cause of the failure to accelerate and takeoff as normal. As the aircraft was rapidly approaching the end of the runway, he made the decision to abandon the takeoff and closed the throttles.

The aircraft's momentum took it beyond the end of the runway and after about 60 yards the main wheels hit two mounds of earth and parted company with the rest of the aircraft. YZ slid for another 210 yards before coming to a standstill almost at the boundary of the airfield. In spite of considerable spillage of fuel, fire did not break out and the crew and passengers were successfully evacuated, the only injury being one cut finger. In the official report the time of the accident was given as 17:58.[1]

A newspaper article on the day after the crash contained praise for the skill of the pilot who, realising that the aircraft was not gaining altitude as it should "piloted it with extreme skill off the runway on to the ground which recent rains had softened thus avoiding harm to the passengers."[3] The stewardess, Miss Margaret Williams, came in for particular praise from some of the passengers because of her calmness. Two South African passengers reported that immediately after the crash she came round and "with a flashing smile told us that 'There is nothing wrong at all – nothing.'"[3] Considering that a minute or two before they had all narrowly escaped serious deceleration injury followed by a good chance of being incinerated in their seats, the aircraft was terminally damaged and at that moment the steward was searching for an axe to break open the jammed cabin door, this would seem to have been stretching the art of reassurance to an almost astronomic extent.

Most of the passengers showed their continued equanimity by completing their journey on a replacement Comet but two would seem to have had second thoughts and continued by sea.[4] *The Daily Telegraph* said that a BOAC spokesman had announced that the accident had been caused by one of the port engines failing on takeoff and explained that jet airliners were particularly vulnerable in these circumstances. On the same page is a photograph of the stricken Comet with the letters 'BOAC' and the word 'Comet' tactfully painted out.[4] A few days later the *Daily Express* helpfully announced that 'Tail skid caused Comet crash.'[5]

Yoke Zebra had sustained considerable structural damage: the starboard inner engine had rotated downwards through the wing, the nose wheel had been pushed up into its housing and the tail bumper torn off. The aircraft was later deemed not worth repairing and was broken up at Rome airport. The nose section was removed and transported back to the UK by sea with the intention of converting it to a simulator. This never happened and it ended its days, like so many unwanted bits of aeroplane fuselage, being used by the fire service at London Airport and was eventually scrapped in the mid-1970s.

Examination of the runway the day after the crash provided considerable help in discovering what had happened. Starting about 650 yards from the far end of the runway, beyond the point at which the aircraft should have become airborne (at about 1,040 yards from the far end), there were ten linear marks. These were interpreted as skid marks from the aircraft's tail bumper, a small projection emerging from the midline of the bottom of the fuselage at a point about level with the middle of the tailplane. These marks ranged in length from 3 to 40 feet. At first they were along the midline of the runway but then deviated to the right. Immediately before the end of the runway there were two parallel marks 30 feet long left by the main wheels, presumably the result of the (non-skid) brakes having been applied and the tyres becoming hot and depositing rubber on the tarmac. The path of the aircraft after it left the runway could be traced by the impressions left on the two earth mounds where the main wheels were ripped off and by fragments of the aircraft found scattered on the ground.[1]

As part of the investigation the aircraft's airspeed indicators and artificial horizons were removed and found to be working normally.

Little was seen of the aircraft's attempted takeoff because of the rain and darkness but there was one witness who came forward. Eugene Kelly, a TWA (Trans World Airways) dispatcher, was about half way down the runway and described the aircraft's attitude as it passed him as 'pretty critical i.e. his nose was up and his tail down. For this reason I continued to watch him as his nose was exceptionally high for this distance down the runway... I might also add that he did not look as though he was off the runway at any time although as it was dark it is difficult to be certain on this point.'[6]

Two things were obvious from the initial examination of the scene of the accident. Firstly the aircraft had failed to become satisfactorily airborne within the available distance and secondly the tail bumper had been intermittently in contact with the runway which meant that at times the fuselage had been excessively tilted nose up and tail down.

The investigation of the crash seemed fairly straight forward and a report was produced and published on 4 December 1952, only about five weeks after the crash. Its conclusion was 'The aircraft's normal acceleration did not build up due to the progressive nose-up attitude of the aircraft which was permitted to develop which resulted in high drag and a semi-stalled condition.' The final opinion was 'The accident was due to an error of judgement by the Captain in not appreciating the excessive nose-up attitude of the aircraft during the takeoff.' In other words 'pilot error.'[1] Even before the report was issued Foote had been removed from the Comet fleet and transferred to flying plodding Yorks. He declined the opportunity to make a statement in his defence or to produce evidence or witnesses on his own behalf, accepted the findings of the report and signed the government form accepting responsibility.[7] But he was left with a feeling of having been unjustly dealt with.*

Captain Foote was an experienced pilot. He was 36 years old and had learned to fly in the RAF during the war winning the DFC and bar. After the war he became an instructor. He was careful and methodical, perhaps even a bit obsessional. At the time of the crash he had 5,868 flying hours to his credit including 71 as first pilot on the Comet and 174 as second pilot. The only previous incident with BOAC for which he had been admonished was hitting an obstruction marker in a Hermes but there was a small shadow on his career with the Comet fleet. The previous May, Captain A. M. A. Majendie, the head of the Comet fleet, had accompanied Foote on a flight to Singapore but had not been impressed. He had reported '...this Captain should be posted back to piston engined aircraft' and that 'further training on Comets is not justified in the light of his progress to date.' In fairness he suggested a second opinion and Foote flew to Johannesburg under the supervision of Captain Rodley who reported 'All his landings have been good and his approaches safe... I can but recommend that he is fit to operate this route on his own.'[8]

The takeoff run had started normally and at that stage there was nothing to suggest any loss of engine power or the failure of any other system. In accordance with the BOAC training manual in use at the time the nose wheel had been lifted off the runway at the correct speed of about 80 knots by pulling back the control column to raise the elevators.[8] The reason for doing this was to avoid damage to the nose wheel as the aircraft accelerated down the runway. The control column should then have been pushed back to some extent and the speed allowed to build up to reach the 'unstick' speed, about 112 knots in this case, and the elevators raised again to rotate the aircraft to complete the takeoff. It was apparent from the skid marks that this phase of takeoff had not been achieved.

When the nose wheel had been lifted just off the runway the fuselage incidence was about 2 to 3°. This required a backward movement of the control column of about four inches which was then reduced to about 1½ inches.[1] The BOAC training manual said that 'care should be taken not to overdo this and adopt an exaggerated tail-down attitude with consequent poor acceleration.'[9] At 'unstick' the fuselage angle was about 6 to 6½°, needing a backward movement of about six inches from the neutral position after which the control column should have been returned to the pre-takeoff position.

* This was the basis of a novel by David Beaty called *Cone of Silence*.[10]

At no stage should the tail bumper have come into contact with the runway.

At the time YZ started its takeoff run neither pilot could see the horizon ahead, there was therefore no distant external reference point for them to gauge the angle of the fuselage relative to the ground. Captain Foote, in his evidence to the internal BOAC inquiry said that as well as looking out of the windows at the runway lights he also looked at the artificial horizon on the instrument panel[11] but it was known that this was unreliable in these circumstances and BOAC emphasised this in a report circulated after the accident.[12] Foote continued, 'Having lifted the nose wheel off I would keep the control (column) in about the same position and then when I got to the unstick position I would make a positive movement backwards – two backward movements.' Foote also said that he 'had been forming the impression that you do need to move the control column fairly far back to get the aircraft off the ground.'[13] First Officer Josling thought that the nose wheel had lifted normally although the control column appeared to be 'a fair way back'. He also thought that the 'unstick' (i.e. the point at which the aircraft becomes airborne) was made by pulling the control column half way back from the neutral position and that it was held there until the left wing dropped. In other words Josling felt that the control column had been pulled back excessively when the nose wheel came off the runway and at the calculated 'unstick' speed.

This was the main cause of the crash; the control column had been pulled back excessively to lift the nose wheel and had then not been returned to about 1½ inches from the neutral position. The 'up' position of the elevators necessary to push the tailplane down and rotate the nose upwards would have progressively more effect as the speed of the aircraft built up and the nose would therefore continue to rise. Once the rumble of the nose wheel had ceased there was no positive indication to the pilots of the attitude of the fuselage except to say that it was no longer horizontal. Foote said 'I was completely unaware that I was in that attitude'[9] and Josling also said that he could not tell what the aircraft's attitude was after the bounce as he had no visual reference points.[1]

The skid marks showed that the angle of attack when the aeroplane had passed beyond the calculated 'unstick' position had to be excessive. The official technique, which undoubtedly worked, and had done so many times, had clearly not been carried out correctly and Captain Foote has to take the blame for that although he could reasonably claim that there were extenuating circumstances. Perhaps it was the lack of an external reference point that had confused him or perhaps it was anxiety to get airborne that had made him do the instinctive, rather than the learned, thing and pull back more than he should on the control column but he also seemed to have learned a faulty technique. With the information available to the investigators at the time their conclusion of pilot error seems reasonable.

Following the crash John Cunningham carried out a series of tests at Hatfield where he repeatedly taxied down the runway lifting the Comet's nose higher and higher. As he put it 'I had to keep grinding my tail bumper on the runway,'[14] although in another account he said they used a wooden skid.[15] Cunningham showed that if the angle of the fuselage was increased to 9° the wings partially stall and there was a considerable increase in drag and consequent poor acceleration and a low-frequency buffet. The aircraft would recover if the nose was pushed well down. Tellingly, for the tail bumper to hit the runway an angle of at least 11½° was needed, and it would have been even greater if the main wheels were off the ground. At the time when the prototype had been tested no specific tests had been carried out at this 'high angle takeoff.'[16] The experience from propeller aircraft had been that stalling speeds were considerably reduced by the airflow over the wings generated by the propellers and that close proximity to the ground also increased lift. During certification tests it had became apparent that the Comet behaved differently but there had been no specific concerns about fuselage attitude.

It was clear from Cunningham's tests and the marks on the runway at Ciampino that after the nose wheel had left the runway the angle of attack of Yoke Zebra's wings was excessive and well into the range at which they would stall. This was supported by the witness statement that the nose had appeared excessively high, the buffeting experienced in the cockpit indicating a stall and the feeling that the aircraft was not gaining speed as quickly as it should. The lack of acceleration was mainly because of increased parasitic drag caused by the wings' excessive angle of attack but there might also have

Fig. 2/10 Passengers embarking on CPA CF-CUN at London Airport on 1 March 1953, (copyright BAE SYSTEMS Heritage)

been some loss of engine power as the air intakes became partially shielded. This explained what happened, leaving the question of why it happened.

David Beaty, in his book on the psychology of aircraft accidents, says that Foote crashed because he obeyed the takeoff rules laid down by BOAC and the manufacturer and that other, less obedient, pilots had realised that there was a problem with the Comet and had developed an unofficial takeoff technique in which they kept the nose down almost until the 'unstick' speed had been reached.[17]

As the crash was judged to have been caused by pilot error it was thought that an alteration to the takeoff procedure would provide the solution. This was illogical. An alteration of procedure by BOAC suggested that they thought the original procedure was incorrect, in which case the crash could hardly be blamed on the pilot. The need, as they saw it, was to keep the nose low but at the same time avoid damage to the nose wheel as the speed built up. The procedure they came up with was to lift the nose at between 80 to 85 knots and then to return it lightly to the runway until the unstick speed was reached. This would provide positive evidence to the pilots that the fuselage was still reasonably horizontal. Pilots under training also had demonstrated to them the excessive-attitude takeoff so that they might be better able to recognise it.[16]

It took another, almost identical, accident, only four months later to provide a more satisfactory solution. This time the consequences were much more serious. Canadian Pacific Airways (CPA) had been the first airline to buy the Comet in its 1A version with the more powerful Mark 2 engines and water-methanol injection to aid takeoff in hot weather. CF-CUN, the 'Empress of Hawaii', was the second example and was being flown on its delivery flight from London to Australia when it crashed on takeoff from Karachi in the early hours of 3 March 1953. Captain Charles Pentland, five crew members and six passengers were all killed. As well as it being the delivery flight there were reports that Pentland was trying to establish an elapsed-time record for the route between the UK and Australia although this has not been established.[18]

Captain Pentland had undertaken the Comet conversion course at Hatfield and had been fully briefed on the Rome crash. This had included being in the right-hand seat while Peter Bois, a de Havilland pilot, demonstrated what had happened in Rome. Cunningham, in his witness statement, said that he had seen this from the cockpit of another aircraft while waiting to takeoff. He had also been trained in the latest technique of returning the nose wheel to the ground until reaching the 'unstick' speed. Nevertheless it is doubtful that Pentland had sufficient experience flying the Comet to undertake the long flight to Australia and de Havillands were later criticised for not providing sufficient training.[19] In fact Cunningham had offered him the services of a de Havilland pilot or engineer for the delivery and proving flights but Pentland had said that he was happy handling the aircraft and only accepted an engineer because he had concerns about some of the radio equipment in the Pacific.[20]

The flight had started from London on Sunday 1 March and the first stage ended at Beirut. After refuelling, the aircraft took off again at 07:26 on 2 March and arrived at Karachi at 12:00. The aircraft was fully serviceable at Karachi but the de Havilland engineers travelling with the aircraft carried out some engine runs using the water-methanol injection system.* Meanwhile the crew had taken rooms at the BOAC rest house at the airport and apart from some administrative duties had several hours to recover before taking off again at 22:54 (02:54 local time).[21] In spite of this they were probably suffering from jet lag and unable to get much sleep and may well have felt tired.

Assuming there was no wind the aircraft was just within its maximum permissible weight, being full of fuel for the next stage to Rangoon and loaded with Comet spares. Even a two knot tail wind would have taken it 468 pounds over the limit. Judging from the radio messages, which came from Captain Sawle, the co-pilot, Captain Pentland was flying the aeroplane. In view of the weather conditions and the heavy weight of the aircraft the plan was to use the water-methanol injection system and the long engine run-up mentioned by several witnesses suggest that it was.

The temperature was 73°F (23°C), there was a full moon, little wind and conditions were said to be 'very favourable for a night takeoff.' Several reliable witnesses near the terminal building were able to see the outline of the aircraft clearly. According to them the start of the takeoff appeared normal but by the time UN was approximately in line with the windsock (about 3,496 feet from the eastern end of the runway where the take-off run had started) it had an abnormally nose-high attitude. This seemed to become more pronounced because sparks started to appear from the underside of the rear of the aircraft, presumably from the tail bumper rubbing along the surface of the runway. Later examination of the runway showed that this started at 5,757 feet from the eastern end. It continued for 1,037 feet when the aircraft levelled out enough for the nose wheels to come into contact with the runway, but by now only 16 feet from its end. Tracks left on the over-run show that both the main and the nose wheels ran along the ground for 960 and 654 feet respectively. The aircraft left the ground about 12 feet before the boundary fence which it just touched. Shortly afterwards the starboard undercarriage struck the wall of a small culvert which carried the airport service road over a ditch. Heavy score marks on this road appeared to have been made by the metal base of the port undercarriage leg which protruded below the wheels after the locking pin had fractured, probably the result of an overload as the aircraft tilted to port after the starboard wheels hit the culvert wall. This may account for the second set of sparks that witnesses described as coming more from the front of the aeroplane. The starboard wing separated at this point but the remainder of the aircraft continued to be supported by the port undercarriage for another 190 feet at which point large volumes of kerosene were spilt. This ignited and the aircraft then exploded, killing everybody on board.

---

* This was a system that injected water and methanol into the engines either just before or just after the compressor. It increased the density of the air entering the engine and so increased the thrust. It also cooled the turbine and allowed a higher rpm to be used at low level, again increasing the thrust, in the case of the Comet by about 10% in all.[22] As the mixture was burned up during the takeoff run it did not add to the weight of the aircraft at the point of takeoff. It was used to assist takeoff in 'hot and high' conditions, par-ticularly when the aircraft was heavy. As the water lowered the temperature in the combustion chambers it led to incomplete combustion of the fuel and produced a trail of black smoke.

There was no evidence that the pilot had attempted to abort the takeoff.[23]

Little remained of the aircraft after the fire and although all the bodies were found it was impossible to identify them individually. There was little or no medical examination of the bodies other than for the purposes of certification. In the circumstances it is doubtful whether closer examination would have added anything to the investigation.

John Cunningham flew to Karachi the day after the crash and examined the runway and was able to interview a BOAC pilot, Captain Rodley, who had witnessed the accident.[24] Cunningham's opinion was that Pentland had 'over rotated... the same problem as Foote.'[25] This was also the finding of the Pakistani inquiry, '...the nose of the aircraft was lifted too high during the takeoff run...' Contributory causes were stated to be the limited experience of the pilot with the type, his electing to takeoff at night and at the maximum permissible weight when a strict adherence to the takeoff procedure was necessary.[23]

Pentland was an exceptionally experienced pilot with over 11,000 flying hours, indeed he had been Cunningham's instructor on Constellations in 1946, but, of necessity, he had relatively little experience flying jet airliners; only eight hours before setting off and another 23 hours on the way to Karachi. He was well aware of what had caused Foote's accident. Cunningham recalled a conversation with him in which Pentland had said 'Holy Jeez, how on earth did the chap do that?'[25] About a week later, presumably anxious to get airborne, and again with reduced visual cues, he had done the same thing.

Carrying out the the investigation was not without its difficulties. It was the responsibility of the state in which the accident had happened, Pakistan, and the State of Registration of the aircraft, Canada. The British investigator, Mr T. R. Nelson, was only accorded observer status. In a hand-written note he described the Pakistani investigator as being 'extremely sensitive' and resentful of any suggestions that he made. On the advice of the British High Commissioner, Nelson organised a lunch party for all concerned and their wives and they 'all finished up the best of friends.'[26] He was later given 'Accredited Representative' status and signed the final report. Curiously this was never published, although type-written copies appear in the National Archives' files, and the British authorities resolutely refused to let the various pilots' organisations have copies stating that Pakistan, and not they, had ownership of it. After the investigation Nelson flew back to the UK in a Constellation.

Cunningham returned to Hatfield determined to repeat the tail scraping and to find a solution. The aircraft used was the other Canadian 1A, CF-CUM, which de Havillands had bought back when CPA cancelled their order after the Karachi crash. These tests confirmed that a large angle of attack considerably increased the length of the takeoff run because of the increased drag. If the over-rocking occurred early in the run, the length to unstick was increased by 50% or more but if the technique described in the Flight Manual was used, keeping the nose wheel on or near to the ground, the distances to unstick were in agreement. More importantly, during the course of these tests a hitherto unknown phenomenon was discovered. This was that as the weight of the Comet increased to its maximum of 115,000 pounds the angle of attack at which it would stall decreased by 2 to 2½° and the lift coefficient of its wings decreased by 25%. Hence the difference of angle between that required for takeoff and that at which it stalls progressively decreased as the aircraft's weight increased.[27] The margin of error between the (power on) stalling speed and the unstick speed, which had been thought to be about 19%, was actually about 3% at maximum all up weight – too small to be appreciated by the pilot. Also it had been reported that the airline pilots were having great difficulty returning the nose wheel to the runway in the new procedure.[28]

Another procedural solution, the second change, was devised by de Havillands and the Accident Investigation Branch (AIB). This time the nose wheel would be kept in firm contact with the runway until just below the unstick speed so there was no chance of over-rocking, a technique remarkably similar to the the the unofficial one allegedly developed by the BOAC pilots. This became the rotation speed, or VR, and continued to be the takeoff procedure for the Comet and its successors. Also the unstick speed was increased to provide at least a 12% margin between stall and unstick. This was passed to the Comet operators by cable on 6 July 1953.[28]

On the basis that 'if a thing can happen, sooner or later it will', these accidents were inevitable. Captains Foote and Pentland were the victims of the Comet's thin, symmetrical wing that had been designed for high-speed flight. It would begin to stall at a relatively small angle of attack and would stall more abruptly than a thick, well-cambered wing. It was easily possible to get into this position as the angles of attack allowed by the fuselage were well within the stall range. This problem was compounded by having the new jet engines rather than the propeller engines that both pilots were more familiar with. Propellers would have provided so much extra air flow that almost any such aircraft would have got off the ground with its tail scraping along the runway at the speeds at which the two Comets had crashed. Any loss of thrust from the jet intakes becoming shielded would have made the situation even worse. Another issue was the relatively-primitive, power-operated control system that did not provide the proportional feedback that might have persuaded the captains that they were pulling the control columns back too far.

Ironically de Havillands already had a structural solution. The first prototype had originally been fitted with leading edge slats to provide more lift at low speeds. Cunningham had found that the aircraft behaved similarly whether they were extended or not, presumably because takeoffs with the tail bumper in contact with the runway had not been tried. Consequently the slats were fixed in the 'up' position and not fitted to subsequent aircraft. Bill Gunston recalled saying to Bishop after Foote's crash that it was surely a mistake to do away with the slats. Bishop had paused and then replied "I hope not."[29] Cunningham said that after the Karachi crash Bishop did a pencil drawing showing a leading edge droop to increase lift and it was made from wood within 24 hours and fitted to a Comet.* Cunningham was then able to "have the tail firmly on the

---

* One suggestion was to have a stick 4 or 5 feet long protruding from the rear underside of the fuselage to prevent the aircraft tilting back too far. Bishop favoured an extending tail bumper. Fortunately neither was adopted.[30]

ground and hold it there until the aircraft took off."[25] Another suggestion was to incorporate a stall warning device that would vibrate the control column. This had already been produced by the Safe Flight Company and would in due course become standard on most aircraft, usually incorporating an audible warning. An 'angle of attack' indicator was also proposed and eventually appeared.[30]

BOAC and the other operators were left with an aircraft that could still get itself into a position from which it could not takeoff although the new procedure made it much less likely. It was a relatively easy matter to incorporate the droops into the Comet 2s which were still being assembled at Hatfield although they would be less extensive than those planned for the Comet 3. According to Bishop they would provide "improved takeoff, landing and approach characteristics giving a substantial gain in safety. In particular the tail-down attitude effect would be overcome." De Havillands would be able to provide three Comet 2s with the droops by January 1954 but only for training purposes as they would not have the thermal anti-icing equipment along the leading edge necessary for service.[31]

This still left the problem of what to do with the existing Comet 1 fleet. The Air Safety Board (ASB) discussed the matter in November 1953 and "learned with satisfaction that a change to the shape of the leading edge had been found to cure the trouble... It was hoped that by March 1954 all the Comets would be modified..."[32]

An internal BOAC letter from C. H. Jackson, the Chief Development Engineer, dated 19 November 1953 mentions that "...there are still takeoff variations in performance which have not been eliminated by the modified takeoff technique..." It continues, "This situation merely confirms what was said some months ago; i.e. that there is an operational case, though not yet an (official) requirement, for the modified leading edge to improve operational reliability..." The letter then suggests getting estimates from de Havillands "...of the cost of incorporating the modification on the basis of an operationally practicable modification programme."[33]

The new droops would make a failed takeoff virtually impossible but it would take some time for them to be manufactured, tested, certified and then fixed to what was left of the Comet fleet. Grounding the aircraft in the meantime would be expensive and damaging to the Comets' sales prospects.* A letter from E. R. Sisson, a project engineer at de Havillands, dated 30 November, says that the droops could start to be supplied from September 1954 and that eight could be delivered within the following six months but it is unclear whether the order was ever placed.[33]

There is no evidence in the material that I have seen that BOAC, de Havillands or the responsible authorities made what Vaughan has called an "amoral calculation"[34] in which the costs of the loss of an aircraft and compensation for deaths or injuries of its occupants were set against the costs of grounding and modifying the aircraft.** It

---

* Bill Gunston in the Principal Films documentary said "Nobody wanted to say 'Well actually it's got a nasty flaw.' So BOAC had tremendous pressure on them not to blame the aeroplane but to blame the pilot..."
** The most quoted example of this is the Ford Motor Corporation's alleged calculation that it would be less expensive to pay any compensation than do an $11 repair to a design defect in the Pinto model that made it vulnerable to a fuel tank explosion. This was later disputed in the so-called Schwartz Memorandum.

would be naive to imagine that BOAC, de Havillands and the authorities were immune to considerations of cost, service disruption and loss of prestige but it seems more that the people involved felt they had an adequate procedural solution and that altering the wing shape would make it even safer and would be sensible to incorporate into future aircraft. Incorporating it into the current aircraft seemed more of an afterthought.

By whatever mechanism it was reached, BOAC et al made the decision for the Comet 1s to continue flying without the leading edge modification and to rely on the skill and obedience of their pilots to avoid another disaster. A safer decision would have been to have grounded the Comet 1s until the droops were fixed and to have pushed de Havillands to do it more quickly than they proposed. As things turned out the procedural change worked and there were no more takeoff crashes in the limited service life of about thirteen months left to the Comet 1s. Had there been another crash of the same type it is interesting to speculate how present day, personal injury lawyers would have viewed that decision.

In January 1954 Captain Foote's union, the British Air Line Pilots Association (BALPA), wrote to Sir Gilmore Jenkins, the Permanent Secretary at the Ministry of Transport and Civil Aviation, saying that as further information had come to light the investigation into the crash of YZ should be reopened.[35] This was passed to Group Captain Tweedie, the Chief Inspector of Accidents, who agreed to consider any fresh evidence they could produce. The following month BALPA submitted a detailed defence of Captain Foote.[36] The basis of this was that after the crash the Comet was found to have previously unsuspected adverse characteristics when on or near the ground. Unfortunately for their case they made a rather complicated argument, much of which appeared irrelevant. The AIB, with the help of a report from Captain Majendie, had little difficulty refuting it, both on grounds of factual inaccuracy and incorrect interpretation.[37]

BALPA had a point though. In the first place the AIB was acting as judge and jury on an investigation they had carried out themselves, albeit under a different chief inspector. Also Captain Majendie might be considered to have been biased against a captain he had recommended be removed from the Comet fleet and in places his report shows the lack of generosity sometimes seen when one professional is given the opportunity to comment on the work of another. A fairer arrangement would have been to have had an independent review. In the third place there was no doubt that some facts about the Comet's takeoff performance had come to light since Foote's accident.[16] It is unclear how much of this information was available to BALPA at the time but as they do not refer to the de Havilland examination of the Comet's takeoff characteristics as its weight increases[27] it is unlikely they had seen it. Fourthly, another almost identical crash had taken place. Fifthly BOAC had seen fit to introduce two changes of procedure as a result of the two crashes and lastly that the manufacturers were incorporating a structural change to future aircraft to eliminate the problem.

The AIB appeared to deal with BALPA's request rather in the manner of an opposing party in a legal dispute, determined to protect their position. Contained in the AIB's internal response to the first BALPA submission, for example, is the sentence "A point which BALPA fail to make is that an attitude on the ground which would not cause trouble on almost any other four engined aircraft will do so in the Comet." Whether BALPA appreciated this at the time is uncertain and it seems unlikely that the AIB told them.

After a meeting between representatives of BALPA and the AIB, a revised case was submitted by BALPA but on 19 May 1953 Group Captain Tweedie wrote to them saying "The opinion expressed in Civil Accident Report No. CA147 is a correct one." He went on to acknowledge that a new technique had been subsequently introduced which had increased the margin for error. It ends " Had the captain applied the technique then in force, one which had been successfully used since before the introduction of scheduled services in May 1952, the accident would not have occurred."[38]

Later the International Federation of Air Line Pilots Association (IFALPA) and the Canadian Air Line Pilots Association took up Captain Pentland's case but they were hampered by the refusal of the authorities in Pakistan, Canada and the UK and de Havillands to release much of the relevant information, in particular the official report of the Karachi crash, the Flight Manual in force at the time and de Havillands' investigation into the Comet 1's takeoff characteristics. This eventually led to the release of a joint IFALPA/de Havillands statement on 16 March 1959.[39] This accepted that the Comet 1 had the takeoff problems described above but also made clear that had the pilot carried out the takeoff procedure then in force the aircraft would successfully have become airborne. It was, therefore, more of a face-saver for IFALPA than an exoneration of Captain Pentland.

On balance Captains Foote and Pentland were at fault for letting their aircraft become too nose-high, although there were certainly extenuating circumstances in both cases, but the Comet was at fault too. The investigators at Rome knew nothing of the Comet's takeoff problems and the opinion they produced was reasonable at that time. It is no doubt difficult to get a government department to change its collective mind but in the light of later information there would seem to be reasonable grounds for at least partially exonerating the two unfortunate captains. Foote, in particular, seems to have been harshly dealt with. Pentland had the advantage of knowing about Foote's accident and how to avoid repeating it and it is less easy to excuse him.

Eventually Foote gave up flying but not before playing a small part in another Comet disaster near Calcutta. He died from ischaemic heart disease at the early age of 53. His widow said of the accident that, "He didn't know what had happened. He couldn't understand why the 'plane hadn't climbed away. It always had before."[40]

Chapter 11

ENTEBBE, DAKAR AND CALCUTTA

At 08:24 on 21 January 1953 BOAC Comet G-ALYY landed at Entebbe Airport in Uganda on the way from London to Johannesburg. Captain E. R. Brown DFC was in the right-hand seat and First Officer S. C. Josling was in the left hand seat, flying the aeroplane – the same S. C. Josling who had been the first officer in the aborted takeoff at Rome the previous October. Strictly speaking this was against BOAC rules as Captain Brown had only done two previous landings at Entebbe and to supervise a landing he should have carried out six. First officer Josling had also done two previous landings at Entebbe. The weather was clear with a surface wind of about 18 knots.[1]

At that time Entebbe was the capital of Uganda and it was an important staging post on the 'Empire' route to South Africa. The airport had been opened in 1929 with a grass runway which had been asphalted towards the end of the war and then extended to 3,300 yards in 1951 in anticipation of the Comets using it. At a little more than 200 feet before the threshold of runway 12 was an escarpment about 60 feet deep. At the base of the escarpment was a swamp which extended for another 1,000 feet or more. On the centre line of the approach to the runway, near the edge of the escarpment, was a switch house where three Africans and one European were working. A tarpaulin 20 feet long had been spread over a steel scaffolding pipe raised about 2½ feet above the ground. This pipe was at an angle of about 45 degrees to the centre line of the runway and at one end was resting on the switch house and at the other on some bricks at the edge of the escarpment on the left side of the runway.

Josling arrived over Entebbe at about 13,000 feet and carried out a wide descending circuit. The final approach started from 4,700 feet at 140 knots and 8,500 rpm on all engines and 40 degrees of flap. Events proceeded fairly normally until the aircraft was at 115 to 120 knots just short of the threshold when it suddenly lost height. Josling responded by asking for increased engine rpm and easing back the control column. He reported that he felt a 'bump' as the aircraft passed over the threshold of the runway. He commented that "there was no feeling that the aircraft had been damaged." In fact the aircraft was damaged and had touched down some 208 feet short of the runway, killing one of the African workmen in the process.

Examination of the scene showed that the aircraft's port wheels had touched down first, right at the edge of the escarpment. The port outer wheels had hit the end of the steel pipe while the inner wheels had hit the workman killing him instantly. It was unclear why this man had not moved out of the way of the approaching aircraft as his fellow workers had. His body was then caught by the port inner flap and carried about twelve yards.

The aircraft port and starboard inner flaps were severely damaged, the number 3 jet pipe and shroud dented, the fuselage dented and scored and the port undercarriage damaged in several places as well as the port outer front tyre having been ruptured.

In the opinion of Captain Brown, expressed in his statement, YY had been caught in a strong down draft just short of the runway and in spite of the throttles being pushed forward a full recovery had not been possible. He had no criticism of his first officer or of the aircraft.[2]

The following day an experiment was carried out with several 'Aix no lift' balloons (presumably ones with neutral buoyancy in air) in conditions thought to be very similar to those of the day of the accident.[3] Six balloons were released about 100 yards along the runway from the edge of the escarpment. Their directions of drift varied slightly but all the balloons sank within about 300 feet of having gone over the edge of the escarpment. As Captain Brown had suspected, with the wind blowing along the runway towards the escarpment there was a down draft.

The conclusion of the investigators was that the aircraft had been affected by the downdraft which had caused it to lose height and to touch down short of the runway. But they also felt that YY was probably already below the glide path and had it been in the correct trajectory it would have been far enough away not to have been affected. The conclusion was therefore 'pilot error.'[1]

As usual there was also an internal BOAC inquiry. This did not reveal any new features although in their questioning both pilots commented on the lag between increasing the power setting and actually getting a response. First Officer Josling was held responsible for the accident and received a severe reprimand. His landing card was withdrawn until he could be checked on approach technique by the fleet training captain. Captain Brown was held to be at fault for allowing the first officer to land. He was severely reprimanded and lost one year's seniority.[4]

Although it was an accident to a civilian aircraft and the official report should have been made public the senior civil servants decided between themselves that it was better not to share the findings with the public as "its publication would, no doubt, produce more adverse publicity for the Comet." Unsurprisingly "The Minister and Parliamentary Secretary agree(d)" and the file was closed to prying eyes until 2029, a date fortunately since revised.[1]

While the conclusions of the report, so far as it went, were undoubtedly correct it makes no comment about whether the characteristics of the Comet had anything to do with what happened. It seems highly probable that a piston-engined, propeller aircraft in the same circumstances would have had a more rapid response to the throttles being opened and would have generated more lift from its propellers, enough at least to have raised the aircraft the few inches necessary to have avoided the workman and the metal pole. This is not a criticism of the Comet, just an expression of the different characteristics of its engines. Characteristics that may not have been fully appreciated by pilots more used to its predecessors. Significantly the same file has a hand-written note enclosed saying "L. & S. E. Division to investigate any reports of Comets undershooting at L.A.P. (London Airport) or Blackbushe." Also "enquiries... which show that crews under training at Blackbushe frequently have a tendency to undershoot."[1]

Failing to stop at Dakar

Later that year, on 25 June, UAT Comet F-BGSC, failed to stop after landing at Dakar, the capital of Senegal in West Africa, on route from Paris to Abidjan and ran beyond the end of the runway and over a 72 feet wide ditch which ripped off its undercarriage. It slid on for another 126 feet but fortunately there were no major injuries among the ten passengers and seven crew. It had flown a total of 133 hours.[5] The aircraft was stored at Dakar Airport and then broken up there.

Details of this crash are sparse. It is unclear whether the aircraft landed in the correct area of the runway and its brakes were not, or could not be applied, or whether it landed too far down the runway to stop within the length of runway remaining. The Comet's engines did not have reverse thrust and it relied heavily on its brakes to stop. It did have air brakes and flaps but the low drag of its fuselage and the absence of the braking effect of propellers, particularly in reverse pitch, would not have helped. Perhaps SC was another victim of the difference between the new jet airliners and what had preceded them. But much worse was to come.

Calcutta, the first of the structural failures

On 2 May 1953 Captain Maurice Haddon, with his crew of five and 37 passengers, took off from Calcutta's Dum Dum airport at 10:59 (16:29 India Standard Time) en route for Delhi. It was the start of the third leg of a flight from Singapore to London, the aircraft having just flown in from Rangoon, landing at 09:40. Six minutes after takeoff Calcutta air traffic control heard G-ALYV calling Delhi; this was the last radio message to be received. At about the same time some villagers working in an area about 30 miles from Dum Dum saw an aircraft coming down in flames through a severe thunderstorm and crashing into a *nullah* (a river or stream). There were no survivors.[6]

The weather forecast supplied to the crew for the route from Dum Dum to Delhi as far as 85° east (Calcutta is about 88°30' and Delhi about 77° east) had been for "scattered thunder-showers, moderate turbulence." At 07:40, about three hours before YV's takeoff, another aircraft reported a "storm developing in the area 24°6' N 89° E" (to the north of Calcutta) "...moving south east with very strong vertical updraft." A special airfield warning for Dum Dum had been issued at 09:45 saying "Thunderstorm accompanied with squalls from north west speed reaching 50 knots likely... between 02 12:00 hrs. GMT and 02 16:00 hrs. GMT." Captain Haddon had visited the airfield's meteorological office at about 10:30 and was personally briefed by the duty forecasting officer. There is therefore no doubt that the captain was well aware of the weather forecast for the route he was about to take. The staff in the office later reported that Captain Haddon seemed more concerned about the weather at Delhi.[6]

The weather at the airport around the time of takeoff was clear with good visibility and was well within company limits; any decision about the weather en route was the captain's. Yoke Victor took off from runway 19 left and headed in the direction of Delhi. Calcutta approach control gave clearance to climb under visual flight rules and to report when they passed 7,500 feet. When the crew failed to make this report, approach control made several unsuccessful attempts to contact them. Approach control then contacted area control and discovered that YV had been in touch with them since 11:02, some three minutes after take off, and that they were climbing to 32,000 feet. At 11:05 YV called Delhi. Delhi acknowledged and asked them to pass their message but no reply was received. There was no further contact with the aircraft. It took until 11:58 for the various centres to realise that YV had become silent and for the police to be informed and a search started. By this time visibility was severely reduced because of darkness and the poor weather and no aircraft were specifically sent out to look for the Comet. However what remained of the aircraft had already been spotted.

Murari Mohon Roy, who was in the vicinity of the crash, near to the village of Jagalgori, and was described rather patronisingly as an "educated observer" (some other witnesses were described as "uneducated"), recounted being in a heavy rain storm and seeing a flash in the sky coming from an easterly direction which was not followed by thunder. Shortly afterwards there were two "heavy sounds" like bombs and then "a fire rising up approximately 2-3 palm trees high... followed by thick smoke." He and his companions ran to the place of the crash to see if they could help but found all the passengers dead "the bodies were in a circle and the bodies were lying off from the place where the plane had dropped." One body, later identified as that of the captain, was strapped in a seat holding what appeared to be a steering wheel. There were also bodies within the plane. They were unable to put out the fire which burned until the following day. He did not know the time of the accident as there was no clock in the village.[7] He said that the severity of the storm was not unusual for the time of year but another witness said that he had only once before seen such a severe storm.[8]

One of the villagers who saw the aircraft parts fall to earth reported it to the local police inspector who happened to be in a neighbouring village on another investigation. He immediately went to the scene and found two parts of the aircraft still burning. He sent a messenger to the nearest police station whose only means of communication was via the railway telegraph office. Unfortunately their main telegraph wire had been damaged by the storm so a less direct line had to be used and the message only reached Dum Dum the following morning. The local police cordoned off the scene but were unable to find any survivors.

The following morning two Indian Air Force aircraft and a BOAC York, piloted co-incidentally by Captain Harry Foote, took off to search for the wreckage which they found in the area reported by the police. A land party was then assembled and transported to the scene. As well as the wreckage they found 40 bodies; three people were unaccounted for and their bodies were assumed to have been consumed by the fire.

The investigation was carried out by the Indian authorities with help from the local BOAC staff and Mr. T. H. Nelson, who had just returned to the UK after investigating the Karachi crash, and several other experts flown out from England. Nelson travelled from London on another Comet but after the investigation flew back on a Constellation. As he wrote later, "I was losing my confidence in fast-jet aircraft."[9]

The main wreckage was found about 24 miles from the airport, on the route from Dum Dum to Delhi. Aircraft fragments were found scattered along a track about 5½ miles long which was in the direction of travel of the aircraft (334° true). The largest piece, consisting of the fuselage from the nose to bulkhead 26 (about half way down the cabin, just at the end of the wing centre section) with both stub wings still attached and all four engines in place, was found furthest along the track towards Delhi. There were no skid marks on the soft ground, indicating that the fragments had been falling almost vertically when they landed. The main piece of wreckage was inverted and had been on fire. The rear portion of the fuselage, several of the wing pieces and the tailplane had also been burned but some of the separated pieces of fuselage showed no evidence of fire damage. All the fragments were severely damaged by their impact with the ground.

Examination of the wreckage showed that the undercarriage and flaps were fully retracted, all four throttle levers were jammed in the half open position, the ailerons and elevators were in normal positions and judging by the spill valves the cabin was in the process of being pressurised. This would not have got very far as the aeroplane probably broke up at about 7 to 8,000 feet so the occupants were at least spared the consequences of an explosive decompression.* The fire extinguishers had not been used nor was there evidence of any emergency procedure having been taken. Both wings had failed outboard of rib seven; the top panels had failed in tension while the bottom ones had failed in compression, indicating a downward pressure on the outer wings which had caused them to bend and then fracture. The main part of the aircraft, which had been found inverted, had probably descended in that attitude for some way.

The port tailplane had suffered a severe impact while still in the air and had been severed close to the number two elevator hinge. The outboard part was undamaged but the inboard portion of the same tailplane had separated at its attachment to the fuselage and been divided in two. The starboard tailplane had suffered impact damage in the air at the inboard leading edge and the front and rear spars had failed at their roots. The fin had separated at the insulation box. The fuselage had failed at frame 26, close to the attachment to the centre section of the wings. The fuselage panels showed a tension failure at the top and a compression failure at the bottom, indicating that either the centre of the fuselage had been pushed up or the ends pushed down, rather in the manner of the wing fractures.[6]

It was clear from the evidence that whatever happened was unexpected, sudden and catastrophic leaving no time for any emergency action to be taken. Nor was a distress call made, although it is only fair to say that making such a call may not be the first priority of pilots in these circumstances. The aircraft seemed to have broken up in flight, some parts showing signs of impact in the air, probably caused at, or soon after, the

---

* 'Explosive' in this context refers to an extremely rapid fall in cabin pressure rather than to a chemical explosion. See Chapter 12 for an explanation of the physiological consequences.

event. According to the witnesses fire had already broken out before the fragments landed. The parts not marked by fire had either already separated before the fire started, indicating that the fire was a secondary event, or had been upwind of the fire. There was nothing to suggest a problem with the engines and it appeared to be a catastrophic structural failure brought about by stresses imposed on the airframe by the storm that Yoke Victor had flown into. The aircraft had flown for a total of 1,649 hours.

One of the Indian assessors, Mr. S. W. Srinivasan from the design department of the Hindustan Aircraft Company, submitted his opinion of the sequence of the structural failure as an appendix to the report on the crash. His view was that the primary failure was of both elevator spars which had bent due to a heavy down-load imposed by the pilot performing a pull-up trying to counteract a sudden down-gust in the storm. In turn this caused the fuselage to fail at bulkhead 26. That the throttles were at halfway position tends to support this as the pilots would have been trying to reduce speed as the aircraft descended. As the aircraft responded and the nose moved up the wings would have experienced a sudden download and both failed at the end of the main spars. The extension wings would have experienced more wind resistance than the fuselage and probably collided in mid-air with the tailplane explaining the impact marks on them. Mr. Srinivasan considered that the power-operated controls, with their lack of proportional feedback, may have caused the pilot to make bigger elevator movements than he might otherwise have done and that this was the cause of the primary failure. He suggested that they be altered to provide feedback.[6]

These conclusions left several other questions unanswered. Why did Captain Haddon, an experienced pilot with 6,512 flying hours as captain, of which 439 were on Comets, takeoff with the storm forecast. He was well used to the route and the problems that its weather could produce. The answer will never be known for certain but there is always pressure on a pilot to keep to the schedule and maybe he felt some of that. He did not have the weather radar that modern pilots take for granted and may not have appreciated the severity of the storm ahead or been able to see a way around it. He might also have thought that the Comet would fly through it without difficulty, perhaps having experienced similar storms before when flying other types of aircraft. Two other aircraft, a DC-3 and a Constellation, were in the vicinity of the storm at about the same time and neither came to any harm. Captain Vlotman of the KLM Constellation stated that he did not feel the storm was anything worse than normal monsoon weather and that he had flown through it for about 25 minutes without any difficulty. He added that he had experienced far more turbulent weather at higher altitudes in monsoon weather.[10] Captain Foote's widow recalled that her husband had said "I've flown through that weather in an old York freighter."[11] On the other hand the force of the gusts in a tropical thunder storm can vary considerably from time to time and from place to place and even modern, much stronger, aircraft occasionally come to harm in them.

Some of the wreckage was flown to the RAE at Farnborough but most was stored at Calcutta and was only taken to Farnborough in May 1954, in a York chartered at some expense specially for the purpose, to help with the later accident investigations.[12]   A ('first summary') report was subsequently produced by P. B. Walker and E. L. Ripley of the RAE in February 1954.[13] They were able to rule out a lightning strike and sabotage and considered that the fire had happened as a secondary event after the structural failure of the wings. They felt that the tailplane had probably failed first and then the wings, both under downloads. The fuselage had then failed, as they put it, under a 'hogging' load from the downloaded tail and wings.* No fatigue fractures were found; all the failures had been from static loads. Reviewing the manufacturer's design calculations and strength tests they felt that there were "no grounds to suppose that the structure was under strength." The conclusion was that the "structural failure had been caused by a severe down-gust in a storm of such violence that no transport aircraft could have been expected to have survived." They conceded that an alternative possibility was that the elevators had been moved excessively either because of a malfunctioning of the power-operated controls or the automatic pilot but most of this material had been destroyed by fire and what evidence there was did not support it.

There was no evidence in either the Indian or the RAE investigations to suggest that the aircraft was structurally weak or that metal fatigue was involved and there was no similarity between this accident and the ones that preceded it. Yoke Victor just seemed to have been overwhelmed by the storm, the implication being that any other aircraft would have suffered the same fate and even in the light of future events this verdict was not seriously challenged.

After the Indian investigation was completed a statement was issued jointly by BOAC and de Havillands that they had faith in the Comet and that the basic design was sound.[14]

---

* 'Hogging' occurs when a horizontal beam, or something similar, is just supported at its centre and its ends bend down as a consequence. It was common in wooden boats whose ends had less buoyancy, and therefore less support, but were still expected to carry loads. Even a modern ship can crack when its centre is supported by a wave but not its ends. To prevent hogging ancient boats sometimes had a 'hogging truss', a rope attached to each end and stretched tight over a series of rigid vertical supports. Sagging is the opposite where the middle of the beam is unsupported and sinks. [15]

Chapter 12

DISASTER OFF ELBA

BOAC Comet G-ALYP, the first production airframe and the first jet airliner in the world to carry fare-paying passengers, took off from Rome's Ciampino airport at 09:31 GMT (local time was one hour ahead) on 10 January 1954, heading for London.[1] It was on the last leg of a trip from Singapore. It had a crew of six with 29 passengers, all of whom had less than half an hour to live. One of the passengers was Chester Wilmott, a well-known BBC war correspondent whose book, *The Struggle for Europe*, had been a best-seller. He had met a friend in Rome Airport, Noel Monks, another war correspondent also on his way back to London, whom he had tried to persuade to change from the BOAC Argonaut on which he was booked, to the Comet. Fortunately for Monks he declined in order to stay with his companions.[2]

The last radio message received by the Ciampino control tower was at 09:50 and reported that Yoke Peter was climbing at 26,000 feet and passing over the Orbetello Beacon on the west coast of Italy to the east of Corsica. Just after this the pilot sent his departure message to London and indicated that he intended to climb to 36,500 feet. Nearby was the BOAC Argonaut heading for London which had taken off before Yoke Peter but which could expect to land in London well after it. At about 09:51 the crew of the Argonaut received a message from Yoke Peter that began "George How Jig from George Yoke Peter did you get my..." and then stopped.[1] Shortly afterwards, at about 10:00, several witnesses saw pieces of aircraft, some on fire, crashing into the sea off the island of Elba. Just like the Calcutta crash something unexpected, instantaneous and catastrophic had happened to Yoke Peter.

At the time of the crash YP had flown a total of 3,681 hours and had been given a Certificate of Maintenance valid for 75 flying hours on 7 January, since when it had flown only 40 hours. The previous November its fuselage had successfully passed a pressure test up to 11psi following a repair to the passenger entrance door. On the trip back from Singapore there had been problems with refuelling at Karachi. The port-wing refuelling valve had failed and the tank had to be filled under manual control. At the end of this process the engineer officer was a little slow in closing the switch and about five gallons of fuel overflowed through the air vent on the underside of the wing. A similar incident also occurred at Beirut, this time the fuel flow was only stopped when the bowser was shut down. There had been two other minor equipment defects on the way back from Karachi but as far as was known the aircraft was fully serviceable. The only effect had been to put the service about 1¼ hours behind schedule.[3]

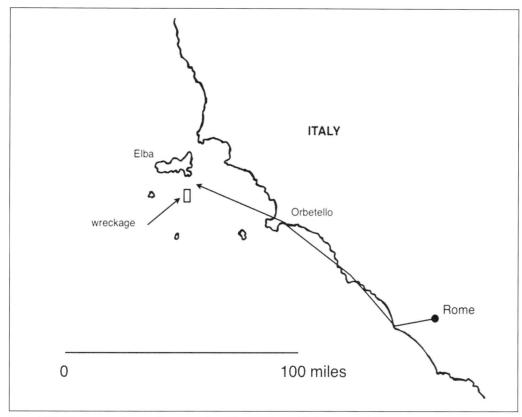

Fig. 1/12 The approximate flight path of G-ALYP on 10 January 1954

The weather after takeoff from Rome was good with thin cloud, little turbulence and negligible icing conditions up to the altitude of 27,000 feet, just below the maximum height that YP was thought to have reached.[4] Captain Alan Gibson DFC, like many of his generation, had learned to fly in the RAF but since then had flown a total of 5,218 hours with BOAC, mostly as first pilot. He had flown 159 hours as first pilot and 78 hours as second pilot in Comets. The first officer, William Bury, although two and a half years older than Captain Gibson, had a smaller total of flying hours but of these 262 were as second pilot in Comets. Both were fully qualified and experienced Comet pilots.[5]

The witnesses who saw the final moments of Yoke Peter described hearing an explosion or explosions and seeing a red flame falling into the sea. This was followed by smoke and a column of water rising up from the surface of the sea. Some of them saw burning wreckage falling. The wreckage appeared to have entered the sea to the south of Cape Calamita, a small peninsula on the south east part of Elba, roughly in the direction of the island of Montecristo. One of the witnesses noted that the time was 11:03 (10:03 GMT). They reported what they had seen to the Harbour Authority at Portoferraio on Elba at 10:50 GMT that morning. The delay in reporting the crash had been caused by there being no telephones in the area and the witnesses having to walk to the sub-harbourmaster's office.[6]

Lieutenant Colonel Lombardi, in charge at Portoferraio, promptly telegraphed to the mainland and requested an airborne search. He then dispatched the only available craft in the harbour, a motor fishing vessel, to the scene carrying the local doctor and his nurse. A fast motor launch, the *Montecristo*, was also got ready and left at 12:25 carrying Lombardi so that he could co-ordinate the search. On the way to the scene other vessels were sighted and directed to take part in the search. By 12:35 the first Italian search and rescue aircraft was in the area.[7] This was followed by a second aircraft after about half an hour, then by a Skyways cargo York that had been flying between Malta and London and ultimately three RAF Shackletons* from Malta joined in.[8]

The first wreckage was sighted by one of the fishing vessels at about 14:30. Shortly afterwards a body was seen floating in the water. From then until about 16:45, when it became too dark to continue, a total of fifteen bodies, mailbags, various pieces of floating wreckage and personal effects were retrieved. No survivors were found. The area where the bodies and most of the wreckage had been collected was calculated to be about thirteen nautical miles from the Cape in an approximately south south-east direction. The lack of a compass (see below) made it impossible to be more precise.

The bodies were brought ashore later that evening and carefully placed in the chapel in the cemetery at Porto Azzurro. The search continued over the next two days and other items and pieces of wreckage were retrieved but no more bodies were found. While this was going on Colonel Lombardi tried to find witnesses to the crash and to collect statements.[7]

The following day, 12 January, a fishing vessel reported that it had trawled up some wreckage from the sea bed in the same area in which the original search had taken place. This was important in fixing the point of impact as this material, unlike the floating bodies and debris, was unlikely to have been moved much by the sea. On 15 January floating debris was picked up on the far side of Elba which showed how far it could drift.[9]

Meanwhile news of the crash had reached the Accidents Investigation Branch of the Ministry of Transport and Civil Aviation at midday and two of their investigating officers, Messrs. Nelson and Morris, set off for Italy that evening. By this time Nelson must have become even more wary of flying in the Comet and they travelled from London in a BOAC Argonaut. The following morning they attended a meeting in Rome of the commission that the Italians had set up to investigate the crash. This posed something of a problem for the British authorities. They were desperate to carry out the investigation themselves but under international law the state in which a crash happens is obliged to instigate the inquiry. The actual site of the crash was just inside the six mile territorial limit that the Italian Government was claiming but outside the three mile limit that the British recognised. The Foreign Office in London sent a forceful cypher message to the British Embassy in Rome, dated 11 January, instructing them to press

---

* The Shackleton was a four propeller-engined maritime reconnaissance aircraft.

for the investigation to be led by the British team.[10]

Nelson was unaware of this message when he attended the meeting with the Italian Commission.[11] On his own authority, but aware of the territorial controversy, Nelson asserted that the crash had happened 'over the high seas' and that responsibility for conducting the investigation lay with the United Kingdom as the State of Registry of the aircraft. The general chairing the meeting retired to consult his colleagues and returned after about an hour to say that the matter would have to be settled by a higher authority but in the meantime he would continue the inquiry as originally ordered. Nelson accepted this but said that he reserved the right to conduct a separate investigation if such was decided by the British authorities. As things turned out matters proceeded amicably with the full co-operation of the Italian authorities, which did them great credit under the circumstances, and what could have been a difficult diplomatic situation was avoided. It was agreed that the Italians would conclude the preliminary investigations and that the British team would lead the technical investigation that followed. Colonel Miniero and Signor Roveri were appointed accredited representatives and worked closely with Nelson and Morris. The second telegram from the Foreign Office, dated 13 January, was considerably happier than the first.[10]

After collecting details of the departure of Yoke Peter from Rome the Italians and the British left for Elba. Their first task was to inspect the debris and wreckage that had been recovered. Nelson then interviewed the witnesses and returned to Rome to report back to Group Captain Tweedie, the Chief Inspector of Accidents. Nelson called at the British Embassy but the ambassador was away in Sicily and the air attaché, an RAF group captain, claimed that the crash of a civilian aircraft was not his responsibility. Nelson was concerned that a search for wreckage on the sea bed should start as soon as possible and the Italians were happy to hand this over to the British. He reported back to London the lack of interest in the embassy and that he needed urgent assistance if the search was to get underway. Alan Lennox-Boyd, the Minister of Transport and Civil Aviation cabled back and asked Nelson to telephone him at home. This immediately raised Nelson's status at the embassy and the air attaché suddenly decided that he was interested after all. The minister flew out the following night to add weight and to provide any necessary assistance. Nelson was given £5,000 to deal with local expenses such as chartering boats and travelled through what he described as 'bandit country' with millions of lira in cash as "bank notes so big we could have used them as wall paper."[12]

The first enquiry about a possible salvage operation was made on Friday 15 January by the Ministry of Transport and Civil Aviation to the Director of Boom Defence and Marine Salvage.[13] A departmental meeting was rapidly convened which concluded that the depth of the sea in the relevant area was 75 to 100 fathoms (450 to 600 feet) which made any form of soft-suited diving impossible. The alternative was to use a mechanical grab and an observation chamber. The only company in the UK that had such equipment was Risdon Beazley Limited of Southampton and a telephone call confirmed that they would make their equipment and crew available for the search. It was also noted that HMS *Sea Salvor*, an ocean salvage vessel, and HMS *Barhill*, a boom defence vessel, were available at Malta. Over the weekend a formal request was made by the ministry to the Royal Navy and a signal was sent from the Admiralty to the C-in-C Mediterranean (Malta), Earl Mountbatten, that he should "Endeavour to locate and salve Comet."

The following day, 17 January, Mountbatten signalled the Admiralty that he intended to sail the *Wrangler*, an anti-submarine frigate converted from a wartime destroyer, and the *Sursay*, a trawler, to lay buoys and to obtain any local information that they could. *Sea Salvor* and *Barhill* would sail when their special equipment had arrived at Malta and been taken aboard. Mr. Risdon Beazley arranged for their equipment, which now included an articulated diving suit, to be packed for air freight to leave on the 20th. Its crew of five would travel separately. Magnanimously he made no charge for the use of his equipment other than for out-of-pocket expenses. Other items of equipment were also sent to Malta by air including two sets of underwater television cameras, again provided by the manufacturers on a goodwill basis.

The position of the point where the burning wreckage was seen to enter the sea had been further refined by the invaluable Colonel Lambardi, often accompanied by Mr. Murphy, the British Vice-Consul at Florence. They had spent several days going with witnesses to the exact spots where they had been at the time of the crash and taking sextant angles to their estimates of the point of entry. The sextant, presumably held horizontally for the purpose, had been necessary because iron ore in the Elba hills made compass readings unreliable. In this way they made sixteen sight lines. Further help was provided by the photograph taken from the York aircraft that helped in the search for survivors. It showed boats picking up bodies, some floating wreckage and a corner of the island of Elba.

This photograph, which had been taken by the navigator of the York, had been the subject of a dispute between Captain G. S. Brown, a BOAC Inspector of Accidents, and Mr. McNally, a *Daily Express* reporter who had offered the crew £200 for it. After a discussion lasting almost two hours a telephone call from an official at Skyways, the owner of the York, settled the matter and it was handed to Captain Brown. Ironically Captain Brown considered it was of little importance.[14] The photograph was sent to the RAF Photographic Interpretation Unit near Oxford who were able to provide an approximate position but this was not available until 23 January.

HMS *Wrangler* arrived at Elba in the early morning of Wednesday 20 January. In the afternoon she sailed to a point twelve miles from Cape Calamita on a bearing of 193°. This was based on the evidence from the fishermen who had picked up the bodies and floating debris but was, in fact, too far south, no allowance having been made for the effects of a current which had taken the material six or seven miles to the south. By nightfall an area of one square mile had been searched by Asdic (Sonar) and one possible contact had been found and buoyed.

Wrangler continued the search for the next six days, moving to the north west, and identified two more contacts which were buoyed by HMS *Sursay*. Meanwhile two trawlers had been searching to the north and had found several small pieces of wreck-

Fig. 2/12 Salvaging YP (BT220/102), (The National Archives)

age and, more significantly, two heavy objects which had been buoyed. In view of their success three more trawlers were chartered and their activities co-ordinated by the 'trawler boss', an officer whose minesweeper was refitting in Malta. These trawlers proved to be the most successful means of finding wreckage.

Sea Salvor and *Barhill* arrived on 25 January, the former carrying one set of television equipment and Risdon Beazley's gear, and the latter the heavy moorings to secure the *Sea Salvor*. Further progress was interrupted by four or five days of bad weather which at least had the benefit of allowing the crews to become more familiar with the new equipment. *Sea Salvor*'s first task was to use the television equipment to identify the heavy objects found by the trawlers. This was first attempted by drifting over the spot but this proved to be unsuccessful and it was decided that she would have to be secured over the relevant object. Further attempts were made with a one-point mooring, then two-point, then four-point but *Sea Salvor* swung around too much and only a full six-point mooring provided enough rigidity over the contact to be successful. This was the method always used by Risdon Beazley but perhaps the navy had to find out for themselves. The situation was further complicated by discovering that the area had been a German minefield. The mines had gone but their sinkers remained to confuse the Asdic operators and to snag on the trawls.

Little progress was made during what remained of January and the first few days of February, mainly because of bad weather. HMS *Wakeful* arrived on 4 February bringing the second set of television equipment and the Captain (minesweeping) Mediterranean to take command. *Wrangler* departed the same day. One of the contacts

was identified as an ancient wreck with amphorae lying around it on the seabed, another
was a more recent wreck and a third an old Italian mine. Meanwhile the trawlers had
snagged another object ('George') which did turn out to be part of the crashed Comet,
reassuring the crews that the system did work. On the 15th *Barhill* began to lay moorings around contact 'George'. This took two days and *Sea Salvor* secured to them on
the 18th and by the evening had brought up the first sizeable piece of Yoke Peter. More
pieces were brought up over the next seven days, the largest one being the pressure
dome, although it was never an easy task. *Sea Salvor* then transferred to another contact
which proved to be a sunken buoy. She then returned to contact 'George' as the trawlers
had snagged more objects. This was a fertile area for wreckage and on 16 March the
centre section and engines were raised together with many other smaller items. By the
end of March all the large parts of the aircraft had been accounted for except for the tail
and wing extensions.

　　After all this heavy work *Barhill* and *Sea Salvor* were badly in need of repairs and
sailed for Malta on 9 April while the trawlers were left to continue. This went on until
late September by which time the tail unit had been recovered (26 May), the wing tips,
most of the starboard wing and, on 12 August, part of the cabin roof containing the ADF
windows. By now about 70% of the aircraft had been recovered, much in excess of
what had been expected and a remarkable achievement in the circumstances. It proved
to be of great importance in working out what had happened to Yoke Peter.[13]

Summary of the main salvage items:[15]

	date recovered	date received at RAE
floating wreckage, private trawling (including one part of the centre fuselage)		26/1/54
pressure dome, parts of rear fuselage	21 to 26/2/54	18/3/54
main items, wing centre section (engines about the same time)	16 to 18/3/54	05/4/54
most of cockpit, human bones	31/3/54	15/4/54
starboard outer wing (ribs 17 to 20) (other parts followed later)	07/5/54	22/5/54
tail unit	26/5/54	28/5/54
centre fuselage - port side piece	16/6/54	21/6/54
fin	09/6/54	30/6/54

search re-orientated 06/7/54

centre fuselage
- piece containing ADF aerial windows   12/8/54   31/8/54

outer portion, port tailplane   21/8/54   31/8/54

On 11 January the bodies of the victims in the mortuary chapel at the Porto Azzurro cemetery were photographed, numbered and examined externally by Dr Perri, the local magistrate, Mr. Bastreri, the Clerk of the Court and Dr. Bellina, the doctor who had taken part in the search for survivors. The doctor's opinion was that the victims had similar head, limb and chest injuries and that death had occurred about 24 hours before (not too difficult) and had been caused by an explosion. At the request of the Italian Commission of Inquiry and Mr. Murphy, arrangements were made to have full post-mortem examinations made by a forensic pathologist. The person selected to do this was Dr. (later Professor) Antonio Fornari of the Institute of Forensic Medicine at Pisa.

Dr. Fornari arrived the following day and started the examinations at 18:00 in the chapel in what must have been less than ideal circumstances, nevertheless Fornari did a competent job. Mr. Nelson attended the following morning and impressed upon Dr. Fornari the importance of looking for any embedded metallic objects that would indi-cate that there had been an explosion although it was unlikely that Dr. Fornari would have needed to be reminded of this.

Dr. Fornari carried out fourteen autopsies during 13 and 14 January, the fifteenth body was examined externally but not subjected to an autopsy for religious reasons.[16] His initial findings would have been available to the investigators within a few days. More information was provided later when the histology became available.*

Dr. Fornari's findings were included in a report he prepared for the public inquiry that would follow in the autumn. It was dated 11 May 1954 although it was actually written in April.[17] What follows is a summary of this report. It amounts to what was probably available soon after the autopsies had been carried out although there would have been less time for thought and discussion. Fornari was careful not to speculate, at least in writing, about the causation of injuries that he could not substantiate and none of his findings was later discredited.[18]

The bodies showed similar injuries composed of severe chest trauma, severe head and limb injuries and what looked like scalding, mainly over the back but in one case over the front of the body. He divided the injuries into events that had happened during life, i.e. the traumatised tissues showed evidence of bleeding, and those that happened after death, which did not. The chest injuries had happened during life and had usually been the cause of death. Some of the head injuries had also occurred during life and had

---

* Histology is the study of tissues at microscopic, i.e. cellular, level. The tissues have to be processed over a few days (longer for the brain) for this to take place and the results are often provided after the macro-scopic findings have been reported. It can reveal important information about what has happened to a par-ticular part of the body which may not have been suspected before.

either caused death or played a major part in causing death. The limb injuries had occurred after death. There was no evidence of drowning, implying that the victims were all dead, or at least not breathing, by the time they entered the water. No metallic fragments were found.

Fornari's findings were also summarised in a report written by Sir Harold Whittingham, the head of BOAC's medical services and Group Captain W. K. Stewart from the RAF Institute of Aviation Medicine at Farnborough, dated 21 January.[19] They were somewhat less cautious about speculating and included the following:

1) There was no evidence of internal fire or hot flame such as the burning of clothes or body hair.
2) There were extensive areas of scalding on the covered parts of all the bodies except that of the stewardess.
3) The head injuries were to the top and the back of the head, perhaps as a result of being thrown up against the roof and then falling back.*
4) The ribs were badly broken in ten cases.
5) The people identified as sitting in the rear seats were less badly injured and more completely clothed than those sitting further forward.
6) The loss of clothing was thought to have been caused by being thrown out of the cabin and then descending from a great height.
7) It was assumed that the passengers sitting in the rear of the cabin were only ejected at a low altitude or when the rear cabin hit the sea.
8) The lungs were damaged in all cases except that of the stewardess, the damage ranged from partial collapse to over distension and rupture. The degree of damage was thought to be more severe than was to be expected from an explosive decompression unless it had been very rapid.** It was most severe in those persons who had been sitting forward of the back two rows of seats.
9) There were severe visceral and spinal injuries compatible with severe trauma.
10) Death was rapid and caused either by the head injury or the other forms of severe trauma or some combination of the two.

This was followed by a suggested sequence of events which postulated that the aircraft had suddenly fallen out of control and the passengers had been flung up against the roof. The aircraft had dived steeply at which time the victims had been scalded by some

---

* Lap seat belts for passengers became compulsory in British aircraft after the crash of the Empire class flying boat Courtier off Athens in 1937[20] but it is unlikely that many, if any, of the passengers in YP were wearing them at this stage of the flight.

** If the ambient pressure is suddenly reduced to any extent the volume of gas within closed, or semi-closed, body cavities, such as the middle ear or the lungs, expands and may cause significant organ damage. This phenomenon is not limited to gas in body cavities. The young Peter Masefield, later Sir Peter Masefield and the head of BEA, went to sleep on some semi-inflated aircraft inner tubes when he was travelling in America in an unpressurised aircraft. While he was sleeping the aircraft gained altitude, the inner tubes expanded, and he awoke to find himself pushed up against the roof of the cabin and unable to move until the aircraft descended. He described it as being "not unpleasant."[21]

hot fluid, perhaps hydraulic fluid. The wings failed during the dive and a fire had developed causing the fuel tanks to explode. The fuselage had then broken at the rear of the main spar and tipped the forward passengers out at some height. They concluded that explosive decompression was not a primary event, but had followed from other events.

All in all it was an accurate account of the post-mortem findings followed by a series of what turned out to be inaccurate and misleading conjectures for which there was little, if any, real evidence.

In the latter part of February Dr. Fornari travelled to London to discuss his findings with Sir Harold, Group Captain Stewart and Dr. Donald Teare, a forensic pathologist of some distinction at St. Georges Hospital in London. (Brabazon called him "the best pathologist in the country... a sort of modern Spilsbury."[22]) Teare wrote to Group Captain Tweedie on 5 March after taking part in several meetings about the post-mortem findings and their interpretation. By this time the lung histology was available and showed areas of emphysema* and atelectasis** in all fourteen specimens, which Teare thought had been caused by "violent decompression due to perforation of the fuselage at height." Dr. Fornari had also taken specimens of heart muscle for histology. He described extensive tears both longitudinal between the cells and transversely across them (see Chapter 20). The skin 'burns' were still a bit of a mystery.[23]

There were also legal consequences to the crash. Although not accused of negligence BOAC would be obliged to provide compensation for the dependents of the victims of the crash. The maximum amount of compensation was determined by the Warsaw Convention of 1929 which laid down a figure of 125,000 French Francs

---

* Emphysema is the enlargement of the alveolae (air sacs) in the lungs caused by the breakdown of the walls between them. In normal medical practice it is a chronic disease commonly seen in the lungs of older cigarette smokers and is usually associated with an increase in the total volume of the lungs. Although the word used in the reports was "emphysema" in this context it was assumed to have been produced by a sudden and large increase of gas volume within the alveolae, produced by an equally sudden and severe fall of ambient pressure, which caused disruption of the alveolar walls. There was probably also an element of interstitial emphysema where the air (strictly speaking alveolar gas) had expanded out of the alveolae into the spaces between the alveolar walls causing them to become distended. Fornari's report says: "wide cavities resulting in rupture of alveolar walls."[18] If the volume increase is large enough, this gas tracks to the hilum (root) of the lung, then into the mediastinum (the area between the two lungs) and up into the neck. It can also move in the opposite direction to form blisters (bullae) on the surface of the lung which may burst to release gas into the pleural cavity (a pneumothorax) and even leak into the circulation to form air emboli.[24] None of these sequelae was mentioned in the report but it was unlikely that they would have been found unless they were specifically looked for, for example by performing the relevant parts of the autopsy under a small volume of water and watching for gas bubbles to escape. In any case some of the the severe thoracic injuries might have obliterated any sign of a preceding pneumothorax and perhaps some of the other sequelae.

Alternatively the emphysema could have been caused by the blast wave from a chemical explosion. This is known to produce alveolar distension and rupture and is associated with extensive haemorrhaging,[25] which was also seen here, but there was no other evidence of a chemical explosion.

** Atelectasis is an area of alveolar collapse, the opposite to emphysema. If the volume of lung stays the same the volume of over expansion is balanced by the loss of volume of the collapsed zones. If the total lung volume increases, which would be likely in these circumstances, particularly if the chest wall was disrupted, the increase in volume of the emphysema exceeds the loss of volume of the atelectasis.

Poincaré. This was defined by a given mass of gold of a given purity but in 1954 amounted to about £6,000[26] (approximately £143,000 in 2013). BOAC also refunded the unused part of the passengers' tickets, they would have to pay for the part of the flight they had completed.[27] In December that year a claim for compensation of $200,000 was made against BOAC and de Havillands by the relatives of Mrs. D. B. Baker.*[28]

The day after the crash BOAC grounded its Comet fleet. Peter Duffey, a BOAC Comet pilot at that time, said in the Principal Films documentary that, "Everybody knew that this was something which should ground the aeroplane until the facts were known. This was unanimous, the government, the airline, the pilots, everybody knew that there was something here that had to be discovered."[29]

---

* The same claim was made at the same time by the relatives of Mr. R. L. Wilkinson who died in the Naples crash (see Chapter 15).

Chapter 13

THE DECISION TO RESUME FLYING

At this juncture BOAC had a serious problem. Not only had their star aircraft just dropped to pieces and fallen into the Mediterranean for some reason or reasons unknown, but they had several other items of identical, and very expensive, hardware sitting around the world, not earning money, indeed consuming money, as well as idle crew, and passengers they were contracted to transport. They must also have been worried about the travelling public losing confidence in the Comet, which they had spent a lot of money building up, and perhaps even losing trust in the airline itself. The Comets' grounding may have been voluntary, and their Certificates of Airworthiness not withdrawn, but they were commercially unusable unless confidence was restored. The corporation urgently had to produce a mechanism for deciding what to do next.

On the day that the Comets were grounded Sir Miles Thomas, the Chairman of BOAC, called a meeting at London Airport. This resulted in a committee being set up under the chairmanship of Charles Abell, the BOAC Deputy Operations Director (Engineering), in effect the head of engineering, to consider the possible causes of the disaster and what might be done to correct them.[1] This was not an investigation into the cause of the accident as such, that would be carried out by the Accident Investigation Branch,* it was more a means of deciding whether the aircraft could be safely put back into service and how this might be achieved. The final decision about whether it could resume commercial service would best be taken by the minister on advice from the Air Registration Board (ARB) and the Air Safety Board (ASB) but at least it would move things along. The Abell Committee, as it became known, included representatives from the de Havilland aircraft and engine companies, the AIB and the ARB. Also, about this time, the minister announced that the crash would be the subject of a public inquiry in due course.[2]

The Abell Committee held numerous meetings, at first almost daily.[3] Their work divided into four parts: the inspection of the remaining aircraft in the BOAC Comet fleet, the consideration of factors that might have caused the crash, deciding whether any modifications were necessary and, if they were, seeing that they were carried out. The committee evolved a detailed inspection programme for the remaining aircraft as well as an investigation of any components and systems that might be implicated. Much of this work was carried out by de Havillands or by the component manufacturers themselves.

---

* After the Naples crash the AIB was largely displaced by the RAE investigation.

The following causes were considered the most likely:

1) Flutter of the control surfaces, possibly exacerbated by the failure of the hydraulic control systems.
2) Primary structural failure, perhaps caused by turbulence although there were no reports of this at the time.
3) Malfunctioning of the flying controls.
4) Fatigue of the structure, particularly the wings. This area was considered the most likely to develop fatigue as cracks had been found on the undersurface of the wings of the prototype near the edge of the wheel-wells.
5) Explosive decompression of the cabin, particularly from the window panels.
6) Fire caused by the engines. This was thought the most likely cause of the crash[4] although it is difficult to see how it could have caused a catastrophe so abrupt that it stopped the pilot's transmission in mid-sentence.

A modification had already been devised to prevent rudder flutter and this had been carried out on the BOAC aircraft and was made mandatory for the others. No other significant control surface defect was found. The investigation into primary structural failure was mainly concentrated on the possibility of a fracture at the insulating box at the base of the fin, the over-stressing of a wing leading to its breaking off and the failure in some way of the fuselage. Some failures of the Redux joints between the skin and the stringers on the underside of the rear fuselage were found and were thought to have been caused by vibrations from the jet efflux. These joints were subsequently riveted. No faults could be demonstrated in the flying controls but the opportunity was taken to make some modifications to them and to the automatic pilot. The fatigue testing of the prototype's wing was underway at Farnborough and cracks had already become apparent. This prompted detailed inspections of the wings of the aircraft in the fleet which revealed more cracks. These were repaired and strengthening modifications put in place. A more detailed examination was made of the two aircraft in the fleet with the greatest numbers of flying hours (YY and YU) which even went as far as removing their tailplanes. No other fatigue cracks were found although a number of small cracks had been found during service in the fuselage skin of several aircraft, mainly around the passenger doors. They were thought to be unimportant and to have been caused by the passenger stairs.[5]

It was appreciated that the various fuselage cutouts were the most likely cause of any explosive decompression and YY and YU were examined closely with this in mind. The paint was removed from around all the fuselage cutouts, including the ADF and cockpit windows, to make inspection easier. The cockpit window structure and several cabin windows were then removed completely for examination. The only significant finding was that one cockpit window was twisted but it was unclear whether it had been fitted in that way or had become twisted in service. In any case tests failed to show that it was in any way weakened.[6]

The committee was told of the preliminary medical findings on 13 January by Dr. Peffers, one of the BOAC doctors, on his return from Italy. This indicated that a fairly large explosion had taken place. In the light of this they decided that "while not giving up any of the other investigations all concerned should concentrate on the possibility of explosions in either the equipment bay or the centre tank area." By this they meant the ignition of explosive material, not the sudden release of cabin pressure from a breach of fuselage skin integrity. Tests were carried out on the electrical systems of a third BOAC Comet (YS) and modifications introduced to reduce the chance of them providing a source of ignition. There were also concerns about the hydraulic fluid, a castor oil derivative, leaking under pressure and forming an inflammable, and possibly explosive, aerosol under the cabin floor. The conclusion reached was that it was about as inflammable as kerosene and modifications were made to reduce the chance of a leak, to screen the electrical cables and to ventilate any closed spaces in which an aerosol could accumulate.[7]

The last area considered by the committee, and the one thought by them to be the most important, was the possibility of a structural failure in an engine or a fire in the engine compartments. The most likely event was a turbine disc or blade fracturing and then forcing its way through part of the aircraft. So far as was known this had not happened previously in a Ghost engine but one turbine disc from the Calcutta crash had never been found. A team was dispatched to the site of the crash to see if they could be more successful. They discovered the disc by digging in the mud underneath the place where the engines had been recovered.[8] All the rotating parts of the Calcutta engines had now been found and showed no signs of failure. Even so steel plates were added to the engine compartments to reduce the chance of blade penetration.[9] The engines from the Elba crash were recovered before the Comet flights were resumed and showed no sign of being the cause of the accident.[9]

Witnesses to the crash had reported that the wreckage was on fire as it entered the sea. It was unclear at this stage which part of the wreckage this was but the most likely area was in or near the fuel tanks. These were just next to the hot engines and any fire here was most likely to be a secondary event caused by the structures being disrupted, a common occurrence in air crashes. Nevertheless the committee considered that there was a strong possibility that a fire could have started here and been the cause of the whole disaster. Four sets of modifications were made in this area: to reduce the chance of any fire occurring, to increase the likelihood of it being detected if it did start, to extinguish any fire and to reduce the chance of it spreading.

In all more than 50 modifications were carried out, the cabins were pressure-tested to 11 psi and then flight tests completed the programme.

Representatives of the BOAC crews, including Captain Cane the Comet Flight Superintendent, had been involved in these meetings. There had also been two meetings with the Comet crews and their unions to discuss progress although the presence of cracks in the aircraft was not mentioned. At neither of these meetings had the unions asked that the Comets stay grounded. At the meeting on 23 January Abell said that he thought it unlikely that much more wreckage of YP would be recovered[10] but towards the end of March he had changed his mind[11] as wreckage continued to be retrieved and he was advised that there was a strong possibility that more would appear.

On 17 February the committee's findings and the details of the aircraft inspections and modifications were forwarded to the operations director of BOAC together with the recommendation that it was safe to resume passenger-carrying flights. On the 19th they were sent on to the Ministry of Transport and Civil Aviation with a covering letter from Sir Miles Thomas saying that if no further information about the cause of the crash emerged prior to the completion of the inspections and modifications they believed that all steps considered as possible (to make the aircraft safe) would have been taken and that when they have been approved by the ARB then "we submit that the resumption of service by the aircraft should be approved." They would need at least two and a half weeks to set things in motion again and they "would like to have your decision by the middle of next week if possible." By the side of this on the original letter is written in ink "Not possible".[12] Before he took any decision the minister sought advice from the ARB and the ASB.

The Air Registration Board was a limited company set up to supervise civil aircraft design, manufacture and maintenance and it derived its income from the industry by these activities. Its council was made up from four representatives from the manufacturers, four from the airlines, four from the insurance world, one nominated by the minister, one pilot and four non-specialists. It had a total staff of about 300 which included some 125 technical staff, of whom about 84 were involved in inspections. Its chairman was Lord Brabazon who later made a memorable appearance at the public inquiry. Given the task of helping to decide what to do Brabazon, in a letter to Lennox-Boyd dated 24 February, admitted that "...the decision as to whether or not to resume Comet services is extremely tricky."[13]

The ARB, in their deliberations, were in full contact with the Abell Committee and approved of their actions. Its conclusions were expressed in a letter that Brabazon wrote to the minister on 4 March in which he said "...I am now able to tell you that the Board has given the fullest consideration to the Comet situation and has reviewed in detail the work of all parties to the investigations which have been undertaken. Although no definite reason for the accident has been established modifications have been embodied to cover every possibility that imagination has suggested as a likely cause of the disaster. When these modifications are completed and have been satisfactorily flight tested the Board sees no reason why passenger services should not be renewed."[14]

The other body consulted was the Air Safety Board. The chairman of this was Air Chief Marshall Sir Frederick Bowhill who had been in the post since its formation in 1946. It was a small group with no statutory powers and reported directly to the minister to provide advice on matters of air safety such as reviewing the consequences of crashes. Apart from the chairman it had four other members which included Lord Brabazon and Dr. Arnold Hall, the Director of the RAE at Farnborough. It had no technical staff of its own.[15]

The ASB met on 2 March to discuss what advice they should give the minister. At this meeting Mr. Tye from the ARB was present and they were provided with all the information that the ARB held about the inspections and modifications of the aircraft and the discussions held with de Havillands and BOAC. Dr. Hall presented some of the medical information; the severe injuries pointed towards an explosion and the scalds towards the leakage of hydraulic fluid. After some discussion the board members considered that it was likely that the Comet had broken up in mid air, that no cause had yet been found and that it might be months or years before all the investigations were complete. They appreciated that while there was a "natural reluctance to continue flying the Comets in the light of *two* (author's italics) unexplained disasters, any decision to ground the aircraft would have extraordinary [sic] important repercussions. In the light of all the information they and the Board felt they were not justified in recommending such a step, and in view of the modifications being carried out the members considered that the Minister should be advised to allow [the] Comets to return to normal service."[16]

The conclusions of this meeting were expressed in a minute issued by them to the minister on 5 March. After saying that they had considered all the available information it continued, "It [the Board] realises that no cause has yet been found that would satisfactorily account for the Elba disaster, and whilst the Calcutta disaster is completely accounted for if the aircraft is supposed to have encountered a gust of very great severity (which would have broken any other aircraft) we cannot eliminate that the accident might have been due to some other cause which was possibly common to both disasters. Nevertheless the Board realises that everything humanly possible has been done to ensure that the desired standard of safety shall be maintained. This being so the Board sees no justification for imposing special restrictions on Comet aircraft. The Board therefore recommends that Comet aircraft should return to normal operational use after all the current modifications have been incorporated and the aircraft have been flight tested."[17] This minute, which was intended only for the minister, contained one or two time bombs that, in due course, counsel would detonate during the public inquiry to come.

In view of the advice received from the ASB and the ARB the minister gave permission for flights to be resumed and passenger services were restarted on 23 March.

The purpose of the Abell Committee was to consider the possible causes of the Elba crash and to suggest modifications to the existing aircraft so as to have some chance of getting approval for restoring the Comet service. The role of the ASB and the ARB, as disinterested and independent bodies, was to check that this was reasonable and that the Comets were safe for passengers to fly in them again. The investigation of the crash by the AIB was still proceeding. The enquiries in Elba and Rome had been completed and they had received the preliminary medical findings and arranged for them to be reviewed by Dr Teare. The salvage operation had started and arrangements had been made for the wreckage to be removed to Farnborough. Group Captain Tweedie, the Chief Inspector of Accidents, in cross-examination at the later inquiry, said that he was not consulted by the ARB or the ASB[18] but any significant finding would surely have found its way to all the interested parties fairly rapidly. At this point there was no thought of the massive investigation and inquiry that was to develop and overtake Tweedie's investigation.

Some time before the flights were resumed Captain Cane, the senior BOAC pilot who had been involved in the Abell Committee meetings, made a rather stiff appearance in an interview for a news film. He expressed the view that "...we have a very good aeroplane and always have had." He added, "all the other pilots are only too keen to get back into service." But behind the scenes the Comet crews were rather less confident. A meeting of all the Comet crews was held in a hanger at London Airport and the chairman of the pilots' local council asked for a show of hands to indicate whether they were prepared to go back to flying the Comets. The vote was evenly split among the 140 crew present and had to be repeated. In the end the decision to resume flying was carried by a majority of one.[19] Sixteen days after flights were resumed, on 8 April, Comet G-ALYY, on charter to South African Airways, crashed in the sea near Naples.

Chapter 14

THE FINAL DISASTER

Once again the point of departure was Rome Ciampino, an airport that seemed to have dire consequences for the Comet fleet. This time the direction of flight was south towards Cairo, on the second leg of a journey from London to Johannesburg. Arrangements had been made some time before for this route, the first of the Comet schedules, to be shared between BOAC and SAA. The South African crews had been trained by BOAC and some of the Comets were leased to SAA and flown with their crews.

Yoke Yoke had a crew of seven and was carrying fourteen passengers. In common with the rest of the Comet fleet it had been grounded after the Elba crash. It had been one of the two Comets to experience a particularly close inspection and had then received the modifications put forward by the Abell Committee. Following this the fuselage had undergone a pressure test to 11 psi on 15 February and had been passed as fit for service on the 24th. On 2 April YY had received a Check 1 inspection* and been issued with a Certificate of Maintenance valid for 75 flying hours. At the time of the accident YY had flown 2,704 hours and was within the 75 hours of the maintenance certificate.[1]

Captain Willem Mostert had learned to fly in the South African Air Force and had joined SAA in 1946 and became a flying instructor in 1949. He had risen steadily to become a senior captain in May 1953. In June that year he had transferred to Comets and became a Comet line instructor. Within the last six months he had flown 86 hours in Comets. In all respects he appeared to be an outstanding pilot. The second pilot, Barent Grove, had also learned to fly in the South African Air Force and had flown some 47 hours in Comets during the preceding 90 days. Neither pilot had been involved in any accidents.[2]

The Comet had arrived at Ciampino at 17:35 on 7 April and was due to depart that evening but after refuelling it was noticed that the gauge for the central tank showed no reading although the tank was known to be full. The fault was eventually traced to a co-axial cable and arrangements were made to fly out a spare from the UK. Rather alarm-

---

* The Comet 1 had a regular maintenance schedule based on a two year cycle which assumed a total of about 4,800 flying hours. There were four checks: check 1 at 75 hours, check 2 at 150, check 3 at 300 and check 4 at 1,200. Check 1 was the most minor and involved en external examination of the whole aircraft for damage, a functional check of all the systems and services and the putting right of any faults reported by the flight crews which had not already been corrected.[3]

ingly, during the process of tracing the fault, a number of bolts were found lying free
within the port wing. Closer inspection revealed an equal number of bolts missing from
an inspection panel in the underside of the same wing. It was also noticed that even the
bolts that were in place were not fully tightened. This had presumably been the case
since the Check 1 inspection on 2 April. Luckily the panel seemed not to have been distorted and the missing bolts were replaced and the others tightened. The inspectors
involved were later disciplined.[4]

Yoke Yoke took off from Ciampino at 18:32 the following day, 8 April. At 18:57 the
flight-deck crew reported that they were level with Naples and were climbing to 35,000
feet. The weather was cloudy but without any significant turbulence. At 19:05 Cairo
received a signal from them giving their estimated time of arrival and saying that they
were still climbing. The cruising height in the flight plan was 35,500 feet and the pilot
was asked to report when they reached this height. No further message was received
and all subsequent attempts to make contact failed. From the position that the bodies
and wreckage were later found, it appears that Yoke Yoke suffered some sort of mid-air
catastrophe at about 19:10.

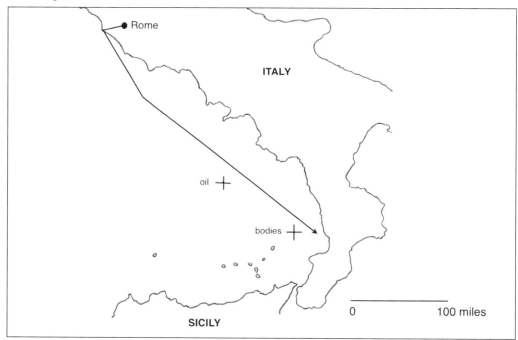

Fig. 1/14 The approximate flight path of G-ALYY on 8 April 1954

The following day HMS *Eagle*, an aircraft carrier, and HMS *Daring*, a destroyer, as
well as some American and Italian aircraft, started a search. At 08:30 four Avengers
were flown off followed by another four half an hour later together with two Sky
Raiders. They searched the likely area for about three and a half hours without success.
After a quick lunch the search was resumed and at about 15:00 a message from an

unidentified aircraft was intercepted by *Eagle* which said that wreckage and some bodies had been sighted. The unidentified aircraft turned out to be a BEA Elizabethan. *Eagle's* aircraft were diverted to the spot and found an oil slick, several bodies and a large collection of floating debris. *Eagle* and *Daring* set course for the area but *Daring* was delayed by investigating some other debris and almost as the *Eagle* reached the area she had to divert to land-on one of the Avengers that was running short of fuel. By the time the boats were launched to start the search and retrieval it was getting dark and most of the work had to be done with the aid of the ships' searchlights and flares dropped by two Shackletons. Nevertheless six bodies were recovered as well as some floating wreckage which included two mail bags.[5]

Four of these bodies were examined by Dr. Teare at Uxbridge on 12 April, one was not subjected to an autopsy and the other was examined by the Italian authorities. The findings of Teare's autopsies were consistent with those of the Elba crash with severe head and chest injuries suggesting that the passengers had been violently flung upwards and forwards. The lungs had numerous emphysematous bullae on their surfaces and the histology showed extensive emphysematous changes. There was no comment about the heart muscle. Tests for carboxyhaemoglobin in the blood of three of the victims proved negative showing that they had not inhaled carbon monoxide from smoke.[6] These findings led to the conclusion that the causes of the two crashes had been the same or very similar. On 18 April, after some heavy seas, another body was washed up on the beach of San Lucido.

The depth of water in the search area varied between about 520 and 580 fathoms (3,120 and 3,480 feet); too deep for any realistic hope of retrieving wreckage from the sea floor although the famous Professor Piccard offered the use of his bathyscaphe. It was politely declined, the problem being that the location of the wreckage was too vague for it to be practical.[7] Any conclusions about this crash would have to be extrapolated from the Elba crash.[4]

On receiving the news of the crash BOAC grounded its Comet fleet for the second time in three months, this time for good, and on 12 April the Comet's Certificate of Airworthiness was withdrawn. Perhaps showing more prescience Air France had avoided this by grounding their Comets permanently after the Elba crash. BOAC once again faced the problem of getting stranded passengers to their final destinations with the minimum of delay and returning to the UK the aeroplanes that had been left scattered along the Comet routes. After a delay of about three weeks YW was flown back unpressurised* to London from Colombo and YX similarly from Cairo. Others were at their various bases in the UK and stayed there until their fates could be decided. Aircraft had to be found to replace the Comets on their routes as well as dealing with the public relations disaster of their star performer crashing, again.

The tragedy of the Naples crash reached even Churchill, then in the very twilight of his political career. Lord Moran, Churchill's physician, recorded in his diary on 8 April

---

* This was before the reason for the Comet crashes had been determined but there were already suspicions about the pressure cabin. See Walker's memorandum to Tweedie dated 15 April 1954 in Chapter 18.

1954, "When I saw Winston this morning he said, 'It is sad about the loss of the Comet. So much of our reputation abroad seems to depend on them.'" Unfortunately, as the conversation continued, the depth of Churchill's sadness was revealed to be somewhat shallower than it had first appeared. He continued, "'The result of the by-election (at Edinburgh East) is disappointing. It is bad; we thought we might win.' He grinned, 'It distresses me more than the Comet.'"[8]

The British authorities now had to deal with the consequences of a second mid-air catastrophe, which appeared almost identical to the first for which no definite explanation had yet been found. It was of utmost importance to the civil aircraft industry, not only in Britain but also the rest of the world, that the cause be found. The Minister of Supply, now Duncan Sandys, instructed Dr. Arnold Hall, the Director of the RAE at Farnborough, to carry out an investigation in collaboration with BOAC and the manufacturer. This was to become one of the longest, most detailed and most exhaustive air accident investigations ever carried out. It was also of a type unlikely to be seen again; testing a whole aircraft to destruction and using real models instead of computer models to test hypotheses. Unlike today there was no flight telemetry, flight data recorders or cockpit voice recorders to provide important, early, reliable and easy-to-obtain information or computer simulations to test theories, but in spite of this, the investigation would provide a convincing explanation for the Comet disasters.

Chapter 15

THE ROYAL AIRCRAFT ESTABLISHMENT INVESTIGATION STARTS

D r. Hall had had something of a glittering career, managing to combine being an academic scientist, an aeronautical engineer, a civil servant and later an industrialist and to excel in all of them. He was born in Liverpool in 1915, the son of an upholsterer. From his high school he won a scholarship to Cambridge where he took a first in the engineering tripos as well as winning, with distinction, the three chief prizes: aeronautics, applied mechanics and heat engines. While he was at Cambridge he collaborated with Frank Whittle on the latter's gas turbine, helping to design its diffuser.[1] In 1938 he moved to Farnborough as a principal scientific officer where he developed the gyroscopic gunsight used by the RAF during the war. In 1945 he became the Zaharoff Professor of Aviation at Imperial College, London but returned to the RAE as its director in 1951 at the age of 36; its youngest ever director. He became Sir Arnold in 1954 and moved on from Farnborough in 1955 to become the technical director of Hawker Siddeley and ultimately its chairman. He died in 2000.[2]

The Royal Aircraft Establishment was part of the scientific civil service and was controlled by the Ministry of Supply. It had several branches but its largest, and best known, was at Farnborough, a few miles to the south west of London. It was a large establishment that had grown out of the Royal Aircraft Factory (the original 'RAF') in the First World War. It had its own airfield, aircraft, wind tunnels and extensive research and test facilities as well as a group of talented and respected scientists and engineers. It did not manufacture aircraft but existed to do original research in aviation and to investigate specific problems, such as crashes, that had arisen in the industry. Its primary role was to deal with military aircraft but it was the obvious choice for such an important investigation. It has now virtually disappeared as a research establishment although some of the original buildings still exist. A few defence and other high-tech companies have taken up residence there as well as the National Aerospace Library. The airfield still exists and is used mainly for business flights and the bi-annual air show. BAE Systems, the successor to de Havillands, has a large office complex nearby.

The RAE investigation started in mid-April 1954 and was completed by September, forming the basis of the Court of Inquiry that was to follow. It was an impressive piece of work, scientifically robust and carried out in an amazingly short time. Their findings were compiled into a large, comprehensive and highly-illustrated report of more than 700 pages from which most of the following account is derived. It was, and still is, a model of accurate and concise writing which would be hard to improve upon. It is the perfect antidote to the sort of baseless speculation that often goes on after air crashes and indeed went on after the Comet crashes.* For the purposes of this account the report, of necessity, has been considerably abridged and some of its twelve parts combined.

Inevitably there is some repetition in the chapters that follow. The causes of the crashes were described and discussed in some detail in the RAE report, the same ground was then raked over in the public inquiry that followed, with some parts expanded and some new, and occasionally dissenting, opinions added. The same topics were then covered for a third time in the report that followed the inquiry, together with the Court's conclusions and the ways they had been reached. There is also some information about stress and its application to airframes in Appendix 5.

When the RAE investigation started on 12 April 1954 only limited information was available. Some pieces of Yoke Peter had been recovered and transported to Farnborough and Hatfield. These included the floating wreckage picked up by the fishermen soon after the crash, the pressure dome and parts of the rear fuselage. The engines and the centre section of the wings followed and shortly afterwards the front part of the fuselage. It now seemed likely that other parts would follow but there was little prospect of recovering much from Yoke Yoke.

The first step was to review the findings of the Abell Committee in the light of the fact that there had been another, seemingly identical, crash.

The possibilities that had been raised by the Abell Committee were:

1) Flutter of the control surfaces.
2) Primary structural failure, perhaps caused by turbulence.
3) Malfunctioning of the flying controls.
4) Fatigue of the structure, particularly the wings.
5) Explosive decompression of the cabin, particularly the window panels.
6) Fire caused by the engines.

It was apparent that flight tests would be necessary to check the control systems to see whether flutter could develop or if they could malfunction in some other way. There were no reports of the bad weather or turbulence that had been used to explain the Calcutta crash but there was certainly concern about fatigue problems with the wings. Explosive decompression of the cabin also seemed to be a possibility. Dr. P. B. Walker, Head of the Structures Department at Farnborough, was struck by the similarities between the two crashes.[3] Both incidents appeared to have happened when the aircraft

---

* Sir Miles Thomas, in a letter to Arnold Hall dated 14 April 1954, mentions that he had received, to date, "462 foolish letters suggesting reasons for the Comet crashes ranging from... conflict between volcanic ash over Italy and radio-active particles blown over from the H-bomb to death rays sent up by spiritual guardians of the ancient Roman civilisation."[4]

had just reached, or nearly reached, their cruising height i.e. the point at which the pressure differential between the inside and the outside of the cabin wall reached its maximum for the first time. Fire as a primary event could be investigated by examining the wreckage and anyway the modifications suggested by the Abell Committee seemed to make this unlikely in the second crash and the medical evidence was also against it.

There would have to be several lines of investigation some of which would inevitably prove to be fruitless. The first, and most obvious, would be to examine the pieces of wreckage as they appeared at Farnborough and use them to reconstruct the aircraft as far as possible. The second would be to carry out flight tests with some of the remaining Comet 1s and the third would be to do tests to determine the static and fatigue strengths of the wings, tailplane and fuselage but these would take some time to set up and carry out. As well as these there would be medical investigations, fuel tank pressure tests and tests using flying and non-flying models of the Comet. For the sake of clarity this account will mainly follow the particular lines of investigation, which were in any case progressing roughly in parallel, rather than a strict chronological sequence.

One of the earliest sets of evidence was the medical findings. The autopsy reports for the Elba crash were already available and those from the Naples crash soon followed and have been discussed above. The RAF Institute of Aviation Medicine at Farnborough reviewed them but had little to add to the sequence proposed by Fornari and Teare.[5] Most of the victims had died from chest injuries, perhaps caused by hitting the back of the seats in front, and then received injuries to the top of their heads, probably from hitting the roof of the cabin, before falling back again. Nearly all had lung damage thought to be compatible with explosive decompression or overpressure. There were also extensive postmortem internal injuries and limb fractures, although there were few facial injuries, lacerations and traumatic amputations to limbs. This suggested that the victims were ejected from the cabin fairly soon after the primary event and received their injuries from hitting the surface of the sea rather than tumbling about in a confined, furnished and probably damaged space. The absence of any signs of drowning and burning was also noted.

There was only one previously recorded case of explosive decompression that they were aware of and this was thought to have been complicated by the subject voluntarily holding his breath and therefore producing an unusual pattern of injury. There was some evidence from animal experiments to suggest that explosive decompression produced the same type of lung damage as that seen in the Comet victims. Against this was the feeling that the loss of structural integrity would have needed to be extremely rapid and complete to produce the effects that it had. An alternative explanation was an explosive overpressure such as from a mist explosion. There was some wartime experience of this but the bodies showed no signs of flash burns or missile injury. Another possibility was the effect on the body of hitting the sea's surface. This was known to produce a shock wave which travelled through the lungs causing a blast-type injury. Some animal work showed that very similar lung damage was produced in these circumstances and was associated with the type of abdominal trauma seen in the Naples

Fig. 1/15 Model cabin used to demonstrate the effects of explosive decompression, from RAE report, Part 11, Fig. 1, (FAST, Farnborough Air Sciences Trust)

victims. The view of the Institute of Aviation Medicine was that it was impossible to distinguish between the effects of explosive decompression and impact with the sea and that it was likely that both had contributed to the final picture.

It was uncertain whether the massive loss of cabin integrity would be powerful enough to blow people out of their seats. Arranging a full scale experiment with dummies would be expensive, dangerous and take some time to set up but a small scale one might do. A Perspex $\frac{1}{10}$ scale model of the Comet fuselage was constructed at Farnborough to reproduce the events that would happen if the cabin roof burst.*[6]

The timing and the sequence of the different parts of the RAE investigation were not included in the report but it seems likely that this experiment was carried out fairly late in the sequence when the evidence from the wreckage suggested that the failure was in the roof of the cabin and towards the front of the aircraft.

The model cabin contained seats of $\frac{1}{10}$ scale size and weight and some similarly-scaled passengers. The whole model was put into a pressure chamber evacuated to represent an altitude of 40,000 feet and the interior of the cabin pressurised to produce a differential of 8.25 psi. The top of the cabin was then made to burst in the same place

* This topic was omitted from the report of the RAE investigation contained in AVIA 6/22292 in the National Archives and is not listed in the index to Part 11. This version also omits Part 12, (Note on the medical aspects) which again is not listed in the main index. AVIA 6/17623 lists Part 12 in its index but contains a note saying that it is closed for 75 years but contains the full version of Part 11. It is difficult to see why either should have been omitted or closed. Fortunately DR 11/112 has part 12.

and to the same extent as YP's was thought to have done and the results filmed. At 0.03 seconds (scaled up to represent the actual time in YP by multiplying the experimental time by the square root of 10) the seat backs were beginning to move forward and the most forward model passenger was also moving in the direction of the burst. At 0.1 seconds the interior of the cabin was in chaos and at 0.6 seconds a model passenger hit the roof with considerable force. At about the same time another passenger was ejected through the defect in the cabin roof. This experiment was meant only as a qualitative demonstration of the probable events at the time of YP's breakup and the timings may not have been accurate but the general picture was highly consistent with the medical findings.

Another puzzle was that the clothes of all the bodies from the Elba crash, except one, were stained yellow. Two samples of clothing were sent for chemical analysis to identify the cause of the discolouration. By this time the yellow colour had disappeared but the cloth was treated with a solvent and the product examined using paper chromatography and ultraviolet fluorescence. The Comet carried various types of fluid such as toilet fluid, beverages, windscreen de-icer, hydraulic fluid and kerosene. The only fluid present in any volume was the kerosene and at the time the bodies had been picked up they had been said to smell of it but no positive identification could be made, perhaps because by this time it had all evaporated.[7]

All but one of the bodies from Elba showed the sort of skin damage seen after scalds or contact with a hot surface rather than having been burned by a flame. Thirteen of the fourteen bodies showed these marks on their backs, the other one on his front. All appeared to have occurred after death. Most of the affected areas of skin had been covered by the yellow-stained clothing they were found in. Three of the victims from the Naples crash showed extensive skin pigmentation. There were sharp demarcation lines between the non-pigmented areas, which had been covered by clothing, and the exposed pigmented areas. There were no signs of burning or scorching of the skin or clothes of any of the victims of either crash.

The two types of skin discolouration appeared to be different and therefore probably had different causes. Various explanations of the skin damage in the Elba crash were suggested and then discounted and it was some time before experimental work produced the most likely explanation. The main difficulty was in explaining the distribution of the scalds, if that was what they were, being mostly on the victims' backs but not at all on their fronts and then one completely the other way around. Various suggestions were made such as that the scalds might have come from burning kerosene at a time when the fuselage was inverted, the victims lying on what had been the ceiling where the kerosene had collected after escaping from ruptured tanks and having caught fire. Another idea was contact with a hot surface, a flash burn or falling through burning fuel but it was unlikely that contact with a hot surface would, in all cases, produce scalding without burning any clothing and that nearly all of the victims would have just their backs affected. Injury on impact with the sea was excluded on the grounds that the bodies from the Naples crash did not show the same damage. Flash burns could be excluded because covered rather then exposed skin was affected. Falling thorough burning kerosene was excluded on similar grounds. Chemical burns from kerosene was excluded by experiments in which kerosene-soaked clothing applied to the skin of freshly dead animals failed to produce the same damage. However if the kerosene floating on the surface of the sea had ignited, which was quite likely as some of the falling aircraft parts were seen to be burning, this might have produced heat damage.

It was found experimentally that a layer of kerosene burning on the surface of water reaches a temperature of about 100°C, rising to over 400° half an inch above the surface and falling to 80°C one quarter of an inch below and not heating the water at all one inch below the surface.[8] The hypothesis that this was the cause of the mysterious scalds was tested at Farnborough by floating dead guinea pigs, dressed in fabric, in a water tank on the surface of which was a layer of burning kerosene. Similar skin lesions to those of the Elba victims were found on the upper surface of the guinea pigs. It also explained their distribution. Most bodies that fall into water but do not sink are found floating face-down with most of the body just below the surface and the limbs hanging down, hence the scalds on their backs where the water was hot. The victim with frontal skin damage was fatter than the others and may have assumed a different posture. The one body that did not show skin damage was assumed to have fallen outside the area of conflagration. The lack of actual burns could be explained by the bodies having been in the water, and therefore having wet clothing, before the fire started.[9]

Against this theory was the fact that the bodies were found over a wide area and no fire on the surface of the sea had been seen by any of the witnesses. However the bodies may well have been dispersed by the wind and waves and the flames of any burning kerosene may have been difficult to see or there may not have been anyone close enough to have seen them for the short time they existed. The cloth binders applied to the guinea pigs also showed a brown coloration which probably explained the similar, although yellow, discolouration of the victims' clothing. On balance kerosene burning on the surface of the sea and heating the water immediately beneath it seemed the best hypothesis.[10]

The pigmentation seen in exposed skin of the Naples victims had a simpler explanation although flash burns and oil contamination were considered and discounted. These bodies had floated in the sea for about 22 hours, some of which was in day light, before being retrieved and it is known that solar skin pigmentation, in other words sunburn, can develop in recently-dead bodies (the Meirowsky phenomenon). This seemed the most likely explanation.[10]

Another puzzle was the partial or complete stripping of the clothes from the bodies. This was thought to be due to the effects of the free fall from around 30,000 feet. To investigate this eight dummy men (Mark V!) were dressed in male clothing and dropped from aircraft flying over military ranges. Two were dropped on rough ground at the Imber range * in the middle of Salisbury Plain, one from 10,000 feet the other

---

* Imber was a village on Salisbury Plain, an area heavily populated by the military in southern England. Its inhabitants were evicted in 1943 to provide a training area for American troops preparing for the invasion of Occupied Europe. It was retained by the British military after the war and its inhabitants not allowed to return.

Fig. 2/15 Dummy man No. 8, turned over in the place where it landed, from RAE report, Part 11, Fig. 17 (FAST, Farnborough Air Sciences Trust)

from 12,000 feet. Three others were dropped from 30,000 feet from a Lincoln bomber in the same area and three more were dropped from 1,200 feet into about ten feet of water at the Pendine range* on the south coast of Wales. The first two lost one shoe between them and the three dropped from 30,000 feet lost one jacket during the descent. When they landed the dummies were travelling at about 150 feet per second (fps) and made depressions in the ground three inches deep. They experienced a mean deceleration of about 1,400 g and, not surprisingly, were quite damaged by the experience. The dummies dropped into water at high tide were similarly damaged and therefore must have experienced similar deceleration. They were seen to be fully clothed at impact with the sea but by the time they were retrieved at low tide their clothing was severely damaged and on the point of coming off completely. The damage was started by the impact and then continued by the action of the waves. The degree of stripping of the crash victims was therefore no indication of their length of free fall except to say that it was at least 1,200 feet. Additional damage to clothing might also have been caused by the event which destroyed the aircraft.[11]

Put together the medical findings suggested that the primary event was a massive explosive decompression caused by the structural failure of the cabin. The rush of air out of the cabin had pushed the passengers, all or most of whom were seated, violently forward and upward either killing or stunning them. At the same time they were exposed to ambient atmospheric pressure at about 30,000 feet, causing their lungs to

---

* Pendine range. Another military acquisition during the war that was never returned afterwards. Before the war it had been used for several attempts on the World Land Speed Record and five records had been made there, three by Malcolm Campbell and two by J. G. Parry-Thomas. The latter was killed during his second attempt.

expand violently. Shortly afterwards they were ejected from the cabin, probably at different altitudes, and then fell into the sea. Impact with the sea then caused a second set of injuries and subsequent loss of clothing. In the Elba crash burning kerosene on the sea's surface heated the water and caused scalds to the clothed parts of the upper surface of the bodies whereas the Naples victims were subjected to strong sunlight and developed pigmentation of exposed skin. The bodies that were not recovered had probably received even more severe injuries, such as large open chest wounds, which had caused them to fill with water and sink. Most of these people had been seated towards the front of YP and may well have received the most severe injuries. In the Naples crash it was thought that most of the passengers had been sitting towards the rear of the aircraft.

The interpretation of the medical findings was essentially no different than before but it was more supported by experimental evidence and, as a result, carried more weight. It also provided an explanation for the scalds which had puzzled Fornari and Teare.

Chapter 16

EXAMINATION OF THE WRECKAGE

Nearly all the wreckage came from the Elba crash and arrived at the RAE at varying intervals and in no particular order. The first parts were the items of floating wreckage picked up soon after the crash which arrived in several consignments starting on 26 January; the rest followed as detailed in Chapter 12. The fuselage wreckage was reassembled as it became available on a wooden frame resembling the Comet in one of Farnborough's hangers.[1] In charge of this was Mr. E. L. Ripley, Head of the Accidents Investigation Section.[2]

Inevitably the damage to the aircraft fragments was the product of the initial event and any resulting fire, combined with the effects of hitting the sea at some speed. More damage was produced by the time spent in the sea and by the process of salvage although this was relatively slight. In spite of all this, important information was slowly gleaned from the material forwarded to Farnborough.

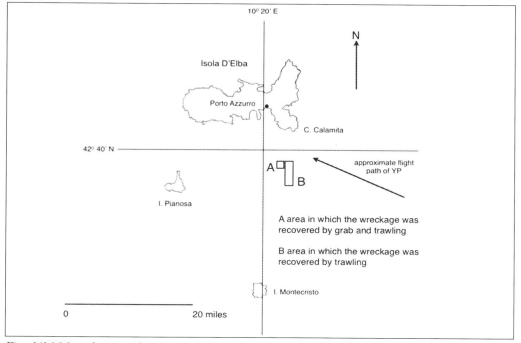

Fig. 1/16 Map showing the areas in which the wreckage of YP was found.

Fig. 2/16 Reconstruction of the fuselage and tail unit of YP at Farnborough, from RAE report, Part 2, Fig. 4 (FAST, Farnborough Air Sciences Trust)

The first tranche of wreckage was found about 5½ miles south of Cape Calamita on Elba. Using the television equipment it was possible to identify pieces of wreckage on the sea bed before hauling them to the surface so the positions of these items could be plotted fairly accurately. Later on when trawling was used it was only possible to get a general idea of the original positions. The parts made from magnesium alloy had corroded badly in the sea water but the damage to aluminium alloy was relatively slight except where it had been in contact with the magnesium. In the end about 80% of the airframe and engines was recovered and some 50% of the equipment and controls; overall about 70% of the weight of the aircraft was salvaged.[3]

The only wreckage recovered from the Naples crash was floating material such as cushions, life jackets and bits of furniture from the cabin, similar to the floating wreckage from the Elba crash. The few items that were retrieved, including the bodies,

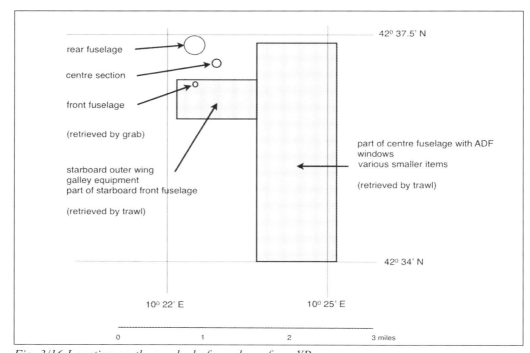

Fig. 3/16 Location on the sea bed of wreckage from YP.

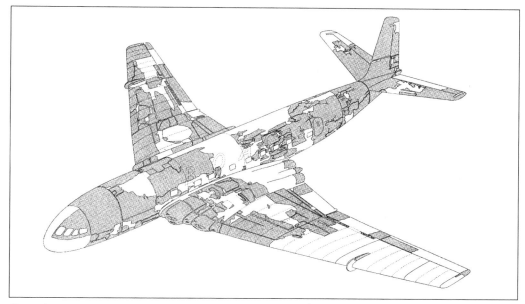

Fig. 4/16 Amount of wreckage recovered from G-ALYP[4] *(FAST, Farnborough Air Sciences Trust).*

showed no signs of burning.[5]

Most of the pieces of wreckage from the Elba crash had been found scattered over a relatively small area. The inference was that the aircraft had either descended intact and then disintegrated on hitting the sea or that it had broken up in mid-air into a few large pieces which had descended more or less together and had only become fragmented after hitting the sea. The latter agreed with the evidence of two of the witnesses on Elba who saw recognisable pieces of aircraft, at least one of which was on fire, falling into the sea.[6] The different patterns of crush damage of the fragments from the Elba crash also supported the idea that the aircraft was not intact when it hit the sea, for example the centre section of the wing was crushed on its upper surface showing that it had separated from the cabin and was inverted on impact whereas the front fuselage was crushed on its lower surface. Fire damage was found only in the wing centre section indicating that it had already separated before the fire started. This fire damage was continuous across several fragments of the centre section showing that it had been on fire during its descent but had then broken up on impact with the sea.[7] Judging from the heat and flame damage to the four rubber fuel tanks and their compartments the fire lasted about three minutes.[8] This was compatible with the fire having started shortly after the accident, an estimated time of descent between two and three minutes and it then being extinguished fairly quickly by the sea. The damage to some of the forgings suggested that the temperature in places must have reached about 680°C. The centre section was presumably the wreckage that was seen by the witnesses to be on fire when it hit the sea.

The impression given by the grouping of the wreckage on the sea bed was that the aircraft had broken up into six large pieces: the fuselage forward of the front spar, the fuselage aft of the rear spar (including the tail), the centre section of fuselage (that part over the wing), the port outer wing, the starboard outer wing and the centre section of the wing complete with engines and undercarriage,[5] not unlike the modules from which it had originally been assembled. The roof of that part of the fuselage over the wing was missing, but would be found later and would prove to be very significant.

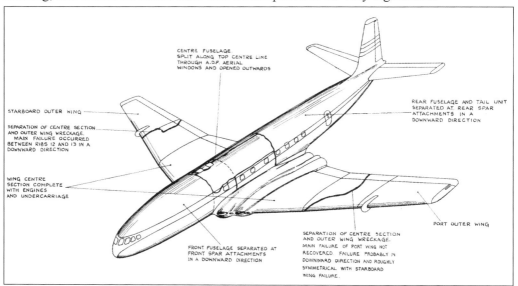

Fig. 5/16 Drawing of G-ALYP showing the location and direction of the main failures,[9] (FAST, Farnborough Air Sciences Trust)

The impact with the sea had caused extensive damage. The centre section of the wing showed evidence of backward bending in the plane of the wing and the remaining fuel in the inner tanks had caused forward bowing of the front walls, both implying that there was forward movement of the section as it hit the water. The rear fuselage section had entered the sea open-end first. At the forward end of this section there was considerable crushing and shattering characteristic of impact with water. The fuselage to the rear of the pressure dome had separated in a downwards direction, probably as a result of the impact, but the dome itself had been pushed off horizontally, presumably blown out by the air pressure generated by water rushing in through the open end and acting like a piston.

The wreckage showed that the mid-air fractures were caused by the downward separations of the front and rear fuselages from the centre section – 'hogging' again. The starboard outer wing (pretty much the extension wing) had separated in a downward direction at the outer end of the outer fuel tank. The evidence for this was a tension fracture of the upper skin, buckling of the lower skin and the failure of the joints in the rear spar at rib 12 in a downward direction associated with a shear failure of the web between ribs 12 and 13. Further evidence came from the aileron control cables breaking in tension as they were pulled downwards over a bracket. The wing folded downwards and under, using the compression buckle as a pivot, and then tore away part of the lower surface of the outer tank, scratching the underside of the wing as far inboard as the undercarriage door. Judging by the fire and water damage the wing finally separated between ribs 10 and 12. Only bits of the port outer wing were found but it also seemed to have separated off in a downward direction in a roughly symmetrical way. The cause of the fractures, however, was not explained by these findings.

There was a fatigue crack at the lower wing skin at the rear edge of the port under-carriage bay. This crack had extended as the wing broke apart and for most of its length it had tension characteristics but there was no evidence that the fatigue part had initiated the break up of the wing. The main undercarriages themselves showed little damage from the incident but were torn out of the centre section by the impact with the sea.[10]

Evidence of a mid-air break-up of the fuselage of some violence was provided by impact marks, scratches and paint traces on the wings. On the upper surface of the inner part of the port wing there were traces of blue, yellow and white paint chemically sim-ilar to the blue band edged with yellow that had been painted along the sides of the white fuselage. The letters BOAC had also been painted along the sides in blue edged with yellow. Combined with the scratch marks on the wing it suggested an impact from a large piece of the centre section of the fuselage moving outwards along the wing at high speed as it had not been blown rearwards by the slipstream. Similar marks were found on some of the fragments of the port outer wing indicating that the wing had been intact when it had been hit. This was confirmed by microscopic examination which showed that the marks had preceded the fractures. The starboard wing had smaller black marks on the leading edge of the wing making it unlikely they could have been made by wing wreckage. The black material probably came from the rubber sealant used in the manufacture of the cabin. These marks, and some scratches, were continu-ous on both sides of the main fracture indicating that they were made before the wing separated.[11, 12]

The rear fuselage had separated in a downwards direction pivoting about its lower pick-up points. There was no fire damage but there were some black marks along the port side which were thought to be rubber from a window or escape hatch. The marks were continuous across a fracture at frame 42 (just forward of the pressure dome) show-ing that they were made before the fracture and were subsequent to a breakup further forward. The close grouping of the wreckage on the sea bed suggested that the tail unit had remained attached to the rear fuselage until it had hit the sea. The pressure dome had been blown out with some force during the impact scattering debris which included carpet, flooring and insulation as well as creating a perfect impression of a one anna coin near the leading edge of the starboard tailplane.[13, 14]

The outer part of the port tailplane appeared to have been struck by another piece of wreckage and had broken off, most likely during the mid-air breakup. A piece of carpet trapped in the fracture suggested that a fragment of fuselage was responsible, probably the port half of bulkhead 18. Judging from the impact marks, blue paint traces and the distribution of the wreckage, the remainder of the tail unit had stayed attached to the rear fuselage until it hit the sea. This blue paint had a different chemical makeup to the paint on the wing and probably came from the seats in the front cabin. These marks were unlikely to have been produced during the descent as the various pieces would have been falling at roughly the same velocity. There were no signs that the tailplane had been subjected to abnormally high loads.[13]

The fin had failed through the wooden insulator box near its base and the rudder had become detached at the same time. There was no evidence that the rudder had exceeded its normal limits of movement. The impact marks on the fin and the absence of much water damage suggested that its separation had come late in the sequence of events, probably after the rear fuselage had hit the water.[15]

These findings suggested that the primary event had been the centre section of the fuselage bursting apart violently, causing its fragments to hit the wings and tailplane with some force before they became separated from the rest of the aircraft. There was no definite explanation of what had caused the central fuselage to explode although there were several possibilities, such as the result of internal stress from excessive cabin pressure or a cabin weakened by metal fatigue or fire damage exploding under normal pressure. Other options included a bomb or excessive structural stresses produced by the fuselage bending or twisting in flight as a result of a violent flying manoeuvre or turbulence. Considered less likely were the consequences of the structural failure of a wing from fatigue, overloading or damage from pressure refuelling, the structural failure of the tail unit or a fire from loose fuel in the wings' trailing edges, but all of them had to be explored.

The possibility of the cabin pressure system building up to a level high enough to exceed the ultimate strength of the fuselage was considered but it was thought that the damage from an explosion at such a pressure (at least 2P) would have been even greater than the damage seen.[16] The fire in the centre section had not damaged a major structural member and appeared to have lasted too short a time to have been the cause rather than the result of the catastrophe and there was no sign of flash damage in the parts of the cabin so far salvaged. No evidence was found in the wreckage of any deposits left by explosive or of missile impact either in the wreckage or the victims. The flying controls and systems indicated that the aeroplane was flying normally when the accident happened. The wing was known to be vulnerable to fatigue and cracks had been found around the wheel housings of the undercarriage in the port wing but the fractures in YP's wings were outboard of the wheels. It remained to be seen whether the pressure refuelling system could cause damage but the wing fractures appeared to be secondary to cabin failure. There was no evidence of the tailplane having failed and it fell into the sea largely intact.

Seats
There were 36 passenger seats, eight in the forward cabin and the rest in the main cabin.

There were six crew seats, four on the flight deck, one in the galley for the steward and one at the rear of the main cabin for the stewardess. Parts of most of the seats in the main cabin were recovered. All of them were severely damaged by an initial forward loading (i.e. being pulled or pushed forward, towards the nose of the aircraft) and then finally pushed backwards and broken away from the cabin floor. The forward loading was thought to have come from a sudden movement of air towards the front of the aircraft during the breakup and the backward loading from the sea rushing into the open end of the rear fuselage after impact. The captain and first officer's seats were identified because they were the only ones fitted with shoulder and waist belts. They were severely damaged and detached from their pedestals which were themselves still attached to the cabin floor. The remains of the engineer's body was held in one of the seats, probably the first officer's, by the waist belt and showed evidence of severe forward loading, presumably on impact with the sea. The reason for his being in this seat became apparent later. Little of the seats in the forward cabin was recovered.[17]

Electrical systems
Most of the equipment from the flight deck had been salvaged and about half that from the equipment bay but little from the rest of the aircraft. Much of what was found had suffered considerable damage consistent with the structural breakup of the aircraft and only limited testing was possible. There was evidence that there was electrical power at the time of the breakup but only a few fuses had 'blown' suggesting that the supply ceased at an early stage and the particular fuses involved indicated that the start of the disruption was in the roof of the centre section of the cabin. No evidence was found of any electrical defect or failure. Similarly the radio equipment appeared to have been functioning normally. Examination of one of the batteries showed no evidence of any overcharging which could have led to excessive hydrogen production leading to an explosion risk.[18]

Controls and instruments
The flying instruments and controls were recovered but were thought to have been so affected by the breakup and what followed that they threw no light on the situation immediately before the disaster and were therefore of no assistance.[19]

Hydraulic system
This provided power for the flying controls, undercarriage, wheel brakes and nose wheel steering. Most of the system was recovered and no evidence was found to suggest any abnormality in its functioning or in the position of the controls just before the accident.[20]

The automatic pilot
The aeroplane was fitted with a Smith's Electric Pilot (type SEP1). Most of the components were recovered but many were severely damaged or corroded. No evidence was

found to suggest any malfunction of the system, nor was it possible to tell whether the system was engaged at the time of the accident.[21]

Cabin pressure system

This system took hot air at high pressure from the diffuser casings of all four engines, passed it through a heat exchanger, humidifier and refrigeration unit and then into the cabin. The cabin temperature and pressure were governed by controllers in the cabin. The controllers operated the two discharge valves in the cabin wall set at a differential of 8.25 psi. In addition there was a safety valve set at 8.5 psi. Two other valves allowed inward air flow if the ambient pressure exceeded the cabin pressure by more than 0.5 psi. Excessive cabin pressure could, in theory, be produced by the discharge and safety valves blocking or the air supply increasing so much that there was insufficient escape through the normally-functioning discharge and safety valves. No evidence was found of any malfunction of the outlet valves, and they were considered to be of a reliable design, and it was found to be impossible for the equipment supplying air to the cabin to overwhelm the valves as long as they were functioning properly.[22, 23]

Fuel tanks

All the fuel tanks were within the wing structure. There were inner and outer integral tanks in the wings and a tank in the central section which contained four interconnected flexible bags. During the mid-air breakup of the aircraft the outer integral tanks were torn open and most of the fuel escaped. The inner tanks were less damaged at this stage and there was evidence from the distortion of the baffles within the tanks that they still contained fuel at impact. Both inner and outer wing tanks were badly damaged by impact with the sea. The four rubber bags in the central section had ruptured on impact with the sea. There was some heat damage consistent with the outside of the compartment walls having been heated to 450-500°C for about three minutes with only slight fire penetration to the starboard side of No. 4 tank. The damage to these compartments was consistent with the damage to the rest of the central section and there was no evidence of primary fire or explosion damage. The remains of the fuel delivery system showed no evidence of any malfunction before the accident.[24]

Tests with components

Although not mentioned in the investigation report, components of Yoke Peter were filmed as they were dropped from balloons to determine their rate of fall. There is also film evidence of YP's tail fin being pushed off the back of a lorry into a pond to discover its rate of descent through water.[25]

Flying models

After the above tests, and no doubt to the delight of the people who would be involved, it was decided that the best way of exploring the breakup of YP and the distribution of its wreckage was by flying scale models of the aeroplane and seeing how they behaved with various parts relevant to the accident removed. The models were made from wood suitably weighted with pieces of metal to raise them to the correct scale weight and were flown at scale speeds.* Six $\frac{1}{36}$ scale basic silhouette models and fourteen $\frac{1}{36}$ scale completely correct models were made as well as four different types of dynamically loaded wing. The $\frac{1}{36}$ scale was chosen because it was the largest that could be launched

Fig. 6/16 Flying model Comet, from RAE report, Part 9, Fig. 3a (FAST, Farnborough Air Sciences Trust).

using a single bungee-powered catapult. The models had a wing span of 3.2 feet and weighed 5.12 pounds.

There were three sets of tests: the first looked at the motion of the aircraft after a particular structural failure had left it with a major part missing, the second looked at the mode and duration of descent of major parts of the aircraft and the third the scatter of these parts on the ground relative to the position of launch after mid-air breakups. The points of fracture of the airframe were suggested by the Accident Investigation Section.

In the first tests the models, each with a particular structural failure, were launched at 91 feet per second from a platform on the roof of a balloon hanger at Cardington in Bedfordshire which had a height of 160 feet. They were filmed as they descended and caught in a net suspended five feet above the ground so they could be used again. The 160 feet fall represented the first 5,760 feet of descent. The time of flight of most of the models was between three and four seconds, equivalent to between 18 and 24 seconds full scale.

With one wing removed from rib seven, and the elevators set to a trimmed climb (-3°), as YP would probably have had at the time of the accident, the models developed a high rate of roll and a large angle of sideslip.** A similar pattern developed with half the tailplane removed as well but if the fin and one wing were removed the model rolled once and descended with its wings at right angles to the horizon. With both wings partially removed the rate of roll was very slow and large angles of sideslip were not developed. Removal of the fin from an otherwise complete model produced

---

* The speed of the launch was $V/n^{1/2}$ where V is the true speed of the aircraft and n is the scale of the model. The weight of the model was $1/pn^3$ where ρ is the relative density of the air at the altitude to be simulated.
** Sideslip is a rotation of the aircraft about its vertical axis, away from the direction of the oncoming airflow, in which the aircraft moves sideways as well as forwards.

inconsistent results.

In order to simulate the descent of large parts of the aircraft from 30,000 feet the wings, part wings and part fuselages were launched by hand from the basket of a balloon tethered at a height of 835 feet. Their descent was filmed and timed by stopwatch. The wings and part wings behaved similarly and if launched with some rotation tended to spin as they descended. Straight launches tended to fall randomly with some tumbling. The rear fuselage with various parts of the tailplane removed also tended to spin during descent but the isolated nose fell randomly with some tumbling. Their full-scale time of descent was calculated to be 2 minutes 25 seconds.

The first launches of the breakup models were from the hanger roof to gain experience and used a silhouette model designed to break up simultaneously into three parts: the wing, the nose and the rear fuselage and tail. The other five launches, using correct models, were made from the ballon at 835 feet. Depending on the test the models were made to breakup into three or four parts by using a tie line 30 feet long which pulled out the two pins holding the model together. As before the parts of the model were filmed as they descended. The places where they landed were then marked and photographed from the balloon. These positions were adjusted to where they would have been without any wind.

In all cases the tail and rear fuselage section descended in a steady spiral while the nose portion descended with a completely random tumbling motion. The wings which had asymmetrical lengths removed tended to spin whereas the symmetrically shortened wings fell randomly sometimes gliding and sometimes tumbling. Whatever the symmetry of the centre wing section it tended to descend in a steady spin as long as some spin was imparted to it at the moment of breakup. Scaling up to full size, the main components would have travelled about 2½ miles in direction of the original flight path before hitting the sea and they would probably have fallen within a circle of three quarters of a mile radius.[26]

The engines

The engines were contained, more or less intact, in the centre section of the wing. Only the turbine disc of the port inner engine (No. 2) was missing and had left through a large hole in the upper casing of the engine in an approximately vertical direction and was never found. Examination showed that it was not rotating at the time and the shaft on which it had been mounted had broken at the flange where the disc was attached. As the centre section had hit the water inverted and its upper surface had been crushed by the impact with the surface the heavy liberated disc had continued in a downwards direction and pushed its way through the casing. The engines were removed and examined superficially by a de Havilland engineer and then sent by air to the company where they arrived on 21 March. They were dismantled and examined in detail by Dr. Moult, the Chief Engineer of the de Havilland Engine Company at Stag Lane.[27]

The engines showed no sign of having seized or failed in any way before the aircraft had broken up. All the signs of fire damage were outside the engines and rubbing marks showed that the engines had continued to rotate for some time before becoming trapped by the distorted shroud rings.* All the compressor impellers and the remaining three turbine discs were intact and were at rest at the time of their impact with the sea but each of the hubs to which the discs were bolted showed cracks and were considered to be on the point of failing. Apart from No. 2 engine there had been no loss of containment of the turbines. The most noticeable thing was the similarity of the damage in each engine which pointed to a common cause.

Assuming that all the engines were running normally at the time of the catastrophe, and there was no reason to assume otherwise, they would have contained considerable rotational kinetic energy. If they continued to rotate they would have exerted a powerful gyroscopic effect tending to maintain their axes of spin in a constant direction. If the wings containing the engines had suddenly rotated downwards, nose first, as they were believed to have done, the gyroscopic couples would have tended to bend the shafts sideways, that is in the plane of the wing.** As the clearance between the tips of the turbine blades and the surrounding case is small, signs of rubbing would be expected and indeed were found in each engine. This confirmed the bending of the shafts which produced the cracks in the hubs. It showed that the engines had not stopped suddenly but had continued to rotate for a short time but the lack of damage to the impeller and blades indicated that they were not turning when they hit the sea. The engines had sustained considerable external damage, mainly to the upper parts of their casings, when they had hit the sea.

These ideas were tested by the company by suspending a Ghost engine from a horizontal beam which was some distance above the engine and at right angles to the longitudinal axis of the engine. This allowed the engine to move back and forth in a vertical plane like a child's swing. The engine was then run at normal speed and pulled backwards (i.e. against the thrust of the engine) and hence rotated upwards. When it was released it accelerated under its own weight and from the thrust it was generating. The rate of rotation could be increased by raising the height at which the engine was released. It was found that when this reached a rate of 180° per second, equivalent to the centre section of the wing turning upside down in one second, the turbine disc hub broke and the engine slowed down and stopped without much further damage. Examination showed the same type of failure as that found in the four engines from the crash.[28] It appeared from all this that the engines had been damaged as a consequence of the aircraft breaking up rather then being the cause of it.

---

* The metal rings that closely surround the tips of the turbine blades.
** This is to do with the rotational force, the torque, of a spinning body. This can be seen seen when a spinning gyroscope is supported on a point and whose axis of spin is not exactly vertical. As well as spinning about its axis, the free end of the axis of the gyroscope moves in a circle around the vertical - it precesses - its axis tracing out the shape of an inverted cone with its apex on the supporting point. Gravity, acting on the mass of the gyroscope, generates a torque in a plane perpendicular to the spinning axis and causes the whole gyroscope to precess. The spinning turbine and compressor acts as a gyroscope with its axis of spin parallel to the fuselage. Gravity generates a torque tending to rotate the engine in the horizontal plane, i.e. into the wing. If the wing becomes inverted, the horizontal rotation would still be in the plane of the wing but in the opposite direction.

The captain's clock

One puzzle was the time of almost 09:50 shown on the captain's clock; several minutes before the time (09:57 local time) at which the mid-air catastrophe was thought to have taken place and the time at which the wreckage hit the water (10:00). Leaving absolutely no stone unturned, the clock was examined closely. This revealed a broken balance staff and a broken main spring. It was thought that the former had stopped the hands and had occurred at the time of the structural breakup or the impact with the sea. The spring had corroded in the sea water and had probably snapped as a consequence. The clock also appeared to have received a glancing blow across its face which had broken the glass and the hand-setting knob. It was likely that this blow moved the hands backwards until they broke when they became superimposed at 09:50, the gearing not allowing the two hands to move at the same rate.[29]

Putting all the evidence from the wreckage together it seemed that the most likely sequence of events was an explosive disruption of the pressure cabin, probably originating in the centre section of the fuselage, probably in the roof and probably at a normal pressure differential for the altitude. This projected fragments of the cabin wall outwards at great speed, scraping along both wings. Parts of the cabin interior, including a passenger seat or seats and part of a bulkhead, were then ejected through the defect in the cabin wall and blown to the rear, hitting and then severing the port tailplane. At the same time the passengers were blown up to the roof of the cabin and began to be pushed out of the aircraft through the hole in the cabin wall. The aircraft continued to disintegrate, the rear part of the fuselage breaking off first, then descending almost vertically and entering the sea 'open end first'. The forward part of the fuselage separated off next and descended in an unknown but probably tumbling fashion and hit the sea horizontally and the 'right way up'. The wings, including the centre section and the engines, now separated from the rest of the aircraft, would probably have turned 'nose down', the outer part of the wings breaking off as the fragment descended. From the evidence of the fire damage the wing centre section fell in a consistent manner, probably spinning, and entered the sea upside down. The conclusion was that the most likely cause of the disaster was a fatigue failure of the cabin wall but there was, as yet, no direct evidence of this.

Chapter 17

THE INVESTIGATION CONTINUES

W hat follows is an account of several avenues of investigation that the RAE had to follow to make sure that nothing was missed. None of them led to anything that could explain the crashes but they provided important information if only in the sense of excluding possible causes and confirming the adequacy of much of the Comet's design and performance.

Fatigue tests on the tailplane

The tailplane used for these tests belonged to the Comet prototype, G-ALVG, which had already flown 686 hours. It was almost identical to the production tailplanes except that the elevators had been removed and a representative mass had to be attached to the elevator hinge brackets to compensate for this. Close examination before the tests were started revealed a one inch crack in the skin on the upper side of the starboard tailplane. The crack had been 'located'* by drilling a small hole at its end.[1]

The steady flight loads on the tailplane depend on the aircraft's weight, the position of its centre of gravity and its speed. Added to this are the loads produced by gusts, mainly while flying at low altitude. For some time BOAC Comets had been flying with counting accelerometers** and the data from these suggested that a reasonable approximation for the gusts was +/- 8 fps. In addition to this were any periods of turbulence that the aircraft encountered and the loads produced by landing. The latter by itself was found to be equivalent to three hours of flight. In the end it was estimated that the total loads on the tail amounted to three times that from the gusts alone.

To carry out the tests wooden formers were clamped around four loading points on each tailplane. The downloads were applied to the front spar by bags of lead shot bolted to the formers. The uploads were provided by two hydraulic jacks via a loading tree.

---

* 'Locating' was a technique used by de Havillands, and others, to stop the progression of an existing crack. It consisted of drilling a small hole, in this case $\frac{1}{16}$ inches in diameter, at one or both ends of the crack. The idea was that the hole removed the crack tip and substituted a more benign stress concentration in its place. The hole would require a significant number of further fatigue stress cycles to start a new fatigue crack tip and with any luck the crack would not reappear before the end of the aircraft's service life. Professor Gordon relates the story of an ocean liner, the *White Star Majestic*, that developed a long crack running down one side of its hull. The crack fortuitously hit a port hole and stopped, thereby preventing the ship breaking in two.[2]
** An instrument that counts and records the number of times a given magnitude of acceleration is exceeded. It is used to document the loads that an aircraft experiences in flight.[3]

The loading cycle was applied 29 times a minute. In order to reduce the number of fatigue cycles and the test time the actual load imposed during the tests was 25% greater than the 8 fps of the gusts. It was estimated that this multiplied its effect on the fatigue life by a factor of 2.25.

Some 600,000 applications of load were made without any significant new cracks becoming visible on the tailplane. The crack noticed before the start of the test did not increase in length. These 600,000 loads were equivalent, in fatigue terms, to 1,350,000 8 fps gusts which would have occurred in 60,000 flying hours. As it was assumed that all the fluctuating loads added up were equivalent to three times the number of gust loads this meant that the test represented 20,000 flying hours. Incorporating a safety margin reduced this by a factor of five, giving a minimum safe life of 4,000 flying hours. This was likely to increase as the tests continued.

In summary the tailplane would be unlikely to have a fatigue problem in the numbers of flying hours that the individual Comet 1s had so far accumulated.

Static strength tests on the tail unit
The crash of G-ALYV after taking off from Calcutta had raised questions about the static strength of the Comet's tail. Mr. Srinivasan, from the Hindustan Aircraft Company, had made the suggestion that the cause of the breakup was the failure of both elevator spars after the pilot had tried to pull up to counteract a sudden down-gust in the storm. In his view this had led the fuselage to fail at bulkhead 26 and the rest had followed. As part of the investigation into this crash the authorities had decided to test the strength of the tail but as yet no progress had been made. The crashes off Italy provided an added stimulus and static testing was started to investigate all three crashes.[4]

The tests fell into two groups: those on the tailplane and elevators and those on the fin and rudder, and were carried out by the Structures Department at Farnborough. It proved impossible to test a tailplane identical to the one in the Calcutta crash as modifications had since been made but it was thought they would not significantly affect the findings. The parts were provided by BOAC and were from G-ALYU which had accumulated about 3,000 flying hours. The tailplanes had symmetrical aerofoils and were interchangeable.

The tailplane and fin under test were mounted on a section of Comet fuselage aft of frame 42, where the pressure dome would have been attached, which was considered to provide representative root attachment conditions. The section of fuselage was held in position by a substantial steel frame with the tailplanes projecting sideways outside the frame. The loads were applied to rubber pads glued to one surface of the tailplane by an overhead crane pulling a loading tree upwards. During the tailplane and elevator tests the rear fuselage and tailplane were inverted so the upward pull represented a download. For the tests on the fin and rudder the fuselage was rotated 90° about its longitudinal axis so that the upward pull represented a side load.

The first test on the tailplane and elevator was specified by the British Civil Airworthiness Requirements and it showed no cracks after a load equivalent to a 50 fps down gust while flying at 278 knots EAS (90% of a 1.5 factored load),* i.e. 135% of the maximum expected load).

The second test represented the conditions thought to have applied in the Calcutta crash with an aircraft speed of 220 knots EAS and a down gust speed of 120 fps, extremely severe conditions. Failure eventually occurred by a compression collapse between ribs four and five at 133% of the basic loading.** The elevator suffered a secondary failure at the same point. These two tests showed that the tailplane was considerably stronger than the minimum demanded by the requirements. Further testing showed that the elevators were similarly stronger than specified in the requirements.

The fin was divided into two parts by an insulating laminated wooden box covered by a moulded faring of resin-bonded fibreglass on its leading edge. This was to allow the upper part of the fin to be used as an aerial. The rudder was similarly divided. The fin failed at 83% of the factored (1.5) load representing a 50 fps lateral gust at a cruising speed of 278 knots. Again this satisfied the requirements, but the ultimate safety factor was only 1.25 instead of 1.5. The failure was at the wooden box. This could not have applied to the aircraft involved in the Naples crash as the fin aerial was no longer needed and the box had been replaced by a stronger arrangement.

The strength of the tailplane and elevators therefore exceeded the minimum specified by the authorities and they would have been strong enough to have resisted the estimated forces in all three accidents. The fin was weaker but should still have been strong enough to resist the maximum gust specified in the requirements. It seemed unlikely that the fin or tailplane was to blame for any of the accidents.

Damage to the outer wing tanks during refuelling

The main selling point of the Comet was its speed but its short range, by modern standards, meant that it needed frequent refuelling stops. To make these as short as possible a pressure refuelling system had been developed. The pumps involved in this delivered a pressure of up to 40 psi but the outer wing tanks, the only ones thought vulnerable, were not designed to withstand more than about 9 psi. Safety measures were installed to stop excessive pressure developing but there was clearly some scope for things to go wrong and for the wing skin to be pushed away from its supports as a result. It was thought that this had happened in service at least once and possibly on a number of other occasions as most of the outer tanks had sustained internal damage at one time or another.[5]

The normal method of refuelling involved connecting the fuel bowser's hose to the connecting valve on the underside of the wing. The fuel then passed through a control valve which could be closed electrically by two float switches. The lower float closed the valve when the tank was about 100 gallons short of being full. The rate of flow from the bowser was then reduced and the valve manually reopened. The tank was then filled

---

* If the maximum expected load was 100 units and the design safety factor was 1.5, the tailplane should have coped with a load of 150 units. Under test it reached 90% of 150 = 135. Not quite as much as it should have been but still above the maximum expected load.

** Other factors, not included here, were defined for the 'basic loading'.

to about twelve gallons short of capacity when the upper float switch closed the valve again. This system should have stopped overfilling but the float switches could be over-ridden by a manual system called 'off-load refuelling'. This was intended for emptying the tank but in an emergency it could be used for filling and there is evidence that it was used more often for this than had been intended. Air was displaced through a vent as the tank filled and there was a pressure blow-off valve which activated at about 3 psi. When refuelling was in progress a cover was removed from the blow-off valve allowing it to function. There were two types of fuel bowsers, the British-made 'Dorset' which delivered a flow of 200 gallons per minute (gpm) at a pressure of 40 psi and the Italian Viberti type, used at Rome for the Elba and Naples flights, which had a flow of 140 gpm at a pressure of 20 psi.

Static water tests showed that a pressure of 6.5 psi broke the outer tank structure of the prototype Comet, mainly by shearing the light-alloy bolts in the rib connections and those holding the skin to the ribs. Most of the service Comets, including those in the two crashes, had steel bolts and these prevented damage until a pressure of 9 psi was reached.

There appeared to be two ways in which excessive pressure could have been pro-duced in service: blocking all the air exits during fuelling and overfilling the tank with a restricted outflow. The first type of damage could have occurred if the air inlet/exit became completely blocked, perhaps with ice, but in tests this was found to be impos-sible to reproduce. The float switches also proved to be reliable. More likely was over filling using the 'off-load' method at a time when ice had disabled the blow off valve or blocked its exit tube or perhaps failing to remove the valve's cover.

Refuelling tests were carried out on an outer tank of G-ALYS with the final float switch and the blow-off valve inactivated. The damage produced depended very much on the flow of fuel into the tank. Below 120 gpm the critical pressure could not be reached as the fuel flowed out through the air vent. Between 120 and 190 gpm damage could just about be avoided by switching off the fuel delivery but it had to be within about ten seconds of the fuel being vented. At flows of 200 gpm damage seemed inevitable. This damage was reproduced in the starboard wing of the prototype (VG) and was shown to reduce its static strength by about 20% (to 78% of the design strength). This damage was unlikely to have been spotted unless suspicion had been aroused by the fuel venting and the noise of the skin being pushed off the ribs.

The port, undamaged, wing of the prototype was also tested for static download strength. It failed at 92% of the design strength by a compressive buckling between ribs 7 and 8 with another imminent failure at rib 12. It was, however, a prototype wing that had probably been weakened by previous fatigue tests. For the climb conditions apply-ing at the time of the Elba breakup a damaged wing would have required a down gust of 83 fps and an undamaged wing a gust of 107 fps.

The conclusion was that the strength of the wings of the service Comets would have been adequate.[6] As this part of the investigation was proceeding evidence from the wreckage of the Elba crash showed that even if this type of damage had occurred it was not the cause of the crash.

The possibility of excessive pressures in the cabin and fuel tanks

An aeroplane is a series of closed compartments in which the internal pressure may rise sufficiently to cause bursting. The most obvious cause is an explosion but the cabin pressurisation system might malfunction enough to cause disruption. Within some of the compartments there are volumes of liquid, such as hydraulic fluid or kerosene, that in some circumstances can vaporise to produce an explosive mixture. This would need a supply of oxygen and a source of ignition to explode but it is quite possible that these could be present.

Below the cabin floor forward of the main spar was the equipment bay which contained hydraulic and electrical equipment as well as accumulators. It was possible that a spray of hydraulic fluid or a leak of hydrogen from the batteries could be ignited by a spark from the electrical equipment and an explosion result. Tests showed that these conditions were virtually impossible to reproduce in practice and even if an explosion had occured it would not have been catastrophic as long as the communicating hatch with the main cabin had been left open.[7]

The obvious source of a large volume of inflammable fluid was the kerosene in the tanks. The conditions in the two Mediterranean crashes were unlikely to have produced much kerosene vapour but it was possible that air dissolved in the fuel at ground level could escape as the fuel was agitated in the tanks and the aircraft climbed. Even if such a situation occurred, and it was difficult to reproduce experimentally, it would still need a source of ignition to cause an explosion. Further tests found this was unlikely to be from the electrical equipment in contact with the fuel or from static discharges. Furthermore there was no evidence in the wreckage to suggest that an explosion had taken place.

The possibility of excessive pressure building up in the fuel tanks was also looked at. The tanks were open to atmosphere to allow air entry to replace the volume of fuel used and to allow air to escape during a climb. The latter might conceivably allow a build up of pressure if the vent became blocked, perhaps with ice. Experiment showed that this was unlikely in the four wing tanks but possible in the central tanks although all attempts to block the vent with ice failed.

The report said that the pressure cabin was designed to contain a pressure differential of 16.5 psi (2P). If all the safety measures failed simultaneously it would take about seven minutes to pump the cabin up to 20 psi, the maximum that could be reached at that altitude. This would (probably) have been sufficient to burst the cabin.* If all the safety devices had blocked at ground level the pressure would build up rapidly and the cabin would most likely have burst before the aircraft reached 10,000 feet. It was considered that it was improbable that all three safety devices would fail simultaneously and be unnoticed and that this could be discounted. Failing to switch on the air conditioning system, and so preventing any air entering the cabin, produced a pressure differential of less than 7 psi.

---

* The cabin was actually designed to have an ultimate pressure capability of 2.5P (20.625 psi). In the static test carried out on AV after the inquiry (see Chapter 28) the cabin burst at 2.34P (19.3 psi). The proof pressure, i.e. the maximum pressure at which there was no permanent deformation, was 1.33 P (11 psi).

Calculations showed that to produce the decompression injuries seen in the victims the cabin would need to be decompressed in about 0.1 seconds at an altitude of 30,000 feet which would need the instantaneous removal of about 100 square feet of cabin wall, rather more than a single door or window.

The possibility of loss of control
Any aircraft that is handled in a particular way can suffer a structural failure. This is most often demonstrated in violent combat manoeuvres during wartime but it could also happen in an aircraft such as the Comet if the pilot lost control for some reason or severely over-controlled. It could also happen in severe turbulence, if the autopilot malfunctioned or if the powered flying controls became defective. All of these possibilities had to be investigated.[8]

Discounting the pilot deliberately flying in a manner likely to break up the aircraft, loss of control could be caused by an accident on the flight deck, for example the pilot's seat suddenly collapsing or the control column being accidentally pushed away from the trimmed position and becoming jammed. Of course the situation might be quickly retrieved without structural damage occurring but a violent manoeuvre producing high g forces may make it impossible for the pilot to reach the controls, particularly if he had not been strapped in, and damage could occur very quickly. As an illustration, moving YP's elevators up at their maximum rate (20° per second) in the conditions applying just before the breakup of YP would probably cause the aircraft to stall before the wings failed. Moving the elevators down might make the wing fail first. This would happen within about one second, leaving the pilot little chance of intervening.

The three most likely ways in which a pilot could inadvertently lose control are: allowing the aircraft's speed to fall to the stalling speed, allowing the aircraft's speed to increase beyond the critical Mach number or applying sufficient normal acceleration to stall the aircraft.*

Using the results of wind tunnel tests and data from de Havillands it was possible to show that the Comet, flying trimmed at about 200 knots EAS, was a relatively stable aircraft. A considerable force of 50 to 60 pounds would be needed to pull the control column back far enough to produce a stall. It was a little easier (25 pounds) to push the control column so far forward that the aircraft exceeded its critical Mach number (0.82) but it was unlikely that either of these commands could happen inadvertently.

There was a problem with the elevator controls though. A force of some 15 to 20 pounds, the 'breakout force', was needed to move the control column from the trimmed position and this increased at a rate of about six pounds for each degree of elevator rotation. This made smooth control difficult and might prove to be a problem in an emergency from over-controlling producing excessive loads on the aircraft, particularly the tailplane, something that had been mentioned in the report on the Calcutta crash.

In turbulence the aeroplane could be stalled by an up gust or a down gust but it was

---

* 'Normal' in this context means perpendicular to the aircraft's flight path. So a rapid movement pitching the nose up, caused partly by the control command and partly by the aircraft's momentum, can produce a stall from an extreme angle of attack.

possible to show that for a Comet flying at 200 knots at 30,000 feet the gusts would have to be very strong; 94 fps and 154 fps respectively. Gusts like these would be quite exceptional although a much weaker down gust (35 fps) would be quite capable of unseating the pilot if he were not properly strapped in.

A simulator was set up to represent a Comet flying through turbulence to find out whether the high breakout force needed to move the elevators led pilots to overcorrect the aircraft and produce excessive loads on the tailplane. A number of BOAC and RAF pilots familiar with the Comet were tested and even with the most severe gusts that could be programmed in (66 fps) the tail loads were only about one third of its ultimate load. It was thought unlikely that this would have led to the crash.

The Comet's autopilot was an electromechanical system using gyros, pendulums and a compass. Limit switches were fitted to prevent excessive commands being erroneously generated by the system. Failure of these switches could lead to maximal movements of the flying controls leading to structural failure. There were other possible failures that could produce excessive commands and a loss of feedback leading to the autopilot 'runaway' that had occurred in service on G-ALYX which had been traced to a loose screw causing a short circuit. Fortunately any excessive manoeuvres had been prevented by the limit switches and the pilot had been able to disengage the autopilot and fly manually. BOAC also reported other incidents but none had led to a serious problem.

On balance it was thought that although problems with the autopilot could occur, and indeed had occurred, they were unlikely to be serious enough to pass unnoticed and cause the loss of the aircraft before the pilot could disconnect the system.

Failure of the powered controls could be caused by a loss of hydraulic fluid, valve seizure or the system becoming unstable leading to oscillations of the aircraft. The hydraulic arrangements had considerable redundancy as well as having several independent sub-systems. It was unlikely that a loss of fluid leading to power failure would develop unnoticed to any serious degree and prevent the pilot switching to a backup system. The equipment seemed well designed to prevent valve seizure and there was no evidence from the wreckage of this having happened. On test, oscillations could be produced, although not easily, and they tended to settle fairly quickly. It was thought that they would also tend to be damped aerodynamically when the aircraft was flying and it was unlikely to be a problem in practice.

Flight investigations

These investigations were carried out on the Comet 1A that had not been taken up by Canadian Pacific after the Calcutta crash. Its registration had been changed from CF-CUM to G-ANAV for its short career with BOAC. It was used partly because it was available and partly because it was a relatively new aircraft having about half the number of flying hours as the Comets involved in the two Mediterranean crashes. The aircraft was prepared by BOAC at London Airport by removing the cabin fittings and installing oxygen and power supplies and some of the instrumentation in the cabin. Strain gauges,* vibration pickups, counting accelerometers and thermometers were installed by the RAE as well as instruments for measuring movements of the control surfaces and the pilots' controls.[9]

The overall purpose of the flight tests was to obtain information which by itself, or in combination with the ground investigations, might have a bearing on the Comet crashes. The test programme was designed to investigate high and low frequency vibrations in the rear fuselage and tail caused respectively by the jet efflux and buffeting or flutter during flight. The stresses in the same areas in normal and turbulent flight were also measured as were the temperatures of the structure. The aircraft's and the pilot's response to turbulence and various manoeuvres was included as well as measuring the stresses around the forward port escape hatch in association with the cabin fatigue tests. Noise and vibration at ultrasonic frequencies and fuel leakage were also investigated. During the flight tests AV was followed at a respectful distance by an RAE Canberra fitted with observation equipment in case the worst happened. The whole programme took about five weeks to complete with about fifteen hours of flying per week.

The flight tests started in May. The aircraft was flown unpressurised and limited in altitude, for this reason, to 38,000 feet. This was later reduced to 35,000 feet as it was thought that the lack of pressurisation was affecting the hydraulic system. Additional fire detectors and extinguishers were installed in the cabin. The centre section fuel tank was kept empty and the wing tanks had at least 100 gallons of free air to reduce any danger from fuel spillage. In addition the pressures in the wing tanks were monitored.

It was found that the general levels of low-frequency vibration was about normal for this type of aircraft. High frequency levels caused by the jet efflux, however, were severe enough to give rise to skin fatigue problems which had needed some repair work in service. Steady flight produced stress levels within design limits and the shear stress measurements near the escape hatch showed that the increase in stress levels in low altitude turbulence (as compared with measurements on the ground) agreed closely with calculated estimates. When flying in turbulence there was appreciable stress amplification at the resonant frequencies of the wing and tailplane. This was expected but its significance was unclear. The various temperature gradients were insignificant. There were no abnormal or dangerous responses to the manoeuvres carried out during the tests and the extra loads generated by the pilots' control movements in turbulence were

---

* A strain gauge is a narrow strip of metal foil configured in a zig zag shape which is glued to the surface of a structure at the place where the local strain is to be measured. A small electric current is applied to the ends of the foil allowing its resistance to be measured. When the structure is loaded the material under the gauge deforms together with the gauge and the resultant change in resistance can be related to the local strain at that site. For elastic strains the measured values can be used to calculate the local stresses by using, for example, Young's Modulus (stress/strain is a constant for the material under test). This cannot be easily done if the local strain exceeds that at the elastic limit of the substrate material (see fig 3/A5 in Appendix 5).

Thomas Young (1773 to 1829) was a polymath, a figure rarely seen in today's world of specialists. As well as devising his modulus he investigated the wave nature of light, made advances in haemodynamics and helped to decipher the Rosetta Stone. He was also notoriously difficult to understand. This was illustrated in part of a letter from the Admiralty to Young, "Though science is much respected by their Lordships and your paper is much esteemed, it is too learned... in short it is not understood."[10]

small. The most significant positive finding was that fuel could spill from the tank vents during climbing. This fuel then re-entered the trailing edge of the wing and penetrated as far as the jet pipes and severe leaks thus constituted a fire hazard.

Although nothing was discovered in these tests that could account for the crashes of YP and YY some problems had become apparent and these would need to be dealt with if the many Comet 2 airframes that were littering de Havillands' factories were to have any future.

Chapter 18

FATIGUE TESTING OF THE
FUSELAGE AND WINGS

The most enduring image of the Comet 1 is not a de Havilland or BOAC publicity shot showing it flying gracefully above the clouds, but the aerial view of one of them being tested to destruction in a water tank at Farnborough. It sits forlorn and humiliated, submerged in an alien medium, surrounded by the steel walls of the tank with its wings sticking out on each side. It is the one thing that the RAE investigation is most remembered for, but tank testing was not an original idea. De Havillands themselves had used it and Walker had already constructed a small tank at Farnborough.[1] What was different this time was that the whole aircraft was to be tested, not just part of it, that it was a production aircraft and not a specially prepared specimen and that flying loads as well as pressure loads would be applied. The decision to do the test was made by Dr. Hall on 18 April, just ten days after the Naples crash, although the idea appears to have originated from Dr. Walker.

The fuselage had two potential modes of failure: failure under a static load by bursting under excessive pressure or breaking in two from a large tensile, shear or compressive flight load and failure from metal fatigue after repeated small stresses from the pressure cycles or flight loads. The tank tests were to discover the fatigue life of the Comet's fuselage. Static pressure testing took place later in the same tank some time after the inquiry that followed the RAE investigation had finished (see Chapter 28).

Walker's arguments for undertaking such an expensive and time-consuming test were recorded in a memorandum he sent to Group Captain Tweedie on 15 April 1954. In it he compared the Calcutta, Elba and Naples crashes but left the first out of the main argument. He made three suppositions for each case: the possibility of the airframe having undergone an ageing process directly related to its flying life,* the occurrence of the disintegration at or near the end of the climb and the suddenness of the event. In Walker's opinion only the fatigue failure of the pressure cabin fulfilled all three suppositions, particularly the second. He concluded that "...there is no direct evidence since

---

* YP had undergone some deterioration even before its service flying life had started. It had been the subject of some correspondence between BOAC, the MoS and de Havillands in1951 because it had developed skin corrosion after having been left out in the open at Hatfield for long periods. De Havillands responded by saying they were cleaning it with Teepol twice a week which, as one of the letters pointed out, probably made things worse by removing any grease.[2]

Fig. 1/18 G-ALYU fuselage being transported to Farnborough, 7 May 1954 (copyright BAE SYSTEMS Heritage)

the chances of finding the initial fatigue failure, if it exists, are slight." [3]

In service the Comet's fuselage was pressurised with air bled off the engines. In the static proof tests carried out by the manufacturers, air was pumped into the cabin from the factory supply to a pressure of 11 psi and the fuselage monitored for deformation, cracks and leaks. The prototypes and all the production Comets had been tested in this way, and were tested again by the airlines at intervals of about 1,000 flying hours. Air was used because it did not damage the fittings of the aircraft in the way that water would. The disadvantage of using air is that if there is a sudden, large, structural failure events happen so quickly that it is difficult, if not impossible, to work out the sequence in which they happened. Also, because air is compressible, energy is stored as the pressure builds up* and is then released suddenly when the structure ruptures, rather like a balloon bursting. Any major failure amounts to an explosion; in the case of the Comet's fuselage at 8.25 psi it was thought to be roughly equivalent to a 500 pound bomb going off inside the cabin [4] and for this reason the tests were carried out in the open air away from the factory buildings. As well as damaging large parts of the fuselage any failure would be something of a threat to the people around it. De Havillands had inadvertently demonstrated this when testing the centre section and this had prompted them to build a small steel safety chamber for the person unlucky enough to be the closest observer.

A less exciting way of testing a pressure vessel is to fill it with water until the desired pressure differential is reached. Water is virtually incompressible and little energy is

---

* This can be visualised as the work done pumping air into the fuselage to reach the required pressure.

Fig. 2/18 Right, safety enclosure used during fuselage pressure testing with air, 13 July 1953, (copyright BAE SYSTEMS Heritage)

stored in it* so that any structural failure does not produce the explosive decompression seen with air. With a relatively flimsy structure like a fuselage, the weight of the water itself would produce damage and the walls would have to be supported. The easiest way to do this was to immerse the whole structure in a tank of water which equalises the pressure on both sides of the skin. The pressure differential was then produced by pumping water inside the fuselage. De Havillands had been pioneers in doing this at Hatfield with the two fuselage test sections.

The aircraft selected for the RAE tests was G-ALYU, Yoke Uncle, which was transferred by road from Hatfield where it had already been used for tests on the strength of its tail unit. The internal fittings were stripped out, the airframe sealed and the floor and one end of the steel tank constructed so that the aircraft could be pushed into it. The rest of the tank, which was made of the same prefabricated sections that had been used for wartime emergency water tanks, was then built around it.** Building the tank took the amazingly short time of six weeks.[5] The most difficult part was the construction of the tank where the wings projected through the sides. Another problem was sealing the tank around the wings but this was eventually solved by using specially-designed inflatable seals, rather like large car inner tubes, which allowed the wing to flex up and down. Only the roots of the wings were inside the tank. The water was pumped into the fuselage from a nearby storage tank to the usual cabin pressure differential of 8.25 psi (P)

---

* When the fuselage was filled with water very little extra pumping was needed to reach the required pressure and hence little work had been done.

** The tank was 112 feet long, 20 feet wide and 16 feet high. It had a capacity of 225,000 gallons.[5]

Fig. 3/18 Aerial view of YU in the water tank at Farnborough, from RAE report, Part 3, Fig. 1 (FAST, Farnborough Air Sciences Trust).

and then pumped out again, mimicking the pressure cycle of a single flight. Each cycle took about five minutes. At intervals of about 1,000 cycles a proving pressure equivalent to 1⅓ P (11 psi) was applied. No preservative was used in the water to avoid the risk of corrosion and as a consequence it became steadily more colonised with algae and occasionally had to be changed.[6, 7]

At the same time as the fuselage was being examined, the wings were tested for fatigue failure and for the effects they had on the cabin strength, by being bent by hydraulic rams. These movements were designed firstly to reproduce the takeoff, flight and then landing stresses by applying a steady load carried first by the undercarriage, then the wings and then the undercarriage again. As well as this the variable stresses that would have been experienced during a three hour flight were represented by 25 cycles of alternating up and down loads equivalent to 10 fps gusts. These figures were arrived at by Dr. Walker from the counting accelerometers carried on BOAC Comets in service.[8] The movements also mimicked the stresses exerted by the wings on the fuselage. Each of these 'three hour flights' was completed within the five minute pressure cycle. The loads were reacted against by the weight of the airframe resting on its undercarriage and by lead weights put on the cabin floor. The rear fuselage load from the downward thrust of the tailplane in level flight was applied by a rod passing through the top of the fuselage and spread over four beams. Later on this had to be increased to eight after a local structural failure. These loads could only be an approximation to what

Fig. 4/18   Inside view of the first failure in YU, from RAE report, Part 3, Fig. 16 (FAST, Farnborough Air Sciences Trust)

the aircraft might have experienced in a three hour flight and no allowance was made for any other stresses such as engine vibrations and the jet exhaust impinging on the cabin wall, the minor fluctuations of cabin pressure during flights and skin temperature fluctuations.[9]

Careful examination of the airframe before the tests started revealed several small cracks. These were a mixture of cracks produced during manufacture, which were to be the cause of much discussion during the public inquiry, and cracks caused by wear and tear in service such as the stairs being pushed up against the passenger door. None of them appeared to be very significant.[10]

Before the tests Yoke Uncle had flown for 3,539 hours, about the same as the Elba Comet (3,681), and had made 1,231 pressurised flights.[9] On 24 June, after the equivalent of another 1,826 flights, making a total of 3,057, the cabin structure failed. A piece of cabin wall about eight feet by three feet was suddenly forced outwards. This was after a total flying life of about 9,000 hours or about 2½ times the life of the Elba Comet. The actual failure occurred at a pressure of 10.4 psi during a proving test although this was thought not to be significant in the sense that it would probably have happened anyway within the next few cycles.

The starting point of the failure appeared to be at a small fatigue crack at a rivet hole in the lower rear corner of the forward escape hatch on the port side, just aft of frame

16. By this time the water in the tank had become colonised by algae and this had discoloured part of the edges of the crack. As the rest of the crack was clean, the discoloured part was assumed to have been present for some time before the length of the crack suddenly increased. The crack extended back along the fuselage to frame 18. At the same time a fracture had started at the forward lower corner of the same escape hatch where there was also evidence of a small fatigue crack preceding the major break. This crack had extended forward about the same distance as the other one, to frame 13A. Both cracks had then extended transversely to the roof, partly along the lines of rivets, raising a flap which had remained attached at the top although the skin had buckled and some rivets had been pulled out of the top of the subframes at each end of the escape hatch. The window itself remained in place but the frame had sprung out at the bottom edge.[11, 12]

By co-incidence that day de Havilland and Bishop had flown over from Hatfield to see how the tests were progressing and had been talking to Hall when he received a telephone call telling him that the cabin had ruptured. They had all gone over to examine the structure as soon as the tank had been drained. De Havilland says in his biography that it was an enormous relief to have found out the cause of the disasters but at the same time he felt that it threw into question their technical design ability.[13]

Had the aircraft been flying and been pressurised with air there would have been an explosive decompression and much more damage. The chances are that it would then have broken up. Because all the flight stresses that would have occurred in service were not mimicked in the test, it is likely that failure would have happened earlier than the 3,057 pressurisations actually undergone by Yoke Uncle, more like 2,500 Walker estimated.[14] This fatigue failure strongly suggested the reason why Yoke Peter and Yoke Yoke had broken up in mid air and focused the investigation, but it fell short of absolute proof.

The fractures at the front part of the fuselage were repaired with a new skin panel and escape hatch. Examination also revealed another crack about 1.25 inches long in the cabin skin at the upper rear corner of the first window forward of the wing rear spar on the port side. It was agreed with de Havillands that this was likely to be the start of another major failure and in order that the tests could continue it, too, was repaired.[15] The reason for continuing the pressure cycles was to use strain gauges to measure the stress levels in the areas shown by the first tests to be most vulnerable, i.e. the corners of the windows and escape hatches.

After 3,881 test cycles (5,112 in total, equivalent to about 15,000 flying hours) a fairly large crack appeared in the skin at the forward top corner of the port number two window. The crack ran forward for about three inches and was then stopped by a rivet hole. There were also small cracks at several other windows. At 5,546 cycles in total (about 17,000 hours) a large portion of the port side of the rear fuselage blew out from frame 26 to frame 34, a length of about fifteen feet. This started from a fatigue crack at a rivet hole in the skin at the forward bottom corner of number seven window. Several other cracks were also found, including one at the rear corner of the rear ADF window.[16]

This provided further evidence that the corners of the various cutouts were vulnerable to fatigue cracking.

The cabin of Yoke Uncle was not the only part to fail under test. Cracks appeared in the bottom skin of the rear of the wheel well of both wings at the equivalent of about 5,410 total flying hours, some 3,600 hours before the cabin failed. By 5,540 hours one crack had extended to 8.25 inches and was beginning to accelerate. At this point the tests were stopped and the wing repaired so that the cabin tests could continue. If the tests had continued without repairs this crack would have made the wing fail. Had the aircraft been in service, and the crack not been noticed, it would probably have crashed soon after. More cracks appeared inside the wing structure at 10,000 hours and a number of cracks appeared in the bottom skin between 10,000 and 15,000 hours. This was known to be a problem area in the Comet and had been the subject of considerable correspondence between BOAC, the MoS, the RAE and de Havillands, mainly about who would pay for repairs or the premature retirement of the aircraft if that became necessary.* The MoS had originally written to BOAC saying that they "cannot advise flight of the Comet beyond 1,000 hours. This is because the wing fatigue life has not yet been demonstrated to our satisfaction... to give assurance that longer life can be permitted."[17] This had caused some alarm in BOAC as it made the aircraft hopelessly uneconomic but as the wing and its various parts were tested at de Havillands and Farnborough the estimated life crept up and the last figure recorded in the BOAC archive, dated 16 November 1953, was 10,000 hours.[18] Alterations and an inspection regime had been put in place and it was thought that this would catch any incipient failure in time as it was likely that crack progression would be relatively slow. Based on the tank tests this fatigue life would seem to have been rather optimistic.

The fatigue crack in YP's port undercarriage bay had extended during the breakup but it was not the cause of the wing failure or the crash. As there were no relevant parts to examine from the Naples Comet it is possible that a wing failure was responsible. However YY had only flown 90 hours since a rigorous inspection had been carried out as part of the Abell Committee's programme. For the wing to have been responsible either the inspection had been ineffective or any crack must have extended much more rapidly than experience suggested it could. Both eventualities were thought unlikely.

More wreckage is found

At the same time as the tank tests were going on more wreckage was appearing from the Elba crash. By the end of June, when Yoke Uncle had already burst apart in the tank, the front part of Yoke Peter's fuselage, the starboard outer wing, the tail unit, the port side of the centre fuselage and the tail fin had been found and transported to Farnborough. None of the fragments so far retrieved showed the primary fracture

---

* Some of these letters, now in the British Airways archive, were used in the Principal Films documentary to imply that de Havillands, the MoS and the airline knew that the Comet was liable to a cabin fatigue failure but had allowed it to continue to fly. In fact the cabin was never mentioned, only the wing, and BOAC were operating the Comet well within its estimated wing fatigue life which anyway was extending as the tests continued. The wings were never implicated in any of the crashes.

DIRECTION OF PRO-
PAGATION OF MAIN
FAILURES

FORWARD

SECONDARY FAILURES
AND FOLD MADE
DURING SALVAGE
(SEE FIG.69)

SEE FIG.71 FOR
DETAIL OF WINDOWS

PORTION OF BLUE
BAND WHICH MADE
IMPACT MARK ON
WING (FIG.11)

Fig. 5/18 Area of wreckage around YP's ADF windows, from RAE report, Part 2, Fig. 68 (FAST, Farnborough Air Sciences Trust)

although it was likely that it was somewhere in the roof of the central part of the fuse-lage. It seemed reasonable to assume that if Yoke Peter had suffered an explosive decompression that the part of the aircraft where it had happened would separate first and therefore hit the water first. This fragment would then be roughly in the line of the aircraft's flight path and closer to Rome than the other wreckage. There is considerable variation in the paths taken by the fragments of an aircraft breaking up in mid air. At the moment of disintegration each fragment is moving forward with the velocity of the aircraft. Added to this is any acceleration produced by an explosion. Each fragment is then subject to gravity and air resistance as it falls, the latter depending very much on the size, shape, attitude and density of the fragment. This makes any calculation of the position and spread of the fragments something of a guess, although it was no doubt helped by the model experiments. Nevertheless the search, which was still going on, was redirected to a new area on 6 July.[19] As the sea quickly became deeper in this direc-tion the only practical method was trawling.

On 12 August, not long after the new search was started, an Italian fishing boat trawled up pieces of cabin skin. The exact position at which this wreckage was found is uncertain as the trawling covered a large area but it was most likely to have been somewhere to the south east of the area where the other wreckage had been found.[20] The pieces were received in Farnborough on 31 August. There were two large pieces of cabin wall; one on the port side extending from frame 13A to about frame 23, and the other on the starboard side from frames 13A to 18. The port piece had been cut after

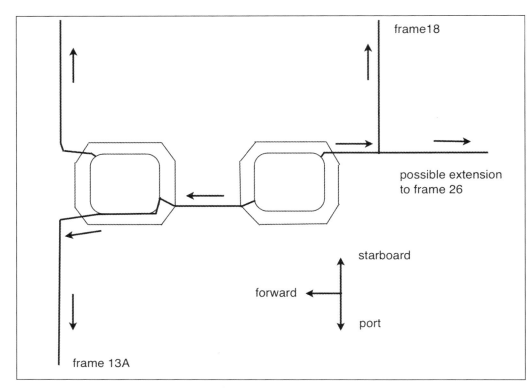

Fig. 6/18 Diagram of the primary fractures around the two ADF windows in YP taken from a more detailed drawing in the RAE report.[21]

recovery and was received in three parts. These pieces came from the centre of the top of the cabin, approximately over the front spar of the wing, and contained the two ADF windows.

Examination of this fragment, and two adjacent fragments received earlier, showed a series of fractures. One extended back from the starboard corner of the rear ADF window in an almost-straight line, parallel to the top centre line of the fuselage. This fracture reached to the end of the fragment but would probably have continued to frame 26 where the rear fuselage had separated from the centre section but this part had not been retrieved. Another fracture had branched off at right angles from the first one at frame 18, a short distance behind the window, and moved down the starboard side of the fuselage. There was a short fracture between the port front corner of the rear ADF window to the port rear corner of the front ADF window. There were then fractures which extended forward from both front corners of this window a short distance to frame 13A and then both turned at right angles to move down the port and starboard sides of the cabin. [21, 22]

Using fracture analysis (see Chapter 21) it was possible to establish the directions of tearing and this suggested that the origin was at the rear ADF window. This was in accord with the findings of the tank tests where the fractures had all started near the corners of cutouts.[23]

The skin on the roof of the cabin was thinner (22 gauge) than at the sides (20 gauge) but was doubled around the two ADF windows. Some of the rivets attaching this reinforcing plate had been placed closer to the edge of the cutout than specified although this had not been the cause of the failure.[24] It proved impossible to say definitely where the split had started but the most likely place was the starboard rear corner of the rear ADF window at a point where a small fatigue fracture had already existed at the edge of a countersunk bolt hole.[25, 26] The bolt was through the doubling plate but outside the double row of rivets close to the cutout edge and was part of the attachment of the skin and doubling plate to frame 17. The fracture had then passed rearwards parallel to the long axis of the fuselage as described above.[21, 22, 23]

An alternative starting point was at the port forward corner of the same ADF window where the fracture had gone though a small crack about 0.2 inches long made in the reinforcing plate during manufacture. It had been 'located' in the manner approved by de Havillands by drilling a small hole at its end. This fracture had then travelled to the front ADF window, extended along the two rows of rivets on the port boundary of the window and then for a short distance further to frame 13A.[27]

At the starboard rear corner of the doubling plate of the front ADF window there was a short crack made during manufacture extending in from the edge of the window. It had been 'located' roughly half way to the first row of rivets but during the life of the aircraft the crack had extended into a rivet hole and then stopped. It was not implicated

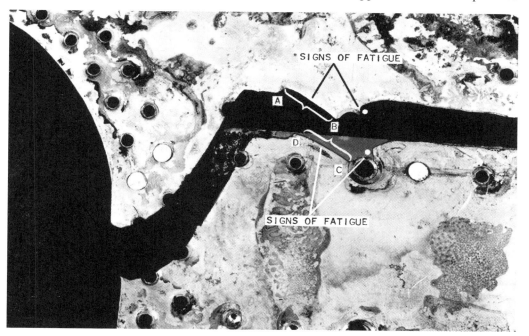

Fig. 7/18 Plan view of the fatigue crack near the rear ADF window in YP, from RAE report, Part 2, Fig. 75a (FAST, Farnborough Air Sciences Trust).

in any of the fractures that destroyed the aircraft but it does not provide much confidence in this method of dealing with cracks. But for the rivet hole being directly in line it would doubtless have extended, possibly with serious consequences.[28]

The nature of the fractures indicated that they were associated with the release of pressure from the cabin.[23] The sequence appeared to be that the cabin roof had split roughly along the centre line from frame 13A to frame 23 or 26. Then each side had peeled back, causing more fractures, this time across the fuselage, as the top of the aircraft burst open.

At the same time as the cabin-roof fragments arrived at Farnborough, two other pieces arrived. One was part of the aileron of the port wing, the other part of the port wing-fence. Both had marks made on them by pieces from the cabin. Taken together with the paint mark on the leading edge of the inner section of the wing, not far from where the outer wing had broken off, which had been caused by the piece of cabin wall containing the first window (an escape hatch) they provided more evidence that the cabin had exploded in the vicinity of the front spar of the wing when the aircraft was essentially flying normally. As it seemed unlikely that much more wreckage would be found and, even if it were, that it would provide significant new information, the search for further wreckage was stopped in September.[29]

Although the explanation of the disaster that befell Yoke Peter was becoming clearer there was no direct evidence that any of this applied to the Naples crash but there was some circumstantial evidence. The altitude at which the event had occurred was about the same suggesting that pressurisation had been involved, like the Elba crash it had been abrupt, catastrophic and without warning and there was no evidence of turbulence or a storm which might have precipitated a wing failure. Also the victims' head, chest and decompression injuries were almost identical. The two crashes appeared so similar that it seemed reasonable to apply the explanation of the cause of the first crash to the second.

Stress and its consequences (see also Appendix 5)
As described in the footnote on stress in Chapter 4, stresses in a structure can be uniform but more often vary with location within the body. Regions of high stress are called stress concentrations, and the shape of the body plays an important role in determining the location and the size of the local stresses. In particular stresses become concentrated around notches and holes, the greater the notch depth and the smaller the radius at the tip the greater the local stress. This phenomenon can often be seen in the plaster around the corners of windows and doors in any house that has experienced even small amounts of movement. Plaster is very weak in tension and cracks readily. The cracks generally start at the edge of the plaster where it meets a corner of the wooden frame and move away roughly bisecting the angle at the corner. Stress concentrations can also occur where a relatively flexible part of a structure, such as a wing, meets a relatively rigid part, such as the fuselage. Stress concentrations cannot be entirely eliminated in structures exposed to stress but careful design can reduce their number and severity.

It cannot have been a surprise to the investigators that the crack in Yoke Peter thought to be the origin of the breakup involved two windows and that the windows were close together and in the longitudinal axis where pressurised cylinders tend to split. Also the fuselage skin was thinner here than at the sides although it was doubled around the cutouts. The Comet pressure-tested in the water tank had also failed in a longitudinal line, although this time involving the windows at the side of the cabin.

After the first cabin-wall failure strain gauges were attached around three escape hatches and one window of Yoke Uncle to quantify the stress levels and pressure testing resumed. It was found that the highest areas of stress were close to the corners of the windows. The strain gauges were about one inch long and some extrapolations from the observed figures had to be made to reach values for stress concentrations at the margins of the windows. The analysis of the strain gauges readings was carried out with the aid of an early computer, the Pilot ACE, at the National Physical Laboratory, at the time the only computer in a government establishment in the UK. Its original architecture had been designed by Alan Turing before he had departed for Manchester in 1948.[30]

With a pressure differential of 8.25 psi. the maximum stress at the edges of the skin at the corners of the windows was estimated to be 43,100 psi. This increased to 45,700 when the stresses that takeoffs, landings and gusts produced were taken into account. The ultimate tensile strength (UTS)* of the DTD 546B alloy used for the Comet's skin was around 65,000 psi, so the usual stress experienced in flight was about 70% of its UTS.[15] When it is considered that in aluminium alloys the fatigue limit stress for smooth laboratory samples is generally taken to be the UTS/3, in this case about 21,600 psi, it is not surprising that these areas were vulnerable. It seemed reasonable to assume that the small fatigue fracture found in YP near the corner of one of the ADF cutouts, and thought to be the origin of the disaster, had happened because of this stress concentration. Also that the manufacturing crack at the other corner, the alternative source, was in a vulnerable area. It was slightly puzzling that all the tank failures had started at the windows or escape hatches at the side of the fuselage rather than the ADF windows but the consistent feature was that they had all started at the corners of the various cutouts. The initial fatigue cracks were quite small and were not a problem in themselves. But a small crack can grow into a big crack and cause a catastrophic failure.

The RAE investigation was now complete. It had shown that the Comet pressure cabin under test had a short fatigue life, much shorter than had been expected, and that the weakest parts were at the corners of the various cutouts. The wreckage of the cabin roof had shown where a crack had started and strengthened the view that YP and YY had exploded when their cabins had reached maximum differential pressure at cruising altitude. All this, seemingly cut and dried, evidence now had to be gone over again in the public inquiry ordered by the government shortly after the Elba crash.

---

* The ultimate tensile strength of a ductile material such as an aluminium alloy is the maximum tensile stress reached before the specimen starts to narrow non-uniformly or 'neck' (see Appendix 5). It is used more for quality control than design as it is uncomfortably close to the fracture stress. It is not to be confused with the ultimate load which is the maximum load to be expected in service – the limit load – multiplied by the safety factor of 1.5.

Chapter 19

THE COURT OF INQUIRY

The Court of Inquiry to look into the two Mediterranean crashes was set up at the request of the Minister of Transport and Civil Aviation, Alan Lennox-Boyd, under an Act passed in 1951, to look into the causes and circumstances of the two Comet crashes. By the time the inquiry had started the ministerial merry-go-round had replaced Lennox-Boyd with John Boyd-Carpenter. It was unusual to hold a public inquiry into an air crash but these particular crashes had excited considerable public interest and the future of de Havillands, and to some extent the British aviation industry as a whole, were at stake. The Commissioner of the Court, Lord Cohen, was appointed by the Lord Chancellor as well as three assessors: Sir William Scott Farren, Professor William Jolly Duncan and Air Commodore Allen Henry Wheeler.

Lionel Cohen was a senior Court of Appeal judge who had started his legal career just before the First World War. He had previous experience of technical commissions and chaired the Royal Commission on Awards to Inventors for ten years (for the use of their inventions during the Second World War).* He was regarded as courteous and sensible and, unusual for a man in his position, was said to lack any arrogance or pomposity.[1] He was to show a masterly control of events and with Sir Arnold Hall was one of the two outstanding professionals in the inquiry. He displayed a quick understanding of technical concepts with which he must have been previously unfamiliar and frequently had to rephrase counsels' incomprehensible questions so that a witness could have some chance of answering. He died in 1973.

Sir William Farren was an aeronautical engineer of some distinction. Less than a year after leaving Cambridge in 1914 he was recruited to Farnborough by Mervyn O'Gorman and became the head of the aerodynamics department. While at Farnborough he learned to fly and in 1917 took the CE1 flying boat, which he had helped design, for its first flight. After a brief period in industry he returned to Cambridge in 1920 as a lecturer in engineering. With the approach of the Second World War Farren left Cambridge for the Air Ministry and ultimately became its Director of Technical Development. In 1941 he became the Director of the RAE and played a large part in setting up RAE Bedford.** During his four year tenure Farren polished his flying skills with every aircraft he could get his hands on, often flying a Spitfire in the

---

* He awarded Whittle the not-inconsiderable sum (at that time) of £100,000.[2]

** RAE Bedford was used for aircraft development and played an important role in the early life of the Harrier. It was also an important site for research and development using wind tunnels. It was largely closed in 1994.

early morning as a way of starting his working day. He was an early enthusiast for the jet engine and supersonic flight after initially being critical of Whittle's work. After the war he returned to the aviation industry and became a director of Hawker Siddeley, retiring in 1961.[3] He was an excellent choice as an assessor and asked many pertinent questions during the hearings and frequently intervened to make difficult technical concepts more understandable to the lawyers.

William Duncan was the Professor of Aeronautics and Fluid Mechanics at the University of Glasgow from 1950 to 1961. He was a graduate of University College London and served in the Royal Army Service Corps during the First World War. After working for his father's marine engineering business

Fig. 1/19 Lionel Leonard Cohen, Baron Cohen, by Elliot and Fry, (copyright National Portrait Gallery, London.)

in Govan he joined the National Physical Laboratory's Aerodynamics Department in 1926. He left there in 1934 to become the head of the Department of Aerodynamics at University College Hull, becoming a professor there in 1938. He worked in Farnborough during the war and became the Professor of Aerodynamics at Cranfield in 1945.[4]

Air Commodore Wheeler was an engineering graduate from Cambridge and had joined the RAF in 1924. He spent most of the early part of the war at Boscombe Down and Farnborough testing aircraft. In 1943 he took over the command of the new RAF station at Fairford and played a major part in organising the dispatch of large numbers of gliders for the Normandy invasion. In 1953 he became the Commandant at Boscombe Down. At the time of the inquiry he was still a serving officer. After retiring he became the aviation adviser for various film productions including *Those Magnificent Men in their Flying Machines*. He bought his first aircraft, an SE5A, for £25 and later owned two Spitfires. In his career he flew over 400 different types of aircraft.[5] Wheeler's role in the inquiry was mainly to advise on any piloting issues and as these were relatively few he played only a small part in the proceedings.

One of the potential problems for the inquiry was that all the technical witnesses knew the results of the RAE investigation. This offered them the temptation to adjust their historic opinions with the benefit of hindsight. It is to their great credit that none of them did so, perhaps encouraged by the knowledge that many of their original opinions had been recorded in contemporary letters and minutes.

Most, probably all, of the protagonists in the inquiry are now beyond the reach of the interviewer's questioning but the transcript of the inquiry recorded their words as they spoke them. Although for the witnesses in particular, these may have been uttered in somewhat stressful circumstances they nevertheless bring the participants more alive than formal letters, minutes and reports can ever do.

The hearings started on 19 October 1954 in the Assembly Hall at Church House in Westminster and moved to the Institution of Civil Engineers, also in Westminster, on 17 November. Church House is where the Synod of the Church of England meets and was used during the war for sittings of the Commons after the Palace of Westminster had been bombed. The Assembly Hall is a large, imposing, domed, circular room, complete with a balcony and challenging acoustics. The Court sat for a total of 22 days and also had a day out at Farnborough. There were 46 witnesses and affidavits were received from 24 others. Twelve interest groups, such as de Havillands and BOAC, were represented by a total of seventeen barristers. As is the way with barristers many had other concurrent commitments and their attendances were sometimes intermittent which must have made their understanding of difficult technical matters even more difficult than it already was.

List of counsel and whom they represented[6]

Sir Lionel Heald	
Mr. Graham	
Mr. Bevan	The Attorney General
Sir Hartley Shawcross	
Mr. Winn	
Mr. Fisher	The de Havilland Companies
Mr. Rimmer	
Mr. Browne	BOAC and SAA.
Mr. Shaw	The relatives of some of the deceased passengers
Mr. Cripps	The Ministry of Supply
Mr. Grant	The Ministry of Transport and Civil Aviation

Mr. Scarman	
Mr. Allen	The Air Registration Board
Mr. Whitford	Aero-Research Limited (The manufacturer of Redux)
Mr. MacCrindle	The British Air Line Pilots Association and two members of the crew
Mr. Tilling	The Navigators and Engineer Officers Union
Mr. Everington	Normalair Limited

Each day the court stenographers took down the words of the lawyers and the witnesses and had them transcribed in time for the Court to have them the following morning. Every few days the proceedings started with a list of corrections compiled by the various counsel. In all some 1,530 pages were typed and multiple copies printed, an average of almost 70 pages per day for 22 days. Although it was a public inquiry, and the final report was published, the transcript was kept closed, the original intention being to keep it so until 2030.

The transcript is of necessity often repetitive as the barristers covered the same ground with different witnesses, sometimes seeking better understanding and sometimes seeking differences between the witness' opinions which, with one or two exceptions, they largely failed to do. The main areas of difference were: the questioning of the reliability of Redux joints by Mr. Jablonsky, Mr. Tye's search for an alternative explanation for the cabin explosions and the different values for the stress levels in the fuselage calculated by de Havillands and the RAE, and even this was eventually settled with an armistice.

Much of the inquiry covered events that have already been related here and it would be tedious to repeat them. What follows is a brief outline of the proceedings except where new material was introduced or areas of contention arose. In order to make the proceedings easier to follow the text sometimes ignores the strict chronology of the hearings and deals more with themes. For this reason some of the witness' separate examinations have been joined together; Sir Arnold Hall, for example, made eight separate appearances, although some ran over from one day to the next. Even so the story that emerges from the hearings is at times confusing as different counsel took up different themes with the same witness or repeated the same themes with different witnesses. The development of the Court's understanding of the important topic of stress and fatigue and how it affected the Comet is particularly tortuous. It is presented here as logically as possible without destroying the feeling that it evolved in a court room by virtue of a sophisticated question-and-answer game rather than the logical progression of a lecture.

Some of the information that emerged during the inquiry has also been used in other parts of the text, such as in the account of the deliberations that took place before the Comets were allowed to fly again.

After such a comprehensive investigation and report from the RAE it might be thought that there was no need for a public inquiry but for a series of events as complicated and important as these it served several purposes. It provided a second look at the RAE investigation, which really just amounted to a very long expert witness statement. It obliged the scientists and engineers to explain, in everyday words, concepts that might have been unclear to non-specialists, rather in the manner of lawyers presenting a complex case to a jury. It allowed the experts to expand on the opinions they expressed in their statements and in the RAE investigation and to be questioned on ideas advanced by the barristers. It also provided an opportunity for other interested parties to air their views and opinions and for some areas not covered by the Farnborough investigation to be explored.

In truth it was unlikely that one of the lawyers would turn out to be a closet stress-mathematician, able to point out a mistake in Hall's calculations and upset the conclusions of the Farnborough investigation. Indeed the barristers frequently made comments to the effect that they neither understood the engineering concepts involved nor the mathematics that underpinned them but that did not stop them testing the witnesses who on occasion almost appeared to be on trial themselves.

At times the inquiry seemed like a clash between C. P. Snow's two cultures: that of the lawyers who preferred statutes, case law, logic and forensic questioning and the scientists and engineers who preferred observation, experiment and mathematics. It led to endless misunderstanding, incomprehension and, at times, irritation. Only a few of the participants managed to bridge the gap, Lord Cohen being one and Sir Arnold Hall and the assessors being others. The barristers were left to proceed in the only way they knew how, by trying to get a superficial understanding of the complex topics they were dealing with, relying on their own technical advisers and, at times, seemingly endless and pointless questioning usually taking as their starting points the pre-inquiry statements made by the witnesses. Many of these were people who, during the course of their careers, might reasonably have expected not to have had to defend their actions in open court. Most coped with it well but for some their hours, sometimes days, in the witness box must have been an ordeal, particularly if they were exposed to the sort of barbed remarks and hostile questioning that barristers usually reserve for people they wish to discredit. On a few occasions Lord Cohen had to rein in the more enthusiastic barristers when their forensic instincts got the better of them.

It might be wondered whether a legal context such as this was an appropriate forum for the truth to be arrived at. Inevitably many of the counsel had their clients' interests as their highest priority. This is not to criticise them, for that is what they were paid to do, but it may be a strategy more appropriate for situations where criminality or financial liability is at issue, which it was not here. On the other hand some of the scientists and engineers, particularly Hall, Walker and Harper, could seem excessively precise and pedantic at times, perhaps mindful that any generalisation they made might be used against them at a later date and perhaps because they knew they were dealing with the main points of contention. It is also possible for barristers, by clever or persistent questioning, to extract an answer that the witness might not have given had he been allowed more time to consider it, perhaps in a less-stressful environment. It is one of the failings of interrogations, or for that matter torture, that the questioner may get the answer he or she is seeking rather than the correct one. Lawyers, in their way of dealing with scientific and medical matters, often expect from witnesses a precision that the real world does not provide and they sometimes have difficulty with the concept of probability that such people have to live with in their professional lives. It takes considerable confidence to resist such pressure, often applied many times and in different forms.

Whether the inquiry produced value for money is debatable. It altered little if anything in the RAE report which the Court accepted in its entirety, indeed it was hard to see how it could have done otherwise. The changes to official procedures and suggestions for improvements to future marks of the Comet would probably have happened anyway but the questions and answers did provide new information, as well as expanding other areas of the report and they certainly made it more understandable. By the end of it no person, or organisation, was found to have been culpable, indeed Lord Cohen seemed to go out of his way at times to make sure that blame was not attributed.

The official task of the Court was to provide answers to five questions set for them by the Attorney-General: (abridged here and for each accident)

1)   What was the cause of the accident?

2)   If several factors caused the accident what were such factors and to what extent was each contributory?

3)   Was the accident due to the act or default or negligence of any party?

4)   At the time of the accident:
   a) Had the aircraft been properly maintained?
   b) Was the aircraft airworthy?
   c) Was there a valid Certificate of Airworthiness?
   d) Was there a valid Certificate of Maintenance?
   e) Was the radio station of the aircraft serviceable?
   f) Was the aircraft properly loaded and trimmed?
   g) Were all members of the crew properly licensed and experienced and if not did this affect the safety of the aircraft or contribute to the accident?

5)   What steps should be taken to increase the safety of civil aircraft?[7]

Chapter 20

THE HEARINGS BEGIN

Sir Lionel Heald, who represented the Attorney-General, and therefore the people, explained in his opening address that the inquiry was a 'fact finding tribunal' and that counsel were not there to 'attack or defend anybody'. The purpose of the inquiry was to present all the relevant facts and technical information and to satisfy the public that 'no stone has been left unturned' in determining the cause of the crashes. The second aim was to see that the cause of the crashes, if possible, would not be repeated while at the same time not making conditions that would inhibit future advances in aviation.[1]

Heald recounted the history of the Comet project and the circumstances of the two accidents.[2] He pointed out the difficulty of making a cabin able to withstand the pressure needed to keep its passengers safe and comfortable at altitude while at the same time being light enough to be able to be lifted into the air.[3] Nothing wrong had been discovered with the alloy that had been used but he said that the cabin had been found wanting in its ability to withstand the stresses of repeated pressurisations. At the time at which the Comet had been designed and built the view of the responsible authorities had been that if a structure had adequate static strength, say to twice the working pressure, then it would have adequate fatigue strength. He gave an outline of de Havillands' tests and the RAE investigation and its findings. Nothing was said by Heald that was controversial or would be disagreed with by any of the counsel present and much of what was to come would only serve to confirm it.

The first witnesses were uncontroversial witnesses as to fact. They were the people who had flown YP to Rome, serviced it there, predicted the weather it would fly through, heard its last, interrupted, message and later brought most of its wreckage to the surface of the sea.[4, 5] Translated affidavits were read out from the people on Elba who had seen its broken parts hit the sea and then searched for survivors.[6] Unfortunately the engineer officer of YP, Mr. F. C. Macdonald, whose few remains had been found by the salvage crews some weeks after the crash, had allowed his licence to elapse. No doubt it was a slip of the memory on his part and it made no difference to the findings of the inquiry, or to anything really, but it provided an opportunity for criticism which was not missed by the Court.

Professor Fornari presented his evidence through an interpreter.[7] He added little to what has already been described in Chapter 12. The head and chest injuries had been the primary cause of death and had been produced by impact with the roof and sides of the cabin and the backs of the seats. The lungs had been damaged by explosive decompression before death but had not been the cause of death but these two sets of injuries had been almost simultaneous. He described lacerations between groups of cells in the heart muscle which he said was characteristic of an explosive decompression.* The upper and lower limb fractures had mostly happened after death and were consistent with hitting resistant surfaces, such as parts of the cabin, perhaps during the descent, and then hitting the surface of the sea. The bodies showed scalds, not burns, which he had initially postulated had been caused by their having come into contact with hot fluid in the cabin but he agreed that this was not based on any hard evidence. All these injuries were consistent within the group.

The first note of dissent from the medical part of the RAE report (Part 12) concerned the cause of the lung injuries.[8] Fornari was quite definite in his opinion that these could only have been caused by an explosive decompression and not by blast or hitting the sea at some speed as Farnborough had said could not be excluded. There were no signs of there having been an explosion to produce a blast injury and hitting the sea would have produced an external injury limited to the front or back of the body whereas the victims' injuries were uniform. Mr. Scarman** (representing the ARB) pressed him on this, pointing out that he had little experience of lung injury caused by explosive decompression which Fornari countered by saying that he had a lot of experience of people falling from great heights into water.[9]

Dr. Donald Teare followed Fornari.[10] He agreed with Fornari's view that the lung injury could only be explained by explosive decompression and he doubted that these injuries were severe enough to cause death almost instantaneously although they appeared to have happened very early in the sequence of events. Dr. Teare said that he had not seen the part of the RAE report (Part 11) which described the model used to demonstrate the effects of explosive decompression. He had seen the RAE medical report (Part 12), however, and was therefore aware of their work with guinea pigs. In addition he had conducted some experiments of his own at Farnborough using dead human skin, covered in clothing, floating on water with burning kerosene on its surface. As in the crash victims the clothing was not burned but the skin was scalded and produced the same microscopic picture. He also disagreed with the Institute of Aviation Medicine's explanation for the darkening of the skin of the victims of the Naples crash having been caused by post-mortem sunburn. He felt that this was more likely to have been caused by heat on the surface of the water although he did not expand on this.

* Fornari said in evidence that this phenomenon had been described in previous cases of explosive decompression[7] but it seems not to be an accepted finding in current forensic pathology practice nor was it mentioned in a NASA paper on explosive decompression[11] although Fornari was quite definite about it in his report. Teare does not mention it in any of his reports and it remains something of a puzzle. It is possible it was an artefact.

** Later Lord Scarman. He is best known for chairing the public inquiry into the race riots in Brixton in 1981. He was called to the bar in 1936 but remained without a brief until the war which he spent in the RAF. He became an appeal judge and later a Law Lord. He had a striking appearance and made several controversial judgements, including upholding a charge of blasphemy.

The areas of disagreement between Fornari and Teare on one side and the Institute of Aviation Medicine on the other were relatively minor and made no difference to any conclusions that the Court reached. Curiously the official report of the Inquiry persisted in referring to the scalds as burns[12] although all the medical evidence had emphasised the difference.

The Court spent some time looking into the decision to resume Comet services after the Elba crash. Events had soon proved this to be wrong and it was clearly an area where blame might be attached to persons or organisations and the barristers' forensic instincts were aroused. The Court was more concerned with whether the process of reaching this decision was a reasonable and proper one rather then whether the decision was correct. The first stage in this process had been the work of the Abell Committee which has been covered in Chapter 13. Abell himself appeared after Air Chief Marshall Sir Frederick Bowhill, the Chairman of the Air Safety Board, who was fitted in early because of his other commitments although, as things turned out, he must have wished that they had prevented his attendance altogether.

Mr. J. M. Shaw acted for the relatives of some of the deceased passengers who were naturally concerned that the Comet flights had resumed prematurely after the Elba crash. He started by asking the Air Chief Marshall whether the ASB had considered all the possible causes of the Elba accident. Bowhill replied that they had. "Did they," Shaw asked, "consider the possibility of the failure of the pressure cabin and that it might have been caused by fatigue" (they had). "Did they consider whether it was due to some inherent design fault in the Comet or just a chance happening" (they had). "The point was," Shaw said, "that an inherent defect would risk the same accident happening again." Sir Frederick declined to accept that, saying that the Abell modifications covered all possibilities. On further questioning he was unable to say which modifications would prevent the fatigue failure of the cabin which he had already acknowledged they had considered a possibility if not a probability.

Shaw then turned to the report on the Calcutta crash which had concluded that the accident had been caused by an intense storm. The board's minute to the minister seemed to suggest that they had some doubts about this and Sir Frederick acknowledged, under questioning, that there might be some factors common to both accidents* (and that there might, therefore, be an inherent design fault). In spite of this, Bowhill agreed, the board still recommended that the Comet could resume flights. Shaw followed this with the sort of unanswerable question beloved of barristers, "How many aircraft" he asked, "would have to crash from an unknown cause before the Air Safety Board recommended that they should not be allowed to fly anymore?" Lord Cohen, rather unsportingly, intervened at this point and the question was left unanswered but the point had been made.[13]

Bowhill's calvary was not yet over. After a more gentle interlude from other counsel Mr. R. A. MacCrindle, representing the British Airline Pilots Association, took up the cross-examination. He asked whether the board was aware of the continuing successful

---

* Hall, a member of the ASB, clearly did not agree with this. See below.

retrieval of wreckage (they were) and that examination of wreckage was the best way of determining whether fatigue was a factor (they were). Would it not then have been 'humanly possible', Mr. MacCrindle asked, to have waited to see if more wreckage might appear that would reveal the cause of the crash. Sir Frederick agreed that it would have been 'humanly possible' to have waited but at the time little had been recovered and it was felt that little more would be recovered.

Mr. T. H. Tilling, representing the Navigators and Engineer Officers' Union, brought up the question of the medical evidence. It was unclear exactly what medical information the board had access to when they were preparing their minute but Sir Frederick said that they were aware that the lungs of the victims showed that there had been an explosion, that there were head injuries and that there might have been a violent disintegration of the aircraft. They did not know how that had come about but thought it was likely to have been caused by some means other than increased pressure within the cabin. (In other words either a primary structural failure at a normal pressure differential for that altitude or a secondary event, caused by something else such as a wing falling off leaving a hole in the cabin or producing such a stressful manoeuvre that the cabin disintegrated.)

The possible connection with the Calcutta crash was pursued. The recommendation of the Indian authorities was that the wreckage should be removed to the UK for further examination and tests and that the tailplane be examined by carrying out static strength tests. The short report from the RAE about the Calcutta crash contained a note that its findings could be revised in the light of further tests on the tailplane. As the board considered that there might be a connection between the two crashes should they not have waited for these tests to have been carried out? Sir Frederick agreed that they had made their recommendation without waiting for these results, that the cause of the Elba crash was unknown and that it might have been the same as in the Calcutta crash. After this Sir Frederick must have stepped down from the witness box with some relief.

Dr. Hall, now Sir Arnold Hall, in his capacity as a member of the ASB, was also asked about his part in the decision to resume the Comet services. Hall agreed with the ASB's advice to the minister and did not in any way try to disassociate himself from it. His view was that no conclusions could have been drawn from the wreckage at the time the ASB gave its advice.

His reasons for supporting the ASB's decision were first that they were very unlikely to get an answer from the wreckage. Even the navy at that time thought they would be extremely lucky if they got much within two years because of the depth of the sea and the presence of an old minefield.

Secondly would any reasonable man think there was a connection between the Elba and Calcutta crashes? If there were no connection then it was not the usual practice to stop an aircraft type flying because of a single crash. A Lockheed Constellation, for example, had disappeared over the Atlantic the previous evening and they were still flying. Most air crashes were not due to a fundamental problem in the aircraft but to a variety of other things such as pilot error or maintenance problems but there was always concern to see if there was any 'family resemblance' in the crashes. The Calcutta aircraft was at 7,000 feet and in a storm, the Elba aircraft was at 30,000 feet and in clear weather, so the circumstances were completely different. The Indian inquiry had found that the crash was due to the storm and, secondarily, to an element of loss of control. Hall felt that there was no reason to doubt that, and even in the light of subsequent events he still felt he agreed with the findings of the Indian inquiry. So there was no family resemblance apart from possibly fire or explosion. They had discussed these topics with the ARB which, in turn, was in touch with the Abell Committee whose members had looked into it and made most of their modifications with fire or explosion in mind.

Thirdly there was concern about whether the sea water would steadily destroy the wreckage. In fact, that turned out not to be the case. On a piece of the tailplane there was a perfect imprint of a newspaper presumably from an impact at the time of the breakup or when it went into the sea.[14] It was still there after five months in the water but it disappeared within a day or two after its arrival at Farnborough, so in some respects the sea water actually preserved the findings.

Without the wreckage, Hall said, they were left with a 'type investigation' and this had been carried out by the Abell Committee. They were happy that that had been done well although the RAE was not involved with it. At the time he did not know about the de Havilland test nose and the number of reversals it had undergone.

Lord Brabazon was then called to give evidence about the same decision.[15] As the 'Grand Old Man' of British aviation he was treated more gently than the Air Chief Marshall had been but in any case he was well able to look after himself. He had an abundance of genial, upper-class, self-confidence not always, perhaps never, supported by a knowledge of detail. Nevertheless his was an entertaining appearance. He had been the chairman of the Air Registration Board since 1946 although the board had originated in 1933. Their chief duty was to issue Certificates of Airworthiness; as Brabazon put it, "Nothing can fly without our consent." From Brabazon's testimony it sounded a rather 'players and gentlemen' organisation with the technical experts being the players and Brabazon very much one of the gentlemen.* He deflected all the technical questions to Mr. Tye, their Chief Technical Officer and told the Court not to regard himself as "a second Hall." Technical matters were left to the technical people, the board dealt with matters of policy.

The ARB considered the Calcutta accident to be completely explained by the storm which, Brabazon said, would have broken any aircraft. They did not connect Elba and Calcutta in any way; Elba was completely unexplained at that time. This was really the only point of difference between them and the ASB. "The Comet was a machine which was being talked of all over the world as being, as it was indeed, the most remarkable machine in the world. We never took the action of grounding them, and I think it is wise to let you know straight away that if you grounded the type of every aeroplane that had an unexplained accident you would scarcely have a machine in the air today... We saw

---

* Bill Waterton, a test pilot for Glosters, later an aviation journalist, referred to the ARB as an "esteemed body of pioneer airmen and shipping experts."[16]

nothing in that accident which justified us in grounding it." He supported his view with the example of the Avro Tudors, two of which, he said, had disappeared but when the aeroplanes had been examined nothing wrong could be found and the Tudors went back in service. Considering what a terrible aeroplane the Tudor was this might not have been the best choice. Out of 33 built, four went on to crash after the two that disappeared, not to mention the prototype that had crashed earlier.

Even if BOAC had not grounded the Comets the ARB, Brabazon said, would not have withdrawn their Certificates of Airworthiness - "a very drastic thing to do."[17] But they did recommend to BOAC that the machine should be looked at very carefully.

Fig. 1/20 Sir Arnold Hall
(FAST Farnborough Air Sciences Trust).

Brabazon went on to say that they had never had much success in discovering the cause of an accident from wreckage recovered from the sea. The general opinion was that they would not get much more wreckage from the Elba crash and that it would not provide much help if they did. Later he said that they did not reconsider their decision in case further wreckage became available. "We came to the conclusion that it was ridiculous and impossible to wait for this remote possibility." Brabazon agreed that by the beginning of April more wreckage was being brought up "...but it was not leading us anywhere." He saw no reason to have another meeting.

The board was aware of the medical evidence but Brabazon said that it was "...extremely contradictory. We never really got much information from it. Some people said that the deaths were due to very rapid decompression. Others said they had hit something first and the decompression came perhaps later. It was all very involved and we could not really derive a lot from it."

Brabazon said that the ARB had been very concerned about metal fatigue over the last few years. However he seemed not to know what was in their own publications which had been related that morning by Sir Arnold. His response was a lordly, "Put that to Tye." Mr. MacCrindle (for the British Airlines Pilots Association) reminded him of the ARB Regulations published in January 1951, "You did not even know that?" "No."

After Brabazon's letter to the minister on 4 March recommending that the Comet services be resumed the board did not revisit its decision.[18]

Following his examination by Sir Lionel, Lord Brabazon made a statement to the Court which was revealing of his views.*[19] In it he said that he had no regrets about the decision he and his board had made with the information they had at the time and that he accepted responsibility for it. He regarded any advance in aviation as carrying a risk and that "every step in progress we have paid for in blood and treasure." The cause of the accident, in his view, was the "pioneering spirit of our race" and that we "...were conscious of the dangers that were lurking in the unknown" although the RAE had "tested every bit (and) it was not found wanting." It also contained the statement that it was "...metallurgy, not aeronautics, that is in the dock."

Brabazon had grown up in the early years of aviation when crashes and fatalities were commonplace and this no doubt had coloured his views, indeed the whole of his life had been one of joyful risk-taking. All of the people involved in the decision to resume services had come through a war where fatal air crashes were frequent and they probably shared Brabazon's views, at least to some extent. Judging by their willingness to continue flying, the public, too, seemed more tolerant of crashes than they are now and it was an altogether different, less safety-conscious and much less litigious, age. Nevertheless some of Brabazon's views seem more appropriate for a test pilot flying an experimental aeroplane in full knowledge of the risks involved than for members of the travelling public who were ignorant of the risks and just wanted to get to their destinations safely and trusted the authorities to see that they did so.

Brabazon no doubt had considerable influence with the board that he chaired and, as the strong character that he was, probably also in the ASB. It was untrue that the RAE had tested "every bit" of the aircraft and "not found it wanting" and his criticism of the alloy rather then the aircraft was later questioned. Nevertheless Sir Arnold had said that he agreed with the decision of the ASB and, judging by his appearances at the inquiry, he would have been well able to stand up to Lord Brabazon had he felt it necessary.

It is difficult to review the correctness of the decision to resume services when one already knows what followed. Even Lord Brabazon acknowledged that it had turned out to be the wrong decision but the question the Court had to answer was whether the process by which the decision had been reached was reasonable and whether it was correct given the information available at the time.

This process of reaching a decision involved the interested airline and manufacturer analysing the crash, examining the aircraft and making modifications to avoid a repeat of what they thought had caused the disaster. Their recommendation to resume flights was then reviewed by two independent, disinterested, authoritative bodies who concurred. Even then the minister could have vetoed the recommendation.

---

* This is reproduced in full in Appendix 3.

The Principal Films documentary suggested that commercial pressures from BOAC pushed the Comet back into service prematurely. Others have mentioned political pressures but there is no documentary proof of either. Of course pressures might have been applied verbally or the documents missed or destroyed so it is impossible to discount the possibility completely. It is quite obvious that BOAC would want its Comets back in service unless they knew that there was something incurably wrong with them. This was the reason for the two independent bodies, with no commercial imperatives to respond to, being asked for their recommendations. Even with the benefit of hindsight it would be hard to devise a more reasonable and balanced process and Lord Cohen's subsequent report made no criticism of it.

The correctness of the decision is less obvious. The circumstances of the Calcutta and Elba crashes were quite different and Hall and the ARB were surely right to consider that there was no 'family resemblance'. Elba was rather like the first of a serial murderer's killings; so far it was an isolated event and it would take another for a pattern to emerge. In the eyes of the people involved the only alternative to resuming services was to wait to see if more evidence would appear. But for how long would they wait? There was no thought of the enormous RAE investigation that was to come, let alone the tank tests, and the view was that little in the way of wreckage would be found and even if it were, it would be unlikely to provide an answer. There must have seemed no point in waiting indefinitely for an answer that was unlikely to come and Lord Cohen did not criticise their decision in his report.

In fact there was some good evidence. The medical findings from the Elba crash definitely pointed to an explosive decompression of the cabin and that it appeared to originate in the roof of the forward part of the cabin although admittedly they did not say why it had happened. There was nothing in the autopsies to suggest a chemical explosion or a cabin fire and there were no reports of turbulence that could have led to a loss of control. There was also nothing to disprove some other spectacular structural mishap, such as a wing falling off, which could have produced a manoeuvre violent enough to have disrupted the cabin. Equally there was nothing to suggest such an unlikely event. The medical evidence seems not to have carried the weight that it should have done, perhaps because it came from a different discipline and was not fully understood or its significance appreciated. Brabazon, in particular, seemed uncomprehending and dismissive of it.

After YY crashed in the sea near Naples on 8 April the ARB promptly withdrew the Comet's Certificate of Airworthiness.[20] This provided the answer to Mr. Shaw's question to Air Chief Marshal Bowhill. It took *two* Comets to crash from an unknown cause before they were not allowed to fly anymore.

Chapter 21

THE STRESS DEBATE BEGINS

(For those preferring a more direct route to the Court's understanding of how stress affected the Comet there is a summary at the end of Chapter 24.)

Sir Arnold Hall made the largest and the most important contribution to the hearings. He provided lucid explanations of the findings of the Farnborough investigation and the events that befell YP and YY as well as explaining much of the science behind them. His was by far the biggest contribution to the Court's understanding of the effects of stress on the Comet's fuselage. He also managed to do this while, almost unfailingly, remaining calm and polite as he repeated the same explanations to different (and sometimes the same) barristers day after day. The gradual unravelling of how stress and fatigue had affected the Comet was to be the most important part of the inquiry.

Sir Arnold explained that he was consulted for the first time after the Elba crash but before Naples. The request had come from Group Captain Tweedie of the AIB and the wreckage was being sent to Farnborough for that reason. This was common practice but it was only after the Naples crash that he had been asked by the minister to start a full scale investigation, quite a different prospect, he said, from just answering specific questions. He had thought it would be a thankless task but took it on anyway.

Under gentle questioning by Sir Lionel Heald on day three,[1] Hall explained that the RAE investigation fell into two parts, the examination of the wreckage and the examination of the technical features of the aircraft although the two were closely linked. They had started with no preconceived ideas and therefore had to consider all the possible causes of the accidents which inevitably meant that many of the lines of investigation would prove fruitless. They had to proceed on the basis that little of YP or YY would be recovered. As things turned out more and more wreckage from YP appeared at Farnborough but it had been a long and difficult task piecing them together on the wooden frame. Using a diagram and photographs of the wreckage of YP Hall pointed out the main failures in the aeroplane and then demonstrated the sequence of the breakup using a scale model* which had been built so that it could be pulled apart in the way that the aircraft was thought to have exploded. They had found nothing in the wreckage that was inconsistent with the sequence of the mid-air breakup described in their report.

Hall was then asked about the ADF windows.[2] This part of the wreckage of YP was

---

* This is preserved at the Science Museum in London but is no longer (2013) on display.

Fig. 1/21 The model Comet used in the inquiry to show how YP disintegrated, (author's photograph courtesy of The Science Museum).

in the Court as an exhibit (also preserved at the Science Museum but again no longer on display) and its dust sheet was removed to reveal the split that ran between the port corners of both ADF windows and then extended backwards from the starboard corner of the rear window and forwards from both front corners of the front window.[3] There was no doubt about the split, Hall said, but the question was whether it had started there. This led to an explanation of the technique of fracture analysis.[4]

Fracture analysis depended on being able to detect the cause of the fracture from the appearance of the fracture surfaces and then using this to work out the sequence of events. A tensile fracture could be differentiated from a shear fracture and both were different from a fatigue fracture. In the wreckage of YP all the fractures appeared to run away from the area of the rear ADF window indicating that the failure started here. There was also a compression buckle lower down which was characteristic of the release of pressure as a flap of the fuselage skin was flung outwards.[4]

The Comet tested in the tank at Farnborough, YU, failed in a similar place to YP in that it was near a cutout, in YU's case the forward port escape hatch. This failure, Hall explained, started at a particular rivet hole and fracture analysis showed that the crack ran away from the window in three different directions. Again a compression buckle had been produced as the internal pressure was released.

Hall thought that YP's breakup happened suddenly when it was flying normally at about 30,000 feet. The medical evidence heard that morning supported the idea of the sudden breakup of the cabin. The alternative aetiologies for the lung damage suggested by the Farnborough doctors did not in any way contradict this.[5]

The conclusion that Hall and his establishment had arrived at was that the pressure cabin had burst and that the burst was in the vicinity of the rear ADF window. The cause of the burst was less certain at first but there was no evidence of a bomb or of any kind of chemical explosion or overpressure and eventually the arrival at Farnborough of the roof of the forward part of the cabin clinched the argument that it was a fatigue failure at normal working pressure. The tank test, Hall said, had been done to cover all possibilities rather than just thinking that they would produce a fatigue failure (although it is difficult to see what else it could have been testing). The day before YU failed in the tank he had discussed the test with James Taylor who was in charge of it. They had both thought it would go on for a long time.[6]

The questioning then moved to metal fatigue. Sir Arnold explained that it was impossible to detect incipient metal fatigue and any crack (a 'fatigue origin') that presaged failure might be so small as to be virtually undetectable. In practice the best way of dealing with it was to determine a 'safe fatigue life', that is the life predicted for a particular structure during which fatigue failure is extremely unlikely. This is based on design characteristics, stress calculations and, most of all, on tests. The results of these tests can be displayed as the S/N curve for the structure where S is the size of the stress cycle applied causing failure and N is the number of cycles completed at the time of failure.[7] The curve is produced by taking a number of nominally identical samples and subjecting them to cyclic stressing, each with different stress amplitude or range, and then recording the number of cycles to failure of each sample. Each failure is then plot-

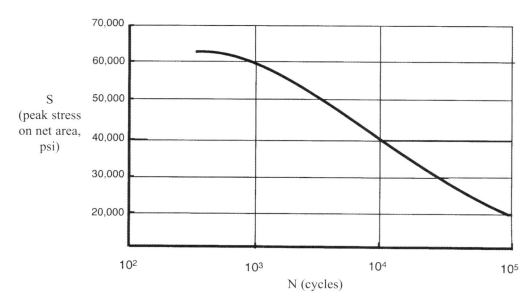

Fig. 2/21 S/N curve for DTD 546B (specimen width 0.5 inches, thickness 0.035 inches with 0.125 inches diameter hole)[8]

ted on a graph of stress amplitude or range against the number of cycles to failure and a curve drawn through the points as shown in figure 2/21.

The N axis has a logarithmic scale to contain the increasingly large number of cycles involved. The static strength of the structure is at the extreme left of the curve (not shown) where $N = 1$ and S is the stress at the point of failure. If S is a large fraction of this stress, 70% or 80%, the structure or sample will fail after 2-3,000 cycles. If the stress is only 30% or 40%, the life of the sample will be much longer, some 10^5 or 10^6 cycles, before failure. For aluminium alloys the stress range at failure continues to reduce with increasing cycles even at 10^8 or 10^9 cycles, although the line is almost horizontal at that stage. The S/N curve was to be an important concept in what followed.

The S/N curve has its limitations, however. Even with simple, nominally-identical pieces the test results show a scatter. The more complicated the structure and the smaller the stress, the greater the scatter. The numbers of cycles causing failure of different specimens of the same structure subjected to the same stress might therefore be different but the complete curve would have the same general shape as the above. To accommodate this, the single line of the S/N curve above would appear as a band which becomes wider as the scatter increases as the magnitude of the stress decreases, perhaps to as big a spread as 1:100. Hall considered that the scatter for the Comet's pressure cabin life would be about 1 to 9, in other words the weakest would fail in about ⅓ the number of cycles as the average and the strongest at about 3 times the average. This 1 to 9 spread came from the experience the RAE had in fatigue testing.[9]

If the fatigue life of YU, the test aircraft, was taken as unity then in comparison YP and YY had lives reduced by factors of 2.4 and 3.4. It was reasonable, Hall said, to assume that YP and YY were the weakest aircraft in the cohort, and for that reason had crashed first at about 3,000 hours, and that among the remaining seven there would be a spread of somewhat longer fatigue lives, perhaps to as much as (3,000 x 9) 27,000 hours. YU was then somewhere about the middle of the spread at about 9,000 hours.[10]

The main cause of stress in the Comet fuselage was the pressure differential rather than buffeting in flight and the taking off and landing, which together only amounted to about 6% of the total.[11] Each flight involved one pressure cycle. The stage length for the Comet in airline service was around three hours, so the ratio of flying hours to pressure cycles was about 3:1. The fatigue life of a fuselage could therefore be best expressed as the number of flights, (pressure) cycles or reversals or, less accurately, flying hours. This was to cause some confusion later on when the barristers mixed up cycles, reversals and hours. The life of a wing was more dependent on inflight buffeting and therefore on flying hours.*

The stress in the skin near the corners of various cutouts was calculated by the RAE to be about 70% of its ultimate strength. This placed it towards the left of the S/N curve with an accordingly much shorter fatigue life than if it had been, say, 40% of the ulti-

---

* For clarity this text will use 'cycle' to represent one pressurised flight rather than 'reversal' which is usually taken to be equal to half a cycle but in the inquiry was used synonymously with 'cycle'. The most commonly used currency in the inquiry was 'hours' but where available the number of cycles will also be given.

mate. This value for the maximum stress was an extrapolated figure because, Hall explained, the strain gauges could not be used right at the edge of the cutouts. This would prove to be a bone of contention between the RAE and de Havillands.

Identifying fatigue in a fracture caused by high-level stress, i.e. the stress towards the left of the S/N curve, was less easy than in a fracture caused by low-level stress, mainly because the process had not gone on as long. It was made even more difficult by having to look at the edge of a thin sheet rather than at a more substantial piece of metal. Nevertheless signs of fatigue were found at the starboard rear corner of YP's rear ADF window in the fuselage skin underneath the reinforcing plate but, Hall said, this was not what he relied on for deciding the cause of the disaster that befell YP. The main factor was the demonstration of the short fatigue life of YU's cabin in the tank test but, as he pointed out, it was interesting that in one of the areas where one would expect a failure there was this fatigue fracture. They had found what they expected to find in a place where they could expect to find it.[12]

Other cracks, manufacturing cracks, identified by the locating holes at their ends, had also been found in the wreckage of YP.[13, 14, 15] One was probably made when the hole for a rivet was dimpled, a second had been 'located' but had then progressed and had only been stopped by running into a rivet hole. Another, at the port front corner of the reinforcing plate of the rear ADF window, had been successfully 'located' but had then run on during the breakup of the aircraft. These cracks, Hall said, indicated that the manufacturing process was capable of fracturing the skin material but he was more concerned about manufacturing cracks that had not been seen, which he called 'incipient cracks', and had therefore escaped being drilled. These cracks would produce stress concentrations in the metal at their ends (see Appendix 5), hastening the development of local areas of fatigue and hence would tend to propagate. There was no proof that they had existed, or had hastened the end of YP, but if they did exist they may have made its already short fatigue life even shorter. They might also have contributed to the scatter in fatigue lives between different fuselages.

It was quite possible that the redistribution of stress produced by the initial fracture would almost immediately have caused the manufacturing crack at the port front corner to extend. It may even have taken that particular route because there was already a crack there but there was nothing to say that it had initiated it.[16] The undoubted existence of manufacturing cracks, and the rather-more-doubtful existence of incipient cracks, generated much questioning. There was no evidence that they were implicated in YP's breakup but they were clearly undesirable.

Hall's replies to Sir Lionel had been rather like the explanations offered by a benign science master to a polite and interested, but rather undemanding, fourth former; the questions were not very testing and the exchanges certainly not argumentative but nevertheless they had covered most of the ground.

Some days later Mr. Shaw continued the questioning by enquiring into the state of knowledge at the time the Comet was designed. Metal fatigue had long been known about as had the existence of stress concentrations at cutouts, and rivet holes were cutouts Sir Arnold pointed out. The magnitude of the stress concentration depended on the design of the cutout. At a sharp corner, for example, the stress could in theory be infinite although in practice it would not be so. The S/N curve was also known about but the part of it dealing with large stresses had only become common knowledge within the last ten years or so.[17] Building a large pressure cabin was also not new; the difference with the Comet was that the pressure (differential) was higher but that was a problem of extending existing knowledge rather then breaking new ground.[18]

The first failure in the tank showed where the highest stress was and so where to put the strain gauges for the later tests to discover the actual stress values. The gauge measured the average stress over its

Fig. 3/21 Hartley William Shawcross, Baron Shawcross, by Walter Stoneman (copyright National Portrait Gallery).

length but was too large to measure the stress over a small area such as a rivet hole. Hall said that strain gauges had been in use for some time, were reliable, and that he would have expected de Havillands to have used them and therefore to have found high stress levels around the windows. He thought a stress level of 70% should have caused some alarm.[19]

An important piece of new information that had emerged from the RAE investigations, Sir Arnold said, was that a specimen that had passed a static test of twice its normal loading could nevertheless have a stress concentration of 70% of its ultimate strength at normal loading.[17] So a pressure of 8.25 psi (1P) in the Comet's cabin produced a maximum stress of 70% of ultimate but doubling the pressure to 16.5 psi (2P), which might reasonably be expected to increase the stress to 100% of ultimate, and therefore cause it to fail, did not, in fact, do so. The reason for this, Hall explained, was that plastic flow occurred in the material when it approached its ultimate strength* and this relieved the stress concentration. The general level of stress in the Comet fuselage

---

* Actually rather before this. Plastic flow would start when the material reached its proof or yield point.

approximated to that in a plain cylinder and was probably about 20 or 25% of ultimate and only rose to 70% at the edge of the cutouts (see Appendix 5).

Hall accepted that de Havillands had tested their fuselage sections to 2P and with the knowledge available at the time they could reasonably have assumed that the stress levels could not have been as high as 70%. Nevertheless he would have wanted to know what the calculations showed and then assessed the situation as a whole.

At this point Sir Hartley Shawcross,* representing de Havillands, intervened. It was his job to see that no mud, or as little mud as possible, stuck to de Havillands' reputation. Shawcross pointed out that de Havillands had done calculations which did not suggest such a high stress level and that they had used strain gauges at an earlier stage which had confirmed their figures and had reassured them.[20]

Discussions about stress levels continued. A rivet hole in the high stress field near the edge of a large cutout would raise the stress even further. The percentage increase with such a rivet hole was the same wherever it was but if it was already in a high-stress field it started from a higher base. As the rate of change of stress increases as the cutout is approached, the nearer the rivet hole was to the edge of the cutout, the higher would be the (absolute) stress. Exacerbating this was the discovery that some of the rivet holes were closer to the the edge of the ADF cutouts in YP than was specified (0.24 inches rather than 0.3) A similar error had been found around the ADF window in the tank Comet (YU) indicating that de Havillands' inspection and quality control systems were not all that they might have been. None of the failures could be attributed to this but, like the manufacturing cracks, it was clearly undesirable.

Under questioning from Mr. Tilling, Sir Arnold agreed that he was unable to say definitely which corner of the rear ADF window had failed first but the presence of the fatigue crack at the starboard rear corner tipped the balance of probability in its favour. In any case these fractures, once they started, would be almost simultaneous.[21]

Mr. Tilling then raised the possibility of the cabin exploding because its internal pressure had built up to the point where it exceeded its static strength. There was inevitably some variation of cabin pressure, Hall said, the system tending to hunt a little, but only between about 8 and 8.75 psi. The two safety valves were independent and considered to be reliable and there was no evidence of a malfunction in any of the valves in the wreckage. The cabin pressure, Hall thought, was therefore unlikely to

---

* Sir Hartley Shawcross (1902-2003) was the best known of the counsel present. He had a firm grasp of the facts of the case and probably the most difficult case to argue but, by his own admission, he was not blessed with the gift of succinctness.[22] Later in the hearings he repeatedly corrected the other barristers but even he struggled with some of the more mathematical concepts. He had been the Attorney-General in the Attlee government and had made his name at the Nuremberg trials and was still a Labour MP at the time of the hearings. He was on the right-wing of the Labour Party and was long expected to cross the floor of the Commons to join the Conservatives, earning himself the nickname of Sir Shortly Floorcross. At the age of 95 he married for the third time, his first two wives having died. His family opposed the marriage but he defeated them by eloping to Gibraltar.[23] In his autobiography Shawcross described Hall as "a man of the very greatest ability" and found him a "most difficult witness to cross-examine." In spite of asking him over a thousand questions he "obtained very little to damage his conclusions." [24]

reach a dangerous level. It would have needed multiple faults and the failure of the flight engineer to notice what was happening.[25]

Sir Hartley continued the questioning. He started by alluding to another aircraft having crashed on the way to Rome on the same day as the Naples Comet crash.[26] This type, which was not British, had had several unexplained crashes but, he said, had been allowed to continue to fly,* implying that the Comet had been treated unfairly.

Shawcross then presented de Havillands' calculations. These showed that the maximum stress around the windows was 26,000 psi and around the doors 24,000 (40 and 37% respectively of its ultimate strength). They had then done strain gauge tests on the test pieces to confirm or rebut their calculations. Some 50 were used and they showed comparable or even lower values. They were not used at the windows of the cabin section but were placed around the door which was thought to be representative. Calculations had predicted that the windows would fail at 20 psi, and in a static test of a separate window panel it had failed at 19.75,[27] suggesting that their calculations were fairly accurate.

De Havillands had gone on to do tests of the nose section, which by that time included an ADF window, up to 2P. It was not possible to attach strain gauges to all of it but they felt it was reasonable to assume that if it survived a pressure of 2P then no part was more than 50% of ultimate strength at 1P. Hall agreed that it might have seemed reasonable at the time but commented that he would still have placed strain gauges around the ADF window but, as Shawcross lost no time in pointing out, he had not used strain gauges until after they had had a failure and de Havillands did not have a failure. Their strain gauges had been used more to detect signs of imminent failure at a time when the specimen could not be observed (i.e. when it was in the decompression chamber). They assumed that the ADF windows were covered by a similar cutout on which they had already used strain gauges.

The RAE's figure of 70% of ultimate strength had been an extrapolation to the edge of a cutout from a number of points further away. Shawcross dismissed extrapolation as "...the fertile mother of error." Hall agreed that it could be but said that he felt confident of these figures. The highest actual reading was 53%. Towards the edge there would be plastic flow, Shawcross said, which would relieve the stress.[28] Hall agreed but said that plastic flow in itself would suggest that the stress was too high. The RAE figures for the ADF windows were lower than for the side windows but not by very much and they had only been able to measure the stress on the doubling plates and, Hall thought, the skin beneath it probably had higher levels. At 8.25 psi the stress at a corner of the doubling plate was 28,000 psi and at a similar place on the number 2 starboard

---

* This was presumably an Italian-operated Douglas DC-3 heading for Rome which crashed on 10 April 1954, i.e. not quite the same day as the Naples crash, with no loss of life. Certainly a lot of DC-3s had crashed over the years but that was mainly because there were a lot of them. Over 10,000 (plus nearly 5,000 of a Soviet version) had been built and thousands of them were still flying in 1954. Production started in 1936 and there are said to be over 400 still in limited use. The number of Comet 1s and 1As that reached airline and military service was nineteen, and some of those were in service for very short periods of time. It was disingenuous of Shawcross to compare the two.

window, 35,100.[29] Hall said that they would have expected the failure to be close to the corner of a cutout but exactly which cutout was impossible to say in advance. It might be in a different place from where the cabin would fail in a static test but it would usually be somewhere similar.

This exchange between Hall and Shawcross was confused by references to different parts of the report and measurements being made at different pressure differentials which made Shawcross increasingly irritated, at one point saying to Sir Arnold "Would you just listen?"[30] This may have been part of Shawcross' court room technique to goad witnesses into saying things they might not otherwise have said but it is difficult to see what purpose it served when dealing with an eminent scientist who was doing his best to help the Court.

Shawcross moved onto the history of fatigue in aircraft. In Dr. Williams' 1946 paper[31] the view was that fatigue strength was adequately covered by static testing and this was what was laid down by the ARB and the international and American authorities. In their 1948 and 1951 regulations the ARB said "Attention is drawn to the fact that certain portions of a pressure cabin structure may be loaded for long periods to a stress which is a large proportion of the ultimate strength of the material. In conventional design the construction will usually be acceptable under such conditions if proof and ultimate (load) factors of 1.33 and 2 respectively are achieved when the aeroplane is in level flight at cruising speed... with maximum differential pressure... applied." But, as Hall pointed out, they also said "special attention should be paid to the prevention of failure from fatigue, crack propagation and creep, associated with prolonged and alternating loading of the pressure cabin structure."[32]

Williams' paper dealt with the occasional very high manoeuvre and weather loads on wings. The loads on a pressure cabin were different in that it was pressurised every flight but nobody at that time thought of fatigue in a pressure cabin as a serious danger. Hall said that discussions about it had started in 1951-52, unsurprisingly Shawcross thought a little later, but it was not until 1953 that the ARB began to consider whether repeated loading tests were necessary. By the time of the inquiry the US regulatory body was contemplating a need for 10,000 cycles and the ARB 15,000, but neither had officially introduced it as a requirement for certification so de Havillands, with (almost) 18,000 cycles of the nose section, was well ahead of the regulations in force at the time and even appeared to be ahead of regulations that were being contemplated.

Was it not reasonable, Shawcross asked, for de Havillands to think from the 54,000 hour (18,000 cycles) tests that they had carried out in 1953 that the aircraft would have a fatigue life considerably in excess of anything that had been flown? Hall demurred and then produced his explanation of why the security offered by this test was a delusion. Its longevity had been achieved, Hall said, by preloading the specimen in a static test to "13.5 psi on several occasions and to 16 psi on some occasions."[33] This had produced plastic flow in the highly stressed areas and had limited the stress concentration in these places and the specimen may then have had a much longer fatigue life. Hall emphasised the word 'may' because, he said, preloading could shorten the fatigue life if it caused a crack. It was impossible to predict the magnitude of the increase in fatigue life produced by preloading but a factor of ten was tentatively mentioned. Even the difference between 11 and 13.5 psi may have been significant and in this case Hall felt that 11 psi was probably very close to plastic flow developing.[33] Hall emphasised that at the time when de Havillands did the repeated loading tests on a pre-loaded specimen they were not in violation of what was generally considered to be good practice.

At the end of day nine, Sir Hartley, in one of his more dramatic moments and perhaps forgetting that there was no jury to impress, unrolled an immense sheet of paper on which an S/N curve was drawn with its N axis having a numerical rather than a log scale. He pointed out that if the stress level was reduced from 70% to 50% then the point of failure was yards, in other words years, away. Sir Arnold agreed that it was a big factor, but was not sure if it implied years. It is hard to see how this demonstration improved Sir Hartley's case but perhaps he had just succumbed to the theatrical.

Sir Arnold continued the following day. This started with some tetchiness on Sir Hartley's part as he demanded a 'yes or no' answer from Sir Arnold to a question about whether there were more manufacturing cracks found in YP than the ones he had already mentioned.[34] The question was re-phrased and Hall answered to the effect that once they had found what they thought was the start of the failure in YP they did not minutely examine the rest of the wreckage looking for locating holes. It is difficult at this remove to see how this exchange moved matters on but there appeared to be an ongoing obsession among the barristers with manufacturing cracks. The importance of manufacturing, and wear and tear cracks, lay in where they were. In low-stress areas they were of little significance but in a high-stress area they might propagate, although there was no evidence that they had done so enough to have caused a problem. The solution, Hall said, was to design an aircraft with low general stress levels.

Sir Arnold returned to the calculated stress levels. Hall said that the previous day Sir Hartley had quoted a figure of 26,000 psi at the windows but on the way home the previous evening he had done a calculation "on the back of an envelope" and could not get anything like that, more like 40,000 psi.[35] The general stress level was about 13,700 psi, multiplying it by a factor of 2.5 for the edge of a cutout, gave 33,000. In practice this would be higher because there was a series of windows. He had made an allowance of 20% for the window frame and nothing for the stringers but they might reduce it by 5 or 10%.[36] Hall referred to a paper by A. E. Green published in the Proceedings of the Royal Society in 1945[37] which solved the problem for the stress concentration at the margin of a square window with rounded corners, just like the Comet's.

Shawcross, somewhat irritated at this, explained that the de Havilland figure was the mean stress about 1.5 inches in from the edge.* Hall, unusually for him, also somewhat irritated by this time, pointed out that the metal will break at the edge "where ...every engineer has known for years the stress is maximum."**[38]

---

* Shawcross later corrected this to an area of three square inches.[39]

** This was only true if there were no other stress raisers, such as rivet or bolt holes, in the immediate vicinity of the cutout.

In the transcript Shawcross comes across, particularly at this time, as being unduly argumentative and repetitive and at times frankly insulting but he had failed to get the better of Sir Arnold, if that had been his intention.

Chapter 22

MORE STRESS

Dr. Percy Walker, as the Head of the Structures Department at the RAE, was also questioned closely about stress levels and their consequences. Not surprisingly he largely agreed with Sir Arnold but on occasion he was less cautious in his phraseology and as a result was to have a more difficult time in the witness box.

Walker had written a paper in 1949 about fatigue in aircraft structures[1] which made three points: that fatigue was a potential problem in aircraft, that this problem was dif-ferent from fatigue in heavy structures such as bridges and that it was less a matter of materials but more to do with structures and the stress concentrations within them.[2]

After Naples, but before much wreckage arrived at Farnborough, Walker had reviewed the circumstances of the two crashes and had come to the conclusion that a fatigue failure of the cabin was a possibility as both had disintegrated at a time when they were approaching their maximum differential pressure. Against that, he said, it seemed incredible that fatigue could occur after such a short life. To test this possibility Walker had devised the tank test as a safe method of finding out the fatigue life of a particular cabin. He agreed that it was accurate as far as producing the first fracture but that it did

Fig. 1/22 Dr. Percy Walker in 1955
(FAST, Farnborough Air Sciences Trust).

not allow full disruption to occur. The structure around the first failure at the port forward escape hatch of YU had been brought into the Court as an exhibit.

Dr. Walker reappeared some days later to be examined by Mr. Scarman.[3] After some
questions about how the repairs to YU's failure in the tank at 9,000 hours had affected
subsequent events (difficult to say),[4] whether manufacturing cracks in general alter
fatigue lives (also difficult to say) the questioning concentrated on matters around YU's
rear ADF window.[5] The stress about 2 to 2.5 inches from the starboard rear corner of
this window at a pressure differential of 10 psi was found to be about 10,000 psi. At a
differential of 8.25 psi, Walker said, the stress would be rather less but it could be raised
significantly by a hole and if there was a load-bearing bolt through the hole then the
stress could be even greater.* This was why the fatigue fracture in YP was not at the
edge of the cutout but two or so inches in from the edge. Walker, ever the careful scientist, cautioned that the values in one airframe indicate general, but not absolute, values in other similar ones so the figures might not have been the same in YP.

Mr. Scarman recalled that as part of the investigation tests had been done on hollow
cylinders 44 inches in diameter, made of DTD 546B sheet 0.036 inches thick,[6] with a
riveted lap joint on one side and a butt joint on the other. The rivets were ⅛ inches diameter and countersunk. The cylinders were pressurised cyclically. At a stress of 30,000
psi the cylinder had a fatigue life of 8,000 cycles, equivalent to 24,000 hours. At 10,000
psi its life had increased to 100,000 cycles, equivalent to 300,000 hours. Mr. Scarman
tried to extend this to the Comet but Walker demurred saying there were no stress concentrations in this cylinder and that this argument was completely irrelevant "I disagree
with everything you say on this point."[7]

Mr. Scarman then tried to extend YU's test into a test of 18 windows rather than a
test of one aeroplane. Dr. Walker disagreed at first, calling it cheating, but to some
extent came round to it under later questioning by Mr. Cripps, representing the Ministry
of Supply.[8] He asked whether the tank test was valid after the first failure at 9,000 hours
(3,057 cycles). Perhaps having had time to think about it Dr. Walker's view now was
that the front part of the cabin, the 8-seater, would have been affected by the fracture
and therefore became unrepresentative. The repair that followed the failure was put into
a structure that was already strained and the loading pattern may have changed and, for
example, the ADF window may not have continued to have been tested under realistic
conditions. So the absence of a failure here may be artifactual. The failure at 17,000
hours (5,546 cycles) in the rear fuselage was far enough away, Walker thought, to have
been uninfluenced by the first failure.

Replying to a question from Mr. Scarman, Dr. Walker said that YU's failure at 9,000
hours (3,057 cycles) would have made the RAE consider that the Comets were not safe
to fly at 2,700 hours. He was asked why they had quoted a 1 to 9 scatter range. He

---

* But not always. If the rivet or bolt is loaded in shear and is a very tight fit in the hole then the material
at the hole's margin is in a state of radial compression and peripheral tension and the hole, in effect, may
cease to exist.[9] This situation probably did not apply here because the rivets were smaller than the sizes
(³⁄₁₆ inches and larger) generally considered necessary to produce this effect so the rivet and bolt holes
were, for the most part, stress raisers.

replied that it was only necessary to use a 1:3 ratio (i.e. a range of ⅓ to 3) to include the crashes,* implying that the range could have been wider. The scatter was based, among other things, on an experiment using tubular spar booms with eighteen holes in each. Twenty four specimens had been tested and the scatter from the strongest to the weakest was 1:10. These facts, Walker agreed, were not known to the scientists before these disasters.[10]

The questioning then passed to Mr. MacCrindle. If they just had the failure at 9,000 hours (3,057 cycles) and no crashes, he asked, how long a Certificate of Airworthiness would they have issued? Walker declined to provide a direct answer. He said he would have taken into account other factors such as the general design, the shape of windows and the method of calculation. "Given the two accidents as well what would be your approximate safe life?" "I think I would say it was not worth flying at all."[11] This was quickly re-phrased by Lord Cohen, "Would you not say 'You must modify the design so as to increase the safety margin and I cannot tell you what I will say until we know what modifications you propose.'" Walker agreed. Sir William Farren took it up saying, given Mr. MacCrindle's question and Walker's answers to the previous questions, "...you would be in extreme difficulty in giving any other answer than the one you have done to the question he put to you..."

Dr. Walker was then asked whether before the crashes he would have been satisfied with static tests to 2 or 2.5P to cover for fatigue. He replied that he would have wanted repeated loading tests and strain gauges around the ADF windows. "If you had known about the three manufacturing cracks around the ADF windows would that have altered what you did?" "Yes. I would have sent it back."[12] Together with the "not worth flying" response these were clearly statements that Sir Hartley would wish to challenge and the fact that he did not do so instantly almost certainly meant that he was absent.

Dr. Walker's cross examination continued the following day (day 11). Professor Duncan wondered if the low temperatures at altitude would affect the fatigue life of the cabin bearing in mind that the RAE tank tests had been done at summer temperatures. In fact, Walker said, some previous tests on Meteor tailplanes showed that low temperatures increased the fatigue life by 30 to 40% although he thought this effect was probably less for high-stress levels, perhaps to as little as 10%.

As expected Sir Hartley was anxious to defuse Walker's damning "Not worth flying" sound bite that had been promptly reported in the press. Inevitably Walker agreed that he didn't really mean that at all and it was re-interpreted by Shawcross to mean that it had a short fatigue life and that it would not be profitable to produce such an aero-

---

* This was not strictly true. If YU was the mean then, using Hall's figures, YY was 3.4 times younger, making the ratio 1:3.4 and the range ⅓.₄ to 3.4, i.e. almost a 1 to 12 scatter. In fact the only definite information was that the lower limit of the cohort of nine Comet 1s put into service was 2,704 hours and the next weakest cabin failed at 3,681 hours. YU failed in test circumstances at just over 9,000 hours but with flight stresses, Walker estimated, was likely to have failed at about 7,500 hours, although the figure of 9,000 hours seemed to be the one used in the inquiry. The other aircraft in the cohort had not failed from fatigue so the upper limit, and therefore the mean and the range, was supposition and the scatter could have been significantly smaller or larger than 1 to 9.

plane. The comment, he pointed out, did not refer to any Comet that might be produced in the future with a thicker skin.

Shawcross once more brought up Williams' 1946 paper which said that static tests were sufficient to predict an adequate fatigue life. Walker reminded him that the paper referred entirely to wings and tailplanes and specifically excluded pressure cabins and high stresses. The RAE, Shawcross said, distributed a (restricted) paper by Mr. Taylor, a member of their staff, in December 1949 which said that it was "... most unlikely that a pressure cabin which has satisfactory static strength will suffer fatigue damage." It was repeated in exactly the same words when the paper was published in March 1952,[13] implying that the same view was still held by the RAE.[14] At this point there was a minor spat between Shawcross and Heald when the latter complained that the rest of them could not follow what was going on because they did not have copies of the documents. Shawcross seemed unsympathetic saying "No, I do not suppose you can. I cannot help that." Heald, sounding miffed, responded, "If my friend does not want to show it to us..."[15]

The point Shawcross wanted to make was that an expert in the field could legitimately hold the view, at least until March 1952, that static strength predicted fatigue life. Walker said that some people believed it, implying that he did not. He suggested that Shawcross refer the matter to the ARB as the responsible body for civil aircraft whereas he dealt mainly with military aircraft.

Sir Hartley then moved onto Walker's 1949 paper[1] which said that there was a lack of knowledge of the nature of fatigue which made constructing complex structures a difficult task. This made testing important but he appreciated that with big structures this was expensive and time-consuming and was generally impractical. However just testing components may be inconclusive. Again the paper made no reference to pressure cabins although Walker admitted that pressure cabins (to paraphrase) 'were not entirely out of my mind.' At that time, Shawcross continued, the danger of fatigue failure in a pressure cabin was not appreciated. He quoted from Walker, "...everything pointed to catastrophic failure being unlikely..."[1]

The latest published opinion on fatigue problems, according to Shawcross, was in a 1953 Royal Aeronautical Society Symposium in which Mr. Tye of the ARB, shortly to make a long appearance at the inquiry, concluded that there was "...no agreed explanation of the mechanism of fatigue... must follow empirical approaches..."[16] Walker agreed. Testing seemed all important.

Walker had been little involved in the de Havilland fatigue tests and had not known until quite recently that they had constructed a nose section for tests. He expressed the view that there could have been more co-operation between the RAE and de Havillands during the design and construction period. Even if this were true it was unwise to have volunteered it as it gave the ever-combative Shawcross an opportunity to quote several instances of members of Walker's staff having attended meetings at de Havillands. In 1947 Walker had written to the MoS about fatigue matters in the Comet prototypes but did not request any repeated pressure tests. At about the same time his staff had asked that the nose section be subjected to 2P although the ARB requirement was 1.33P and 0.1% proof (i.e. that it should only elongate by 0.1% at this pressure). De Havillands had started the repeated loading of the nose section as a fatigue test at their own volition in 1953.[17]

By this time Walker seemed defensively pedantic and even a little wise after the event which made Shawcross even more aggressive in his questioning. It was evident, Shawcross said, that the cabin could withstand 2P on the static test but that 1P produced a dangerously short fatigue life in service. Walker concurred. He also agreed that if the stress in a particular area was 70% of ultimate at 1P then he would have expected a failure at 2P but in practice it did not happen because of the plastic flow it produced. Shawcross then asked that if the stress at 1P had been a little higher would it then have failed at 2P. Walker replied that he could not answer that question. Shawcross, in a rather bullying fashion went on "Very well. If you cannot answer that question, there will be other people who will. You do not want to answer that one?" "No, I did not say I do not want to answer it. I cannot, I do not think anyone else can either."[18] The point of all this, it later transpired, was to test whether Walker subscribed to Hall's plastic flow theory, which he largely did.

Even if the wreckage containing the ADF windows had not been found Walker said that he would have been happy that the tank tests had shown that the primary cause of the accident was a failure somewhere in the cabin. Finding the section with the ADF windows showed where the failure had started and provided confirmation that the cabin had suffered a fatigue failure.

Chapter 23

MR TYE'S DOUBTS AND
PROFESSOR MURPHY'S CERTAINTIES

The next witness was Mr. Walter Tye who had been the Chief Technical Officer of the ARB since 1943.[1] His examination was opened by Mr. Graham for the Attorney General. Mr. Tye answered for the technical side of the ARB which Lord Brabazon had largely ducked. He said that the Comet was designed to meet the requirements current in 1946. The ARB had kept de Havillands informed of draft requirements as they had developed and the design was fluid enough to take account of them up to about 1950. The main issues of new requirements were in January 1948 and January 1951 but some of the Comet's new features were in advance of the requirements and so great attention had been focused on them.

In October 1949 there had been a meeting about the sudden loss of cabin pressure. At this meeting the RAE representative recommended that the designed ultimate strength of the Comet pressure cabin should be 2.5P and that it should be tested to 2P, but the actual ARB requirements were watered down to an ultimate of 2P and a test to 1.33P. The draft for this was circulated in February 1952 and agreed the following April. The international and US requirements amounted to the same thing. By June 1953 things had moved on and the ARB circulated a discussion paper for a repeated loading test of 15,000 reversals at 1.25P, (about 10 psi for the Comet) which might mean an ultimate strength of 3P in certain areas such as the windows. These papers were circulated to the industry to let them know what the ARB was thinking, to get feed back, and to give them notice of future requirements that they might need to provide for in aircraft they were designing at the time.

In December 1948, with a number of the main parts at a fairly advanced stage of design, representatives of the ARB visited de Havillands to discuss progress. By this time the nose and centre sections of the cabin had already passed the proof test, and 2,000 cycles using strain gauges, and work was continuing to reach 2P. The ARB, Tye said, thought them adequate and even in advance of current practice. They had considered the significance of cracks but reasoned that they would be able to be seen and repaired before reaching dangerous dimensions at P, but not at 2 or 2.5P.

In January 1952 the situation was reviewed and a general Certificate of Airworthiness was issued for the Comet. By the end of 1952 there was some concern about wing fatigue although this was not just in the Comet. This had led to an increased interest in fatigue in pressure cabins but there was no sense of urgency as far as the Comet was concerned because it was thought that the maximum stress at P was 40%, or at least not more than 50%, of ultimate and this implied a very long fatigue life. The figures came from de Havillands' strain gauge readings and their design statement and took account of the cutouts but not rivets except in the sense that a small area of metal had been removed.*[2] From this, and work on other riveted structures, the ARB thought that the average life would be at least 10,000 cycles,[3] i.e. 30,000 hours and therefore the safe life would be 30,000/3 = 10,000 hours. The ARB did not change this view until YU burst in the tank test. The surprise to them was that the cracks were catastrophic.

The Calcutta crash did not alter their views. The Elba crash occurred near the top of the climb so cabin failure was considered but was discounted because of the calculated safe life of 10,000 hours and the ongoing testing of the nose section which by that time had reached 18,000 cycles (54,000 hours). They were aware that static loading would reduce the stress levels by producing plastic flow but they did not know by how much it would increase the fatigue life. Even recognising the past history of the specimen, as they were beginning to, it still seemed inconceivable that YP's cabin could have burst at only 3,600 hours (1,286 flights), a reduction by a factor of fifteen.

The ARB had relied on the firm's stress calculations and did not check them. Some calculations, Tye said, are mathematically rigorous, such as the stress level around a circular hole in a sheet being increased by a factor of three. But if the hole is reinforced, as it was in the Comet cutouts, then the calculation becomes much more complicated and opinion and experience come into it. This can produce a big difference in the answer, so tests are important after the calculations. In spite of this Tye was surprised that the RAE got a level of 70% and de Havillands 50% (actually 40%) of ultimate.

De Havillands had put the strain gauges mainly around the cockpit windows because they were the most complicated shapes and they thought the highest levels would be there. Further aft the gauges were just to check the general levels and reliance was placed on calculations followed by tests, although one or two gauges were placed around the doors.[4] The results, Tye said, could not be extrapolated from the cockpit windows to the cabin windows. The ARB had thought that the number of nose section tests (2,000 at that stage) was sufficient.

Tye explained that the ARB was also responsible for seeing that the company's inspection system was working properly. They would do the odd inspection of an aircraft themselves but would not see all the concession notes.**[5] In Tye's view whether locating the cracks was adequate depended on where the cracks were and their

---

* "...that certainly it would take account of rivets in the sense that where an area of metal is removed by virtue of the presence of a rivet hole, the load is then carried by a smaller area of metal, and the stress is thereby raised by virtue of the absence of metal where the rivet holes are. It would not, on the other hand, include the factor of about three, which there is on the stress immediately adjacent to a rivet hole."[2]

** This was a system used by de Havillands for dealing with deviations from the designers' specifications that had happened inadvertently during the manufacturing process. When one of these deviations happened a decision had to be made about how to correct it. This depended on the nature of the fault and where it was. A concession note was the official instruction of how to proceed.

direction. Not all of them needed to be recorded for future checks, for instance if they were very visible such as in a doubler plate around an ADF window. Those in YP's doubler plate were short and the plate was not highly stressed, Tye thought, and he considered it proper for them to have been drilled. There were no signs, Tye said, of any dangerous extension of 'located' cracks in YU after the tank tests. With the benefit of hindsight Tye said that he was more conscious of cracks now than before and would pay more attention to them in the future.[6]

Tye was not convinced by Hall's theory of incipient cracks because there was no evidence that they existed.[6] If they had existed the only way they could have extended would be by fatigue and there was no evidence of fatigue cracks in the wreckage except at the corner of the rear ADF window. Also Tye was not convinced that it was possible to deduce this new term 'high-level fatigue' from this small fracture. However he did not suggest an alternative theory to the fatigue failure of the cabin. He accepted that it had burst and that if it had burst at 1P then the weakening was most probably caused by fatigue. He did not consider that the alternative ways in which the cabin could have burst, such as a high external load or high internal pressure, were likely. He thought his answer was "an unhappy one" in the sense that he was "not very enthusiastic about the conclusion that fatigue was present from looking at a particular specimen of fatigue. On the other hand I cannot produce any shattering alternative."

The Commissioner asked Mr. Tye whether he thought that YU and YP had failed for the same reason. Tye thought YU had certainly failed from fatigue but he was less confident about YP. He could provide no alternative explanation and he accepted that there was no evidence of any other cause of cabin disruption.

Tye did not think that the manufacturing crack in the port front corner of YP's rear ADF window had great significance. If it had extended it would have done so by fatigue and there were no signs of that. With the belief that the aircraft's safe life was 10,000 hours there seemed to be such a large margin of safety that even if they had known of the manufacturing cracks they would have believed that they were adequately covered by this margin.[7] Their knowledge of de Havillands' ongoing tests only served to strengthen this belief and provided even more confidence than the calculations.

There had been no discussions, Tye said, with the US authorities about the Comet 1 and Comet 2 and they were only held about the Comet 3 because an American airline was intending to buy it. They had therefore looked at the US requirements at an early stage. Their proposals were for 10,000 cycles of 1P just on windows and doors, not the cabin as a whole.[8] The proposed American tests were significantly less than de Havillands had already done with the Comet 1. They were more concerned with windows or doors blowing out than the cabin bursting. The Americans were satisfied that the Comet 3 tests, if they were the same as the Comet 1's, would more than meet their proposed policy.

Tye said that the ARB would like to see future aircraft tank-tested but that it might not be necessary in the longer term as more became known. It would also probably not be necessary with evolved designs. The ARB would hope to reach a situation where an aircraft could incur a long crack (such as 24 inches) but still land safely ("...would like to get to a state of affairs where an aeroplane can crack safely").*

There was some discussion about a crack in the skin of the starboard front corner of YP's rear ADF window,[9] for which there was no concession note. Presumably, Tye thought, there was no concession note because it had not been seen by an inspector and the workman had just drilled it and covered it with the doubler plate. It was difficult to construct a system that would always spot this sort of thing, but it did not extend in the accident and it was therefore not implicated in its cause.

By this time the questioning had passed to Mr. Tilling. If the (extrapolated) strain gauge figures from YU were correct, Tilling said, then de Havillands' calculations and strain gauge figures must be wrong.[10] Mr. Tilling had a point here and Tye agreed that it was a fair conclusion, but he suggested that de Havillands may have been more interested in values 'inland' of the cutout edges where the rivet holes were, rather than the edge which had no rivet holes. Their view may have been that the stress in this area was going to be the highest so there was no point in calculating the value at the edge. They had found it to be about 40% of ultimate here.

Tye appeared to contradict himself here. The only reason that the stress would have been significantly greater 'inland' of the cutout edge was as a consequence of the stress-raising effect of the rivet holes in an area that already had a high stress level. But Tye had already said that the ARB's understanding of the information that de Havillands had provided them with as part of the certification process was that they had not allowed for the stress-concentrations at the edges of the rivet holes, merely for the effect of removing small amounts of metal. ("... it would not on the other hand, include the factor of about 3, which there is on the stress immediately adjacent to a rivet hole.")[2] The area of metal removed by the rivet holes in the frame at the corners was about 12.5%** of the whole, so on this basis it would have increased the stress levels by the same amount; rather less than the 250% (see Appendix 5) that would, at least theoretically, have occurred at the edges of the rivet holes. This seems a surprising omission and it is equally surprising that it was not followed up by the Court. If de Havillands had arrived at a figure of 40% of ultimate without allowing for the edges of the rivet holes then in reality the stress here would have been much greater and well into the range where plastic flow would occur and fatigue would be sure to follow.

In YU, Tye said, the strain gauges had to be placed away from the rivet holes and therefore "...the curves which are drawn are the stresses in the material away from the immediate locality of the rivet holes." In other words the stresses at the edges of the

---

* This is, in fact, what has happened;[11] see Chapter 29. Full-scale testing of aircraft, including pressure cycling of the cabin, became mandatory in airworthiness regulations for all new designs of fixed wing aircraft after the Comet.

** Considering just the curved part of a corner of a window frame,
  The inner radius at the window corners was 3 inches and the width of the frame was 0.75 inches.
  The area of the quarter annulus = $\pi(3.75^2 - 3^2)/4 = 4$ inches^2
  The total area of 10 rivets of ¼ inches diameter = $10 \pi 0.125^2 = 0.5$ inches^2
  The percentage reduction in area produced by the rivet holes = 12.5.

rivet holes were even higher than the values obtained by the RAE and even more different from the de Havilland figures. He declined to comment further about de Havillands' calculations but thought there might be some variation in allowances for frames and stringers between different calculators, but probably not as much as 40%.[10]

Mr. Tilling, starting on another tack, and clearly trying to show that de Havillands had cut corners, quoted from Bishop's forward in the de Havilland *Maintenance Engineer's Lecture Notes* which said that the decision was made to start with a production line before the first prototype had flown.* This was thought by Bishop to have saved two years. The ARB, Tye said, had been aware of this and considered it to be normal practice. He explained that the manufacturer designs the aircraft and if it looks satisfactory goes ahead and builds one or two of them and at the same time starts making arrangements for larger-scale manufacture. They take a risk that if something is wrong with the prototype(s) they may have to alter parts of the production aircraft and this quite often happened. It did not affect safety considerations. As Bishop later said in his evidence, they delivered the Comets ten months ahead of their contract dates so there had been no pressure on them to rush things.[12]

The following day Mr. Tye's doubts about fatigue being the cause of the breakup were pursued by Mr. Scarman. If it were assumed that YU had the average fatigue life of 9,000 hours, Tye said, then the safe life for the type would be 3,000 hours and it would be very unlikely that any of them would fail at this age. In practice two out of a fleet of eight or nine had failed which Tye thought was statistically unlikely. Therefore from the tank tests alone he found it difficult to accept that fatigue was the cause. Unlike Dr. Walker he considered that the tank test was a simultaneous test of eighteen (independent) cutouts, so one had failed at 9,000 hours (3,057 cycles), the next at 17,000 (5,546 cycles) and the rest had not failed at 17,000 hours, so the average life of the cutouts was up in the 17,000s and not 9,000 hours and some other reason for the two crashes would have to be found. He thought that the RAE had eliminated all the other causes and were then driven to decide it was fatigue. It was put to him that if 9,000 hours were not the average, and it was only one sample, but was actually above the average, then a failure at 3,000 hours becomes more probable.** Tye accepted this and had no alternative explanation which considerably weakened his case and, in the end, led to it being discarded.[13]

The next witness was Professor A. J. Murphy, the Professor of Industrial Metallurgy in the University of Birmingham.[14] He had been called in by de Havillands to help with the inquiry but had not worked with them before.

He said that it was acceptable to use the Comet's thin gauge sheets because their intrinsic strengths were known and if the engineers knew the loads to be carried the

---

* The Principal Films documentary about the Comet alleged that this was an unusual practice and that de Havillands would have been reluctant to deal with any faults discovered in the prototypes because they had already tooled up for the production aircraft.
** This seems a reasonable explanation for the two failures at about 3,000 hours. In any case 9,000 hours was probably optimistic for YU as it had not been exposed to the full gamut of flying stresses and Walker had thought that 7,500 was more realistic.

required thickness could be calculated. The manufacture of this type of material was tightly controlled and specified by the Directorate of Technical Development, part of the MoS, hence the designation DTD. The alloy used, DTD 546B, offered the best combination of tensile and fatigue strengths and fabricating qualities available in aluminium-based alloys at that time. The samples removed from YP had been tested and met the specifications.

Professor Murphy had examined samples from the starboard rear corner of YP's rear ADF window[15] and agreed that the fracture had been produced by fatigue. He thought de Havillands would use a thicker skin in future, in certain parts definitely. This would increase the static strength of the cabin but perhaps they would need to do this to a considerable extent to give an adequate fatigue life.[16]

Under questioning by Mr. Shaw, Professor Murphy said that the ultimate strength of DTD 546B was 65,000 psi. A published S/N curve showed that a specimen with two rivet holes would allow 100,000 cycles with a stress of 28,000 psi and 35,500 cycles with a stress of 35,000 psi, a little more than 50% of ultimate. Therefore the de Havillands' figure of 26,000 psi (40%) would suggest a life in excess of 100,000 flying hours. The difference between suggested and experienced lives was accounted for by the complexity of the Comet's fuselage* so he did not agree with what Lord Brabazon had said ("It is metallurgy, not aeronautics, that is in the dock").** Mr. Tye had calculated that the de Havilland figure of 40%, or at least not more than 50%, suggested a mean fatigue life of about 30,000 hours. Professor Murphy felt that the failure at 9,000 hours (3,057 cycles) in the tank was just compatible with this. The failures around 3,000 hours were not compatible with 40 or 50% but were consistent with a maximum stress of 70%.[17]

Perhaps surprisingly after coming to this conclusion Professor Murphy had doubts about the RAE's extrapolation of the stress at the edge of a cutout to be 70%. He felt that the last reading might have been affected by the proximity of a rivet hole and did not feel happy going higher than that actually recorded by the strain gauges.[18] In his view there was a stress concentration near the countersunk hole with the bolt that was probably high enough to account for the cabin's short fatigue life. He felt that the extrapolation to the edge of the cutout was irrelevant because the general level of stress was known and there was a stress raiser close to where the fatigue was seen. This hole was drilled and the bolt through it generated more stress because it fastened the skin to a frame and did not just join two pieces of skin together. For a fatigue fracture to develop there needed be a high general field of stress and then a stress raiser on top of that. It would not necessarily need to have been this bolt hole because so long as the

---

* Or the inaccuracy, or inappropriateness, of de Havillands' stress calculations.

** Nevertheless there have been suggestions that DTD 546B did crack more easily than some other alloys that came after it[19] and some of de Havillands' workers were said to have expressed the view that the sheets were stiff to work and showed signs of cracking.[20] Ramsden related that the Comet's high-strength, but more-brittle, zinc-containing alloys later gave way to ones containing copper and that Bishop had said that the zinc alloys had "led everyone up the garden path."[21] In fact DTD 546B did not contain zinc[22, 23] and later tests showed that it was not particularly prone to cracking.[24]

general stress level was so high the structure was vulnerable to any number of stress raisers. "... one does not...have to search around for one particular feature and say that that, and that alone, must be present in order to lead to fatigue failure." The solution was to get the general stress level down.[25]

Professor Murphy considered that the failure in the rear ADF window started with the fatigue crack they had discovered but he could not exclude other places, such as the opposite corner or even somewhere else in the aircraft ("it shows that that was the initial point of failure in the area which you are examining"). Around the ADF windows was a doubling plate which made them stronger than other windows. "Therefore," Mr. Shaw asked, "one would have expected (the) initial failure to take place at the other windows rather than at the ADF window?" Murphy refused to be drawn "I think I would be going further than my knowledge would justify me in doing if I agreed to that. I have concerned myself with examining the specimens of material."[26]

At this point the Commissioner intervened saying "I had better warn you, Mr. Shaw, that my assessors tell me your question is scientifically all wrong. It depends on the general design. You cannot say merely from the fact that one window has strengthening on it and the other does not that the one without it is more likely to go. It depends on the general stresses, which in their turn depend on the design, as I understand." Mr. Shaw replied "I am grateful for these interventions by your Lordship's assessor, because I have no one scientific advising me, and if I am on the wrong track I am glad to be put off it." In view of what transpired later this was a particularly ironic intervention.

Mr. Shaw continued. In YU up to 17,000 hours (5,546 cycles) there was no catastrophic failure involving the ADF windows suggesting that there was nothing inherently weak about their design. Would it, he suggested, then be reasonable to look for something on YP that was not present in YU that caused the failure? Murphy's view was that there was such a high general level of stress that it was not necessary, or even relevant, to find "the last final speck" which set off the fatigue failure. It would require only a mild stress raiser, such as a manufacturing crack or a bolt hole, to set off a failure.[27]

Professor Murphy appeared an informed and objective witness. His answers were decisive and seemed sensible and when he did not know the answer he said so, always a useful attribute in an expert witness.

Chapter 24

THE DE HAVILLAND WITNESSES

Mr. R. H. T. Harper, the Chief Structural Engineer at de Havillands since 1949, appeared next and was examined first by Mr. Graham.[1] Robert Harper had started as an apprentice at Boulton and Paul (a British engineering company that had aviation interests) in 1923. From 1928 to 1937 he had worked in their stress office and then joined de Havillands as Assistant Chief Stressman, becoming Chief Stressman in 1941. Harper was responsible for the stress calculations in the Comet and could be expected to provide an alternative view of them. There were to be some discrepancies between Harper's testimony and the, presumably more reliable, information contained in the de Havillands' records but they appear to be just errors of detail produced by imperfect recall.

Mr. Harper said that he was aware of Williams' 1946 paper but that this only covered wings and was not relevant to fuselages. When they designed the cabin to an ultimate strength of 2.5P and tested a representative portion of it to 2P they were just considering static strength not fatigue. Under a contract with the RAE they had started fatigue tests on a Dove wing and in 1949, after discussion with the ARB, they had decided to test a Comet wing as well. This was also to test for leaks from the fuel tanks in the wings and to investigate the distortion of the wing under load. At first there were no data on gusts but the RAE later devised the counting accelerometer which provided this. In 1949 and 1951 there were wing fatigue failures in some American and British aircraft and then in June 1952 in a Dove in Australia. Their thoughts about fatigue were entirely focused on wings.[2]

When they started, Harper said, there was no published material on fatigue in fuselages. He had come across it for the first time in October 1952 in a Joint Airworthiness Committee paper which proposed that transport aircraft should have repeated loading tests as they were expected to have longer lives than other types.[3] It was only following this, in 1953, that de Havillands began to consider the Comet's fuselage in terms of its fatigue life.

Testing of the Comet's components had begun in January 1946 and had continued up to the present. The individual components were then assembled into structures and retested. In all, these amounted to thousands of tests, making the Comet the most tested civil aircraft in the UK. To test the cabin pressurisation and temperature and humidity controls de Havillands had installed a large decompression chamber at Hatfield to simulate high-altitude flying. The final pressure tests on the nose section were in the water tank and reached a maximum of 16 psi. There were similar tank tests of the centre section to the same maximum pressure. They used water for the same reasons as the RAE had, particularly as they had already had a burst with air.

It had been the company's practice to subject test specimens to proof, ultimate and some repeated loads but they realised they would have to go further and that the tests should be applied to larger units. The 2,000 cycles of 9 psi that the nose section had already been subjected to was not regarded as a fatigue test. These 2,000 cycles were equivalent to about 6,000 flying hours and in July 1953 no Comet had flown more than 2,500 hours but they would need more cycles to cover their expected service lives. They then did a further 16,000 cycles of the nose section.* They thought that the results of these further cycles would by no means be completely invalidated by their previous loading to 2P although some earlier work on the Dove spars had shown that preloading did tend to increase the fatigue life. They felt that their tests so far exceeded the current flying hours of the Comet fleet that this pre-loading effect would have been covered. They always tried to have a test programme that was ahead of the flying hours of the aircraft in service, taking into account the effect of scatter, so the 54,000 hours they had reached would adequately cover 10,000 flying hours. As the fleet aged so the test cycles would increase and keep ahead.[4]

One static test involved a separate section of cabin wall which incorporated a window. This had a primary tensile failure at 19.75 psi at one corner and a secondary fracture at the opposite corner. This was the reason why strain gauges were not used around the windows in the later tests at much lower pressures.[5]

The ADF window in the nose section, Harper said, had failed at 11.9 psi of air pressure** and they had considered themselves fortunate that they could trace the origin of the failure. After that they used the water tank. This failure led them to put the reinforcing plates on the ADF windows and they had no more failures. Like YP this ADF window had rivets placed closer to the edge than specified (0.16 instead of 0.25 inches). It also had an additional ⅛ inches rivet at the point of failure. In future rivets were placed 0.3 inches from the edge and were spaced further apart (max 0.43 inches) to allow for errors in placing the rivets in the production aircraft.[6]

There were two further series of tests (March 1948 and February 1949) after which the cabin was considered proved for a pressure of 16.5 psi.*** The last set of tests was the 18,000 cycles in 1953.

The centre section was tested in a similar way, the static pressure being raised in steps to the ultimate load. It was used mainly to test the big cutout for the wing[7] but it was also

---

* The actual total was 17,900 cycles.[8]

** The test report says 12.75 psi and that water was used. This particular test was identified by its containing the report of the extra rivet.[9] Other reports say that it was the centre section that exploded catastrophically and that it was in the high altitude chamber.[10]

*** There may be some confusion of dates here. The date of the test at which the ADF window failed and the extra rivet was noticed was recorded in the Type Record as 2 December 1948, the date of the test to 16.5 psi was 31 December 1948 and the date of the report saying that the fuselage was proved to 16.5 psi was 8 February 1949.[9]

used for the wing fatigue tests.

Harper's team had done the stress calculations to design the test specimens and they had been confident that the maximum stress did not exceed 50% of ultimate. In view of this, Harper said that he would not have expected an aircraft to have failed at around 3,000 hours. Nevertheless he did not agree with the RAE's extrapolated figure of 70% at the edge of the cutouts.[11] His interpretation of the RAE strain gauge readings was that there was a maximum stress at 1P of 35,000 psi near the rivets but that it then dropped to about 30,000 towards the edge of the cutout, making it about 50% of ultimate. He thought his original calculations were about right.

Under questioning by Mr. Shaw, acting for the relatives, Harper gradually changed his

Fig. 1/24 Robert Harper in 1948
(copyright BAE SYSTEMS Heritage).

position to agree that there must have been places, such as at the edges of rivet or bolt holes, where the stress levels were considerably higher than 50%. It was difficult to allow for this by calculation or by referral to S/N curves, he said, and the only way was by testing. Harper agreed with Professor Murphy that the countersunk bolt hole near to the starboard rear corner of the rear ADF window was the most likely starting point for YP's failure. He accepted that a general level of stress at 50% of ultimate was too high to provide a safety margin for the inevitable local stress raisers. Any future aircraft would have to be designed to have a much lower general stress level and they would then have to do a lot of fatigue testing with special attention paid to the stress values around the cutouts as well as doing the static tests.

The cabin test sections had not been exposed to external loads but these were relatively small and pressures had been increased a little to 9 psi in the first 2,000 cycles and 8.75 in the last 10,000 but not directly to compensate for external loads. Most of the failures had been around the cockpit windows where the stresses could not be accurately calculated as they were too complex. They did not have gauges around the other windows and, Harper admitted, they may therefore have missed the higher stresses. Also their gauges were not very reliable at this time.

Behind the scenes discussions had been going on trying to reconcile the differences between Hall's[12] and Harper's stress calculations.[13] It appeared that their methods did not differ fundamentally although they did in detail. Hall's were 'novel' according to Mr. Coles, the person who had actually done de Havillands' calculations, and he considered them of "great value and use."[14] Some of the differences had come from different assumptions.

Mr. R. E. Bishop, the Chief Designer, followed Mr. Harper into the witness box.[15] He said that he accepted responsibility for his team's work, even for the decisions he did not know about at the time. In the transcript he appeared a dignified figure, willing to admit where they had made mistakes and to give credit for the work done at Farnborough.

He had written an article about the design problems of the Comet which had been published in *The Aeroplane* in 1952.[16] They had made great efforts to keep the weight down, including using the smallest fuselage diameter possible that would seat four people side by side, the most efficient wing structure and using Redux rather than rivets. They needed a differential pressure twice as great as that on existing passenger aircraft and they were aware that the consequences of failure were so serious that the cabin must be designed 'like a submarine.'* He personally thought it was one of the biggest problems they had faced but "We obviously missed the main point."[17] After the (catastrophic) failure with air (of the centre section in the high altitude chamber)[10] they went on to testing with water and de Havillands had built the first water tank in the UK for this purpose. The windows had been treated as a special case and were tested to 10P (82 psi). It would have been a lot easier, he said, to design an aircraft without any windows or doors.

They had used the decompression chamber, a cylinder 12 by 25 feet, to test structures at low temperatures and pressures and had people inside the fuselage sections as they went for 'flights'. In 1947 he had not been aware of any repeated-loading tests on fuselages being done elsewhere but by 1952 things had changed and repeated-loading tests were being discussed and the ARB produced some draft proposals. He knew that tests were being done on the Apollo** and on one or two others and he thought it wise to submit the nose section to a large number of similar tests in 1953. "We felt it was all right at the time." Like Harper he thought their tests were so far ahead of the service aircraft that "we had no need to worry." They had been talking to BOAC and they knew that some wing parts would have to be replaced.

After the Naples crash he was involved in discussions with the RAE and he felt it was right for them to do the cabin pressure tests. He had wanted to do 16.5 psi on the oldest BOAC fuselage but Walker had preferred to do a test with wing loads and 1P loads first and "in the light of what happened there is no doubt that that was a very wise decision."

---

* Hardly. Weight is of little relevance to a submarine but of immense importance to an aircraft. Both structures are designed to withstand a transmural pressure differential, although in different directions, but it seems a curious analogy.

** The Armstrong Whitworth Apollo was a British, four-engined turboprop airliner which first flew in 1949. As well as being unstable it was beset with engine problems. It was intended as a competitor to the Viscount but failed miserably. Only two were built.

Bishop complemented the RAE on its tank tests; he had not thought them possible. Before the Naples crash explosive decompression had been considered but then ruled out in view of their tests. Even after Naples their thoughts had not been directed towards cabin fatigue; they thought it might have been caused by damage from heavy landings or steps. "...it was a very great surprise to me personally when the fuselage blew up in the tank at 9,000 hours. We thought it had a very much longer life than that." The general view had been that "provided the structure had been demonstrated to be capable of taking something like a factor of two then we had no worry from the fatigue point of view." He agreed with the RAE diagnosis of the cause of Elba crash and thought that the same explanation probably applied to the Naples crash. His view of the RAE report was that it was "magnificent".

His opinion was that the Comet's problems could be fixed but he thought it would be less expensive to test small specimens first, then move to larger structures such as cutouts and then to the whole fuselage in a tank.

Bishop[18] accepted Hall's and Walker's opinions that they should have put strain gauges around the ADF and cabin windows. Harper's staff had positioned the gauges but at the time they had seemed satisfactory to Bishop. In the future, Bishop said, they would increase the thickness of the skin and reduce the local stress concentrations around the cutouts. Thicker skin was less prone to fatigue problems. It was a trade-off between strength and weight.[19]

Following Bishop was Harry Povey, Hatfield's General Production Manager. Povey was asked about the crack in the skin near the rear ADF window in YP that was drilled at each end but was not covered by a concession note. After some discussion this was taken up by Sir William Farren. He referred to a photograph in the RAE report which showed the relevant corner of the ADF window.[20] The crack was shown going through the rivet hole and onto the edge. The locating must have been done before the doubling plate was fixed in place. Povey explained, in some detail, how the cutout was made using a 'landing strip' which had been accurately drilled in a jig. This strip was then clamped in position on the outside of the skin and used to guide the drill making the holes for the rivets. This was then inspected and, in this case, passed. All the parts were then reassembled and, as Povey put it, the skin was "very thin" and could easily have become distorted. He thought that correcting this distortion could have caused the crack. This was "located" and he thought the workman had just forgotten to call an inspector's attention to it and it had then become invisible under the doubling plate.

A less charitable explanation is that having made the crack and thinking that he might be criticised for so doing and knowing that once the doubling plate was in position it would be invisible, he just went ahead and dealt with it. Even drilling it without prior approval was against the rules. Again it did not say much for de Havillands' quality control but inevitably any such system depended on the integrity of the individual worker and a non-accusatory inspection and correction system being in place.

Sir Arnold was then recalled to be asked about his having come to an agreement with de Havillands about the stress calculations.[21] The de Havillands' calculations, he said, were directed to the question of what the stress would be over a region of about three square inches at a working pressure of 17.5 psi in a test of a panel containing a window.[22] The figure they got was then scaled down to 8.25 psi which gave the answer as 26,000 psi. Hall's 'back of an envelope' calculations were directed towards finding the maximum stress at the edge of a square window with rounded corners, not the average over an area. His assumptions were based on a flat sheet of metal with a large cutout and adapted to be a cylinder. It applied only to the elastic range but that was reasonable because it referred to a pressure below proof. No account was taken of structures attached behind the skin or, like de Havillands, the rivets. It was possible only to estimate these. He would not have been surprised if a test had given a slightly different result, but would have been surprised if the difference had been large, say more than 20 or 30%, but it was possible to do calculations with a maximum and minimum figure. The information for de Havillands to have done the same calculation as Sir Arnold's was available at the time although he thought it possible that they were not aware of Green's paper in the Journal of the Royal Society.[23]

It had already been established in the inquiry that what mattered was the maximum stress. As the Commissioner had pointed out early on, it is the worst case that is important because that is where the failure will start.[24] The two calculations thus had different purposes but Hall's seems the more relevant. Both would have got even higher figures if they had allowed for the stress concentrations at the margins of the rivet holes.

If the loads went above the elastic limit, Sir Arnold continued, then the material, up to a point, will readjust itself and flow without any change of stress, in other words it is ductile. This is expressed as a percentage of the original length to which it will stretch before it breaks. It is quite a large figure compared with the small figure that it would stretch to before it reaches its plastic limit. This would have the effect of limiting the stress at the corners to something like proof stress. Up to the elastic limit doubling the pressure doubles the stress but once the elastic limit is exceeded the stress increases much less and possibly not at all.

By this time, day 17, the Court had finally found its way through the stress maze. Although the lawyers had the RAE 'Report on the Comet Accident Investigation' to hand, if they wished to explore it, and explore beyond it, they had to ask the right questions. For the most part all the witnesses could do was to answer the questions put to them although occasionally they broke away and made short statements. It was quite clear that the barristers struggled with some of the concepts and it was unsurprising that they should do so. Nevertheless for an imperfect process it seemed to arrive at most of the answers and in so doing extended the scope and the understanding of the RAE report.

Summary of the stress explanations arrived at by the Court
The sequence that the Court eventually arrived at built upon the basic idea of metal fatigue to reach a sophisticated understanding of the cause of the destruction of the two Comets. It started with the S/N curve that showed that large, repeated stresses produced short fatigue lives. Tests had shown that the fatigue lives of different examples

of seemingly identical structures exposed to high and medium level stress varied by some factor, in the case of the Comet's pressure cabin it was thought to be about 1:9. Within such a structure the stress level could vary from place to place, in particular it rose considerably towards the edge of any cutout and even more so at any corner the cutout might have. It had also become apparent that if a structure developed a stress of 70% of its ultimate strength with a particular load it was possible for the structure to withstand twice the load without failing. This happened because plastic flow in the highly stressed area kept the stress level below 100%. This meant that it was impossible to argue that any structure that withstood twice a particular load could only have stresses less than 50% with the base load.

At the time that the Comet was being designed and manufactured the general belief was that a static test to, say, twice the working pressure would guarantee a satisfactory fatigue life. This idea was replaced by the need to use repeated pressure cycles but only after the Comet had entered service. De Havillands' repeated pressure tests had proved misleading because the fuselage test sections were not truly representative of the complete aircraft. This was partly because the bulkheads that had to be inserted at the ends of the sections to provide seals supported the adjacent fuselage structure but also because the sections had been preloaded. This caused plastic flow at the corners of the cutouts which produced a permanent increase in size of these area leaving them in compression when the whole structure returned to its original size. At the next pressure cycle the plastic areas would start to experience tensile stress later than they would otherwise have done and at full pressure (1P) would therefore reach a lower stress level and therefore fatigue more slowly.

The calculations done by the manufacturers to estimate stress levels in the Comet's skin were directed towards average values over an area a little removed from the cutout edge rather than to the maximum which was more relevant to the probability of fatigue developing. They also made no allowance for stress-raisers such as rivet holes. They therefore missed the high stress values that might have made them think that the structure would be liable to develop fatigue. This explained why the cabins had a much shorter fatigue life than the manufacturer's calculations had predicted. The conclusion was that the general level of stress was too high because the skin was too thin for the loads it was expected to carry. This made the structure vulnerable to any stress raisers, particularly if they were in an area which already had higher-than-base-level stress.

Put like this the problems seemed straight forward but discovering the principles behind them had been anything but. Although the RAE report and the papers relating to the inquiry, with the exception of Lord Cohen's report, were closed to the public for many years to come this information was made available to the aviation industry in general, not just in the UK. Some credit is due for this although it leaves open the question of why so many other papers, including the transcript of the public inquiry were kept closed for so long.

Chapter 25

MR. JABLONSKY'S THEORY

Mr. Bruno Jablonsky was an experienced aeronautical engineer who had written letters to Lord Brabazon, Sir Miles Thomas and the Commissioner volunteering his knowledge of glued joints to the inquiry. He had been a pupil of Orville Wright, no less, and was the holder of pilot licence number 30. His involvement in the aircraft industry had started in World War One and had continued after the war with the development of laminated plastic materials which by the start of the Second World War had become extensively used in the aircraft industry. His company had also supplied some jigs and tools for the Comet.[1]

Jablonsky's original experience was with gluing layers of compressed wood to make propellers. This, he said, was similar to gluing metal as there was no keying effect. Later on he had had experience with wood to metal and metal to metal joints but this was with aircraft components rather than whole aircraft. He had used Redux as well as other types of glue.

Mr. Jablonsky agreed with Sir Arnold that the cabin had burst because it was too weak but was less convinced that the primary cause was metal fatigue.[2] He was more concerned about the integrity of the Redux bonding. During their day at Farnborough looking at the wreckage the Court had seen Redux joints in the wreckage that had failed. This had been explained by Hall and Ripley as having been caused by the remains of the aircraft hitting the sea but Jablonsky disagreed. He felt that impact with the sea would have bent the skin inwards alongside the stringers whereas an explosion would have bent it outwards and produced the damage they saw.[3]

According to Jablonsky there were three areas of potential difficulty with these glued joints.[4] The first was making them. The process of making a Redux joint was technically demanding and could easily be jeopardised by minor infringements such as a workman's greasy finger touching one of the surfaces. This sort of thing, Jablonsky said, was easy to avoid in a laboratory but extremely difficult to prevent in a full-scale workshop.[5] Also the Reduxed joints between the stringers and the skin were extremely long and it was difficult, if not impossible, to be sure that the glue, pressure and heat had been applied correctly throughout the whole length. Once made, a glued joint was impossible to inspect without destroying it. A riveted joint, on the other hand, could be expected to be secure if the rivet was still intact and in place.

The second problem was that glue was known to lose strength at high temperatures.

The Comets were used on many tropical routes and Jablonsky thought that the temperatures on the ground might reach 80°C, even 100°C at times.[6] When standing the structure of the aircraft was stressed by being supported on its undercarriage. On takeoff this stress pattern abruptly changed which might make some of the stringers separate from the skin, a process that could progress with time and subsequent takeoffs.

The third problem was that any temperature gradients that developed between the skin, as it cooled, and the stringers during the initial climb, particularly in the tropics, would produce different contraction rates and generate shear stresses across the glued joints. Jablonsky thought there were considerable similarities between the three mid-air breakups in that they were all in the early parts of their flights and would have experienced considerable skin temperature drops.

Unfortunately for Mr. Jablonsky the various barristers lost no time in destroying his arguments one by one and he must have wondered why he had involved himself in the proceedings.

The failed joints that he referred to were in the rear fuselage and had indeed failed because of raised internal pressure. But according to Hall and Ripley, this had been caused by the largely-intact rear fuselage falling into the sea open-end-first and the sea rushing in, compressing the air ahead of it and bursting the skin away from the stringers. Evidence from the scrapes along YP's wings strongly suggested that the front part of the cabin had exploded when the aircraft was flying at normal speed and that this was the primary event.[7] The RAE's view was that the joints in the rear fuselage had failed as a consequence of the breakup rather than being the cause of it. Some failed joints had been found in the lower rear fuselage in the Abell examinations and been put down to vibrations from the jet efflux although Jablonsky felt it was more likely to be due to the heat. These stringers had then been riveted and there was no evidence that they were implicated in the crashes. Ripley's evidence was that as many riveted joints in the wreckage had failed as had Reduxed ones. Also no Reduxed joints had failed in the tank test.

In fact Jablonsky had a valid argument both with the difficulty of making full-strength glued joints and the impossibility of examining them after they had been made but de Havillands did have a quality control system in place. A length of glued stringer was cut off each end and destructively examined; altogether some hundreds had been inspected and none had been found to be faulty. The joints could fail by peeling, a form of progressive tensile fracture, and by sliding causing shear. Peeling was the dominant stress and was most likely to start at the ends of the stringers which were accordingly riveted. De Havillands' tests had shown that the shear strength of the joints was about 3,000 psi whereas in service they were exposed to a maximum of about 400 psi, so there was a large reserve of strength.[8]

There was no doubt that the aircraft were exposed to high temperatures when on the ground in the tropics although it was unlikely to have been as high as Jablonsky thought. The manufacturer of Redux had done peeling tests at temperatures of - 70 to + 80°C and shown that its strength was at a maximum at 80°. Also on the ground the cabin wall pressure differential was zero so the main stress was absent.

The temperature differentials that Jablonsky relied on were almost non-existent. As Sir Arnold had pointed out[9] the thermal barrier was inside the stringers and the maximum difference in temperature between the skin and the stringers was only about 10°C. Little differential contraction was produced and this would generate only about 150 psi shear stress.[10] De Havillands had done shear tests on stringers exposed to - 50 to + 60°C for 10,000 cycles with no deterioration compared with the controls.[11] Shear strength was at a maximum at 20°C, at 40°C it was 86% as strong and at 80°C 56%, leaving the joints with a comfortable safety margin. The change in diameter of the fuselage at 30,000 feet was 0.02 inches as the cabin pressure expanded it by 0.18 inches and the temperature fall contracted it by 0.16 inches.[10]

Although Jablonsky said that he disagreed with some of the points raised against him, his arguments had been comprehensively dismantled. He was supplied with the various test results to read through and recalled several days later to comment on them. On this occasion he started by saying that he wished to correct some misunderstandings that had arisen from his previous appearance and then read out a statement.[12]

He was, he said, grateful for the Court letting him express his opinion. His first letter had been to Lord Brabazon at the beginning of April, this was forwarded to Sir Arnold and he had then sent a further letter to Sir Miles Thomas which was forwarded to de Havillands. He had not known at that time that there would be an RAE investigation. He had hoped that the de Havilland report on the reliability of the glue lines, one of those he had been given to read, would come to his rescue and would give him an excuse for an honourable retreat but the opposite had happened.

The tests did not show how the adhesive would have behaved if loads had been applied to one side and if expansion and contraction had occurred under the normal stress loading of the fuselage. The test pieces were nine inch lengths cut off the ends of stringers but he was uncertain how representative they were of long lengths of stringer of up to 100 feet which would have to have been glued in sections and whose ends were probably better made than those stretches further in. During the temperature tests they had been free to expand and contract without being anchored and no loads had been applied. He reiterated his previous arguments adding that Redux was used more extensively in the Comet than in any other aircraft and moreover that it was used there in a pressure cabin. There was also exposure to ultraviolet radiation at altitude which might cause deterioration of the resin. He felt that the fuselage had burst at places other than at the windows which, in his view, were adequately reinforced with doubling plates or frames and that fatigue in the glue lines and splitting of the skin happened before metal fatigue.

By now Jablonsky was beginning to ramble and Lord Cohen was clearly becoming irritated, at one point commenting, "What are you going to read now? You seem to be wandering a very long way from what you were asked to do."

It is easy to see why Jablonsky's arguments were not accepted and the logical reasoning of the RAE was. He must have found his experience in the witness box an uncomfortable one. He was examined by the lawyers more as if he had been a fraudster than an honest engineer trying to be helpful; traps were set for him, his ideas exposed as illogical and he no doubt felt humiliated. Nevertheless he had a point, but perhaps only one, and had he stuck to it he might well have had an easier time. This was that glued joints depend for their integrity on the conscientiousness of the person making the joint and that once the joint has been made there was no means of checking it without destroying it. This valid point was lost in arguments about temperature differences and how YP broke up. But in spite of this there was no evidence to suggest that a failed Redux joint had any bearing on the disaster and it was the lawyers' job to make this apparent.

Chapter 26

LAST WORDS

The inquiry was coming to an end; the last words from a witness, fittingly, were from Sir Arnold on day 17. The various counsel then made their speeches, some quite short and some less short. Inevitably Sir Hartley's was the longest, stretching over three days. Early in his speech he made reference to a series of articles in *The Daily Telegraph*.[1] The first was written by their air correspondent on 26 February 1952, before the Comet entered passenger service. This said that MoS experts and aircraft designers were investigating metal fatigue in post-war aircraft which they thought might cause structural failure at about 9,000 hours. Failures had already happened in Vikings and Doves and it may be that jet aircraft were particularly vulnerable because of their high speed producing more buffeting. The only mention of where this fatigue might strike referred to wing spars and the suggested solution was to limit the flying life of certain aircraft or to replace the affected parts. Some experts thought American aircraft were more robustly made and used stronger alloys.

The second was a leading article dated 8 November 1954, while the inquiry was still in progress. This time the author was not named but the article was apparently not written by their air correspondent. It referred to speculation in the British and foreign press about the sales prospects of the Comets. The futures of the Comet 3 and the reconstructed Comet 2, it said, looked bleak unless large orders materialised, particularly from overseas airlines, and the evidence from the inquiry was unlikely to encourage this. Most airlines, the author thought, would continue to use "piston and turbine engine planes" (presumably turboprops) rather than (pure) jets. Recalling the earlier article, it said that it had long been known that metal fatigue could make small cracks spread and cause aeroplanes to "fall to pieces." It pointed out that the Comet fuselage in the tank test had failed at 9,000 hours, just as predicted. It was likely, it continued, that de Havillands' existing customers were going to ask for compensation for their unusable aircraft and the government would probably have to fund further research into the problem. The question was whether the jet airliner could ever be made into a commercial proposition.

Sir Hartley reacted to this with predictable outrage. He blamed the subeditors rather than the reporters for the more sensational headlines and singled out the *Telegraph's* leading article about which, he thought, "everyone in the Court feels extremely indignant." The newspaper, which normally had high standards, he said, seemed oblivious to the fact that the Court was still sitting. Contrary to their view that foreign buyers were reluctant to buy British aircraft they were impressed by the industry's integrity and by the fact that it had confidently submitted itself to a public investigation. He mentioned an (unnamed) American aircraft of which three, or possibly four, had fallen out of the skies for no apparent reason and that three others of the same type had been found to have fatigue problems in their fuselages. The well-known, low-level fatigue in the wings, he said, was a totally different thing to the high-level fatigue in the cabin, although this "miserable article", as Sir Hartley put it, had implied they were the same. Their pointing out that YU had failed in the tank at just their predicted time of 9,000 hours was made, Sir Hartley said, "with complacent satisfaction of a most distasteful kind."

The *Telegraph's* editorial response was published on 20 November. After reporting Shawcross' criticisms it said that they had never found fault with the RAE investigation, indeed they considered it excellent, nor had they found fault with de Havillands or the British aircraft industry. Mindful of being found in contempt they emphasised that they did not in any way anticipate the findings of the inquiry and had merely suggested that special attention should be paid to those points that would discourage future buyers. The main anxiety expressed in the first article had been about metal fatigue and had foreseen the risk of trouble with it. The newspaper did not blame the manufacturer for what had happened because the state of knowledge of fatigue at the time was "clearly insufficient." They accused Sir Hartley of being "selective" in his account and reminded him that fatigue in a wing or a fuselage was a distinction of place and not of type.

In some ways the *Telegraph's* criticisms were a foretaste of the Principal Films documentary in that the newspaper used the knowledge of fatigue problems in wings to say that the fatigue problems in the pressure cabin should have been predicted. It certainly did not go as far as the programme and say that de Havillands, the MoS and BOAC knew all along that there was a problem with the cabin but had kept it quiet.

Sir Hartley was protecting his client's reputation and his comments should be viewed in that light. He stopped short of suggesting that any action be taken against the newspaper and by his actions probably gave the article more publicity than it would otherwise have received. In any case many of the newspaper's comments were not unreasonable and selling more Comets in the UK, let alone overseas, was unlikely to be easy, making de Havillands' future prospects look precarious.

Sir Hartley later acknowledged that the *Telegraph's* response was more sympathetic to his client's predicament and said that he was content to let the matter rest. He even managed to get in another newspaper reference, this time to the *Schenectady Gazette** whose headline was "Mental Fatigue Blamed for Crash of Comet Airliners."[2] No doubt by this time many of the participants in the inquiry were feeling something of the same.

The closing speeches were mainly reiterations of the barristers' arguments and discoveries in the witness box. All of them were peppered with references to the parts of the proceedings that would support the point of view of their particular client or clients in the hope of influencing the Commissioner's opinions in his report although it is

---

* Schenectady is a town in New York State. It was the site of Edison's first electric lamp factory and the company that made many of America's steam locomotives.

doubtful whether they had much effect in this respect.

As well as these speeches, counsel representing the Crown and de Havillands each made a statement. Sir Lionel Heald presented the ARB's intentions. In the future complete pressure cabins would be submitted to tank tests to determine their static and fatigue strengths, more scientists would be appointed to the council of the ARB, more extensive instrumented flight tests would be carried out on the proposed routes and more resources would be put into research on aircraft structural problems.[3]

Sir Hartley put forward de Havillands' proposals for the future. They would use thicker gauge materials for the pressure cabin skin to lower the general level of stress and would strengthen and redesign the cutouts. Specimen sections and then whole fuselages would be subjected to repeated loading tests in tanks. Their manufacturing methods would be changed to avoid, so far as possible, the occurrence of cracks. Any crack that did occur then or later in service would be repaired so that it was as strong, and would have as long a fatigue life, as it would have done had there been no crack. The parts of the wings shown to be prone to fatigue would be redesigned to reduce stress and some parts of the bottom skin would be increased in thickness. Modifications had been designed to prevent fuel venting during takeoff and climb and work was being done to avoid damage to the tanks during refuelling although a complete solution had not yet been found. Consideration was being given to reducing the high breakout force that had been criticised and a search for non-inflammable hydraulic fluid was being carried out. The damage caused by jet buffeting was being reduced in future Comets by angling the jet efflux so that it pointed away from the rear fuselage. The thicker skin would also help. The areas susceptible to damage from loading passengers or freight would be reinforced. Finally the company was anxious to show that it had learned several lessons from the proceedings and that it would try to do better in the future.[4]

The expensive and lengthy inquiry had finally come to an end and the Commissioner and his assessors were left with the task of producing their report. As well as providing an account of the crashes, the RAE investigation and the Court proceedings the Commissioner and his assessors would have to pass judgement where views had differed, answer the five questions that had been set by the Attorney-General and make suggestions for the future.

Chapter 27

THE COMMISSIONER'S REPORT

The Report of the Court of Inquiry into the Accidents to Comet G-ALYP on 10th January, 1954 and Comet G-ALYY on 8th April, 1954, to give it its full title, was published on 12 February 1955.[1] The first part described the participants and the proceedings of the inquiry and the events that had preceded it. Apart from relating the views of the ARB and the ASB the report made no comment on the decision of the minister, on advice, to allow BOAC to restart services after the Elba crash and therefore presumably found no fault with it.[2] The various parts of the RAE investigation were briefly described and the Commissioner accepted their overall conclusion that the Comet's cabin had a short fatigue life. He thought it most likely that the failure in YP had started near the rear ADF window and had spread fore and aft from there. He considered it impossible to say at which corner the failure had started but the starboard rear corner which showed the evidence of an existing fatigue crack made it the most probable site. The opposite corner with the small, manufacturing crack was the alternative. Although the subsequent fracture had run through this crack the Commissioner accepted that 'location' would have been a satisfactory method of dealing with it had it not been for the high stress in the area.[3]

The Commissioner's opinion was that the fundamental cause of the failure of the cabin was that the level of stress around the corners on the cutouts was higher than was consistent with a long fatigue life. This was even more the case bearing in mind the inevitable presence of stress raisers such as rivet and bolt holes in these areas. This opinion was strongly supported by the failure of YU in the tank tests. The views expressed in the RAE report, supported at the inquiry by Sir Arnold, Dr. Walker and Mr. Ripley, were accepted by de Havillands and BOAC and Lord Cohen paid tribute to the work done by the RAE.[4]

The alternative view expressed by Mr. Jablonsky was rejected and the Commissioner went to some lengths to explain why he had done so: there was no significant temperature gradient across the Redux joints to cause differential expansion or contraction producing a shear failure or fatigue, there was no evidence that temperature fluctuations weakened the joints significantly, de Havillands' quality control, at least in this respect, appeared good, there was no history of failure in other aircraft in which Redux had been used and Mr. Ripley's explanation of the failed Redux joints in the rear fuselage was convincing.[4]

The only other witness who did not completely accept the views of the RAE was Mr. Tye of the ARB. He accepted that the cabins had burst but was not entirely convinced that the cause was fatigue. Bearing in mind his position as the technical officer of the ARB and that he had the responsibility for advising the board when a new application was made for a Certificate of Airworthiness for the Comet, the Commissioner thought his caution was understandable. His dissension had been based on the view that if YU's 9,000 hours was an average life then it was unlikely that as many as two aircraft of such a small cohort would have failed after only about 3,000 hours, right at the bottom of the scatter range. However his argument was severely weakened by his being unable to suggest an alternative explanation. He had conceded that YU had failed through fatigue and that all other causes for YP's failure seemed to have been eliminated. On this basis the Commissioner said he had little hesitation in being confirmed in his view that the RAE's explanation was the correct one.[5]

The likelihood of the cabin bursting because of overpressure was easily dismissed because of the reliability of the equipment of the controlling and safety valves.[6] The Commissioner then discussed the significance of the other defects in the aircraft discovered by the RAE. The fractures of both wings could not have been the primary cause of the accident because of the evidence of continuous marks left by cabin parts flying at high speed along the span of the wings when they were clearly still intact. The problem of the fuel venting from the wing and possibly catching fire was equally dismissed because the evidence from the wreckage showed that the fire did not start until after the cabin had disrupted. The risk of damage to the wing tanks from the pressure refuelling was remote and even if it had happened it could not have caused the disaster. The weakening of the Redux joints in the underneath of the rear fuselage had already been noted and dealt with before the second accident and if the two accidents had the same cause it must be something other than this.[5]

There was no suggestion that any person or persons wilfully disregarded any point that they ought to have considered or took any unnecessary risks but, as might be expected, the Commissioner did make several comments about de Havillands' practices.[6] The stress calculations that de Havillands made during the design and construction phases had come in for some criticism during the inquiry as did their structural tests and Lord Cohen's assessors had prepared a memorandum to help in resolving this.[7] The purpose of the calculations done by de Havillands was not to arrive at an exact figure for the maximum stress level near the corners of the cutouts, they were more to estimate the average over an area about two to three inches wide to help in the design of a test piece. They relied more on the actual tests to see that the design was adequate. As their estimate of a stress of 28,000 psi at a pressure of 8.25 psi (1P) was less than half the ultimate strength of the material (65,000 psi) they were confident that the structure around a cutout would withstand a pressure of 16.5 psi (2P). Their tests of a window panel of 'about three feet square' substantiated this as it withstood almost 20 psi. However this window and panel was supported on the face of a stiff 'pressure box' which may have affected the results.*

In a similar way the static tests on the cabin were carried out on two specially-prepared sections which gave de Havillands confidence that the cabins would withstand about 10,000 pressure cycles, suggesting a life of about 30,000 hours or ten years service. This met the requirements of the ARB and was in tune with current practice in the industry but again these sections were not fully representative of the whole pressure cabin. In the first place the open ends of the sections had to be closed with stiff bulkheads, which must have affected the stress patterns, and secondly they did not contain the full complement of windows, in particular the one ADF window in the nose section was very close to the bulkhead and was probably significantly affected by it.

During the second half of 1952 and on into 1953 there was an increasing awareness of the dangers of cabin failure from fatigue. De Havillands had responded to this by carrying out 16,000 pressurisations of the nose section, suggesting a safe life well beyond their target of ten years.[7] It was therefore something of a surprise that YU's cabin failed in the Farnborough tests after around 3,000 cycles although this was about three times the lives of YP and YY. After YU's first failure, strain gauges had been placed around the windows which had appeared to be the places of highest stress. This led to an estimate of maximum stress at the edge of a cutout to be about 43,000 psi at P. This was regarded by de Havillands as unreliable, partly because it involved some extrapolation but also because it implied a stress of 86,000 psi in the static test of the nose section at 2P, well above its ultimate strength. The figure of 43,000 psi was supported by calculations done by Sir Arnold on the stress distribution in a cylinder made from sheet metal with a cutout shaped like that in the Comet although these were not claimed to be exact.

Taken together, these calculations and the tank tests strongly suggested that the stress at the corners of the windows was far higher than had been estimated by de Havillands and probably over 40,000 psi. In fact the extrapolated figure of 43,000 could be increased even more by taking into account loads other than just the cabin pressure, perhaps to about 45,700 psi which was around 70% of the ultimate strength of the material. It was not a case of de Havillands having made a mistake in their calculations, more that they were calculating a different thing. They had, the Commissioner said, the natural approach of a designer using methods based on their previous experience. At the start of the inquiry there was a 'sharp disagreement' between the interpretations put forward by the RAE witnesses and those of de Havillands but the differences had largely, but not entirely, disappeared by the end of the proceedings.

There remained the problem of reconciling de Havillands' fatigue tests with those of the RAE. Sir Arnold had put forward the theory that the preloading of the de Havillands' test sections had prolonged their fatigue lives by producing plastic flow at the corners reducing the stress levels. Mr. Harper had said that he was aware of this

---

* Actually the panel measured 60 inches by 48 inches and had the same radius of curvature as the Comet's fuselage. It was subjected to seven separate tests using air or water as the pressurised medium. The last, static, test, using water, reached 19.75 psi before developing a tensile failure at one corner and a secondary failure at the opposite corner. There was no mention of strain gauges being used. The panel was said to be representative of the window frame construction used in the Comet but photographs show that it was riveted around the whole circumference and not just at the corners.[8]

possibility but considered that the number of cycles their sections had been exposed to amply compensated for it. Bearing in mind the state of knowledge at the time the Commissioner accepted this conclusion as reasonable.

Another question was whether de Havillands' method of dealing with manufacturing cracks by 'location' was satisfactory.[9] It was accepted that cracks also appear in aircraft skins as a result of general wear and tear and that these cracks do not materially differ from those produced during manufacture, except that the latter may indicate an unsatisfactory manufacturing process. For small cracks in areas not highly stressed the process of 'location' was accepted as reasonable, provided that the holes were accurately drilled at the extreme ends of the cracks. Cracks thought likely to progress were dealt with by carefully-considered repair schemes drawn up in collaboration with the designers. Further progression of the crack might require the part to be redesigned to reduce the stress it experienced. Both of these processes were accepted by the Commissioner as reasonable.

The procedure adopted by de Havillands to deal with cracks, or other deviations from the design specifications, when they were discovered by a workman or inspector was to issue 'concession' notes. Cracks were considered major deviations and proposals for dealing with them would have to go to the chief inspector and if approved by him would have to be submitted to the design department for final approval. In the case of YP three cracks were discovered in the reinforcing plates of the ADF windows, all of which had been 'located' using $\frac{1}{16}$ inches drill holes. This would have been appropriate if the stress level had been as low as de Havillands thought it was but was inappropriate with the stress level that actually pertained. As de Havillands cannot be blamed for their ignorance of the actual stress level, their management of these cracks must therefore be considered reasonable.

There was also evidence that the 'concession' procedure did not operate perfectly. There was a crack in the skin at the starboard front corner of the rear ADF window that had been drilled but no concession note could be found for it. This crack had spread beyond one of its drill holes but it was not involved in the failure and there was no evidence of fatigue. As de Havillands had already put forward proposals for improving their management of cracks the matter was not pursued further.

The statements made by Sir Lionel Heald about the ARB and by Sir Hartley about de Havillands were accepted but Lord Cohen also had some other suggestions to make.[10] The first was that more effort needed to be made to secure a satisfactory safe life for the pressure cabins of new aircraft. He accepted that the scatter of fatigue lives was a great problem in the sense that testing large numbers of specimens was impractical. The RAE investigation had increased the understanding of the problem both in terms of better methods of calculation and a means of testing whole structures. A wider use of strain gauges would also be helpful as would the greater use of the RAE's considerable expertise and resources.

On the advice of his assessors Lord Cohen also made suggestions for further research. The first suggestion was to do more work looking into the effects of plastic flow in relieving stress at the corners of the various cutouts. The second was to find out the true static strength of a whole Comet pressure cabin. The third was to reconsider the high breakout force in the Comet's controls that had come in for some criticism, in part from the Indian authorities after the Calcutta crash.

The Commissioner went on to dismiss two other suggestions that had been brought up by counsel in the course of the inquiry.[11] One was a criticism of the system of inspection in the factory and the suggestion that the inspectors should report to the ARB rather than to the manufacturer. Lord Cohen felt that responsibility for the product should rest with the manufacturer and that any other system would reduce their sense of responsibility and would lead to duplication and added expense for no gain. The second criticism was aimed at the ARB and their relatively small flight-testing capability with the suggestion that an active airline pilot should also be involved. Lord Cohen suggested that serious consideration should be given to more use of the existing flight-testing facilities, presumably those at Boscombe Down, but he felt that any airline pilot would have to be a permanent appointment and that he would soon lose the expertise for which he had been appointed.

The answers to the Attorney-General's five questions came at the end of the report and by this time were pretty self-evident.[12] The cause of the accident to YP was the structural failure of the pressure cabin and it was assumed to be the same for YY. The second question relating to whether other factors were involved, did not arise. The accidents were not due to any wrongful act or negligence, the aircraft had been properly maintained and were airworthy, they had valid Certificates of Airworthiness and Maintenance, their radio stations were serviceable, they were loaded properly and, apart from YP's flight engineer, all the crews were properly licensed and experienced.

As might have been expected from Lord Cohen's performance during the inquiry, the report was a succinct, balanced and accurate representation of the proceedings as well as logically and fairly deciding all the points that had to be decided. Its suggestions for future research were taken up by the RAE and the results published in due course.

Chapter 28

THE AFTERMATH

Further fatigue tests

The first of the assessors' suggestions was that further work should be done on the effects of plastic flow relieving stress at the corners of the various cutouts. This was carried out in late 1955 and early 1956 at Farnborough on G-ALYR, which had already made 747 pressurised flights.[1] The same water tank method was used although the wings were not included and the fuselage was supported by the centre section and was only subjected to pressure loads. Strain gauges were placed at the corners of the third starboard window and the forward port escape hatch and readings were taken at intervals during the pressure cycles and the stresses deduced for a differential of 8.25 psi. Detailed visual inspections were made at frequent intervals and when a fatigue crack was found its progress was followed continuously using an inverted periscope. When it was thought that a crack was about to extend catastrophically the pressure cycles were stopped, the tank drained and the crack repaired to prevent excessive damage to the fuselage.

A total of 11,319 cycles of 0 to 8.25 psi were applied to YR's fuselage. Fatigue cracks developed in the skin at the corners of nine windows and two escape hatches; in all, sixteen corners were involved. None occurred at the corners of the ADF windows, the doors or the freight hatches. The first crack was seen after 5,248 cycles and by 8,941 cycles all six windows in the centre section had developed one or more cracks. Nine cracks were observed throughout their development. All of the cracks started at countersunk rivet holes at the cutout corners, not at the edges.[2] Initially they increased in length at the rate of about one inch in 500 pressure cycles. As all the windows and hatches, except the forward escape hatch, were placed between fuselage frames the cracks had to cross a frame when they were about 4.5 inches long. Experience showed that when the cracks had spread about 2 inches beyond the frame, i.e. to a total length of about 6.5 inches, they began to accelerate towards a catastrophic failure. The critical crack length for the thickness and general stress level of the DTD 546B used in the Comet 1 was therefore about 6.5 inches.

The growth of the cracks could be considerably slowed by the frames. The frames had two different means of attachment to the skin. Most frames were attached by only two countersunk bolts at each stringer flange but in the centre section of the fuselage the frames were riveted to the skin in the region of the windows. Where the frames were bolted to the skin they had no effect on the spread of the cracks. The riveted frames had more effect. If the crack passed between two rivet holes they were slowed but not stopped but if they happened to enter a rivet hole they were stopped temporarily; one crack was stopped for 1,800 cycles. The critical length for the window cracks generally varied between 5.6 and 6.75 inches but at the port escape hatch a catastrophic failure occurred at 2.75 inches.

The stress level measured by the strain gauges was highest at the window corners, being around 40,800 psi at the top rear third starboard window. This extrapolated to 47,700 at the edge of the cutout. However the cracks started at the rivet holes, not the window edges, and the ones that subsequently became catastrophic started at the outer rivet holes. The few that started at the inner holes spread to the edge of the cutout and then stopped. In other words the cracks did not start in the areas of highest measured stress. This strengthened the belief that the rivet holes themselves created local stress concentrations that were even greater than those created by the large cutouts, as well as the rivets causing fretting.*

The fatigue cracks were more frequent, and started earlier, at the windows in the centre section although the first failure in YU had been at a forward escape hatch. This was explained by a combination of three factors: the average stress at the corners of windows was about 20% higher than at the corners of the escape hatches, probably because the radius of curvature of the window corners was 3 inches and that at the escape hatches was 4 inches, secondly it was thought that the floor reacting against the internal pressure produced distortions whereas the rest of the fuselage approximated to a complete cylinder and lastly, during its service life, the centre section would have experienced more stress from flight and ground loads.

Most of the cracks were only about 0.25 inches long when they were first noticed but the circumstances for finding them were ideal and it was considered unlikely they would have been spotted in normal service life, particularly as all the paint had been removed from around the test cutouts. It was found that when a crack of this length had developed, about 90% of the total life of the pressure cabin had already been used up. It was also thought probable that crack propagation would have been faster in service life with its extra loads, indeed in YU, which had some of these extra loads, they progressed between two to six times faster. There was some correlation between these results and experimental findings using cylinders with diameters of twelve feet but not with tests using flat sheets which did not have the radial pressure. The failures in YR happened after about twice the number of cycles as in YU. Also they happened over a larger spread of cycles and the cracks progressed more slowly; it seemed the less realistic the test, the later the failure.

The final conclusions were that for a test to be of any use in estimating fatigue life the flying and landing loads must be represented as fully as possible, the attachment of reinforcing material, such as the rivets in the window frames, produces its own stress

---

* Fretting is the wear caused by two surfaces, which are never completely smooth, rubbing together under load. It can result in a particularly potent form of fatigue resulting in a greatly reduced fatigue life and fatigue strength.

concentrations and that by the time a crack first becomes noticeable nearly all the fatigue life associated with that crack has been used up.

Static tests of the Comet fuselage

The second of the assessors' suggestions was to find out the true static strength of a whole Comet pressure cabin. The same apparatus that had been constructed at some cost for the fatigue testing of YU could fortunately also be used for the static test and was later used for the fatigue studies on YR described above. The Comet selected for this was G-ANAV. This was the youngest available fuselage, with 1,255 flying hours, and it was the least likely to have any existing cracks which could have invalidated the test. As well as being the youngest it was also rigorously examined for cracks and none were discovered. The test was carried out in summer 1955 and the results published that December.[3]

After a few preliminary trials a steadily-increasing pressure load was applied to the fuselage in a single operation to destruction. This happened at a pressure of 19.3 psi, i.e. at 2.34P. The failure was confined to the starboard side and consisted mainly of two separate longitudinal cracks: the first extended along the tops of the windows from the rear pressure dome to the rear spar of the wing and the second along a line of rivets above the windows extending from the rear spar to the pilots' compartment. The two cracks were on either side of the internal frame which supported the rear spar and did not connect. There were also numerous small cracks and some internal damage, particularly fractures of the fuselage frames.

It was difficult to determine the exact sequence of events and the indications were that the structure was near to its breaking point in several places. This might mean that it was a 'well-balanced' design and was almost equally strong throughout or that the areas of highest stress had deformed plastically and provided some local stress relief. The view at the time was that both were probably true. The sequence appeared to be that the rear crack was the first and that it started at one of the two top corners of the starboard rearmost window. Almost instantaneously the front crack started at the crew entrance door. Both origins were in similar places to the fatigue cracks in YU and YP in that they were at the corners of cutouts.

The airworthiness requirement in force at the time of the inquiry was that the cabin should have an ultimate strength of twice the operating pressure (2P) and this cabin exceeded it by 0.34P. It did not, however, meet the designed ultimate strength of 2.5P. The Calcutta crash was a failure of static strength in the sense that no fatigue failures were found but the break up was caused by excessive external loading from the storm, and perhaps from over correcting, rather than excessive internal pressure.

More wreckage is found

In the afternoon of 24 June 1956 the crew of the fishing vessel *Isolda Madre* were trawling in an area about ten miles north east of the island of Montecristo (42° 28' N, 10° 27' 30" E). To their surprise the weight of the trawl suddenly stopped their boat. When they managed to haul it in they found in the net a large, irregular piece of metal on which was painted the letter A and 'following it' the letter O, both in blue surrounded by yellow. The top part of the skin was painted white and the bottom part finished with blue paint and parts of a gold line. The process of lifting the wreckage broke their net and the fishermen had to cut the metal sheet into five pieces to get it into the vessel. The wreckage was brought ashore at Porto Santo Stefano on the mainland and kept in the vessel owner's store.[4]

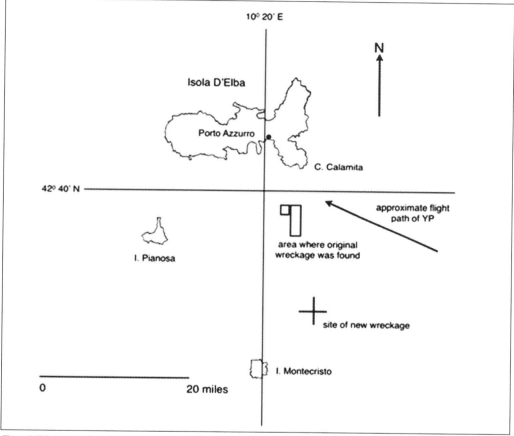

Fig. 1/28 Map showing the relationship of the new wreckage to the earlier wreckage[5]

News of the find reached the BOAC representative in Italy who arranged for a Mr. A. Holt, described as a Comet engineer, to view the wreckage *in situ*. He reported that the material was in excellent condition and would measure about twelve feet by two feet if it were pieced together. As well as the two big letters it also had a stamp with several identifying codes which included the date of 31/8/49. This information was referred back to the Ministry of Transport and Civil Aviation who discussed it with de Havillands (Wilkins) and the RAE (Ripley) who were both "very keen" that the wreckage be brought back to the UK for examination.[6]

Arrangements were made, "without it involving a large amount of expense", for BOAC to fly all 44 kilograms of it back to the UK. It arrived at London Airport on 29

August and Mr. Ripley made arrangements for it to be transported to Farnborough. On 31 August Ripley described the piece as being from the starboard side of the top of the fuselage between frames 18 and 26 and six to eight feet wide in places. He added that it was "of considerable interest" and "could cause some modification of exact sequence of failure." By 13 November he had decided that the wreckage "strongly indicates D/F* cut-out was not primary failure."[6]

No photographs of the new fragments survive in the files although it is difficult to imagine that none were taken. Nevertheless it is possible to deduce some details about it using the information in the files and the development drawing of the wreckage around the ADF windows that was prepared for the RAE report and reproduced here.[7] This is a drawing of the original wreckage stretched out flat and viewed from above. It shows the positions of the ADF windows, four of the port and starboard side windows and the front port and starboard escape hatches as well as the BOAC lettering on both sides of the fuselage. On the starboard side there is an 'empty' area stretching from frame 18 to frame 26 where the new wreckage came from. There is no scale on the drawing but the frames are drawn in and they were 21 inches apart.[8]

The new pieces are variously described as twelve feet by two feet "if pieced together" and six to eight feet wide "in places". It seems reasonable to assume that the latter referred to one or more of the fragments on their own rather than to all five of them pieced together. The distance between frames 18 and 26 is just over thirteen feet and

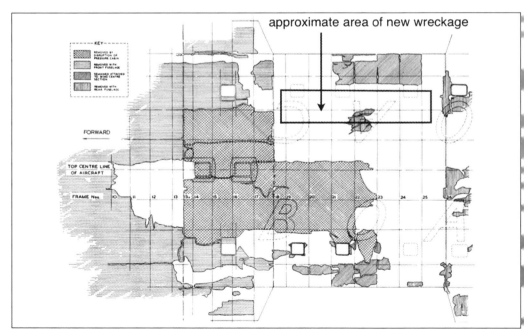

Fig. 2/28 Development drawing of the wreckage around the ADF windows from YP showing the area of new wreckage.[7] (FAST, Farnborough Air Sciences Trust, with additions by author)

* i.e. the rear ADF window.

the 'empty' area on the development drawing is just under six feet wide so the assembled piece would fit most of the length but only part of the width of this area. The bottom limit of the wreckage had blue paint and parts of a gold line. On BOAC Comets there was a blue band all around the aircraft at the level of the windows with a gold line at the top and bottom, corresponding to the top and bottom of the windows. So the bottom limit of the wreckage was around the top of the side windows. No windows parts were mentioned so presumably they were not found and the wreckage did not extend far into the window line. The letters A followed by O were said to be present. Part of the skin where 'A' was painted had already been retrieved but enough new skin must have been found to identify it as coming from here. However O precedes A and if the assembled pieces ended at frame 26 only a small part of the letter O could have been present. It is more likely that the left hand part of the letter C was present and was mistaken for the letter O. The approximate area of the assembled new pieces is shown above although it would have been much more irregular and may not have been continuous.

There must have been a considerable amount of thinking going on at Farnborough about the implications of the new piece wreckage. In December Dr. Walker wrote to Group Captain Tweedie at the AIB with their conclusions.* Walker outlined some of their recent views about the mechanism of structural break up. Some of this had been prompted by the static test on the Comet fuselage described above. At the inquiry the view had been that if a pressure cabin burst at one point then the pressure was released and it could not then burst at another point. But the static test-to-destruction of AV had disproved this by producing two major fractures which had happened almost simultaneously but which were not in physical continuity. Unless the two areas had been absolutely identical in their static strengths and therefore burst at exactly the same moment, which was stretching co-incidence a bit far, then there had to be a connection between the two events in the sense that one had triggered off the other. Walker's new theory was that the sudden release of stress at one point caused the production of a shock wave which travelled at very high speed over the whole structure and might then induce subsidiary origins of failure elsewhere almost simultaneously. In AV the rear crack was the primary and the front crack secondary. Instrumentation on AV indicated that the shock wave produced several areas of what Walker called 'super stress', about 50% higher than elsewhere.[9]

Walker's letter continued, explaining that with a static failure the subsidiary origins might be almost anywhere but for a fatigue failure the likely spots were where there were already small cracks. This theory could explain some of the crashes in the past that had appeared to have multiple simultaneous failures. Walker said that for some time he had felt that YP's failure had started at a side window, much as it had in the tank test, without there being any conflict with the evidence given at the inquiry regarding the failure at the ADF window.

Ripley and his team reviewed the original wreckage from YP and still thought that

---

* The text of this letter is reproduced in full in Appendix 4.

the rear ADF window was an origin of failure causing cracks to propagate out from there for some distance. The new wreckage showed cracks radiating outwards from an origin in the region of the three starboard windows between the main spar bulkheads. The actual point of origin was not found and must have been in a piece of wreckage not retrieved and presumably still at the bottom of the Mediterranean but the most likely place was at a corner of one of the windows. This would probably have produced a linear fracture along the top or bottom of the line of windows, depending on where it had started. As this was likely to extend along several windows and there was no mention of it in any of the blue or gold-painted fragments from the tops of where the windows had been, it is more likely that the fracture ran along the bottom. Some of the skin under windows two and three had already been found in the original salvage operation but nothing had been retrieved from under the first window which therefore seems the most likely site although it is impossible to be sure. The area between the two origins was, in Walker's words, "a kind of no-man's-land where the direction of propagation is uncertain... a circumstance which is not inconsistent with crack propagation from two distinct sources."

There were, then, at least two cracks in YP which acted as 'origins of failure'. It was difficult, Walker said, to decide which crack went first but he felt that as a group the Comet 1s were more likely to have a primary failure at a side window than at an ADF window. This opinion was based, to some extent, on work done at the RAE since the inquiry (presumably including the fatigue tests on YR and the static test on AV) and "some really first class experimental work done independently by de Havillands." In any case the two failures would have been almost simultaneous.

Walker's letter ended with a request to "let the matter rest here." He did not want to start another Comet inquiry, even an unofficial one. His view was that there was nothing they now knew that was inconsistent with the evidence given at the inquiry or with the findings of the Court; if anything, the new information strengthened the view that pressure cabin fatigue was a major hazard to the Comet 1.

Dr. Walker, with Tweedie's agreement, copied this letter to Professor Duncan, Sir William Farren, Walter Tye, Ronald Bishop and Sir Arnold Hall asking for their views on the technical aspects and whether they agreed that the matter should be kept quiet. They replied that they were all in full agreement that no purpose would be served by publicising the matter. It was also Tweedie's view that under the regulations controlling the investigation of accidents the new material did not constitute a reason for re-opening the inquiry. Just to be absolutely sure, or perhaps to spread any blame that might ensue, Sir William got in touch with Lord Cohen, who also concurred.

As well as agreeing on a vow of silence several of the respondents at the same time thought it should not preclude the publication of Walker's ideas about shock waves and pressure cabin break-ups. Walker agreed but said that he would have to find some way of doing this without "dragging the Comet through the mire." Tye felt rather vindicated by the new material. His mild dissension at the inquiry had been caused, he said, by the feeling that YU's ADF window had remained undamaged at 17,000 hours (5,546 cycles) whereas YP's had failed at about 3,000 hours, which implied an improbably large scatter. The new material reduced this considerably to 9,000 and 3,000 hours.[10]

The most considered reply was from Sir Arnold who had left Farnborough and was now the technical director of Hawker Siddeley. He thought the matter quite trivial from the legal point of view. He was strongly of the opinion that Walker's hypothesis should be published if only to avoid rumours about the Comet's demise becoming common currency. He thought Walker's ideas should be combined with the report on the static test and should be prefaced with an explanation of how a structure with stresses exceeding 50% of ultimate can nevertheless survive twice the original load and why the wreckage of YP suggested a failure at one point whereas the tank tests suggested another.[11]

Sir Arnold said he was not clear why if a stress wave from the failure at a side window could produce a stress concentration sufficient to cause a failure at the ADF window, it had not happened in the tank tests. This may have been, he conceded, because YP already had cracks which YU did not. A second point was that it would be necessary to show that the geometry of the structure increased, or at least did not reduce, the power of the stress wave as it propagated. Walker responded that the latter would be difficult although the magnification had definitely occurred in the tests. He thought the inertia, damping and the low energy content of the water in the tank might account for the survival of YU's ADF window. The later fatigue tests also had the failures repaired before they became catastrophic.[12] Hall accepted the water inertia and damping but disagreed that it would be difficult to explain the stress magnification[13] although he had already said that he had no intention of working it out himself.[11]

The last to reply was Ronald Bishop who had been away in South Africa. He agreed, as might be expected, that there was no virtue in re-opening the inquiry. Their tests after the inquiry had "tended to show" that the crack originated at a side window or escape hatch but that it was "quite immaterial" which. "The accidents were due to fatigue in the pressure cabin."[14]

They were right. The new wreckage made no material difference, in fact it removed at least one of the inconsistencies between the original wreckage and the tank tests. Whether it was also right to keep the new findings secret was another matter. They were all understandably anxious to put the Comet inquiry behind them for the sake of de Havillands and the British aircraft industry in general. There might also have been an element of not wanting to seem professionally discredited after coming down heavily in favour of the source of all the trouble in YP being the rear ADF window. It was a more secretive and authoritarian age then, with more of the feeling that the authorities knew best. It is less likely now that such a cover-up would take place and if it did, it would be more likely to be leaked. Even then it was probably unnecessary as all the inquiry had said was that the cabin had a short fatigue life and that, of the wreckage found, the rear ADF window was the most likely site.

The files were closed and as the people involved were used to keeping official secrets it did pretty much stay a secret. Mike Ramsden, the de Havilland apprentice who saw the first Comet being built, mentioned it in an article in *Aeroplane Monthly* in 1989[15] but it seemed not to attract much attention.

In 1995 Mr. A. J. Lucking, who was something of an airline passenger activist, start-ed his own investigation.[16] He had attended a lecture at the Royal Aeronautical Society that September given by Sir Peter Masefield which implied that the later wreckage had shown that failure of the Redux joints had played a bigger part in the crashes than the inquiry had thought. He confirmed this in a letter to Lucking.[17] He recalled a meeting in the Skyport Hotel at Heathrow at which Bob Hardingham (the administrative head of the ARB) and Walter Tye had announced "the latest findings." These were that, as well as the failure at the side windows, there had been a "simultaneous failure of some of the redox [sic] bonding so the top of the fuselage largely tore off." The meeting had decided that there was no purpose in re-opening the inquiry so "the whole thing was hushed up."

Following this Lucking wrote to Tye who reminded him that the Court had dis-missed Jablonsky's theory although it had served the useful purpose of pointing out that gluing had to be treated with care and that a degree of poor adhesion had to be expected.[18] Tye's view was the accepted one of high stress levels producing a fatigue failure and that any Redux failure had only a minor effect. He was unable to recall any meeting at the Skyport Hotel and thought it "a figment of someone's imagination." In any case it would not have have been the job of the ARB to have made any such announcement, more that of the AIB.

Lucking, with the help of Mr. Ken Smart, the then Chief Inspector of Accidents, said that he had managed to get the relevant files opened at the National Archives. These files provided the basis for this account. They make no mention of any Redux failure and it would seem to be a false trail.

At this distance it is not easy to assess the significance of this second centre of fail-ure. The actual point of failure was never found but the evidence for its existence and its general vicinity seems robust. The results of the tank tests also support the probabil-ity of a failure along the side windows and the position of the wreckage on the sea floor, roughly in the line of flight but closer to Rome than the other wreckage, strongly sug-gests that it separated first. Nevertheless, judging by the medical evidence of the head injuries, most of the cabin air escaped through the roof of the fuselage pushing the pas-sengers up to the cabin ceiling. This implies that the major breach was in the roof and it may be that the other centre was more of a split than a large flap opening up.

The most probable sequence of events was that the first failure was a crack suddenly lengthening along the bottom of one or more of the starboard windows. This, almost simultaneously, caused the fatigue fracture at the starboard rear corner of the rear ADF window to extend along the centre line of the cabin roof so opening up two flaps which hinged outwards. This allowed most of the cabin air to escape which pushed the pas-sengers up towards the roof of the cabin and inflicted the head injuries. The area of skin near the starboard windows came away first and the disintegration of the aircraft then followed in the way described in the RAE report and again at the inquiry.

Chapter 29

CONSEQUENCES

Aafter the close of the inquiry the lawyers became advocates for other causes and the scientists and engineers went back to their laboratories and workshops but BOAC and de Havillands were left with the wreckage of their project. The corporation, and to a lesser extent Air France and UAT, had lost the most modern and effective aircraft of their fleets. There was no hope of BOAC using the remaining four Comet 1s for anything other than experiments or scrap. There were also eight remaining 1As that were equally unusable, one owned by BOAC, AV, which had been used for the RAE flight tests, three owned by Air France, two by the RCAF and two by UAT. Five of the original complement of nineteen 1s and 1As that entered service had had crashes severe enough to become complete right offs and two more had been badly damaged and because of subsequent events were never repaired. Compared with the present day this is an astounding casualty rate of about a third for an aircraft that had only been in service for around two years. It was excessive even when compared with contemporary aircraft such as the Lockheed Constellation, which had a write off rate (excluding hostile acts but including pilot error) of 11%, the DC-6 at less than 7% and the slightly later Boeing 707 at about 14% and all of them had far longer service careers than the Comet 1.

Also exercising the minds of de Havillands and the airlines must have been the prospect of not being able to use the Comet 2s of which three had already been completed for BOAC and were undergoing flight trials. The first (G-AMXA) had its maiden flight on 27 August 1953 and had performed at the Farnborough Show that year. It had received its Certificate of Airworthiness on 21 January 1954, eleven days after the Elba crash. XA continued with its flying programme, which included a trip to South Africa with John Cunningham in charge, but was grounded with all the other surviving Comets after Naples. Just before this Cunningham had been carrying out the pre-delivery tests.

All in all 1954 was a bad year for BOAC, Sir Miles Thomas described it as a "swine of a year."[1] Not only had the Comet fleet been lost to the corporation but a Constellation had crashed in Singapore in March, just after the Elba crash, with heavy loss of life and a Stratocruiser would go on to crash at Prestwick in the early hours of Christmas Day. There were delays to the introduction of the Britannia, wrangles with the government and Vickers over their V1000 project and uncertainty about the future of the Comet. As a nationalised company BOAC was bound to be bailed out one way or another and anyway they had insured the Comet 1s for twice what they had paid for them[2] and other aircraft could be bought to fill the gaps. For the time being the corporation battled on

Fig. 1/29 Comet 2 G-AMXA, first flight near Hatfield, 27 August 1953,
(copyright BAE SYSTEMS Heritage).

with a mixed fleet of Argonauts, Constellations and Stratocruisers. After the Comet no doubt these all seemed old-technology aircraft but in reality they were no different from the fleets of their competitors, at least for the present. Eventually dealing with the political and bureaucratic constraints imposed on the chairman of a nationalised company became too much for Sir Miles and he resigned in early 1956.

It was not long before American competition in the shape of the large, four-jet-engined Boeing 707 and the Douglas DC8 were in prospect and BOAC must have felt that the tables were being turned on them. The Britannia's engine troubles seemed never ending and the future for later marks of the Comet looked doubtful. Even when the Britannias were eventually delivered they fell short of their specifications and BOAC held back some of the payments for them.[3] By the time they did enter full and reliable service the world had moved on from turboprops to pure jets for the trans-Atlantic routes and BOAC wanted some of the new 707s for themselves. In October 1956 the corporation was given permission to order fifteen. As a concession to British manufacturers they were to use Rolls-Royce Conway engines. The first was delivered in May 1960. Part of the government's deal with the corporation to buy the 707s was that it would also purchase twenty British-built aircraft for the eastern routes where the airfields were less developed and the 707 would have difficulties. One possibility for this was the Comet 5 but de Havillands wanted an order for at least 50 which did not seem likely.[4] The challenge was taken up by Sir George Edwards of Vickers who went on to produce the beautiful VC10 which, in its first version, entered service in 1964.[5] It remained in service with the RAF until 2013.

In the meantime de Havillands were facing bankruptcy and had to find a survival route. Before the crashes the Comet 2 had sold quite well, 32 had been ordered, twelve for BOAC, nine for France, three for Canada, four for Brazil, two for Japan and two for Venezuela.[2] Shortly after the Naples crash W. E. Nixon, the managing director of de Havillands, called a meeting of the senior executives and stopped production. At this time there were about 25 Comet 2 airframes at various stages of construction in the factories at Hatfield, Chester and Belfast[6] and there were rumours in the press that they would all have to be scrapped although some of their equipment might be salvaged. At the Chester factory a fitter recalled, "It nearly flattened this place. There were people standing around for weeks afterwards. They had no work to give them."[7] Development work on the Comet 3 was continued.

Certainly things looked grim for de Havillands. The figures they gave to the government showed that they had invested £8m in jigs and tools, £12m in work-in-progress and had reserves of only £6m. If 21 aircraft were sold and no compensation were paid to the French (an optimistic view) they would use up all their reserves and not recover any of their £8m investment, leaving their position "parlous."[2] One comment made in an internal civil service letter after the RAE investigation, but before the inquiry had started, said that "…unless HMG (Her Majesty's Government) weighs in horse, foot and artillery, the firm will be bankrupt…"[8] At this stage the government was hoping that it would be possible to buy back the Comet 1As from the French and that they, and BOAC, would still buy the Comets 2s they had on order.

The Comet 2 was virtually a Comet 1 but with the more powerful Avon axial turbojets which delivered 7,300 pounds of static thrust compared with the 4,450 pounds of the first Ghosts. It had a fuselage that was three feet longer, wings that were slightly smaller (2,027 square feet compared with 2,105 for the Comet 1) with leading-edge droops and it carried more fuel and weighed more. Crucially it had the same windows and fuselage skin as the Comet 1s and was therefore unusable as a pressurised commercial airliner. The options were to scrap all 25 Comet 2 fuselages, which de Havillands certainly considered,[6] or to strengthen them in some way. The problem with the latter was whether any airline would buy them and, if they did, whether any paying passenger would set foot inside them. As things turned out no airline would touch them. In view of this, and after much consideration and negotiation behind the scenes, and some reluctance from HM Treasury,[9] the government eventually came to de Havillands' rescue.

At a Cabinet meeting on 16 March 1955, presided over by Churchill, R. A. Butler, the Chancellor of the Exchequer, said that he had discussed the future of the Comets 2 and 3 with the Secretary of State for Air, the Minister of Supply and the Minister of Civil Aviation and they proposed that the government should buy nineteen of the Comet 2s and that after modification most of them be used by RAF Transport Command for moving troops, one or two by the MoS for test purposes and one should be sold to BOAC for training. The remainder of the fuselages should be scrapped.[10]

   This was quite fortunate for the RAF which had been considering buying six or even eight Comet 2s but had been holding back from making a firm commitment until the results of the inquiry were known.[2] It was thought that these proposals would allow the company to concentrate on producing the Comet 3 which should be available by about 1958 to compete with the American aircraft which would be emerging by then. A discussion followed in which it was suggested that the use of Comet 2s for transporting servicemen and their families might be criticised on the grounds that the aircraft were not considered fit for commercial use. In response it was pointed out that the aircraft would not be used unless Certificates of Airworthiness were forthcoming and the decision could be presented as a means of getting the Comet 3s into production more rapidly. If the modified Comet 2s failed to get certificated they would have to think again.[10] The Comet 1As that the French had bought for considerably more than BOAC had paid for them (£469,000 compared with £250,000)[2] had to be bought back to stop them starting proceedings that would jeopardise any future Comet programme.

   In the circumstances this was about as good a solution as could have been devised and it saved de Havillands from serious financial difficulties if not total collapse.* It was not an entirely altruistic act on the part of the government however. If the company had collapsed the government stood to lose considerably more than the cost of the rescue as de Havillands had contracts with them worth about £39m and they would also be unable to recover development costs of about £4½m. In addition they would lose one of the country's most innovative aircraft firms and its products and would incur considerable dollar expenditure buying American replacements to say nothing of the unemployment it might cause.[11] In any case the government expected eventually to recoup the cost of the rescue. Also the RAF had a genuine need for transport aircraft, particularly to go backwards and forwards to the developing rocket range at Woomera in South Australia and service personnel would not get a great deal of choice about how they travelled. But the aircraft still had to be made safe. For various reasons only fifteen of the Comet 2s were purchased by the MoS, thirteen for the RAF, one for testing and another for BOAC trials.

   It was thought at first that just local strengthening would be sufficient but de Havillands came to the conclusion that a more extensive rebuild to commercial transport standards would be better.[2] In the end the RAF settled for local strengthening which was both cheaper and quicker but meant a limited fatigue life of 5,000 hours compared with an estimated 30,000 hours for the complete rebuild.[12] The aircraft's problems were well understood by now and it was relatively easy to work out a practical way of reducing the general stress level. It was proposed to cut out a complete section of the side of the fuselage where the windows were and replace the 20 gauge (0.036 inches) skin with 19 gauge (0.04 inches). It would incorporate elliptical windows whose frames would have an extra layer of reinforcing. The frames would no longer be Reduxed to the fuselage in situ but would be Reduxed to this oval reinforcing plate; the

---

* Duncan Sandys said in Cabinet on 15 October 1957, "I had to save de Havillands after (the) Comet disaster." [13]

Fig. 2/29 RAF Comet 2 XK671, 15 August 1956, (copyright BAE SYSTEMS Heritage).

edge of the fuselage cutout would be similarly reinforced with an oval Reduxed plate and the window frame would then be riveted to the fuselage.[14]

The long axes of these elliptical windows were horizontal. This was the shape pioneered by the Comet 3 and then continued into the Comet 4. It is unclear why this orientation was chosen as it produces a stress concentration greater than vertical ellipses, circular windows or even the rounded rectangles of the Comet 1.* It is even more puzzling that it was continued in the designs produced after the investigation and inquiry although it was not necessarily dangerous so long as the frames were strong enough but strength generally translates into weight. Perhaps it represented a triumph of the marketing department over the engineers but circular cutouts would have allowed almost as good a view for the passengers.

The ADF windows would be redesigned to be stronger and circular and the passenger and freight doors would be reinforced with 16 gauge light alloy. The emergency exits in the eight-seater cabin would be eliminated. In places the fuselage seams would

---

* Horizontal ellipses produce a stress concentration of about 4.5. Had they been vertical they would have produced a much smaller stress concentration of around 1.5, particularly if the proportions had been close to the ratio of $\sqrt{2}:1$.[15, 16] Sir Frederick Handley Page, a pioneer aircraft manufacturer, said of them that they looked like the perforations in lavatory paper, "And you know what they are for".[17] In theory the Comet 1 windows had concentrations of about 3.1 and circular windows would have been about 2.5, in practice a little more. See Appendix 5 for a fuller explanation.

be reinforced with external plates large enough to bridge three stringers and strong enough to take the full pressure load by themselves. The wing would be strengthened with a 10 gauge plate added to the bottom skin between ribs three and eight just forward of the rear spar. The periphery of the wheel well would also be reinforced with the same material. Some other improvements were made to the wing as well as to the tail unit. In addition the control-column breakout force would be reduced, there would be improved fuel venting and the jet pipes would be angled out to reduce buffeting of the rear fuselage.[18, 19]

The RAF wanted other changes as well so that the aircraft could be used as a passenger, mixed passenger and freight or an aero-medical transport. This involved strengthening the floor in the forward passenger compartment and providing racking for six stretchers. It was decided that eight of the aircraft would be finished to this specification and were designated C2. Of the three early aircraft that were finished and intended for BOAC, two were considered too costly to convert fully and just received the stress-reduction modifications but retained their original interiors but had 44 rear-facing seats installed. They were designated T2.

These aircraft were originally given a flying life of 5,000 hours but for some of them carrying counting accelerometers this was later extended to 8,000 hours as the tank testing continued.[20] Unfortunately this fatigue life was predicated on the assumption that each flight lasted about three hours but with many short training flights taking place this was no longer true and the airframes were ageing at twice the anticipated rate.[21] A further complication was the corrosion and accumulated accidental damage of the fuselages which was more related to calendar years than flying time and an upper limit of five or even four and a half years was suggested by the RAE. There followed something of a disagreement between Mr. Atkinson of the RAE and Mr. Harper of de Havillands, the latter feeling that a longer life of up to six years was justified particularly if certain modifications were carried out.[22] After more corrosion was found this was changed again to flying with a maximum pressure differential reduced to 5 psi after 6,000 hours. This 'pitting' corrosion attacked the aluminium cladding of the stringers and caused them to become separated from the skin but so far only in the lower rear fuselage.[23] In effect this was the failure of the Redux joints that Mr. Jablonsky had been so concerned about although the glue itself was not to blame and this new finding had no relevance for the 1954 crashes. The reduction of the pressure differential to 5 psi had the effect of reducing the aircrafts' operating altitude and therefore range.

Another three aircraft were not altered structurally, apart from some strengthening of their windows, and were only flown unpressurised with limited flying lives of 2,000 hours and were designated 2R. They were modified internally by Marshalls of Cambridge to become electronic intelligence gatherers. Two aircraft were used for trials with their outer engines replaced by Avon 524s and were designated 2E. The partially-modified Comet 2s (C2, T2 and 2E) proved to be satisfactory aircraft and had relatively trouble-free service lives. In many ways they were the aircraft that the Comet 1 should have been.*

The fates of the individual aircraft were as follows:[24]

06023, G-AMXA, converted to 2R, withdrawn from RAF 1974, nose now on display at Gatwick.

06024, G-AMXB, converted to T2, withdrawn from RAF 1966, scrapped 1967.

06025, G-AMXC, converted to 2R, withdrawn from RAF 1974, scrapped 1981.

06026, G-AMXD, converted to 2E, used by BOAC and RAE, withdrawn 1973, scrapped 1977, ultimately burned 1986.

06027, G-AMXE, converted to 2R, burned accidentally in an RAF hanger 1959.

06028, G-AMXF, converted to T2, withdrawn from RAF 1966, burned 1968.

06029, G-AMXG, converted to C2, withdrawn from RAF 1966, dumped 1973.

06030, G-AMXH, converted to 2R, withdrawn from RAF 1975, scrapped 1995.

06031, G-AMXI, converted to C2, withdrawn from RAF 1966, scrapped 1969.

06032, G-AMXJ, converted to C2, withdrawn from RAF 1973, scrapped 1988.

06033, G-AMXK, converted to 2E, BOAC route trials 1957, de Havillands 1958, Smiths trials 1960, RAE 1965, scrapped 1975.

06034, G-AMXL, converted to C2, withdrawn from RAF 1969, scrapped 1973.

06035, XK 699, converted to C2, withdrawn from RAF 1967, gate guardian RAF Lyneham 1987.

06036, C2, RAF prototype, used for water tank tests at Hatfield 1955, assumed scrapped there date unknown.

06037, XK 715, converted to C2, withdrawn from RAF 1966, scrapped 1973.

06045, XK 716, first Chester-built Comet, converted to C2, withdrawn from RAF 1967, scrapped 1973.

---

* They had their eccentricities however. The C2 had a tendency to 'snake' (repeated alternating yaws) on the approach and to Dutch roll at altitude when approaching the limiting Mach number but it was generally more nimble than the C4. Both the C2 and the C4 (and presumably the C1 and C3) had the unpleasant habit of dropping cold water on the pilots' knees as the aircraft descended. This happened because the frozen condensation on the inner surface of the fuselage roof melted during the descent and travelled forward to the flight deck between the skin and the insulating lining as the aircraft tilted nose-down. The cabin staff would provide towels for the pilots at the beginning of the descent.[25]

As well as the Comet 2s there were also several Comet 1As and one Comet 3 to consider. The life histories of the 1As has been covered in Chapter 8 and will only be briefly re-capped here. Ten 1As had been manufactured (06013 to 06022) but two had already crashed and been written off. The rest were either bought back by the MoS or de Havillands or their owners compensated to avoid proceedings being started against the manufacturers or the ARB with all the attendant bad publicity that would produce. The MoS then had the job of finding new uses and owners for the ones they had acquired.

The first of the series was intended for Canadian Pacific Airways but was not taken up by them after the Karachi crash. It was transferred to BOAC as G-ANAV for a short time and then after the Naples crash transferred to the RAE and used for flying trials and eventually water-tank tests. It was ultimately scrapped at Farnborough but its nose was acquired by the Science Museum. The second, the other CPA aircraft, 06014, met its end at Karachi. The next two were bought by UAT and withdrawn from service after the Naples crash and were scrapped in France. 06017 and 06018 were bought by the RCAF and withdrawn from service after Naples but in 1956 were flown (unpressurised) to Chester to be converted to 1XB standard. This involved a partial re-skinning in the same way as the C2s and the other modifications except that their Ghost 50 Mk. 2 engines were replaced with the more powerful Mk. 4s. They were used by the RCAF until 1963. The next aircraft in the series was bought by UAT and crashed at Dakar and was written off. 06020 was bought by Air France and grounded after the Elba crash and its fuselage ultimately found its way to the de Havilland Aircraft Museum at London Colney. 06021 was also bought by Air France and after its grounding was purchased by de Havillands the following May, converted to 1XB standard then bought by the MoS and used for trials at Boscombe Down. The final 1A aircraft, 06022, another Air France purchase, was modified to become a 1XB and was retained by de Havillands and was eventually preserved at Cosford. Out of the original ten, four were converted to 1XB standard and had useful service lives.[26]

When it was designed and built the Comet 3 was thought to be the future for the Comet. It was bigger, faster and carried more passengers for a longer distance than its predecessors* but apart from the shape of its windows it had pretty much the same fuselage construction as the 1s and 2s and therefore had no commercial future as it was. BOAC had signed a contract for five Comet 3s on 1 February 1954 to be delivered in 1956 but after the crashes the contract was cancelled. The prototype of what were intended to be many, 06100, G-ANLO, was finished in May 1954 and flew for the first time in July, four days after the prototype Boeing 707 had had its maiden flight.[27] A second Comet 3 was started but not completed. It was not worth re-skinning a single aircraft and it was decided to use it unpressurised, or with limited pressurisation, in trials to develop the Comet 4. It had a long and useful career as a test aircraft which included an engine change to the Avon RA29 and several long-distance proving flights. It even survived a crash with a BEA Trident at RAE Bedford. The Trident was practising blind

---

* The Comet 3 had a fuselage length of 111.5 feet, a wing span of 114.8 feet and a maximum all up weight of 145,000 pounds giving it a range of 2,800 miles with a maximum payload.

Fig. 3/29 Comet 3 G-ANLO near Hatfield, 25 February 1957,
(copyright BAE SYSTEMS Heritage).

landings and unfortunately descended on top of the Comet which was sitting at the start of the runway. It was withdrawn from service in 1972. Even then its career was not over and LO was used in the development of the Nimrod (see below). It was eventually scrapped in 1992.

The Comet 3 evolved into the Comet 4, the last of the series. It was almost the same size as the 3 but had slightly more powerful Avon 524 and 525 engines and a stronger cabin built to have a minimum safe life of 30,000 hours, around ten years of airline service. To complete the quotation (above) from the Chester fitter "...the management just wouldn't get rid of them (the workers) because they had enough foresight to realise that they would need them again as soon as things picked up. And sure enough they did pick up, when we started work on the Mark 4 Comets."[7]

The Comet 4 flew for the first time on 28 April 1958 and then made several long demonstration flights. It entered service with BOAC later that year and one of them, 06404, G-APDC, carried out the first non-stop trans-Atlantic crossing of a jet aircraft with paying passengers on 4 October. Two hours after DC left London its sister aircraft G-APDB left New York for London. This achievement was somewhat overshadowed by PanAm's first commercial jet crossing of the Atlantic in both directions about six weeks later. Significantly the Boeing 707 carried more passengers (140 to 179 compared with 60 to 81 in the first Comet 4 variant) and the later versions could do the Atlantic crossings with a full load, non-stop in either direction whereas the Comet had to refuel at Gander on the east-west flight. Even with a lower load factor the Boeing's operating costs were less than half those of the Comet* (see next page).[28] Although not really suited to the all-important Atlantic route the Comet 4 was used by BOAC until they could get their hands on the American aircraft. It found a more appropriate niche on shorter routes with many airlines all over the world. A total of 76 complete aircraft were built (06401 to 06477 with 06402 used for tank tests)[29] compared with 1,010 Boeing 707s.

The Comet 4 was built in three versions tailored to different passenger loads and route lengths, 28 of the original type, eighteen Bs, 25 Cs and five RAF versions which were essentially Cs.** BOAC received nineteen of the original type and BEA eighteen of the Bs. The rest were bought by a variety of foreign airlines except for the last two which were built 'on spec.', failed to find a buyer and were converted into Nimrod prototypes for the RAF.***

Production of the Comet variants finished in 1962. Most ended their flying days with Dan Air, a smaller British airline, now defunct, and the last one flew commercially in 1980.[30] The Comet 5 would have been bigger again and able to cross the Atlantic without stops but could not elicit any interest from BOAC and it never emerged from the drawing board.[31]

The Comet 4s gave good service although fourteen of them were written off in crashes. Most of these were due to pilot error but there was one instrument failure on takeoff and one landing gear failure. One crashed into a mountainside near Barcelona after confusion between air traffic control and the flight deck crew about the position of the aircraft. One was destroyed in mid-air over the Mediterranean by a bomb and the Israeli Army blew up three Middle East Airlines Comet 4s in a reprisal attack on Beirut Airport. Another was so severely damaged after landing at Newcastle that it had to be scrapped; the crew had forgotten to lower the undercarriage.[32]

De Havillands survived the Comet years with its turnover dipping only transiently and then continuing its upward trend,[33] but the company and its reputation were seriously damaged. Martin Sharp in his history of de Havillands suggests that the company lost about £10m, equivalent to more than £200m today, but without government help this would surely have been much more. New aircraft were increasingly expensive to design and manufacture and cash flow at the company was severely constrained. Their successful aircraft, the Dove and the Vampire and Venom were at the end of their production runs and the Comet 4 was not selling as well as was hoped. Nevertheless de Havillands embarked on another civil airliner project, the three-engined Trident, but not unexpectedly ran into financial difficulties.[34] It was a good-enough aircraft, very similar to the

---

* When Hives was shown the 707 by George Schairer, the Boeing aerodynamicist, he said, "This is the end." "The end of what?" asked Schairer. "The end of British aviation," Hives replied.[35]

** The Comet 4 had a fuselage length of 111.5 feet, the B and C 118. The wing span of the 4 was 115 feet and the B 108 and the C 115. The B and C carried more passengers over shorter distances.

*** The Nimrod was a maritime reconnaissance aircraft that provided a second life for the Comet design. It had what amounted to a second fuselage fixed below the original for holding munitions and other equipment. It also had the more-modern Spey turbofans. It was retired in 2010. Two later variants were the airborne early warning version with an impressive bulbous nose and extended tail which was abandoned after running into trouble with its electronics and the re-engined and improved reconnaissance variant which again was abandoned, this time as a economy measure, after a difficult, prolonged and expensive gestation.

Fig. 4/29 BOAC Comet 4 G-APDA, first flight 27 April 1958,
(copyright BAE SYSTEMS Heritage).

best-selling Boeing 727, but it was too closely tailored to BEA's requirements which, in any case, kept changing. Because of this it ended up too small and failed to appeal to foreign airlines. Only 117 Tridents were produced compared with 1,832 of the 727.

De Havillands' military business, such as making the carrier-based Sea Vixen, continued and they developed a thriving missile division within the propellor company. They later became the principle contractor for Blue Streak, the liquid-fuelled intercontinental ballistic missile whose military role was overtaken by events but ultimately became the first stage of the European satellite launcher.

For some time the feeling in government had been that there were too many airframe and aero-engine companies in Britain. They were partly to blame for this because they had kept companies going for military and strategic reasons that should really have been allowed to go to the wall. The individual companies were too small to compete effectively with their American rivals, some of which were more than ten times as large. In 1959, just before the consolidations, de Havillands, as one of the larger firms, employed about 37,000 people.[33] Also the cosy relationship that had sometimes grown up between the companies and the government had allowed some of them to become insufficiently commercial. Many of their civil aircraft had been technically poor, such as the Tudor and the Apollo, too late, such as the Britannia, or inappropriate such as the Brabazon and the Princess. Even the competent Vanguard failed commercially because the world had moved on from turboprops to pure jets and the VC10, like the Trident, was too tailored to British needs, this time BOAC's, to reach a world market. The Comet was just the most spectacular of the failures, the Viscount the only real success. In the government's eyes the solution was an amalgamation into two airframe and two engine groups.

Some amalgamations had already happened. Airspeed had been bought by de Havillands in 1940 and fully integrated in 1951; Miles had gone bankrupt and was bought by Handley Page in 1948[36] and Metrovicks had left the engine business. The biggest group was Hawker Siddeley which was made up of Avro, Armstrong Whitworth, Gloster and Hawker. In 1959 the civil and military agencies of the government concerned with aviation were merged into the Ministry of Aviation (MoA) with Duncan Sandys appointed as the minister. He had had a rather mixed career in aviation having been responsible for the infamous 1957 announcement that there would be no more manned military aircraft. Nevertheless he was determined to consolidate the British aviation industry and produced what amounted to a government-sponsored marriage bureau.[37] The government for their part undertook to maintain a basic research programme and to provide financial support for exports and to reintroduce launch aid by providing finance which could be recouped from future sales, assuming there were any.

By this time de Havillands were struggling to finance the Trident even with government launch aid and on 17 December 1959 [38] they bowed to the inevitable and announced that they would be joining the Hawker Siddeley Group together with Folland and Blackburn. In the new group what had been de Havillands did most of the civil aircraft work while Hawkers concentrated on the military. Bristol, English Electric, Vickers and Hunting merged to make up the rival British Aircraft Corporation (BAC) while Saunders-Roe, Fairey and Bristol's helicopter interests joined the Westland Group. Handley Page and Shorts, the latter government-owned, stayed away. Handley Page found life difficult as an independent and ceased trading in 1970.[39] The engine companies consolidated into two groups, one inevitably Rolls-Royce, the other Bristol Siddeley. In the long run the two big airframe groups consolidated even further into British Aerospace, now BAE Systems, and Rolls took over Bristol Siddeley. By 1965, after the first consolidations had settled down, no doubt with some 'rationalisation' of the workforce, the whole of Hawker Siddeley, the larger of the two groups, employed only 50,580 compared with Boeing's almost 130,000.[40] The runway and buildings at Hatfield survived for many years after the amalgamation and were used for the production of the Trident and the early British Aerospace 146 feeder liners. Gradually as the group became bigger the work went to other sites. The runway was dug up in the early 1990s but some of the de Havilland buildings still survive, including the large hanger, the art deco administration building and the control tower which are now part of the University of Hertfordshire.

Any amalgamation or take-over is a difficult and painful process, particularly if the participants have been commercial rivals beforehand. The amalgamations of these proud companies with famous names that had been formed at the very start of aviation and led by strong personalities must have been particularly traumatic. But the amalgamations were inevitable and they were the right thing to do. It was part of an evolutionary process of the survival of the fittest that an immature industry often has to go through, particularly if the industry is one in which the financial risks are high. Interestingly, according to Stanley Hooker, this pain did not extend to everyone "...at the technical and engineering levels it all took place with scarcely a ripple."[41] Even Sir Geoffrey seemed at accept it without rancour.[42] It is doubtful that the Comet debacle brought about or even hastened the consolidation of the industry much. Consolidation was well overdue and its timing was mainly controlled by the government. If the Comet did have any effect on the process it was probably quite small.

There were also consequences for the aircraft-building industry throughout the world and the Comet's nemesis, the Boeing 707, was extensively tank tested.* A second, bigger, tank was built at Farnborough to test the Britannia.** It used a more sophisticated and flexible system for loading the fuselage and its storage tank served as another test tank, this time for fuselages without wings.[43] The future was clearly going to be with fast, high-flying, jet-powered passenger aircraft and some way had to be found to make them immune, or relatively immune, from the troubles that had brought the Comet down. Components could be designed to minimise stress concentrations but they would still occur. Hall had said that the way to prevent crashes caused by fatigue failures was to arrive at a 'safe life' for individual components, or even a whole aircraft, during which a crash from fatigue was very unlikely. Because of scatter the safe life was usually considered to be one third of the mean life of a sample of components large enough to reach statistical significance. During its life the component would be inspected and changed if any fault was detected and then changed regardless when the end of its safe life approached. Alternatively the whole aircraft could be retired (see Chapter 21). This was certainly an improvement on what had gone before but testing a number of large structures such as fuselages was expensive and scrapping a whole aircraft because the weakest link had reached its safe life seemed extravagant.

In July 1956 new BCAR requirements for the fatigue of pressure cabins specified that:

> The pressure cabin and local structure shall have satisfactory fatigue characteristics which shall be confirmed by an appropriate programme of tests. The tests shall be used either
>   a) to show that all possible failures are of a 'safe' variety (i.e. that the type and rate of propagation of cracks are such that they would be noted in normal inspection before they introduced any significant likelihood of catastrophic failure)
> or
>   b) if (a) cannot be shown, to establish 'safe' lives for the pressure cabin as a whole or its parts.

In time the concepts of 'fail-safe' and 'damage-tolerant design' were added to 'safe

---

* To about 50,000 cycles.[44] It was said that Boeing swopped information about engine pylons with de Havilland in exchange for their fatigue data.[45]
** It was 160 feet long, 20 feet deep but still 20 feet wide as much of the internal bracing structure had been eliminated so wider fuselages could be accommodated. It held 400,000 gallons.[43]

life' so that the failure of a component did not lead to the loss of the whole aircraft.[46] Some components, such as engine discs and undercarriages, are still designed as 'safe life.' This is because their high strengths (and therefore high stresses they are exposed to) mean that their crack-propagation lives are very short which makes a 'damage-tolerant' design difficult. Engine components do occasionally disintegrate and in an application of the 'fail safe' approach they have containments which should be strong enough to prevent the escape of high-velocity fragments into the cabin or wing structure. On occasion even this fails and in yet another application of 'fail safe' the aircraft should still be able to land safely.* All modern twin-engined aircraft are designed so that they can fly on one engine in the event that the other has failed

More relevant to the Comet's problems, a fuselage can be designed to be strong enough to tolerate an extended crack, say up to 40 inches, before it accelerates and destroys the aircraft.[45] Long before it reaches this size the crack should have been seen and repaired and even if it were missed a crack this big would probably prevent the aircraft becoming pressurised. The difficulty with this is that small cracks, in themselves far from being critical and undetectable in practice, can suddenly join up to become catastrophic.[47] This applies particularly to cracks that are close together such as in a row of rivets and was demonstrated in a Southwest Airlines 737-300 in which a section of fuselage roof nine inches wide by 59 inches long was peeled back in flight and sudden decompression resulted. The fracture connected 58 rivet holes of which 42 showed fatigue cracks.[48]

The cabin can also be designed to decompress less explosively. The fuselage skin is made with 'tear straps', thicker pieces of skin that either stop a crack extending or turn it through 90 degrees. This allows a flap to open and the cabin can decompress in a relatively controlled fashion. This removes most of the load from the skin and stops the crack extending. The straps are made by gluing two sheets of the aluminium alloy skin together, masking off a grid-like pattern on the inner sheet and then etching away the material in between, leaving a matrix of straps about ten inches apart.

Modern aircraft are vastly more tolerant of the consequences of fatigue cracks than the Comet 1 was. The Southwest Airlines 737 mentioned above was able to land safely and an even better demonstration was provided by Aloha Flight 243, another Boeing 737, in 1988. Twenty minutes after take off the flight deck crew heard a load bang followed by screams and a whooshing sound. The captain turned around to find that the cockpit door had vanished and that he could see sky where the cabin roof should have been. He began an emergency descent and managed to land the aircraft safely. Fortunately the passengers were all strapped in but one member of the cabin staff, who was towards the front end of the aisle, was missing. Several of the passengers were

---

* In November 2010 a turbine disc in a Rolls-Royce Trent 900 on a Quantas A380 failed; three fragments from it were not contained and the adjacent wing, and some of the systems within it, were damaged. In spite of this the wing remained structurally intact and the aircraft was able to land safely. During the inspections after the incident small cracks were found in the attachments (feet) of the ribs to the skin of the wings. These are thought to be relatively benign and rather than being grounded the aircraft are being allowed to continue in service and to be fitted with a new design of feet in due course.

injured, some seriously, but things could have been a lot worse. A section of fuselage roof towards the front of the cabin, 18 feet long and 14 feet wide, had been blown out, but in spite of this colossal damage the rest of the aircraft had remained intact and controllable.[49] Like the Comet the cause was metal fatigue, but unlike the Comet the damage was contained.

Chapter 30

THE REASONS WHY

There are two pitfalls that are best avoided when commenting on complicated past events like the Comet crashes. The first is to assume a knowledge of technology that only became available, or generally available, at a later date and the second is being wise after the event. The difficulty with the former is knowing now what was known then. In this case the most reliable sources are the published papers and the dated letters and memos in the files. Also useful are the opinions of the witnesses expressed at the inquiry although these do sometimes vary, Dr. Walker, for example, was much more critical than Sir Arnold. Being wise after the event is an occupational hazard of writing about accidents. Knowing what came later can often make a decision made at the time seem wrong or even foolish. In fairness it can only be expected of people that they act in good faith, using their special knowledge and skills, and make the most reasonable decision with the facts available to them at the time.

The Comet's jet engines meant high speed and high altitude. The high speed led to the thin symmetrical wings which in turn led to the failures to take off at Rome and Karachi and to the power-operated controls which may have played a part in the Calcutta crash. The high altitude led to the need for a cabin with a large pressure differential and the two Mediterranean crashes. The crashes at Rome and Karachi are well understood, were dealt with in the Comet 2 and do not need further exploration. Some questions remain about the Calcutta crash but in the absence of any new information they will probably stay unanswered. The Elba and Naples crashes, which were fundamental to the demise of the Comet 1, can be usefully explored further.

The root cause of the mid-air breakups in the Mediterranean was the failure to appreciate that a lightly-constructed, large-differential, aircraft pressure cabin could be so susceptible to metal fatigue. At the time of the Comet 1's design and manufacture this lack of understanding was universal within the aviation industry* and the research community and it was to be de Havillands' misfortune that they discovered it.

As well as needing to construct a pressure cabin de Havillands also had to use a relatively-primitive jet engine. Compared with modern engines the Ghost had limited thrust and very high fuel consumption.** The provision that the designers made to

---

* Sir George Edwards, the well-respected head of the Vickers Aviation Company, said of his Valiant bomber, a contemporary of the Comet 1, "...nobody worried about fatigue, particularly cracks, in those days."[1]
** See Appendix 7 for a comparison with a modern engine.

incorporate rocket engines between the jet exhausts suggests that there were concerns right from the start about the lack of thrust at takeoff. There was nothing wrong with Halford's engines as such, they performed reliably to their specification, it was just that their specification was constrained by the technology of the time. When the Comet was designed, and the first ones made, there was no alternative to using centrifugal engines and as there was little to choose between the Ghost and the equivalent Roll's centrifugal engine, the Nene, it seems only natural that de Havillands would use their own engine. The Rolls axial engine, what would become the Avon, was not yet available and it was uncertain when, or even if, it would become available. Rolls were having trouble with it and some engines take years to get right.

The limited thrust of the Ghost meant that the aeroplane had to weigh as little as possible so that it could get into the air* and one of the ways of doing that was to use thin sheeting for the fuselage skin. Ralph Hare, who worked in de Havillands' design department, said that they "went for the thin skin at the dictate of Mr. Bishop to get the minimum weight possible."[2] The Comet's airframe does seem remarkably light; 48,000 pounds** compared to 87,000 pounds for the Airbus A318, the closest modern equivalent. Bishop, in his testimony at the inquiry, said that it was a trade off between strength and weight,[3] but in de Havillands' view the skin thickness was adequate. Their calculations showed that the stress was not excessive and this had been confirmed by their tests. They had met, more than met, all the official strength requirements and there is no evidence that de Havillands felt that the structure was wanting in any way. Even if they had waited for the Avon, and that would have been commercially difficult, it is unlikely that the extra thrust would have been used to allow a thicker skin, it would probably have been used to carry more passengers or more fuel. Even when the Avons did become available for the Comet 2 the extra thrust was not used to provide a thicker skin. Without the crashes there was no perceived reason to change.

The Comet's skin was certainly on the thin side and it has been criticised as being too thin.[2] It is true that the later Boeing 707 had significantly thicker fuselage skin, 0.04 to 0.07 inches compared with the Comet 1's 0.028 to 0.036 inches, but the even-later Boeing 737, which was closer in size to the Comet 1, had the same skin thickness (0.036 inches) in places as the early Comets'.*** The difference was that the 737 had the crack-limiting technology described in the previous chapter and different cutout designs but even so it has not been without its fatigue problems.

YV's breakup in the storm near Calcutta did generate some questions about the Comet's structural strength both before and during the inquiry[4, 5] but there was little to substantiate these doubts. There was no evidence of fatigue in the wreckage and later tests confirmed that the fuselage exceeded the ARB's requirements in terms of static pressure strength,[6] although this had limited relevance for the Calcutta crash as the aircraft was only starting to be pressurised at the time of the breakup. The RAE's static

---

* At a constant speed the (weight) induced power requirement varies as the load squared.

** Gunston says 46,300 pounds and comments that it was "astonishingly low".[7]

*** Boeing 777 0.070 inches, DC-10 0.071, Boeing 747 0.063.[8]

tests on the tailplane[9] and the manufacturer's fuselage flexing and torsional tests[10] both showed adequate strength. The bulging floor noticed in the Comet prototype flying at Farnborough suggests it was more flexible than other aircraft, at least when it was not pressurised, but not necessarily that it was any weaker. There is therefore no objective evidence that the Comet was statically less strong than it was required to be or less strong than other aircraft of its time.

The general level of stress, i.e. the stress in a representative section of fuselage skin away from the effects of any cutout, depends on the pressure differential and any other relevant loads, the radius of the fuselage and the thickness of the skin. This stress was said more than once in the inquiry to be too high in the Comet and to be one of the main causes of the Mediterranean breakups. No doubt when compared with contemporary, non-pressurised or less-pressurised aircraft, the general level did appear high but at about 14,000 psi (see Appendix 5) it was similar to that in later jet transports* but they had the benefit of the design features mentioned above.

Keeping the original design of the Comet 1, but using a thicker skin, would have made the pressure cabin more resistant to fatigue. It would have reduced the level of stress and consequently increased the time to crack initiation, reduced the growth rates of cracks when they did form and increased the length of the cracks at which they would become catastrophic. This would have postponed, but probably not prevented, the disastrous events that befell YP and YY. In all probability cracks would eventually have started at the corners of the cutouts and once they had started they would have progressed, albeit more slowly. Every pressure cabin has a finite fatigue life, the ideal is to make this long enough for the aircraft to be economically viable and for any cracks to be large enough to be spotted by an inspection regime before they become catastrophic. The crack-stopping technology of the later jets was developed as a consequence of the Comet breakups. Without them, or some similar event, it is unlikely that the need for it would have been foreseen.

Making matters worse was the high fuel consumption of the Ghosts. This meant that much of the Comet's carrying capacity had to be for fuel and even with this it could only fly short stages lasting about three hours. As the aircraft was used on long-haul routes these had to be flown using multiple stages, hence the popular London to Johannesburg route had to be done in six stages whereas nowadays it is flown non-stop. For that reason the Comet fuselage, in fatigue terms, aged about six times as quickly as a modern, long-haul jet used on the same route.

Bishop said at the inquiry that he was aware of the serious consequences of a cabin failure and that designing it was "one of the biggest problems"[11] and Walker had published calculations about the destructive energy involved[12] but their concerns were about having adequate static strength. The general belief at the time was that if a structure was statically strong enough it would have satisfactory fatigue strength.[13, 14] The regulatory authorities in Britain and abroad endorsed this view but at the inquiry neither Hall nor Walker appeared to embrace it wholeheartedly,[15, 16] although Hall did at least

---

* Boeing 737 15,400 psi., 777 15,000, DC-10 14,500, 747 18,300.[8]

acknowledge the ARB's position.[17]

In retrospect it may seem surprising that nobody at the time appreciated that the repeated pressurisations were likely to lead to fatigue but de Havillands were merely reflecting the generally accepted view. As late as October 1953 Walker published a paper on the fatigue life of transport aircraft in which only wings were discussed and gusts were considered to be "the main fatigue hazard."[18] There was no mention of pressure cabins.

Nevertheless stress calculations and tests were routinely carried out on all parts of a new airframe and had de Havillands done these differently they might have discovered the high stress levels and the consequent vulnerability to fatigue. The calculations were done to provide an idea of the general level of stress in components and structures so that pieces could be constructed and then tested for static and fatigue strengths.[19] De Havillands' calculations were for "...an area of the skin in the neighbourhood of the corners... an average value over a width of two or three inches" rather than an attempt to find the maximum. The Commissioner accepted this explanation in his report[20] although Hall was clearly critical of it, "that is where the metal is going to break, and you want the stress where it is the maximum."[21] Harper's belief that the stress level did not exceed 40% of ultimate arose partly from these calculations and at the beginning of his testimony he still held this view.[22]

Small areas of high stress concentration were therefore not picked up and the designers were left with a false idea of the strength of the cabin sections. Information about where these stress concentrations would occur was readily available in the literature. Inglis' work on the stress concentration at the tip of a crack (see Appendix 5) in the early part of the twentieth century provided the rationale behind de Havillands' 'locating' of cracks and must have been known to them unless they were working on a purely empirical basis. Green's work on rectangular cutouts with rounded corners had been published in a major British scientific journal in 1945[23] but there is no evidence that de Havillands were aware of it. Even without this detailed information it was common knowledge that all cutouts generated stress concentrations and that these were highest at the margins, as Hall said "where... every engineer has known for years the stress is maximum,"[24] and even more so at any corners. The vulnerability of these corners had also been revealed, if it needed to be, in the static tests that de Havillands carried out in 1947[25] and the fatigue tests of 1953.[26] Even Hall's 'back of an envelope' calculation produced stress values greater than 60% of ultimate. Had de Havillands arrived at similar figures they might well have reconsidered their design.

It was particularly regrettable that no account was taken of the stress-concentrating effect of the rivet holes in the high-stress fields at the corners of the windows other than the minor effect caused by the removal of metal.[27] Although the concentration they produced was very local[28] it would prove to be significant. This phenomenon was well known and was specifically mentioned in Williams' 1946 paper, "At low loads... the stress raisers are fully effective in reducing the fatigue strength, which then approaches that appropriate to the nominal stress concentration."[29] It might be said that de

Havillands' calculations, no doubt mathematically correct, produced the right answer to the wrong question and they must bear some responsibility for this.

As it was, de Havillands preferred to rely on tests which was a common and accepted practice and might well have revealed the high stress levels if strain gauges had been placed around the cabin window cutouts. The use of large numbers of strain gauges ('several hundred') for this type of work was not novel and had been reported by Mr. Taylor of the RAE in 1945[30] and was presumably known to the designers.* For their part the company seemed to have had less trust in the gauges than the RAE had and used them more sparingly, mainly to predict any failure of the admittedly more-complicated cockpit windows when they could not be observed in the decompression chamber. Both Hall and Walker said they would have used gauges around the cabin cutouts.[15, 31]

De Havillands' were further misled by believing that cabin sections that could withstand 2P could not have had any part stressed more than 50% of ultimate at 1P. This implied that there was a linear relationship between the cabin pressure and the percentage of ultimate strength reached, which turned out not to be the case.** Hall accepted that "it might have been a reasonable assumption... not... an objectionable deduction" at the time although he may just have been being diplomatic.[32] Again strain gauges could have pointed out the error of their ways.

The early pressure cycles on the cabin sections were not regarded as fatigue tests. In common with other manufacturers, the regulators and the RAE at that time, any concern that there was about fatigue was with the wings. This problem was well understood, was being monitored and was under control. It was not a feature in any of the accidents and was certainly not peculiar to the Comet.

Perhaps prompted by the Comet's entry into airline service in 1952, it was beginning to dawn on the aviation community that pressure cabins might be vulnerable to fatigue and the RAF and the ARB began to require fatigue tests for new pressure cabins. The best that de Havillands could do at this stage was to start tests on the nose section and by September 1953 they had completed 17,900 cycles before the first failure occurred.[26] This was well ahead of what the service Comets had experienced, and were likely to experience before they were retired, and the view was that this represented an adequate safety margin.[33]

It was unfortunate that these tests were inadvertently rendered invalid by preloading and only served to produce a false sense of security. Preloading had long been known to be capable of strengthening structures and again was specifically mentioned in Williams' 1946 paper, "As is well known such stress raisers (he is referring to rivets) have little effect on the static failing load owing to plastic deformation relieving the high stress. This relief also helps the structure to withstand a much greater number of high load repetitions than it would otherwise."[29] De Havillands said they were aware of it but

---

* The copy of this paper in the Kings Norton Library at Cranfield University is stamped in two places with the de Havilland logo and the caption 'Research Information Service.' The stamp is undated but one of them appears to be overlain with an 'A.V. Roe Canada Ltd' stamp dated 13 November 1947.

** See Appendix 5.

felt that the number of test cycles they had carried out was so far ahead of the aircraft in service that they could ignore it[34] but it is unclear what this belief was based on. Using the same specimen for static and fatigue testing had already been condemned by Walker in a letter in June 1951 ("...in no circumstances could we agree to static and fatigue tests being planned for the same specimen"), although in the case he was referring to the sequence was reversed.[35] In the inquiry Hall was more accepting "...they were in no sense in serious violation of what one terms good practice or... of widespread opinion."[36] Later work, carried out by the RAE after the inquiry and published in 1956, showed that tensile prestressing could significantly increase the fatigue life of extruded specimens incorporating stress raisers, in one case by a factor of 100, and also on whole aircraft structures, but the effect on DTD 546B sheets with a single hole exposed to high-level fatigue was very little if any.[37] The effect of preloading on the Comet test sections, which were structures rather than just sheets, is therefore difficult to quantify but it probably did extend their fatigue lives and the last safety barrier had been removed. Had the test sections been truly representative a fatigue failure would probably have occurred early enough to have retired the Comets before the Mediterranean crashes.

The rectangular shape of the Comet's windows has often been blamed for the accidents, and they certainly changed shape in the later versions although Bishop said this was to save weight. Compared with modern aircraft the Comet 1 windows were larger with straighter sides and long axes that were horizontal, mainly to provide a good view for the passengers, although fewer were needed and they were relatively more spread out. Overall the Comet had almost twice as much window-to-fuselage area as the A318. As the windows were surrounded by a flexible seal they carried little of the skin stress and so a large window area meant less load-bearing metal although in the Comet the skin thickness along the line of windows was greater than elsewhere.[38] At the time the size and shape of the windows was not unusual, the unpressurised Dove and DC-3 and the pressurised DC-6 and 7 had similar ones, but the almost-contemporary, jet-powered and therefore higher-flying, Avro Canada C-102 and the Avro Ashton (a Tudor with jet engines) both had small circular windows.

The margins of fuselage cutouts are reinforced with frames which carry some of the hoop stress. It is theoretically possible to make a reinforced window cutout that does not affect the stress pattern in the fuselage skin, the so-called 'neutral hole', although the weight of the frame is usually rather greater than the weight of the metal removed for the cutout. The most efficient shape for this approximates to a vertical ellipse with dimensions in the ratio of $\sqrt{2}:1$.[38, 39] The window shape used in the Comet 1 was significantly different and even with a circumferential frame it would be likely to produce some degree of stress concentration at the corners. Having said that, the theoretical stress concentration factor at the rounded corners of the Comet cutouts (3.1) was not vastly greater than that for circular ones (2.5), (see Appendix 5).

The tank tests carried out at Farnborough on YU and YR using strain gauges around the corners of the cutouts showed that the tensile stress levels at 8.25 psi rose markedly as the margins were approached (see next page):

	YU	YR
strain gauge readings	7,600 psi	12,560
remote from cutouts	6,900	11,360
		11,570
		17,700
mean	7,250	13,297
maximum stress @ 8.25 psi		
at cutout corner (extrapolated)	43,100	38,975
stress concentration factor	5.9	2.93

Stress values and concentration factors at window corners.[40, 41]

Given the scatter between specimens and between different locations in the same specimen the above maximum stress concentration factor of between three and six is compatible with theoretical predictions for un-reinforced cutouts of the same shape and dimensions as those in the Comet.

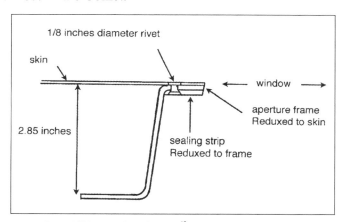

Fig. 1/30, window frame [42] *(adapted by author).*

The frames used on the Comet windows had two layers of DTD 546B, 0.064 inches thick and 0.75 inches wide, glued and, at the corners, also riveted to the skin of thickness 0.036 inches, making the skin around the window margin about four and a half times thicker. The middle layer of this sandwich then projected inwards for 2.85 inches making a Z shape. The curves plotted from the strain gauge figures in YR and YU illustrate the increasing stress as the the corners of the cutouts are approached but show no discernible change of gradient at the outer margin of the frames[43, 44] although this may just be a consequence of the curves being drawn from a limited number of values.

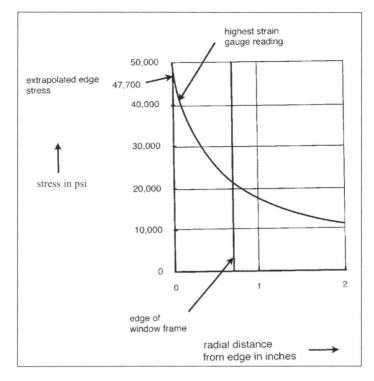

Fig. 2/30, stress in the skin at the top corner of the third starboard window in YR for an internal pressure of 8.25 psi[45] (adapted by the author).

In Povey's description of making the Comet (Chapter 6) the frames are Reduxed to the fuselage skin; there is no mention of riveting.[46] John Wilson, the de Havilland test pilot, recalled that he went to see Bishop about four months before he died and he had said to Wilson, "My biggest mistake was the day that Harry Povey came into my office... and he said 'Bishop, I can't Redux these bloody windows.'" Bishop had said, "What do you want me to say? What do you want me to do, because that's the way it's designed." Povey replied, "I want to rivet it." And Bishop said "My biggest mistake was saying, 'All right, go on then. You rivet it.'"[2]

The rivets were used only at the corners of the windows and escape hatches so whatever problem Povey had with the Reduxing seems to have been confined to these areas. It is difficult to see what the problem with the Reduxing could have been other than some failure of adhesion between the skin and the frame. This possibility had already been explored in the Abell Committee's inspection of YY and YU. The bonding of the frames around the two front escape hatches was examined in both aircraft as well as that in the No. 4 port and No. 8 starboard windows in YU and the No. 3 port and No. 4 starboard windows in YY.[47] All the bonds were said to be 'satisfactory', although this was presumably just based on an external examination of the edges of the joints.

It was unfortunate that rivets, with all their stress-raising effects, had to be used at the corners where the stress was already high. In YR the stress level in the area of the outer row of rivets was around 20,000 psi[48] but the strain gauges were too large to measure it at the margin of a rivet hole. Such a hole would, in theory, multiply the stress by about 2.5, taking it up to, and possibly above, the ultimate strength of the DTD 546B (about 65,000 psi and not less than 58,240)[49, 50] although plastic change would have started at these levels. The fact that the rivets were countersunk[51] would have produced an even greater stress concentration.[52] In YU nearly all the cracks started at rivet holes at cutout corners, including the two that caused major failures.[53] In YR all the cracks started at rivet holes. Those starting at the inner row extended to the cutout margins and stopped there. Those starting at the outer row moved either towards the cutout margin, often ending at an inner rivet hole, or away from it. The catastrophic cracks all started at the outer row and moved away from the cutouts.[48] It seems reasonable to assume that the crack along YP's side windows started in a similar place and behaved in a similar way.

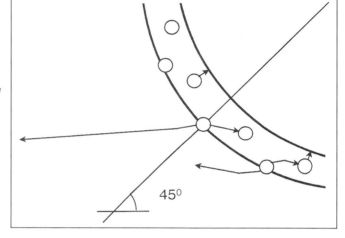

Fig. 3/30 Cracks in the third window on the port side in YR[54] (adapted by author).

It is relatively easy to calculate the maximum theoretical stress concentration for a cutout in an infinite, thin sheet but, as Walter Tye said at the inquiry, it becomes difficult, and at the time the Comet was designed probably impossible, to calculate when the structures become more complicated. This was the reason for testing actual components and structures. In late 2012, while this book was still being written, an opportunity arose to explore the effects of the window frames and the internal structure of the fuselage by building a digital model of the area around a window. Finite element analysis (FEA) was then used to calculate the static stress values as the structure was built up in stages and subjected to the same forces as if it were in a Comet fuselage pressurised to 1P. This work was carried out as a research project by Paul Johnson, supervised by Ian Sewell, in the Design Unit of Newcastle University using ANSYS software. A more complete report can be seen in Appendix 6.

The most significant results were as follows:

The maximum stress concentration (Kt) at the inner margin of the corner of a single, un-reinforced, cutout of the size and shape of those in the Comet 1, with applied forces equivalent to those generated in a Comet fuselage pressurised at 8.25 psi was approximately 3.4. This was larger than the theoretical value of 3.1 but was considered close enough to validate the FEA model. The figure generated by the model for the general level of stress at 1P was 13,865 psi, hence the maximum stress at the cutout margin was 47,141 psi.

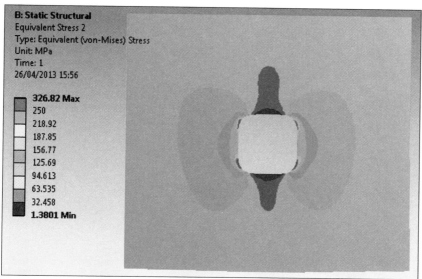

Fig. 4/30, Equivalent* stress areas around a cutout of the same shape and size of a Comet window at 1P.

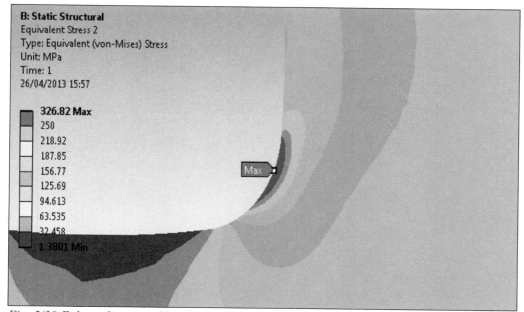

Fig. 5/30 Enlarged image of bottom left-hand corner of the above cutout (now viewed from the inside of the fuselage) showing the area of maximum stress.

* Equivalent, or Von Mises, stress is the resultant of stress applied in the x, y and z axes. In thin sheets, such as fuselage skin, it amounts to two axes.

Adding the window frames and bonding them to the skin reduced Kt at the inner margin of the cutout to approximately 3.

Adding the stringers and fuselage frames and bonding them to the skin reduced the stress at the window margin by about 4.5%.

Adding rivets at the corners increased Kt at the margin of an outer rivet hole to 4.9.

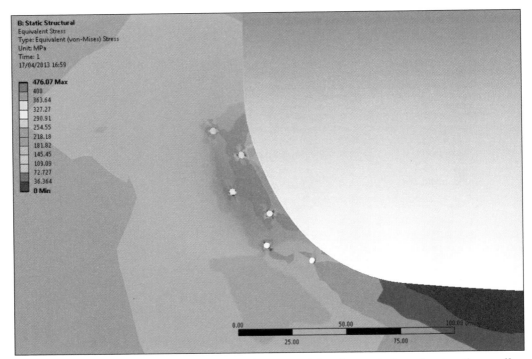

Fig. 6/30 Enlarged image of the lower left corner of the above window showing the small areas of high stress at the margins of the rivets (note change of colour scale).

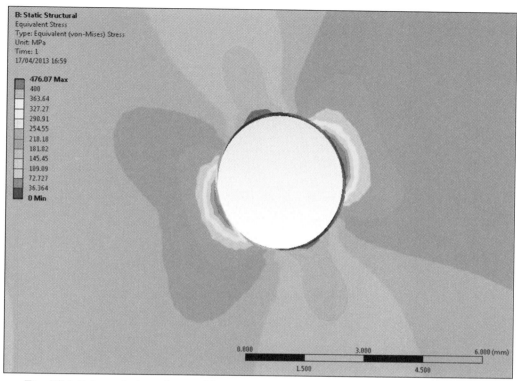

Fig. 7/30 Enlarged view of one of the rivet holes in the same orientation as in Fig. 6/30

The software can produce a plot of stress against displacement along a line moving away from the margin of the corner of a window and passing through an outer rivet hole.

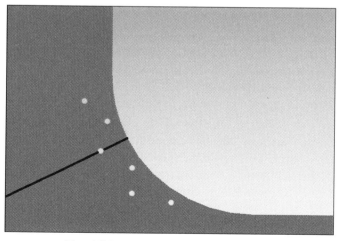

Fig. 8/30 Diagram of a cutout corner showing the line mentioned above.

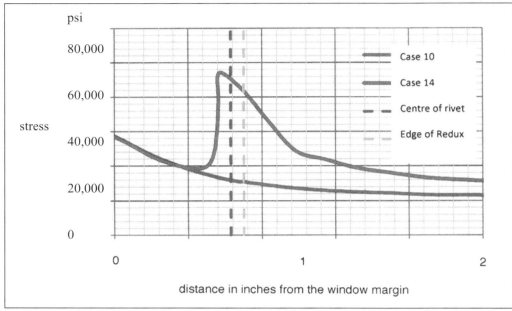

Fig 9/30. The upper (blue) line shows a plot of stress against displacement along the line through the rivet hole shown in Fig. 8/30. The lower (red) line shows the stress along the same line but without any rivet holes being present.
(For an explanation of the 'cases' see Appendix 6.)

This shows the considerable increase in stress at one of the outer rivet holes compared with what it would have been if the frames had just been Reduxed to the skin, i.e. as it had originally been designed. Removing the bonding (i.e. the Redux) from the corners had little effect on Kt at the rivet holes.

The ANSYS model gives a maximum stress value of about 68,000 psi at the margin of an outer rivet hole, just above the ultimate strength of DTD 546B (65,000 psi). In practice with the extra stresses created by flying and any fretting that the rivets caused the figure would have been even larger and it is easy to see that these areas, although small, would have been very vulnerable. Nevertheless it is important to remember that this model is just a simplified approximation of the real thing and that there would have been considerable scatter between different fuselages.

It is uncertain when the decision to use rivets was made but they were present in a photograph dated 10 August 1949,[55] and also in the photograph of the crack at the corner of the window in the nose test section that developed after 17,900 cycles.*[26] Riveting the corners was clearly a change to the original design and the decision to do it seems to have been made almost casually giving the impression that the stress implications were not fully appreciated. Povey's failure to mention the rivets in his account of building the Comet, delivered well after the rivets had been used, suggests that he

---

* The crack is longitudinal, about four inches long, and may start at the edge of the cutout in the area of maximum stress but is more obvious between two of the outer rivets.

Fig. 10/30 The inside view of a Boeing 747 cabin window. It is relatively smaller and more vertical than in the Comet 1, and more robustly constructed, but not greatly different in shape, (author's photograph courtesy of the Science Museum, London).

considered them of little importance.

Rivets and bolts are inevitable in aircraft construction and most windows in modern passenger aircraft are similar rectangles with rounded corners although their long axes are usually vertical rather than horizontal and they are relatively much smaller. This can be seen at any airport but in some museums the inside of a window can also be seen. In the Science Museum in London, for example, the windows are fully exposed in the transverse section of a Boeing 747. The window frame is also riveted although the construction appears more robust than the Comet's.

If the rivets had not been used the maximum stress would have been about 40,000 psi at the margin of the corners (Fig. 9/30). The SN curve for DTD 564B (Fig. 2/21) suggests that a failure could then have been expected at about 10,000 cycles. However the test pieces for this study had a ¼ inches hole with a theoretical stress concentration factor of 2.42. This implies a considerably longer life for a complete specimen, much longer than the failures in YP (1,286 cycles) and YY (about 900) and the less-stressed YU (3,057) and YR (5,248).

Even without the window rivets it is likely that the Comet's fatigue life would still have been on the short side. There were significant stress concentrations in the skin at the holes for the bolts in the fuselage frames on either side of the notches accommodating the stringers.[56] Any crack propagating from or towards the vicinity of one of these notches was likely to cause the frame to fracture at the notch. This design was typical of early unpressurised fuselages such as the DC-3 but was changed in later aircraft.[57] One of these bolts was the site of the fatigue fracture at the rear ADF window in YP and it would probably not have been long before this crack accelerated and destroyed the aircraft.

There is no suggestion in the surviving letters and files that anyone in de Havillands, the RAE or the various civil service departments knew of, or even suspected, any of these problems and was involved in a cover-up. Of course any doubts might not have been written down or the relevant documents lost, destroyed or just missed so it is impossible to be certain but it is hard to imagine that such knowledge would have remained a secret in the long run. Keeping quiet about the discovery of the wreckage found after the inquiry was understandable and a completely different matter and even this news leaked out in the end.

It is always tempting to ascribe a disaster to a single factor – if only that one thing had not happened all would have been well. In practice there are usually several factors that generate a sequence of events leading to the disaster and this was so for the Comet. The windows were larger than they needed to be, the shape of the windows generated more stress than some other shapes and the window frames were relatively ineffective in reducing the stress at the corners. The rivets then made things significantly worse. The Comet's thin skin, notched frames and lack of any of (the later) crack-controlling technology allowed the cracks to propagate easily and the short stage lengths meant that the fuselages aged quickly. Nothing in the science was new; it was just not put together, its relevance appreciated and then communicated to the people who made the important choices. Bishop was right to regret the rivets though.

De Havillands, then, must bear some of the responsibility for the sequence of errors that led to the cabin failures. Several of what turned out to be serious errors were common beliefs or common practice at the time but others, such as not calculating the stress values at the corners of the cabin cutouts and at the margins of the rivet holes and not using strain gauges around the corners are less excusable. Assuming that the relationship between cabin pressure and ultimate strength was linear and using preloaded specimens for fatigue tests also came in for some criticism in the inquiry but the failure to realise the consequences of Povey's difficulties with Reduxing the cutout corners and using the thin skin would seem to have been the most significant errors. As Bishop said at the inquiry, "We obviously missed the main point." [58]

This raises the question of whether de Havillands were up to the job. The British preference for 'practical men' in industry has often been compared unfavourably with the German and American use of highly-educated and trained personnel.[59, 60] The men who created the Comet had mainly come up through the company and had learned their business there. Before Air Marshall Sorley was sent to the United States there had been an earlier mission, headed by Sir Alexander Dunbar, the Controller-General of the MAP, which visited 29 American factories in September and October 1942. They reported back that there was a much greater proportion of trained engineering staff to production staff than was usual in Britain. Furthermore the engineering staff were often the holders of university degrees and not "shop-trained ex-apprentices as is generally the rule in the United Kingdom." [61, 62] Bishop said of his design team that "They nearly all came up from our own show," meaning The de Havilland Technical School.[63] A little later Fedden's 'Mission to America' pointed out the limited technical and human resources of British aircraft manufactures compared with those in the USA but had been met with some disdain. After the war Sir Roy Fedden and Sir William Farren, the then head of the RAE, led missions to Germany and both had been amazed by the research facilities available to the German aviation industry[61, 64] and the quality of their technical staffs.[65]

Bill Waterton, a test-pilot-turned-aviation-journalist, published a book in 1956 in which he recorded his concerns about the British industry.[66] He had become increasingly frustrated by his experiences testing the Gloster Javelin which had included a crash caused by elevator flutter in which he was very nearly burned to death. The same type of aircraft later killed another of their test pilots, probably by demonstrating the deep stall that high-tailed aircraft are prone to. In his book Waterton described British aircraft factories as being like "back-alley garages" compared with American and Canadian ones, lacking the large, and even some of the small, tools of their transatlantic competitors.[67] They lacked research facilities as well as the best engineering and mathematical brains, often because they refused to pay the going rate for them. Waterton had left Glosters, under something of a cloud, to become a journalist with the *Daily Express* in 1954 but the publication of his book ended this second career. Messengers carrying unwanted truths are rarely appreciated and the newspaper's advertisers threatened to move their business elsewhere, so Waterton had to go.[68]

The following year Sir Roy Fedden published a book which, as might be expected, expressed much the same view as Waterton's.*[69] Fedden recalled that the part of his 'Mission to America' that detailed the high technical standard of the staff in the American industry had been "universally disbelieved."[70] He felt that this attitude had continued after the war leaving the British industry with a deficiency of high quality engineers and managers and that there was even some prejudice against them, "Those who had come up the hard way mistrusted what they called 'mere theory' and were afraid of them."[71] Fedden backed his views with data: in 1954 the annual output of graduates in aeronautical engineering in the UK was 60, in the USA it was 738, giving a ratio of 0.265 per 1,000 employees in the UK and 0.863 in the USA. Similarly the percentages of all types of qualified engineers and scientists in the aviation industry was 1.9 in the UK and 9 in the USA.[72]

The aircraft industry was a relatively young one and at the time the Comet was designed the early aviation pioneers were still running the companies. With one or two exceptions, such as Frise of Bristol's and Volkert of Handley Page, the heads of department in the various firms were not university-trained engineers.[73] Camm, the designer of the Hurricane and Typhoon, had started as an apprentice in the carpenter's shop and Chadwick, the designer of the Lancaster, began in the drawing office. Halford had started a degree but had not finished it and Bishop had left after failing an examination.[74] This is not in any way to diminish them as people, just to say that it may have

---

* Fedden himself had not always seen the future clearly. In the early days of the jet engine he had written to Air Chief Marshall Freeman protesting that a 400 mph (at sea level) fighter could be more easily made with a piston engine than a jet engine. Freeman passed the letter to Hives who passed it to Hooker for comment. This was the stimulus for Hooker's calculation that the engine for such an aircraft would need to have about 36 cylinders and would therefore be impossibly complicated, (see Chapter 3).[75]

given them, in scientific terms, closer horizons. Perhaps they had thought they could learn faster working in the business as it developed. At that stage they may well have been right but it might have left them with the feeling that what had worked for them would work equally well for the people coming after them. Archbold Russell, who rose to be the managing director of the British Aircraft Corporation at Bristol, and his class-mates, were told by their professor on graduation in 1924 that unless directly asked they should not mention that they had an engineering degree as many of the managers in the industry preferred apprentices.[76]

In addition to a feeling that university-trained engineers were unnecessary, "half-a-dozen at the utmost,"[77] there were not many to be had, as Fedden had pointed out. At least before the Second World War there was still prejudice in some circles against engi-neering as an academic discipline. One view, said to have been expressed in Oxford, was that engineering was "an appropriate subject for illiterate artisans, and that academ-ic engineers were men with oily rags stuffed into the pockets of denim overalls, who were ill-suited, metaphorically as well as literally, to enter the senior common-rooms of the colleges."[78] Departments of aeronautical engineering were few, Cambridge and Imperial being notable exceptions, and engineers from other specialities were under-standably reluctant to enter a business as precarious as aviation. There was, then, a shortage of supply as well as a deficiency of demand,[73] and what talent and resources that did exist were spread too thin among too many projects and too many companies.[79]

Although Britain entered the war with several excellent aircraft such as the Hurricane and Spitfire, many of the innovations in pre-war aviation had come from abroad, principally the United States. The variable-pitch propeller had its origin in sev-eral countries, one of which was Britain, but when de Havillands wanted it for their Comet racer they had to go to French and American companies for practical devices. The various British aeroplane-manufacturing companies lacked much in the way of research facilities and relied on government resources such as the National Physical Laboratory, the RAE or the universities. Perhaps this was more a reflection of the industry's fragmented nature leading to small companies than any deliberate intent, but it did mean that a company had to be aware of a problem before it could seek outside help. In spite of this the industry had performed well during the war and built consid-erably more aircraft than the German manufacturers although in part this was due to the political interference the latter suffered. Also some British aircraft, such as the Spitfire had been continually updated during the war and excellent new designs, such as the Mosquito, had been produced. The war had massively increased research and develop-ment in Britain as well as promoting cross-pollination with the Americans but nearly all the British aircraft produced during the war were conventional developments of what had come before, only the Whittle and the Meteor were fundamentally new. This was probably inevitable given the constrained resources and the urgency of the situa-tion but it did mean that there was nothing to compare with the German swept-wing jet and rocket fighters or the large American transports and the Superfortress bomber.

Building up resources, particularly human ones, takes time. Rolls-Royce was better than most in this and Hives had shown great foresight in employing people like Hooker and Griffith. Whittle, too, preferred to recruit engineers with "high academic qualifications," even if they were young and inexperienced, to those who "had become inflexible through years of experience."[80] Bishop, on the other hand, was said to distrust academics and theorists who had never actually made anything and to regard them as fools. Waterton, who wrote a contemporary book on the Comet crashes, said that "Bishop epitomizes what is probably the key characteristic of de Havilland plane building. For he is a 'practical' designer. Not for him the boffins' theories and scientific speculation. He just wants to make things work, and work quickly."[81] It is hard to imagine Bishop employing anybody like Griffith to 'go on thinking'. He appears to have had the disdain of the practical man for the theoretician but as aeroplanes became more sophisticated there was an important niche for the occasional original thinker with a strong academic background who had the status to question accepted wisdom. The need now was for the best scientific and production staff to be working together, both having regard for each other's special knowledge and skills. Significantly Rolls-Royce has been the great survivor of the British aviation industry.

The Comet was a considerable advance over anything that de Havillands, or any other British, or for that matter American, company, had attempted before and one wonders in retrospect whether it was a leap too far, or at least a leap too far by themselves. Collaboration with another company such as Vickers might have made a difference but, judging by George Edwards' remark ("...nobody worried about fatigue, particularly cracks in those days."[1]) it seems unlikely.

Another resource, the RAE, was not too distant and perhaps more use could have been made of its talents. Judging by his comments at the inquiry Walker certainly thought so. To paraphrase an American politician "The problem is not what you don't know but what you don't know that you don't know." [82] Fatigue in the pressure cabin was an "unknown unknown" so help was not sought. It is true that the state of knowledge at the RAE at the time when the Comet was being designed was not greatly different from that at de Havillands but the engineers at Farnborough were not designing a large pressure cabin and were therefore not specifically researching the topic. De Havillands were certainly not behind the contemporary state of the art but they were not ahead of it either. A different and more scientific approach, from either within or without the company, might have spotted some of the problems earlier but even a very competent company such as Rolls had had one or two wobbles in its time, such as the wartime Vulture,* which promised much but then had to be abandoned. The Americans, too, were not immune from disaster. In the late 1950s Lockheed produced the Electra, two of which crashed after their wings separated from the fuselage in flight,** (see next page).

Perhaps there were just too many new things put together in one aeroplane to expect

---

* The Rolls-Royce Vulture was a complex, 24 cylinder, 42 litre, X-configuration engine intended for the Tornado, a version of the Typhoon. It proved too complex and suffered lubrication failures and overheating. It was used in the Manchester bomber but was cancelled in 1941 so that Rolls could concentrate on the Merlin.

that everything would work perfectly from the start. Among other things the Comet combined a new engine, a new airframe, new controls and a new pressure cabin. All of these were inevitable once the decision had been made to build a jet airliner but it was a lot to get right at one go, particularly as most of them were produced 'in house' unlike the modern practice of assembling parts from specialist manufacturers.

There was also some concern about de Havillands' quality control and documentation. Both YP and YU had several of the rivets around the ADF windows placed closer to the edge than specified. In addition they were using a manufacturing process or processes that caused cracks. This was not inevitable and they later changed to a technique that avoided them. Their method of neutralising cracks by drilling the ends may have been a common practice in the industry but it clearly did not always work, particularly in highly-stressed areas, as some cracks had progressed. Also not all the cracks had been recorded and dealt with in the approved fashion. Sir Peter Masefield commented in a letter to A. J. Lucking about the crashes, that de Havillands "...were not exactly renowned for the structures of their aeroplanes over the years. As many in the industry used to say 'de Havillands are aerodynamically splendid but structurally dodgy'."[83] Perhaps de Havillands were unlucky in that several of their products were exposed to minute scrutiny and any defects found in them received massive publicity. In the absence of any 'controls' it is difficult to say whether they were any better or any worse in this respect than other manufacturers but the remark made by the visitors from Boeing that the Hatfield factory was more like "a small town auto-repair shop" makes one wonder.

Would the Americans have done any better? They certainly had more and better engineering resources and more people with engineering qualifications but these do not necessarily translate into the sort of original-thinking scientists and engineers who could predict and solve problems not seen before. Judging by Tye's reports of their official requirements the Americans were just as unaware of the dangers of pressure cabin fatigue as the British, perhaps even more so, but at the time they were not building a jet transport. Boeing certainly learned from the Comet debacle and the 707 was a robust aircraft but it is quite possible that they would have had the same problems as de Havillands if they had been first.

The question of whether the Comet was commercially flawed can also be raised. Like the Brabazon and the Concorde, the Comet was designed to carry small numbers of the personally wealthy, businessmen travelling at their companies' expense and those with their hands deep in the public purse, and few aircraft were sold, whereas the Americans produced the Boeing 707 and 747 for the masses and sold thousands. At the

---

** The Electra was a four-engined, turboprop passenger aircraft, in size somewhere between the Viscount and the Vanguard. About a third of the 170 Electras produced were lost because of crashes, a record that rivals that of the Comet 1s. Like the Comet, two Electras had mid-air disintegrations from a hitherto-unsuspected phenomenon. This was eventually traced to the gyroscopic effect of the propeller disc causing the engine to precess if one of the three struts connecting the gearbox to the engine failed. This became known as 'whirl mode'. If this happened to an outboard engine at cruising speed it caused immediate and severe wing flutter which tore the wing off the fuselage.[84] Like the Comet (4) it was reworked to become a successful maritime reconnaissance aircraft, the Orion.

time of the Comet's design and introduction into service all flying was an expensive and exclusive business. The Comet certainly provided only a premium service for a small number of people but BOAC reckoned they could make it pay.[85] With the contemporary engine technology it would have been impossible to produce a jet aircraft large enough to provide economy travel although this rapidly changed. For its time the Comet was by no means as out-of-step as the Concorde was in its.

One of the questions set by the Attorney-General for the public inquiry was whether the accidents were caused by "the act or default or negligence of any party". Sir Lionel Heald, representing the Attorney-General, seemed to dismiss this in his opening address saying that counsel were not there to "attack or defend anybody". Lord Cohen certainly seemed to go along with this, perhaps to encourage more candid testimonies from the witnesses. Nevertheless it is interesting to speculate whether de Havillands and BOAC could have been successfully sued by the relatives of the deceased had the accidents happened in today's more litigious age. To prove negligence it is necessary to show that a person or persons had a duty of care (a contract) towards the claimant, that on the balance of probabilities they acted without reasonable care, bearing in mind their special knowledge and skills, that the claimant suffered harm and that the act of carelessness caused this harm.

De Havillands certainly had a duty to design and manufacture a safe aeroplane and BOAC had a duty of care for its passengers, who undoubtedly suffered harm. There is no question that de Havillands, BOAC or any of the government agencies did or did not do anything knowingly that led to the accidents in the way that the Principal Films documentary implied. Although de Havillands had made an aeroplane which turned out to have serious faults they had acted in good faith and, as they saw it, within the bounds of knowledge at the time and within the normal practices of the industry. Nevertheless they made serious errors which led directly to the two Mediterranean crashes, and it might well be argued that some of these errors were avoidable. BOAC, on the other hand, acted competently and professionally and did all that they could have done in the circumstances and it is hard to see that they had any liability beyond their statutory obligations. Perhaps one of the effects of the Court of Inquiry was to reduce the probability of litigation by finding that nobody was at fault. Nevertheless at least two cases for increased compensation were started against BOAC in New York.[86]

Neither the government nor BOAC can be blamed for de Havillands' misfortune. The government, via the MoS, provided the specification and ordered the aircraft and stayed loyal to the programme. Similarly the airline enthusiastically supported the Comet as long as it reasonably could do so. Even after the crashes the government, this time in the form of the RAF, provided a lifeline for de Havillands and BOAC bought the Comet 4 when it could reasonably have hung out for American aircraft. Unwavering government and airline support for the industry did not continue much longer and the future was littered with cancellations and airline complications. Denis Haviland, a senior civil servant said "From 1954... the Treasury never missed an opportunity presented by a proposed new programme... to mount a major attack."[87] Duncan Sandys' 1957 pronouncement that in future the RAF would not require manned combat aircraft seriously damaged confidence in the industry as well as in the RAF. The great hope of Vickers, the V1000 military transport that could have been the forerunner of a commercial trans-Atlantic jet, was cancelled by the government at the last moment, the de Havilland Trident was made too small at the request of BEA and consequently failed to appeal to foreign airlines and BOAC, for its own reasons, publicly criticised the VC10, which had elegantly met the airline's requirements, and as a result damaged its sales. Maybe the opinions of the government and the national airlines had been soured by the events that befell the Comet but the VC10 and the Trident, at least in its original form, were fine aircraft and deserved to do better. Only the BAC 111, a twin rear-engined, short-haul aircraft, did well but its projected successor, the wide-bodied BAC 311, failed to get government support and was cancelled.

The Elba and Naples crashes were a sad end to a courageous and innovative project that for a short time catapulted de Havillands to the leadership of the industry. But even without the crashes it is doubtful they would have stayed there very long. Boeing and Douglas, with a new generation of engines and their massive resources, would surely have eclipsed de Havillands within a few years. The Comet 3 would have been no match for the 707 and the DC-8 on the all-important transatlantic route, just as the Comet 4 was not. Nevertheless, looking at the photographs of the de Havilland people standing in front of the Comet prototype, it is easy to appreciate the sense of pride they felt in their achievement. How much greater then must have been their sense of despair and anguish after the Mediterranean crashes. Mike Ramsden in a 2012 BBC documentary said "Did we feel guilty, you mean, of killing a hundred people? Yes is the short answer."[88] They must have felt the crashes, the RAE investigation and the public inquiry as a deep humiliation but there is no escaping the fact that the Comet 1 was a deeply flawed aeroplane. Bill Waterton's verdict was damning, "...a brilliant conception, let down by its aerodynamics, engineering and handling – nothing like a 100 per cent. aeroplane."[89] But, given the technology of the mid-to-late 1940s, it would have been very hard, perhaps even impossible, for anyone to build a jet airliner that could carry a large enough number of passengers over a large enough distance for a sufficient number of times to make it commercially viable. The most important outcome of the Comet project was its legacy to the aviation industry. Its failure, although a disaster for the people who died in its crashes and for de Havillands, resulted in the design of the fail-safe, damage-tolerant aircraft of today's airline fleets that we now take for granted.

APPENDICES

1
Some more things about aeroplanes

The parts of an aeroplane

A conventional aeroplane consists of a hollow cylinder called the fuselage where the crew, passengers and luggage or cargo are accommodated. The aircraft is controlled from the cockpit or flight deck. With passenger-carrying flights there are at least two pilots and with the Comet there was also an engineer and a navigator/radio operator. The wings provide the force that keeps the aeroplane in the air as long as the engines move them forward. The front edges of the wings are called the leading edges and the rear the trailing edges. The trailing edges have symmetrical movable surfaces to allow the pilot to control the aircraft, the control surfaces. The ones closest to the fuselage are called flaps and the ones closest to the tips of the wings are called ailerons. Although they look similar they have quite different functions. The leading edge may have a flap-like device, called a slat, or a fixed or deployable, down-facing lip called a droop. The tail consist of small wings, called the horizontal tailplane, (American, horizontal stabiliser) with a central 'wing' projecting upwards from the rear fuselage called the fin (American, vertical stabiliser). Like the wings the horizontal tailplanes have movable surfaces on their trailing edges, this time called elevators. The fin has a similar device called a rudder. The Comet's elevators and ailerons also had small movable surfaces of their own called trimming or balance tabs.

The forces acting on an aeroplane

When an aeroplane is flying it is subject to four forces. They may be made up from more forces but they add up to four, each one pulling or pushing in a different direction. Pulling the aeroplane down to earth is its weight – the acceleration due to gravity acting on the aeroplane's mass. The bigger the mass of the aircraft the bigger the force pulling it down. Pushing the aircraft up is the lift, generated by the wings and in level flight exactly equal to the force of gravity pulling it down. Increase the lift and the aeroplane goes higher and vice versa. If the mass of the aircraft decreases, for example by using up its fuel, and other things remaining equal, it will fly higher. The force that pushes the aeroplane forward is the thrust provided by the engines. The force acting in the opposite direction is the drag, more precisely the parasitic drag. This is produced by the viscosity, or 'thickness', of the air the aeroplane is flying through. The magnitude of the drag depends on the shape and size of the aircraft, the speed at which it is moving and the density of the air it is moving through. At a constant speed the magnitude of the drag is exactly equal to the magnitude of the thrust. Increasing the thrust increases the speed of the aircraft which then increases the drag so that the aircraft reaches a new equilibrium speed where the thrust equals the drag again.

Aircraft designers are obsessed by these four forces and are right to be so. Aeroplanes are designed to be as light as possible, while retaining sufficient strength, and to have as streamlined a shape as possible. Their engines need to generate enough thrust to produce the required performance while at the same time using as little fuel as possible. The wings need to produce sufficient lift to keep the aeroplane in the air but at the same time produce as little drag as possible. How well the designers manage these, often conflicting, demands is a measure of how efficient and safe their aeroplane is.

Centre of gravity (c of g or cg)

This is the place in the aircraft where it could balance on a point. If the aeroplane changes direction in flight it rotates around its centre of gravity, for example if the nose is pushed up by a gust of wind the fuselage will rotate about its centre of gravity and the tail will move down. The position of the c of g varies with the design and loading of the aircraft but is very important for the aircraft's stability in flight.

Axes of movement

An aircraft flies in three-dimensional space. It can therefore move about three axes, all of which pass through the aircraft's centre of gravity. These movements have particular names which recur in aircraft literature. Rotation about the longitudinal axis, the line running lengthwise through the fuselage and the c of g is called a roll. Rotation about a vertical axis passing through the c of g, a waggling of the nose and tail from side to side, is called a yaw. Movement about a lateral axis passing horizontally through the c of g, is called a pitch (up or down according to the direction the nose moves).

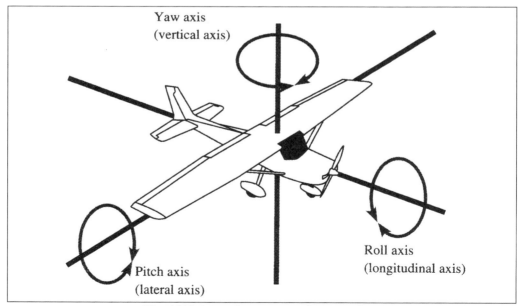

Fig. 1/A1 Axes of movement of an aeroplane
(reproduced with permission from The McGraw-Hill Companies, from Anderson D. F.,
Eberhardt S., Understanding Flight, Second Edition, 2010, McGraw-Hill.)

How an aeroplane is controlled

Flight movements can be quite complex and may be produced in different ways. The direction of flight of an aircraft can deviate to the right or left in the horizontal plane and up or down in the vertical plane. An aeroplane is controlled by moving the control surfaces on its wings, tailplane and rudder and increasing or decreasing the thrust of its engines. Vertical and horizontal movements can be combined just as thrust changes can be combined with control surface movements.

The primary flight controls are the ailerons, the elevators and the rudder. The ailerons are moved by turning the control wheel, or moving the control column, right or left, the elevators by moving the wheel and control column backwards or forwards and the rudder by pushing on the right or left foot pedals. Modern fly-by-wire aircraft, such as the Airbus family, use a small joystick rather than a wheel or control column but the principle is the same. When the control wheel is turned left the left aileron rotates up and the right rotates down. This decreases the lift of the left wing and increases the lift of the right wing, rolling the aeroplane to the left. As well as rolling to the left the aircraft also turns to the left.*

Once the desired degree of bank and turn has been achieved the wheel is centred and the degree of bank stays constant. The aircraft is straightened out again by turning the wheel to the right. This is the usual method of turning in flight, a banked turn, as it keeps the crew and passengers comfortably in their seats and the coffee safely in their cups. Moving the rudder with the foot pedals also produces a turn, or yaw, but this time it is a level turn and the occupants of the aircraft will feel a sideways push and risk losing their coffee. The rudder is used for minor adjustments and at times when banking is inappropriate, such as when the aircraft is just about to land or is actually on the ground and moving along the runway.

Pushing the control column forwards moves both the elevators down. This increases the lift of the horizontal tail plane and it moves upwards. The aeroplane then rotates about its centre of gravity, its nose pitches down and its speed increases. If the elevators move up they decrease the lift of the tailplane and the nose pitches up and the aircraft's speed decreases. The elevators are one of the means of controlling whether the aeroplane climbs or descends. The other, and often the more important one, is by altering the thrust of the engines. If the configuration of the control surfaces stays the same but the thrust is increased the aeroplane will climb and vice versa. The actual combination of thrust changes and elevator changes depends on the circumstances at the time and the pilot's choices.

---

* In level flight the direction of the lift is vertically upwards, perpendicular to the long axis of the wings. If the aeroplane rolls, the direction of lift is still perpendicular to the wings but is now angled towards the inside of the roll. This force can be resolved into vertical and horizontal components. The vertical component keeps the aeroplane in the air by pushing upwards but the horizontal component pushes towards the inside of the roll and causes the aeroplane to turn. At a constant speed the vertical component of the lift reduces as the aeroplane rolls, hence the aeroplane will lose height. There is yet another complication which produces a yaw in the opposite direction to the turn ('the adverse yaw') which has to be opposed by rudder movement.

2

Hooker's Comparison of the Power of the Rolls-Royce Merlin and Whittles' Engine

(This is adapted from Sir Stanley Hooker's biography *Not Much of an Engineer.*)[1]

James Watt used the idea of comparing the power of a horse, with which his customers were familiar, with that of his new steam engines.

Power is defined as the rate of doing work.

Power   = work done/time taken
                                       = (force x distance)/time
                                       = (pounds force x feet)/minutes

Watt's estimate for the power of one horse came out, in round figures, at 33,000 foot pounds force per minute.

Brake horsepower is the power delivered by an engine before it is reduced by any gearing or other transmission losses. The Merlin in its earlier forms produced about 1,000 bhp ('the driving force of a thousand horse'). Its propeller efficiency at this time (1940) was about 80%, hence the Merlin produced about 800 horsepower when it was flying.

Therefore the power output of the Merlin at full throttle in a flying aeroplane = 800 x 33,000 foot pounds force per minute.

Consider an aeroplane flying at 33,000 feet per minute (375 mph, a reasonable speed for a Spitfire).

From above, the power output of an engine = work done/time taken
work done = force (thrust) x distance travelled in one minute
                      = thrust x 33,000 feet
therefore 800 x 33,000 = thrust x 33,000
and thrust = 800 pounds force

Therefore, in these particular circumstances, the 800hp of the Merlin/propeller combination is equivalent to 800 pounds thrust and one pound of thrust is equivalent to one horsepower.

Whittle's engine at this time produced 800 pounds of thrust so the two engines had about the same power. This simple calculation convinced Hives that there was something to jet propulsion.

3

Lord Brabazon's statement to the Court of Inquiry

Day 9, 2 November 1954.[1]

"It is a little difficult. First of all I know you, my Lord, are charged with this duty of trying to find a physical reason for these disasters, and you may even try to find a scapegoat. I am quite prepared to be that scapegoat, because it is true to say, is it not, that the Air Registration Board, of which I am Chairman, could have forbidden the Comet to fly at all. I do not mind what other people think; the only thing is whether one thinks one has done the right thing, and as I look back at it all, there is nothing that I did, with the knowledge that I had at the time, which now I would have done otherwise. That is from the personal point of view in the Air Registration Board.

"Now there is something which I should like to say, which has got nothing to do with my official position in any way. As you know I am not connected with the trade, and I never have been. I am a freelance. I would like to say this to you, my Lord, if I may. You and your colleagues are charged with this Inquiry. You will search here and there among the debris for troubles. I know perfectly well you will do it very well. But I do implore you not to lose sight of the wood because of the trees. You know and I know the cause of this accident. It is due to the adventure of pioneering spirit [sic] of our race. It has been like that in the past, it is like that in the present, and I hope it will be in the future. In this Inquiry there is nothing to be ashamed of; much more to be proud of.

"Here was a great imaginative project to build a machine with twice the speed and twice the height of any existing machine in the world. We all went into it with our eyes wide open. We were conscious of the dangers that were lurking in the unknown. We did not know what fate was going to hold out for us in the future. Of course we gave hostages to fate, but I cannot believe that this court or our country will censure us because we ventured. You would not have the aeronautical people in this country trail behind the world in craven fear lest they be censured in such a court as this for trying to lead the world. Everything within the realm of human knowledge and wisdom was put into this machine. The Royal Aircraft Establishment tested every bit. They thought they would find weaknesses. It was not found wanting. I would like you to remember this, my Lord, that when we gave this certificate of airworthiness to these machines they were airworthy. True they deteriorated in a way no one on earth at the time could foretell, and they deteriorated, so I am led to understand, by a slowly developing molecular metallurgical fault. It is metallurgy, not aeronautics, that is in the dock.

"My Lords, I have had fifty years now connected with aviation, and if I may say something about it I would like to say this, that in every step in progress we have paid for it [sic] in blood and treasure, and God knows that in this case we have paid in full.

"Finally, I do hope that the threat of having to face an Inquiry such as this, with all its publicity, if anything goes wrong, will not stop adventurous spirits pioneering in the future. That is a danger of which I know you will be conscious. Thank you for listening."

4

Royal Aircraft Establishment,
Farnborough,
Hants.
19 December 1956

Confidential at the discretion
of the Chief Inspector of Accidents

P. G. Tweedie Esq.,
Accidents Investigation Branch, (C.A.)
Ministry of Transport and Civil Aviation,
Berkeley Square House,
London, W1.

Dear Tweedie,

I am now reporting to you the results of our investigations into the further Comet wreckage that you sent us recently. At the same time I am bringing to your notice some research work that we have been doing at RAE following the closure of the Comet Inquiry. I hope you do not feel that I am, by this addition, complicating what could be a simple story, but I am satisfied that you need the extra information if you are to have events in true perspective.

In order to give the complete story it is necessary for me to go back to the time immediately following the Comet Inquiry. It was then that I put forward a new theory for structural break-up in certain kinds of structural accident. According to this theory the sudden release of stress brought about by fracture in a particular place may lead to the radiation of shock-waves over the entire structure. These shock-waves, which travel with extreme rapidity, may then induce subsidiary origins of failure elsewhere. Owing to the speed of wave travel, what may be described as primary and subsidiary origins can be created virtually simultaneously; and under normal methods of wreckage analysis each origin, when examined individually, would appear as a primary cause of structural disruption.

The effect is by no means present in all structural accidents, although pressure cabins are among the most likely victims. The consequences, moreover, depend on whether the original failure is produced by static or fatigue loading. For static loading subsidiary origins might develop almost anywhere. For fatigue loading, on the other hand, subsidiary origins are normally only to be expected where small cracks already exist. Thus, if a structure has two fatigue cracks, the sudden growth of one could cause the sudden growth of the other, and both would appear as primaries in a wreckage examination. In many cases, moreover, it may not be possible to determine at which crack catastrophic effects first developed.

This theory was not evolved exclusively for the Comet 1 or even for pressure cabins. Over the years, there have been many apparent discrepancies in accident evidence, and many of these have never been satisfactorily explained. There have been instances, for example, of wing spars that have, to all appearances, failed in different places under up-load and down-load simultaneously. The evidence of one of your people at the Tanganyika Court of Inquiry into the Viking accident impressed me considerably. As is to be expected of a professional witness, no attempt was made to make the evidence fit preconceived ideas, or deliberately to avoid apparent inconsistency. It was, in fact, the evidence in this particular case which first set me thinking seriously on the lines I have described.

At this stage the story ceases to be a purely personal matter. Special investigations were planned by R. J. Atkinson, the Head of the Fatigue Division of Structures Department, assisted by one or two specialists in other Divisions. The static test on the Comet 1 was chosen as the medium for experiment, and plans were made to avoid any interference with the main objective for the test, which was to establish the static strength of the Comet pressure cabin. Some special instrumentation was devised by J. R. Sturgeon, and followed by mathematical analysis by L. S. D. Morley.

It is of interest to note that the first evidence of shock effects was obtained without the aid of the special apparatus. As you will remember, the pressure cabin cracked nearly the whole of its length, but there were two cracks, one forward of a main bulkhead and one aft of it. The two cracks were not connected and later analysis indicated that the rear crack was primary, and the front crack secondary. For various reasons a shock through the water was ruled out as an explanation, and this left only a shock-wave through the structure as the cause of failure in the forward part of the cabin.

The analysis of the special instrument recordings, which took some time to complete, was still more impressive. It would be wrong to regard the results as quantitatively accurate in view of the speed at which events took place, but the conclusions were definite. Conditions of appreciable super-stress were widespread, and there were indications that an excess stress of at least 50% occurred in several places.

You may well be wondering why I did not mention this work to you before. The answer is that the theory began as only the germ of an idea, and I was determined to obtain proof for or against before taking any action. By sending the additional wreckage you have rather forced the issue, but you may consider that you have also provided still more evidence to substantiate the theory. In the light of the work I have described you will be able to appreciate that some months before the wreckage arrived I was convinced that the Elba accident could have been caused by a fatigue failure at a side-window, such as occurred in the tank, and without there being any conflict with the evidence as given at the Court of Inquiry regarding the ADF hatch on the roof.

The investigation just completed by Ripley and his people has embraced not only the study of the new wreckage but also a re-study of the wreckage in the neighbourhood of the the critical ADF hatch. The first conclusion is that the ADF hatch is still an origin of failure, and has definitely propagated cracks for some distance outwards. The second conclusion is that in the new wreckage there are cracks running from another origin in the region of the three starboard windows between the main spar bulkheads. The origin itself has not been found in the wreckage, and presumably is still at the bottom of the Mediterranean. Finally, between the two origins is a kind of no-man's-land where the direction of propagation is uncertain if not controversial; a circumstance which is not inconsistent with crack propagation from two distinct sources.

In brief, therefore, the conclusion is that there were two cracks in the Elba Comet, both of which acted as origins of failure. There is insufficient evidence to say which went first. It would be possible to hazard an opinion, but this would be entirely out of keeping with the rest of the work which has been as factual as we could make it. I am less reluctant, however, to venture an opinion of the Comet1's in general; and this is that they were more likely to have a primary failure in a side window than in the ADF hatch. In forming this opinion I have been influenced to some extent by the results of work done since the Inquiry by RAE and some really first class experimental work done independently by de Havillands.

In giving you these conclusions I am fully aware of the danger of distorting evidence, and even facts, to fit a preconceived theory. I have therefore taken special steps to ensure that no such influences have been at work in this case. Ripley was aware of this shock-wave work, but quite clearly has not been influenced by it until forced to the conclusion that it provided the only possible explanation. Almond and F. H. Jones, who have done most of the detail work, moreover, were hardly aware of it and, in any case, were obviously determined to find out the truth by their own well-established methods.

There is now only one other matter for consideration. If you accept these findings as reasonable, I would like you to agree to let the matter rest here. I am anxious not to start another Comet Inquiry, even an unofficial one. So far as I can judge there is nothing in this letter that is inconsistent with the evidence given at the original Inquiry, and with the findings of the Court. Subsequent work done by RAE and de Havillands, moreover, substantiates the belief that pressure cabin fatigue was a major hazard to the Comet 1.

If you agree, I propose to send copies of this letter to the ARB and de Havillands, and possibly also to one or two people who have been directly concerned, and then take no further action. Whatever is decided upon, however, I would like there to be agreement between us, since I regard this as essentially a joint investigation.

Yours sincerely,

(signed) P. B. Walker[1]

5

Stress, strain, cracks and cutouts. A summary[1]

*(The units of measurement used in this text are the same as those used
when the Comet was made i.e. Imperial.)*

Stress and strain have quite specific meanings in engineering. If a weight is suspended from
an overhead beam by a wire, the weight, acting under gravity, pulls down on the wire causing it to lengthen. The force (or load) acting on the wire is the mass of the weight being
accelerated downwards by gravity. The stress in the wire is this force divided by the cross-
sectional area of the wire. With a weight of 10 pounds and a wire of cross-sectional area of
0.1 square inches then the stress is (10/0.1) 100 pounds (force) per square inch (psi). Other
units of stress are Newtons per square metre, Pascals or something similar. The stress is the
same throughout the length of the wire regardless of its length. This appendix will only deal
with the special case of tensile (pulling) stress.

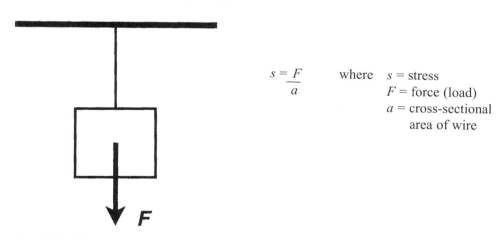

$$s = \frac{F}{a} \qquad \text{where} \quad \begin{array}{l} s = \text{stress} \\ F = \text{force (load)} \\ a = \text{cross-sectional} \\ \qquad \text{area of wire} \end{array}$$

*Fig. 1/A5 Weight suspended by a wire
from an overhead beam*

Strain is the change in size or shape of the body on which the force is acting. In this example
the wire lengthens when the load is applied to it and the strain is the increase in length compared with its original length. Strain is a ratio of sizes and therefore does not have units of
measurement. If the force remains constant the strain has the same value regardless of the
original length of the wire.

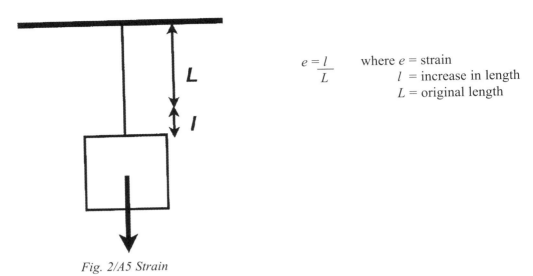

$$e = \frac{l}{L}$$

where e = strain
l = increase in length
L = original length

Fig. 2/A5 Strain

If the load and stress in the wire are steadily increased from zero, the extension and strain in the wire will be directly proportional to the stress. This is the linear region in Fig. 3/A5. This was an observation first made by the irascible Robert Hooke in about 1676 ('as the extension, so the force'). If the load is removed while the stress and strain are in this linear region, the wire will return to its original length. This is termed 'elastic' behaviour. If the wire is extended beyond the linear region it becomes permanently deformed and removal of the load will leave the wire stretched. The permanent deformation is called 'plastic' strain. The stress at which plastic behaviour begins is called the yield or proof strength of the material. Further increases in stress result in increasing plastic strain, achieving a maximum or 'ultimate strength' soon after which the material fails. This stress is also the stress in the plastic region at which 'necking' or non-uniform narrowing of a test piece begins (see Fig. 4/A5).

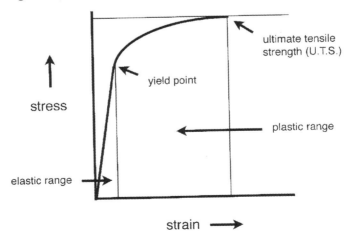

Fig. 3/A5 Plot of stess against strain in aluminium showing the elastic and plastic ranges.

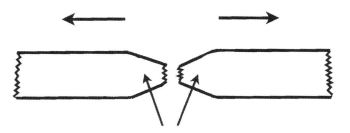

Fig. 4/A5 Necking in a test piece.

All of this can be applied to a sheet of metal in place of the wire. The relevant cross-sectional area is the product of the thickness of the sheet and the width of the surface to which the load is attached (i.e. the length perpendicular to the direction of the stress). Applying this to the Comet the sheet is the cabin skin and the load is the cabin pressure differential.

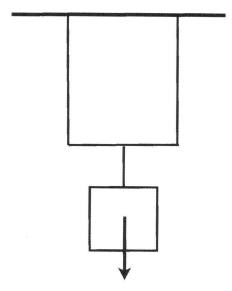

Fig. 5/A5 Sheet of metal stressed by a weight.

At sea level, i.e. with zero pressure differential between the inside and outside, the cabin is at its original size. At a pressure differential of 8.25 psi (1 P) the cabin increases in length and diameter but when the pressure differential falls back to zero the cabin returns to its original size. In other words the deformation (the strain) has been within the elastic range (Fig. 6/A5).

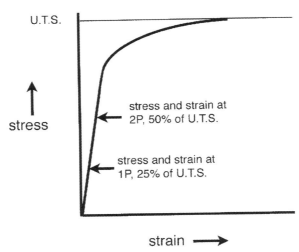

*Fig. 6/A5 In areas remote from the cutouts all the stress and strain is within the elastic range.
Up to 1P even the highly-stressed areas near the cutout corners were still within the elastic
range (UTS = ultimate tensile strength)*

The transition from the elastic to the plastic range, the yield point, is difficult to determine in practice in aluminium alloys and an offset yield point at a specified amount of (permanent) strain is often used. In the Comet the offset yield point at a strain of 0.1% occurred
at a differential of 11 psi (1.33P – the proof pressure). By this point the most-stressed areas
of the cabin skin were just into the plastic range. At pressures greater than 1.33P these areas
would increase in size and deform at increasing rates (Fig. 7/A5).

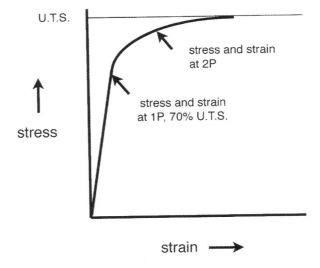

*Fig. 7/A5 At pressure differentials greater than 1.33P the stress and strain values in the more
highly-stressed areas near the cutout corners move into the plastic range.*

The highly-stressed areas that experience permanent, plastic deformation are left in compression when the pressure differential returns to zero (Fig. 8/A5)..

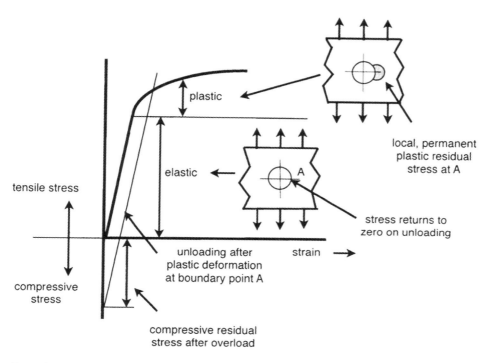

Fig. 8/A5 The effects of plastic deformation at the point of maximum tensile stress (A)
(redrawn from a diagram by Tom Swift)

The fuselage test specimen had been demonstrated not to burst up to 2P and was designed to remain intact up to 2.5P, the designed ultimate strength. At some point the cabin would burst when part of it had reached its breaking strength but this was intended to be greater than 2.5P. In fact AV's cabin, the only one tested to destruction, failed at 2.34P, 19.3 psi, although by this time it was not a new structure.

The relationship between stress and strain in the Comet's pressure cabin can also be expressed as a plot of cabin pressure differential against percentage of ultimate strength.

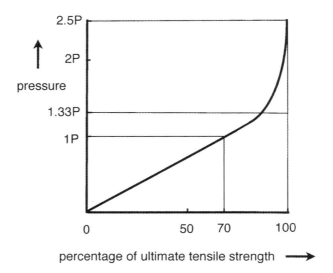

*Fig. 9/A5 Relationship between cabin pressure and ultimate tensile strength in the Comet.
In this illustration the UTS is taken as 2.5P.*

After the cabin section survived the test to 2P de Havillands reasoned that at 1P no part could have been at greater stress than 50% of that at its ultimate tensile strength (in fact more like 40% as its designed UTS was 2.5P). When Hall said that the new information was that a specimen that had passed a static test of twice its normal loading could nevertheless have a stress concentration of 70% of its ultimate strength at normal loading (Chapter 21) he was just expressing the non-linearity of the above graphs beyond the yield point.*

Lines of stress
One way of visualising how stress behaves in a body is to imagine lines of stress passing through it from the points or areas where the acting and reacting forces are applied to it. If a uniform sheet of metal is stressed evenly in the plane of the sheet, as before, lines of stress of equal magnitude stretch parallel to each other and equal distances apart, in the direction of the stretching axis.

---

* In fact it was not new. An expression to calculate stress and strain in elastic/plastic regions had been devised by H. Neuber, in 1945. It was published in German and may well have been unknown to Hall. It was re-published in English in 1961.[2]

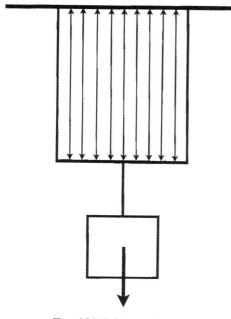

Fig. 10/A5 Lines of stress

If some of the sheet is removed, so that it is narrowed, but the same load is carried, the lines of stress become more concentrated in the narrowed part. If the narrowing amounts to half the original width of the sheet then the stress in the narrowed part is doubled. The distribution of the stress, and hence the stress lines, in this part is not necessarily uniform and concentrations develop at, for example, any corners, shoulders or margins of holes. In general the sharper the corner the greater the stress concentration.

Over the years engineers have developed mathematical solutions to calculate stress concentrations Kt (defined as S/s, where S is the local stress at the edge of the notch and s is the remote or general stress), for a range of component geometries. One solution of considerable importance was published by Inglis[3] for the case of a round or elliptical hole. Some examples of the application of the Inglis solution for ellipses are given below and demonstrate that very large values of Kt can develop at the edge of such holes.

From Inglis

(a) $S = s (1 + 2 \sqrt{[L / r]})$ where S = local stress at the hole edge
  s = remote stress
  L = length of the elliptical hole
  r = radius of the elliptical hole

For example for an ellipse where $L = 0.25$ inches
  $r = 0.001$ inches

$S = s (1 + 2 \sqrt{[L / r]})$
then $S = s (1 + 2 \sqrt{[0.25 / 0.001]})$
$S = 32.6s$ or $Kt = 32.6$

When a crack was 'located' a $\frac{1}{16}$ inches hole was drilled at each end.

then $S = s (1 + 2 \sqrt{[L / r]})$ where $L = 0.25$ inches
  $r = \frac{1}{32}$ inches $= 0.0313$

$S = 6.65s$ or $Kt = 6.65$

a reduction by a factor of 5

Kt values and the Inglis equation assume elastic conditions with no yielding. If the predicted local stress at the hole edge exceeds the yield or proof strength, then plasticity will occur. This reduces the predicted elastic stress values and ensures that if the stress is removed the region at the hole edge, where the proof strength was exceeded, has irreversibly deformed.

Fatigue, fatigue crack growth and unstable (rapid) fracture

Metal fatigue is the process by which cracks start and then grow in a metal structure under the influence of repeated cycles of stress well below the ultimate static strength of the material. It was first identified at the beginning of the 19th century when large numbers of railway axles began failing suddenly after significant periods of service. The failures were caused by a (then) mysterious process which resulted in fractures with a bright appearance quite unlike the dull grey fractures that resulted from static overloads. One railway accident resulting from axle failure at Versailles in 1842 caused the deaths of at least 55 passengers as the carriages piled into the locomotives and caught fire. This crash initiated the first serious research into fatigue by a Scottish engineer called William Rankine. The term 'fatigue' was coined by the British engineer Frederick Braithwaite in a paper to the Institute of Civil Engineers in 1854, a century before the Comet. The fatigue process is irreversible, the metal does not recover if rested.

The essential characteristics of the process: that repeated applications of stress were necessary, that the cracks first developed at stress concentrations, and that the damage process began from the first load applications in service and grew with further stress cycles, were established at that time. There was considerable debate over the significance of the bright appearance of the fractures which almost up to the present day promoted the erroneous idea that the metal under the influence of repeated cycles becomes 'crystalline' and therefore brittle. More recent understanding of fatigue emphasises the role of localised plasticity to initiate the cracks and fracture mechanics allows the prediction of fatigue crack growth and eventual failure.

Aircraft built of aluminium alloys are susceptible to fatigue failure under the influence of cycles of pressurisation and of gust loadings on the wings. At the time of the Comet design prediction of fatigue failures and design against fatigue was still an imperfect art, but the basics of fatigue had been established by research over the previous century. A useful way of illustrating the effects of fatigue on a particular metal or structure is to use the S/N curve that was introduced in Chapter 21. S/N curves were first determined by a German railway engineer called August Wöhler in the middle 1800s. They are produced by taking a number of nominally identical samples and subjecting them to cyclic stressing, each with different stress amplitude or stress range, and then recording the number of stress cycles to failure of each sample. Each failure is then plotted on a graph of stress range or amplitude against the number of cycles to failure and a curve drawn through the points as shown in figure 11/A5.

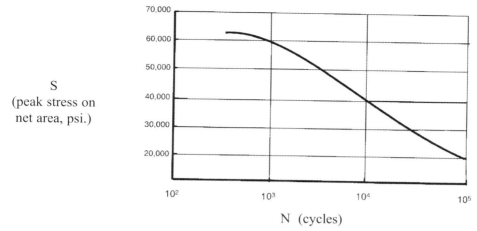

*Fig. 11/A5 S/N curve for DTD 546B (specimen width 0.5 inches,
thickness 0.035 inches, with 0.125 inches hole)*[4]

In aluminium alloys the stress range at failure continues to reduce with increasing cycles but under laboratory conditions of constant amplitude loading ferrous and titanium alloys have a lower limit to the stress that causes failure, the fatigue limit. In this case the S/N curve does not reach the x axis and any stress that is below this level will not cause a fatigue failure no matter how often the stress is repeated. This was a great comfort to the designers of (for example) engines where high frequency stress reversals are inevitable. Unfortunately more recent work shows that in real service conditions of variable amplitude stressing, this fatigue limit does not exist and fatigue failure is always a possibility.

The process of producing a fatigue crack is described as being in three stages:

initiation
propagation
failure

Initiation
Microscopic cracks, which may be just 0.05 inches long, or even less, start at stress concentrations caused by the design features of a structure or the surface imperfections, grain interfaces or persistent slip bands of the material. At a microscopic level metals are composed of crystals made up of sheets of atoms laid one on top of another, rather like sheets of paper in a stack. Occasionally one sheet is shorter than the others and the sheets above and below are distorted slightly to accommodate it. Each of these distortions is an area of weakness and if the material is strained repeatedly the 'short sheet' appears to move through the structure by a process called dislocation. The crystals themselves do not move but they cause a progressive slippage in sheet after sheet. These dislocations accumulate and produce persistent slip bands. These may protrude from or intrude into the surface of the crystal and act as stress raisers.

Propagation

After it initiates, the fatigue crack will grow a small increment per stress cycle. The size of the increment on each cycle is small at first, perhaps only 0.00001 inches. As the crack length increases, the increment size increases rapidly and at the end of the propagation stage it could approach 0.1 inches per cycle. Each growth increment leaves a mark on the fracture surface called a striation, indicating the point at which the crack momentarily paused before the next application of stress. The presence of striations can be used to distinguish fatigue cracks from cracks produced by static fracture. Static fracture cracks are described in the next section.

Failure

The third stage of failure is a sudden, rapid extension of the crack and complete failure of the structure on the next application of load. The crack length at which this occurs depends on a property called fracture toughness, which might be loosely defined as the resistance of a material to the unstable propagation of cracks. Fracture toughness is in part a property of the material, approximately related to ductility and partly dependent on the stress conditions in the cracked structure.

In the years following the Comet accidents, the development of a branch of mechanics called fracture mechanics has allowed the prediction of conditions for the onset of unstable failure in metallic engineering structures. This knowledge was not available to the designers of the Comet.

Some materials, such as modelling clay or soft, high purity gold or copper, are largely insensitive to the presence of cracks. Other materials such as glass or ceramics are highly sensitive to the presence of even small cracks and will fracture at very low stresses. Aerospace aluminium alloys fall between these two extremes.

The conditions for the onset of unstable fracture depend on the material toughness, the overall stress levels and the existing crack length. High stresses and low toughness cause unstable failure at small crack lengths; high toughness and small stresses allow fatigue crack growth to proceed to long crack lengths before unstable failure starts. The principle underlying the onset of unstable failure is energy based. Up to the crack length at which instability occurs, the energy required to increase the crack length is greater than the energy released if the crack extends. At the point of unstable failure, the balance between energy input and output becomes favourable for growth; the energy released by further growth becomes greater than the energy required to grow and crack extension causes a net release of strain energy in the body.

Work carried out by the RAE after the investigation showed that for the Comet's pressure cabin exposed to 1P cycles, the critical length for cracks was between 2 and 7 inches, generally about 6 inches. After this length had been reached propagation was very rapid.

Pressure vessels

(It is not suggested that the calculations that follow in this section are the same as those of de Havillands or Sir Arnold Hall. They are included here just as an illustration.)

The next section is a derivation of the equations to show that hoop stress has twice the magnitude of longitudinal stress and can be omitted without losing the sense of the remainder of the argument.[5]

The most efficient shape for a pressure vessel is a sphere.

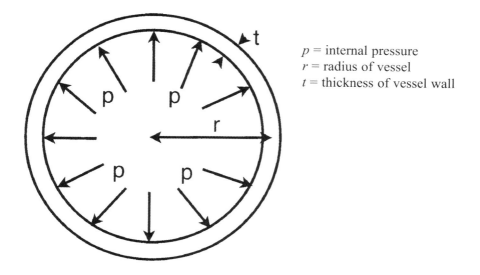

p = internal pressure
r = radius of vessel
t = thickness of vessel wall

Fig. 12/A5 A pressurised sphere

This is impractical for an aeroplane fuselage and some form of cylinder is used.

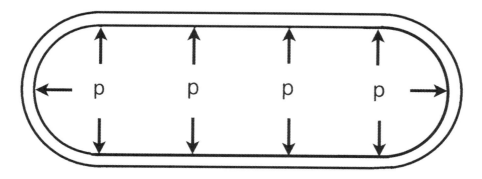

Fig. 13/A5 A pressurised cylinder.

The longitudinal stress in the cylinder is the stress in the parallel parts of the wall and is the same as the stress pushing the two hemispherical ends apart. This is equivalent to bisecting the pressurised sphere we started with.

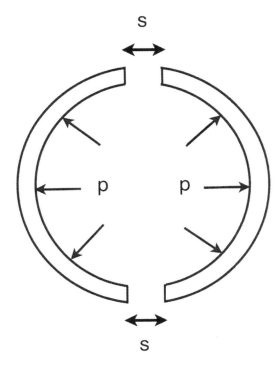

s

p   p

Fig. 14/A5 Sphere bisected.

Assuming that the wall is relatively thin and the sphere is cut into two hemispheres but the same pressure, *p*, is maintained, then the stress *s* = force / area of the cut surface.

s

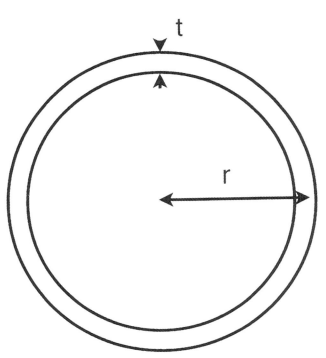

Fig. 15/A5 Cut surface of bisected hemisphere.

The area of the cut surface
$$= 2 \pi r t$$

*Fig. 16/A5 Bisected hemispheres closed
by discs*

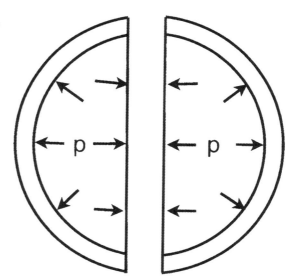

Assuming that the cut surface of each hemisphere is closed by an imaginary circular disc, then the force per unit area acting on each disc is p. The area of the disc is πr^2, therefore the total force is $p \pi r^2$. If the circular disc is removed this force is applied to the cut surface whose area is $2 \pi r t$.

Therefore stress = force / area it is applied to

$$= (p \pi r^2) / (2 \pi r t)$$
$$= (p r) / (2 t)$$

Hoop stress

If a cylinder is sliced longitudinally, the hoop stress is the stress in the cylinder wall produced by the upper and lower halves being pushed apart.

If the cylinder is also sliced transversely, producing a segment one unit long, and the top and bottom of the two half segments are closed with rectangular plates, then the force per unit area is p and the area of each plate = $2 r 1$

Therefore the total force = $p 2 r$

The area of the cut surface of the cylinder wall is $1 t 2$

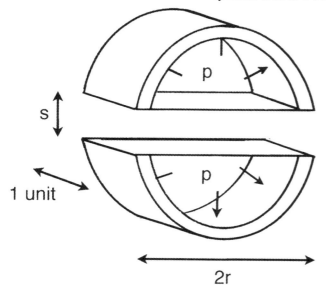

Stress = force / area
$$= (2 p r) / (2 t)$$
$$= (p r) / t$$

The circumferential or hoop stress is therefore twice as large as the longitudinal stress.

Fig. 17/A5 Cylinder sliced transversely.

Going back to equation (a), Inglis' equation for the stress at the end of the major axis of an ellipse,

$$S = s (1 + 2 \sqrt{[L / r]})$$

where S = local stress at the end of the ellipse
s = general level of stress
L = length of crack
r = radius of apex of crack

If $L = r$ i.e. a circular hole (in the middle of an infinite elastic plate) then:

$$S = s (1 + 2 \times 1)$$
$$Kt = S / s = 3$$

where Kt = stress concentration factor

Therefore the maximum stress concentration factor produced by a circular hole within a sheet subject to stress in one axis is 3. The maximum stress will be at two areas on the margin of the hole. If the stress is in the y axis then these two areas will be at 90° and 270° using the convention that 0° is at 12 o'clock.

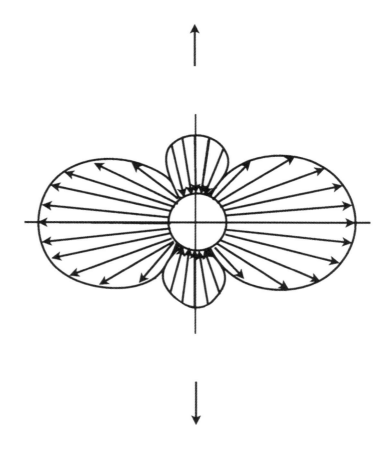

Fig. 18/A5 Stress concentration pattern around a circular hole in a uni-axial stress field.[6]

The length of the arrows around the hole at approximately 10° intervals represent the magnitude of the circumferential stress concentration. Outward-pointing arrows indicate tension and inward compression. The remote arrows indicate the direction of the stress field.

Moving away from the margin of the hole the stress decreases rapidly in a non-linear fashion.[7] Using a different equation, (b), this can be calculated.

(b) $S\varnothing = \dfrac{s}{2} \left(2 + \dfrac{r^2}{a^2} + 3\,\dfrac{r^4}{a^4}\right)$ where $S\varnothing$ = stress at edge of hole at right angles to direction of the stress field

r = radius of hole
a = distance away from centre of hole as multiples of radius
s = general level of stress

If $a = r$, i.e. the margin of the hole, then $S\varnothing$ = s. 3
If $a = 2$ then $S\varnothing$ = s. 1.2188
If $a = 3$ then $S\varnothing$ = s. 1.0741
If $a = 4$ then $S\varnothing$ = s. 1.0371

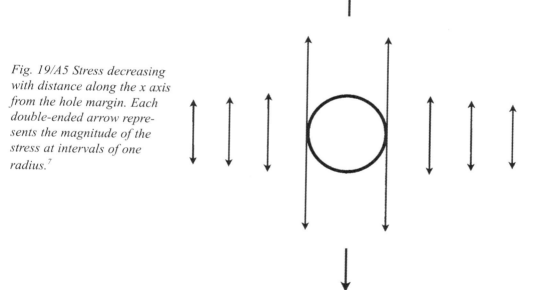

Fig. 19/A5 Stress decreasing with distance along the x axis from the hole margin. Each double-ended arrow represents the magnitude of the stress at intervals of one radius.[7]

With rivet holes of ⅛ (0.125) inches in diameter the stress has significantly decreased at 0.0625 inches (one radius from the margin) and would tail off almost to the general level at 4 x 0.0625 inches = 0.25 inches.

However in a pressurised cylinder, such as the Comet's fuselage, the stress was in the x-axis as well as in the y. If the two stresses are of equal magnitude, such as in a pressurised sphere, it can be shown that for a circular hole the circumferential stress concentration factor becomes 2 at all points on the hole's margin. In the case of a pressurised cylinder the stress in the y-axis, the hoop stress, is twice the magnitude of the longitudinal stress (x axis) and the maximum stress concentration factor becomes 2.5 at 90⁰ and 270⁰ to the hoop stress direction and 0.5 at 0⁰ and 180⁰. All the margin is now in tension.

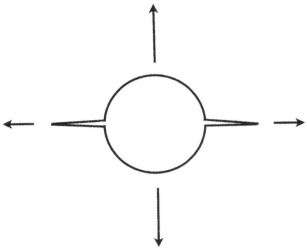

Any fracture would most probably start at the hole margin at one of the two points of maximum stress. Once started the crack would tend to progress in the direction of maximum stress, i.e. along the x axis, its rate of propagation increased by the stress concentration at the tip of the crack, until it reached its critical length when propagation would become very rapid.

Fig. 20/A5 Two fractures developing at the points of maximum stress.

In the Comet

circumferential (hoop) stress = $(p\,r)\,/\,t$ where $p = 8.25$ psi.
$r = 61.5$ inches
$t = 0.036$ inches (20 swg.)
$= (8.25 \times 61.5)/0.036$
$= 14{,}094$ psi.

At the sides of the fuselage this level of stress would have been increased by the presence of the windows and escape hatches, which carried little, if any, stress. The mean stress value in YR from the 4 strain gauges most remote from the side cutouts was 13,123 psi but from 4 readings in YU it was rather less at about 7,500. Hall's estimate was 13,700 psi.

The stress magnitude around a rectangular cutout with rounded corners was calculated by Green, in the paper

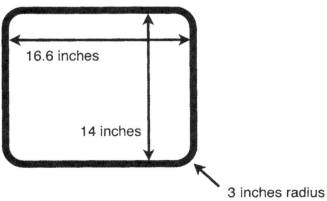

Fig. 21/A5 Comet cabin window

that Hall referred to, for tensile stress in one axis.[8] This gives a maximum stress concentration factor of approximately 2.9. More accurately, using later work[9] and applying the shapes and dimensions of the Comet's windows to the bi-axial stress field described above, the figure comes out to a maximum of about 3.1 at the corners.

Within this zone of raised stress near the corners the inner and outer rivet holes would raise the stress even further by a factor of about 2.5. The maximum stress, even at the outer row of rivet holes, is therefore about the ultimate strength of the Comet skin. This stress would have been further increased by flying loads and any fretting that the rivets produced.

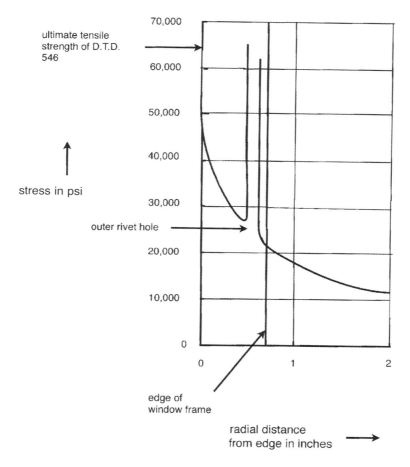

Fig. 22/A5 Theoretical stress concentrations at the outer rivet holes near the corner of a Comet window

This shows a maximum stress of 63,000-64,000 psi at the outer row of rivets. Although this was for an un-reinforced cutout it shows some correlation with the ANSYS model of the complete window frame which generated a figure of almost 68,000 psi. There are no figures from YR or YU with which to compare.

6

Finite element analysis of the static stress levels in the vicinity of the cabin windows in the Comet 1 fuselage

A summary of the project carried out by Paul Johnson, supervised by Ian Sewell, in The Design Unit in the Engineering Department, Newcastle University.

The structural models representing various parts of the Comet 1 cabin were built using AutoDesk Inventor and were then imported into ANSYS, an FEA program produced by Structural Mechanics Solutions. ANSYS generated the results in S.I. units but for reasons of continuity with the rest of the text the results will also be given in Imperial units (to the nearest 10 psi and 0.1 inches). The S.I. figures are the definitive ones.

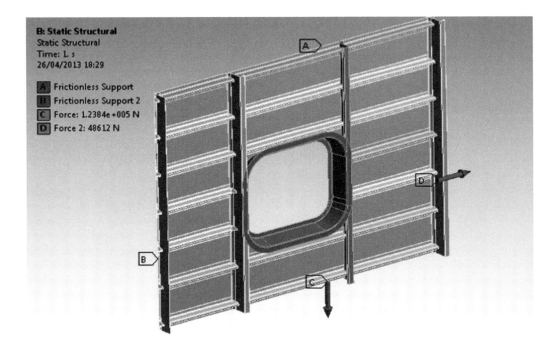

Fig. 1/A6 A fully built-up Comet window showing the frictionless supports (A, B) and the tensile forces (C, D).

In order for an FEA program to solve the analysis a mesh of elements has to be produced and refined around the areas of interest so that the calculated stress in that area converges. Without this convergence the results produced by ANSYS are meaningless. The elements used to mesh the structures were initially quadrahedral but became tetrahedral as the complexity of the model increased. This required more computing power which meant that the models had to be progressively reduced in size to stay within the capacity of the available equipment. Each of these reductions then had to be validated.

An early problem was that the program was unable to mesh a cylindrical structure and a flat sheet had to be used. The model reproduced the hoop and longitudinal stresses of the pressurised Comet fuselage by applying an appropriate tensile force to two of the faces at the same time as attaching frictionless supports to the opposite faces (Fig. 1/A6). The forces necessary to produce constant hoop and longitudinal stresses varied with the changing areas of fuselage skin as the model evolved. The attachments of the various structural parts were defined as they were acquired, for example the stringers were fully bonded to the skin.

Another problem was that the rivet holes were very small compared with the overall size of the model so the element size had to change from being relatively large for most of the model to very small at the margins of the rivet holes (Fig. 2/A6).

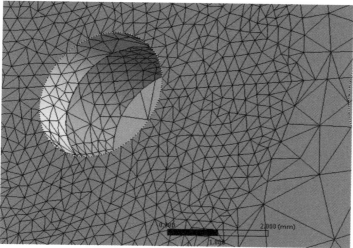

Fig. 2/A6 Small elements close to a rivet hole.

In all fourteen different cases were considered:

Case 1 This was a comparison of the ANSYS results for a cutout of the same shape, dimensions and stresses as a Comet window at 1P located in the centre of a thin sheet with an empirical analysis using data from Peterson.[1] The FEA model generated a maximum stress value of 327 MPa (47,430 psi, $Kt = 3.4$) at the corner margins, whereas the figure from Peterson was 306 MPa (44,380, $Kt = 3.1$), a difference of 6.4%. This may be explained by some extrapolations that were necessary to use Peterson's graphs and that their sheet was of infinite size but in any case the difference was considered sufficiently small that the model could be validated.

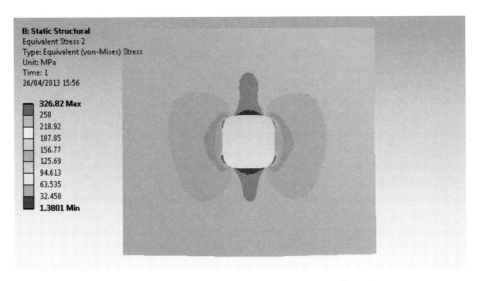

B: Static Structural
Equivalent Stress 2
Type: Equivalent (von-Mises) Stress
Unit: MPa
Time: 1
26/04/2013 15:56

326.82 Max
250
218.92
187.85
156.77
125.69
94.613
63.535
32.458
1.3801 Min

Fig. 3/A6 Equivalent stress-range areas in Case I.

Case 2 This was a thin sheet with three cutouts arranged in the same way as those in the centre section of the Comet fuselage. The cutout-margin stress increased to 347 MPa (50,330 psi, $Kt = 3.6$).

Case 3 Removing the most-distant end cutout increased the stress at the margin of the central cutout to 352 MPa (51,050 psi, $Kt = 3.7$). This was considered so small a change that this cutout could be excluded.

Case 4 Removing the cutout at the other end reduced the stress at the central cutout to 326 MPa (47,280 psi, $Kt = 3.4$). This reduction of 7% was larger than the mesh convergence error of +/- 5 MPa (725 psi, 1.4%) and was considered large enough to invalidate this model.

Case 5 Reducing the size of the sheet increased the stress to 391 MPa (56,710 psi, $Kt = 4.1$). This was caused by the sheet being too small to allow the stress to fall back to the general level of 95.6 MPa (13,870 psi) at its periphery. Accordingly cases 6 and 7 used a sheet large enough to allow this (but see case 8).

Case 6 This was the same as case 2 (three windows) but with the window frames fully bonded to the skin. This reduced the maximum stress at the window margin from 347 MPa to 301 (50,330 psi to 43,660, $Kt = 3.6$ to $Kt = 3.1$).

Case 7 This was the same as case 3 (two windows) but with the frames fully bonded. The window margin stress reduced from 352 MPa to 286 (51,050 psi to 41,480, $Kt = 3.7$ to Kt = 3.0), a similar pattern to the changes between cases 2 and 3.

Case 8 This was the same as case 7 (two bonded windows) but with the sheet size reduced to that of case 5 because it was anticipated that the limitations of available computing power would prevent the internal structure of the fuselage being added to the model with the large sheet size. As a consequence the maximum stress level increased to 331 MPa (48,010 psi, $Kt = 3.5$), showing that the window frames reduced the effect of using a smaller skin size but not sufficiently for the model to be valid.

Case 9 In this case the internal structure of the fuselage was added to case 8, reducing the stress to 273 MPa (39,600 psi, $Kt = 2.9$). This is a similar value to that in case 7, allowing the assumption to be made that when the stringers and frames were added the maximum stress at the window margin is so localised that it is little affected by the size of the sheet.

Case 10 This was the same as case 9 but with the left-sided window removed. This allowed a better mesh convergence and produced almost the same value as in case 7, 287 MPa (41,630 psi, $Kt = 3.0$), indicating that this was a valid model. This is a close approximation to the Comet windows before the rivets were added at the corners, i.e. its original design.

Case 11 Fifteen rivets were then added to each corner of the cutout in case 1. The maximum stress at the margin of a rivet hole was 688 MPa (99,790 psi, $Kt = 7.2$) and the maximum stress at the cutout margin increased from 327 to 367 MPa (47,430 to 53,230 psi, $Kt = 3.4$ to $Kt = 3.8$).

Case 12 The number of rivets in case 11 was then reduced to six. This had minimal effect on the stress at the margins of the rivet holes and the frame (690 and 368 MPa) (100,080 and 53,370 psi, $Kt = 7.2$ and 3.8).

Case 13 This was the same as case 12 but with the window frame added. The stress at the window margin increased to 373 MPa (54,100 psi, $Kt = 3.9$), compared with 331 (48,010 psi) in case 8, an increase of 11%. The stress at the rivet hole margin decreased by about 18% to 582 MPa (84,410 psi, $Kt = 6.1$).

Case 14 This was the same as case 13, i.e. window frames full bonded and 6 rivets at the corners, but with the internal fuselage structure added. This is a reasonably accurate model of the Comet window in its final form. It produced about the same stress at the window margin (284 MPa, 41,190 psi) as in case 10 (287 MPa, 41,630 psi). This shows that with the stringers and frames in place the rivet holes do not affect the stress levels at the window margin. The stress at the edges of the rivet holes decreased to 470 MPa (68,170 psi, $Kt = 4.9$).

Case 15 This was the same as Case 14 but with the bonding removed from the corners but retained at the straight parts of the frame. This model was used to see whether the stress at the rivet holes would increase if the Redux bonding had failed at the corners. The stress at the window margin (303 MPa, 43,950 psi, $Kt = 3.2$) did increase (by 7%) but there was relatively little change at the edges of the rivet holes (460 MPa, 65,250 psi, $Kt = 4.8$). This was because there was no significant physical change in the area of maximum stress at the rivet hole margins between cases 14 and 15.

This process has allowed the following conclusions to be reached:

1) Only one window needs to be present to provide realistic stress values when the window frame, fuselage frames and stringers are present.

2) The model is valid when only six rivet holes are present.

3) The skin area can be cut down to a small size as long as the internal structure of the fuselage is present.

4) To achieve mesh convergence with the computing power available and with the window frames, rivet holes, stringers and fuselage frames present, only one window can be used.

The results obtained from the above cases can be displayed as graphics showing areas of equivalent skin stress range in the same colour.

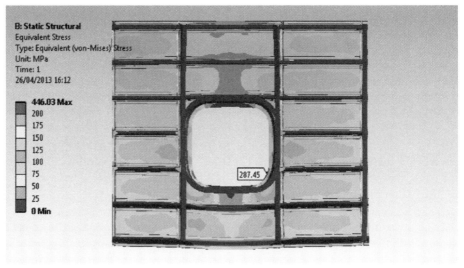

Fig. 4/A6 Equivalent stress areas seen from inside the fuselage in case 10.

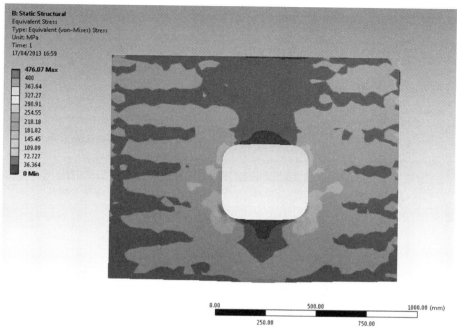

Fig. 5/A6 *The same window as above, seen from outside. Showing the influence of the internal structure of the fuselage on the skin stress.*

An alternative is to plot stress magnitude against displacement along a line projected away from the margin of a cutout corner.

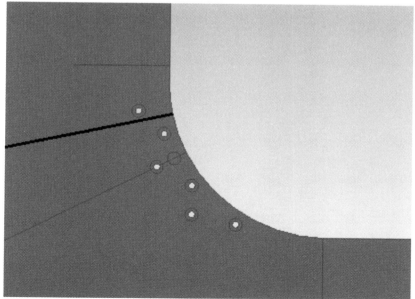

Fig. 6/A6 *Diagram of a line projected out from the corner of a cutout in approximately the same place and orientation as the line of strain gauges in Atkinson.*

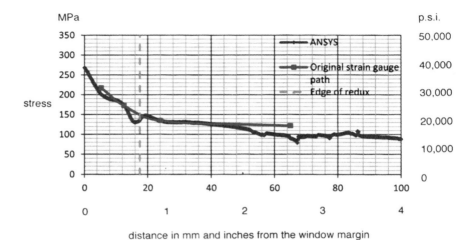

*Fig. 7/A6 Plot of stress against displacement along the line shown in Fig. 6/A6,
window frame fully bonded with Redux and six rivets (Case 14).*

This shows a close correlation between the ANSYS model and the figures from the strain gauges in Atkinson and helps to validate the model. The reduction of stress just inside the window frame was not detected by Atkinson because the strain gauges were too large. This approximates to the situation before the rivets were added to the corners.

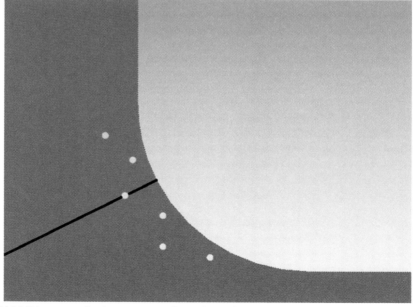

*Fig. 8/A6 Diagram of a line projected out from the corner of a cutout passing through an
outer rivet hole.*

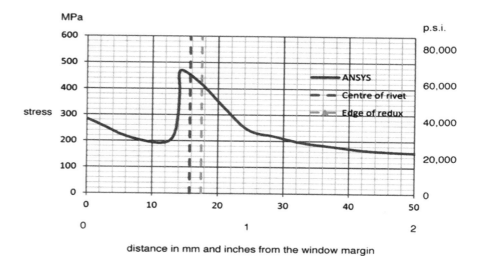

Fig. 9/A6 Plot of stress against displacement along the line shown in Fig. 8/A6, window frames fully bonded (Case 14).

The maximum stress concentration is at the margin of an outer rivet hole.

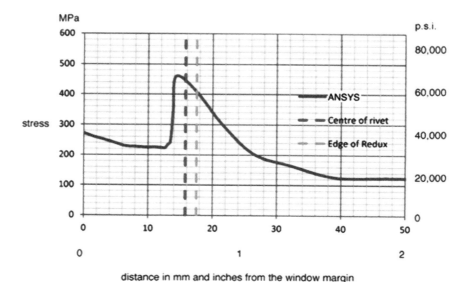

Fig. 10/A6 Plot of stress against displacement along the line shown in Fig. 8/A4 with the Redux removed from the window frame corners but the rivets retained. (Case 15).

There is little difference in the stress values at the window margin and at the edge of the rivet hole between this case and the previous one. This shows that if the Redux bonding at the window frame corners had failed it would not have made the rivet holes more vulnerable to a fatigue failure.

In the pressurised Comet fuselage these areas of high stress at the rivet holes would have exhibited plastic, i.e. non-linear, deformation. ANSYS is a linear-modelling program and assumes that all the relevant material is within its elastic range hence the figures it calculates for stress in these areas are larger than they would have been in practice. Nevertheless the conclusion that the edges of the rivet holes were subject to high stress and were therefore vulnerable to cracking is valid.

7

Comparison of the Comet 1 with the Airbus A318

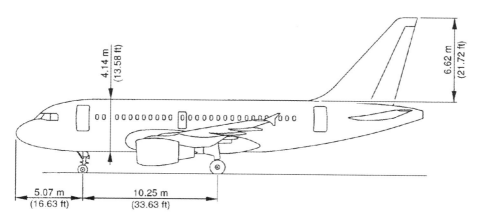

Fig. 1/A7 Airbus 318 (above) and Fig. 2/A7 Comet 1 (below).
Reproduced with permission from Airbus and copyright BAE SYSTEMS Heritage.

(Slightly different dimensions for the Comet 1 are given in the two referenced sources although both were official de Havilland productions.)

	A318 [1,2,]	Comet 1 [3,4,5]
passengers	107 to 132	36
flight deck crew	2	4
length	103' 2"	93' 1", 93' 7"
wing span	111' 11"	115', 114' 8"
wing sweep back	25⁰	20⁰
tail height	42' 3"	28' 4.5" to 29' 4.25"
cabin diameter	12' 10"	9' 9"
fuselage diameter	13'	10' 3"
empty weight	87,000 pounds	48,420 pounds
max. takeoff wt.	150,000 pounds	105,000 pounds
cruising speed	511 mph	460 mph (at 9,500 rpm)
service ceiling	39,000 feet	42,000 feet
max. range (full load)	3,600 miles	1,500 miles
max. fuel capacity	5,330 imp gallons	5,976 (usable) imp. gallons
	(44,481 pounds)	(49,872 pounds)
engine thrust (total)	43,200-47,600 pounds	20,000 pounds (at sea level)
engine weight (dry)		
CFM 56 - 5B8, 9	5,250 pounds	
PW 61-22A, 24A	5,046 pounds	
Ghost 50		2,345 pounds
thrust to weight ratio	4.1:1 to 4.7:1	2.13:1

The two aircraft are similar in size but have considerable differences in performance. The most notable differences are:

> the much larger number of passengers carried by the A318,
> the larger loaded and unloaded weights of the A318,
> the greater combined thrust of the engines of the A318,
> the greater range of the A318.

Overall, in round figures, the A318 carries 132 passengers over 3,600 miles using 5,330 gallons of fuel i.e. approximately 90 passenger-miles per gallon. The Comet 1 carried 36 passengers over 1,500 miles using 6,000 gallons of fuel i.e. 9 passenger-miles per gallon. Using these criteria the A 318 is about ten times as efficient as the Comet 1. Most of this can be put down to the A318's greater thrust enabling it to carry more passengers (and their luggage) and the greater fuel efficiency of its engines giving it a greater range in spite of its being a heavier aircraft when fully loaded.

8

The names of the people who lost their lives in the Comet accidents

G-ALYY Entebbe [1]
Silvani Swakiseke, airport worker, Entebbe

CF-CUN Karachi [2, 3]
C. N. Pentland, Captain
C. N. Sawle, First Officer
P. D. Roy, Navigator and radio operator
J. R. Cook, Navigator and radio operator
J. A. Smith, Engineer

Mr. J. A. Wilson, passenger
Mr. D. H. Edwards
Mr. H. Waters
Mr. B. W. H. Rees
Mr. D. Morgan-Tipp
Mr. N. H. Gardiner

G-ALYV Calcutta [4, 5]
M. W. Haddon, Captain
R. G. W. Strange, First Officer
A. L. Gilmore, Engineer
A. S. Wood, Radio operator
G. W. Irwin, Steward
P. Rawlinson, Stewardess

Mr. M. B. A. F. Aris, passenger
Mr. A. B. Avila
Mr. E. W. Bateman
Mr. P. R. Brown
Mr. J. T. Cartwright
Miss. J. S. Cohen

Mr. N. B. Collins
Mrs. P. Farquharson
Mr. G. K. Farquharson
Mr. B. K. Featherstone
Miss A. A. Hamilton
Mr. F. J. Kemlo
Mr. E. A. Landsman
Mr. F. J. L. Leonard
Mr. W. J. London
Mrs. D. H. Maltman
Miss. M. G. Maltman (child)
Dr. B. Maung
Mr. I. C. G. Milne
Mr. J. E. Milne
Mr. F. Mitchell
Mr. H. A. Morton
Mrs. H. P. Morton
Mr. B. A. R. Nasarudin
The Hon. T. D. Oldham
Mrs. K. M. Oldham
Mr. H. G. Pearson
Mrs. H. G. Pearson
Mr. C. C. Po
Mr. J. J. A. Boxas
Mrs. K. M. Smythe
Miss. P. A. Smythe (baby)
Mr. P. K. Snead
Mr. D. P. Storey
Mr. K. Teck Ee
Mrs. K. Teck Ee
Miss. A. M. Whistler

G-ALYP Elba [6, 7]

A. Gibson, Captain
W. J. Bury, First Officer
F. C. Macdonald, Engineer Officer
L. P. McMahon, Radio Officer
F. L. Saunders, Steward
J. E. Clarke, Stewardess

Mrs. R. E. Geldard, passenger
Miss. G. Geldard (child)
Mast. M. Geldard (child)
Mrs. E. S. Maclachlan
Mr. S. F. Naaman
Mr. J. Y. Ramsden
Mr. D. Leaver
Mr. A. Crisp
Mr. B. Butler
Mr. J. Israel
Mr. J. B. Crilly
Miss. B. Crilly (child)
Miss. R. Khedouri
Miss N. Khedouri
Miss L. Yateen
Mr. J. M. Bunyan
Mrs. J. M. Bunyan
A. Bunyan (infant)
Mrs. D. Baker
Mr. H. E. Schuchman
Mr. T. Moore
Miss E. Fairbrother
Mr. C. Wilmot
Mr. F. J. Greenheugh
Mast. R. Sawyer Shelling
Captain V. Wolfson
Mr. J. P. Hill
Mr. J. Steel
Captain C. A. Livingstone

G-ALYY Naples [8, 9]

W. K. Mostert, Captain
B. J. Grove, First Officer
A. E. Sissing, Navigation Officer
B. E. Webstock, Radio Officer
A. R. Lagesen, Engineer Officer
J. B. Kok, Steward
P. Reitz, Stewardess

Mr. A. B. Brooks, passenger
Mrs. A. B. Brooks
Miss. D. M. Eady
Mr. R. L. Wilkinson
Miss. N. Young
Mr. E. S. Hack
Mr. O. L. Anderson
Mr. J. Rosenberg
Mr. Saltzman
Mr. F. H. Harbinson
Mr. M. A. Lamloum
Dr. J. Stuart
Captain J. A. Collins
Mr. J. F. Murray-White

Total 111

Selected Bibliography

Anderson D. F. and Eberhardt S., *Understanding flight*, 2nd edition, 2010, McGraw-Hill, New York, USA.

Barnett C., *The Audit of War, the Illusion and reality of Britain as a great nation*, 1986, Macmillan, London, UK.

Barnett C., *The Verdict of Peace*, 2001, Pan Macmillan, London, UK.

Beaty D., *The Naked Pilot: The human factor in aircraft accidents*, 1995, Airlife, Shrewsbury, UK.

Beaty D., *The Story of Transatlantic Flight*, 2003, Airlife, Shrewsbury, UK.

Bibell, G., *Beyond the Black Box, the forensics of airplane crashes*, 2008, The Johns Hopkins University Press, Baltimore, USA.

The Daily Telegraph Book of Airmen's Obituaries, 2002, Grub Street Publishing, London, UK.

Brabazon, Lord Brabazon of Tara, *The Brabazon Story*, 1956, William Heinemann, London, UK.

Bramson, A., *Master Airman, a Biography of Air Vice-Marshall Donald Bennet*, 1985, Airlife, Shrewsbury, UK.

Brown E. Miles, *M.52 gateway to supersonic flight*, 2012, Spellmount, Stroud, UK.

Brown E. M., *Wings on my sleeve*, 1961 and 1978, Airlife, Shrewsbury, UK.

Bulman G.P., *An Account of Partnership – Industry, Government and the Aero Engine, The Memoirs of George Purvis Bulman*, 2001, Rolls-Royce Heritage Trust Historical Series No. 31, Derby, UK., Edited and with a commentary by M. C. Neale.

Caygill P., *Sound Barrier, the rocky road to Mach 1.0 +*, 2006, Pen and Sword Aviation, Barnsley, UK.

Clark R. W., *Tizard*, 1965, Methuen, London, UK.

Darling K., *de Havilland Comet*, 2005, The Crowood Press, Marlborough, UK.

Davies D. P., *Handling the Big Jets*, 3rd edition, 1971, Civil Aviation Authority, London, UK.

Davies R. E. G. and Birtles P. J., *de Havilland Comet, the world's first jet airliner*, 1999, Paladwr Press, McLean, Virginia, USA.

de Havilland Sir G., *Sky fever*, 1961, Hamish Hamilton, London, UK.

Fedden Sir R., *Britain's Air Survival*, 1957, Cassell, London, UK.

Fort A., *Prof The life of Frederick Lindemann*, 2003, Jonathan Cape, London, UK.

Furse A., *Wilfrid Freeman, the genius behind allied survival and air supremacy 1939 to 1945*, 2000, Spellmount, Staplehurst, UK.

Gardener R., *From Bouncing Bombs to Concorde, the authorised biography of aviation pioneer Sir George Edwards OM*, 2006, Sutton Publishing Limited, Stroud, UK.

Golley J., *John 'cats-eyes' Cunningham. The aviation legend*, 1999, Airlife, Shrewsbury, UK.

Golley J., *Genesis of the Jet, Frank Whittle and the invention of the jet engine*, 1996, Airlife, Shrewsbury, UK

Gordon, J. E., *The New Science of Strong Materials*, 1968, Penguin Books, London, UK.

Gordon, J. E., *Structures or why things don't fall down*, 1978, Penguin Books, London, UK.

Gunston, B., *Faster than Sound*, 1992, Patrick Stephens, Yeovil, UK.

Gunston B., *Fedden – the life of Sir Roy Fedden*, 1998, Rolls-Royce Heritage Trust, Historical Series No. 26, Derby, UK.

Gunston B., *Nimrod the Centenarian Aircraft*, 2009, Spellmount Publishers, Stroud, UK.

Gunston B., *The Development of Jet and Turbine Engines*, 2nd edition, 1997, Patrick Stephens, Yeovil, UK.

Gunston B., *The Development of Piston Aero Engines*, 2nd edition, 1999, Patrick Stephens, Yeovil, UK.

Gunston B., *World Encyclopaedia of Aero Engines*, 5th Edition, 2006, Sutton Publishing, Stroud, UK.

Hamilton-Paterson J., *Empire of the Clouds*, 2010, Faber and Faber, London, UK.

Harvey-Bailey A., *Rolls-Royce – Hives, the Quiet Tiger*, 1985, Rolls-Royce Heritage Trust Historical Series No. 20, Derby, UK.

Hooker, S., *Not Much of an Engineer*, 1984, Airlife, Shrewsbury, UK.

Hünecke K., *Jet Engines. Fundamentals of theory, design and operation*, 1997, Airlife, Shewsbury, UK.

Jackson A, J., *de Havilland Aircraft since 1909*, 1987, Putnam, London, UK.

Kay A. L., *Turbojet History and Development 1930-1960*, 2007, The Crowood Press, Marlborough, UK.

Lumsden A., *British Piston Aero-engines and their Aircraft*, 1994, Airlife, Shrewsbury, UK.

Masefield Sir P., Gunston B., *Flight Path*, 2002, Airlife, Shrewsbury, UK.

Ottaway S. and Ottaway I., *Fly with the Stars, British South American Airways*, 2007, Sutton Publishing, Stroud, UK.

Owen G., *From Empire to Europe, the decline and revival of British industry since the Second World War*, 1999, Harper Collins, London, UK.

Painter M., *The DH 106 Comet, an illustrated history*, 2002, Air-Britain, Tunbridge Wells, UK.

Penrose, H, *Wings Across the World, an illustrated history of British Airways*, 1980, Cassell, London, UK.

Phipp M., *The Brabazon Committee and British airliners 1945-1960*, 2007, Tempus Publishing, Stroud, UK.

Postan M. M., Hay D., Scott, J. D., *Design and Development of Weapons, studies in government and industrial organisation*, 1964, HMSO, London, UK.

Pugh P., *The Magic of a Name, the Rolls-Royce Story, Part 1, The first 40 years*, 2000, Icon Books, Cambridge, UK.

Pugh P., *The Magic of a Name, the Rolls-Royce Story, Part 2, The power behind the jets*, 2001, Icon Books, Cambridge, UK.

Rivas B., Bullen A., *John Derry, the story of Britain's first supersonic pilot*, 2008, Haynes Publishing, Yeovil, UK.

Rolls-Royce, *The Jet Engine*, 2005, Rolls-Royce Technical Publications, Derby, UK.

Russell Sir A., *A Span of Wings, An autobiography*, 1992, Airlife, Shrewsbury, UK.

Sharp C. M., *D H the history of de Havilland*, 1982, Airlife, Shrewsbury, UK.

Shawcross H., *Life Sentence, the memoirs of Hartley Shawcross*, 1995, Constable, London, UK.

Simons, G. M., *Comet! The world's first jet airliner*, 2013, Pen and Sword, Barnsley, UK.

Smith J. R. and Kay J., *German Aircraft of the Second World War*, 1972, Putnam, London, UK.

Taylor D. R., *Boxkite to Jet – the remarkable career of Frank B. Halford*, 1999, Rolls-Royce Heritage Trust, Historical Series No. 28, Derby, UK.

Timoshenko S., Goodier, J. N., *Theory of Elasticity*, 1951, McGraw-Hill, New York, USA.

Thomas Sir M., *Out on a wing*, 1964, Michael Joseph, London, UK.

Walker T., *The First Jet Airliner: the story of the de Havilland Comet*, 1999, Scoval Publishing Limited, Newcastle upon Tyne, UK.

Warterton W. A. and Hewat T., *The Comet Riddle*, 1955, Frederick Muller, London, UK. (republished 2012, Grub Street, London, UK.)

Whittle F., *Jet, the story of a pioneer*, 1953, Frederick Muller, London, UK.

Chapter Notes

TNA – The National Archives, Kew, London, UK
BAA – The British Airways Archives, British Airways Heritage Centre, The Waterside, Harmondsworth, London, UK.
Public Inquiry – Public Inquiry into the accidents which occurred to the Comet aircraft G-ALYP near Elba on 10 January, 1954, and to the Comet aircraft G-ALYY near Naples on 8 April, 1954.

Introduction
1 Peters A., Newman D., letter, *The Daily Telegraph*, 22 June 2002.
2 Ramsden J. M., letter, *General Aviation*, Bodmin, UK, August 2002. (available @ pprune archive).
3 Adjudication of the Broadcasting Standards Commission 11 November 2003.
4 Cherry R., The Cover-up that never was, *The Aerospace Professional*, April 2004, p14. et seq. (also in RS/1/8337, BAA).
5 Kynaston D., *Family Britain*, 2009, Bloomsbury, London, UK, p124.
6 Ramsden J. M., Wings of Change, *Aeroplane Monthly*, Cudham, UK, September 1989.
7 RS/1/8337, Lucking A. J., BAA.

Chapter 1: The people who made the Comet
1 de Havilland Sir G., *Sky Fever the autobiography of Sir Geoffrey de Havilland*, Hamish Hamilton, 1961, London, UK, p20.
2 ibid., p22
3 ibid., p30
4 ibid., p43
5 ibid., p25
6 Sharp C. M., *D H the history of de Havilland*, 1982, Airlife, Shrewsbury, UK, p19.
7 de Havilland Sir G., *Sky Fever the autobiography of Sir Geoffrey de Havilland*, Hamish Hamilton, London, UK, 1961, p52.
8 Jackson A. J., *de Havilland aircraft since 1909*, 1987, Putnam, London,UK, p31.
9 Sharp C. M., *D H the history of de Havilland*, 1982, Airlife, Shrewsbury, UK, p25.
10 ibid., p20.
11 Gunston B., *World encyclopaedia of aero engines*, 5th edition, 2006, Sutton Publishing, Stroud UK, p243.
12 Sharp C. M., *D H the history of de Havilland*, 1982, Airlife, Shrewsbury, UK, p26.
13 Jackson A. J., *de Havilland aircraft since 1909*, 1987, Puttnam, London,UK, p33.
14 ibid., p36.
15 de Havilland Sir G., *Sky Fever the autobiography of Sir Geoffrey de Havilland*, Hamish Hamilton, London, UK, 1961, p81.
16 Sharp C. M., *D H the history of de Havilland*, 1982, Airlife, Shrewsbury, UK, p38.
17 de Havilland Sir G., *Sky Fever*, Hamish Hamilton, 1961, London, UK, p90.
18 ibid., p95.
19 Sharp C. M., *D H the history of de Havilland*, 1982, Airlife, Shrewsbury, UK, p39.

20 de Havilland Sir G., *Sky Fever*, Hamish Hamilton, 1961, London, UK, p106.

21 Clark R. W., Tizard, 1965, Methuen and Co., London, UK, p224 et seq.

22 Fort A., *Prof, The Life of Frederick Lindemann*, 2003, Jonathan Cape, London, UK, p143.

23 Sharp C. M., *D H the history of de Havilland*, 1982, Airlife, Shrewsbury, UK, p91.

24 ibid., p93.

25 Taylor D. R. *Boxkite to jet – the remarkable career of Frank B. Halford*, Rolls-Royce Heritage Trust, Historical Series No. 28, 1999, Derby, UK, p86.

26 Sharp C. M., D H the history of de Havilland, 1982, Airlife, Shrewsbury, UK, p161.

27 Bulman G. P., An Account of Partnership - Industry, Government and the Aero Engine, 2002, Rolls-Royce Heritage Trust, Historical Series No. 31, Derby, UK, p219 et seq.

28 Gordon J. E., *The New Science of Strong Materials*, Penguin Books, 1968, Harmondsworth, UK, pp43, 235.

29 de Havilland Sir G., *Sky Fever*, Hamish Hamilton, 1961, London, UK, p157.

30 Ramsden J. M., R. E. Bishop de Havilland designer. An appreciation, August 1989, *Aeroplane Monthly*, Cudham, UK, p461.

31 Peters A. G., R. E. Bishop, (Obituary) *The Independent,* London, UK

32 Obituary R. E. Bishop, *The Times* (14 June 1989), London, UK.

33 Obituary R. E. Bishop, *The Daily Telegraph* (13 June 1989), London, UK

34 Sharp C. M., *D H the history of de Havilland*, 1982, Airlife, Shrewsbury, UK, p183.

35 Crowdy T., *Deceiving Hitler Double Cross and Deception in World War II*, Osprey Publishing, Oxford, UK, 2008, p99 et seq.

36 Lumsden A. S. C., *British Piston Aero-Engines and their Aircraft*, 1994, Airlife Publishing, Shrewsbury, UK, p178.

37 Postan M. M., Hay D., Scott J. D., *Design and Development of Weapons*, 1964, HMSO, London, UK, p99.

Chapter 2: The Brabazon Committee

1 RS1/946, Newman D., Notes on early Comet history, 1952, BAA.

2 Tuttle G., Sir Ralph S. Sorley, (1898-1974), *Oxford Dictionary of National Biography*, 2004-11, Oxford University Press, Oxford, UK, (on line edition, accessed 14 February 2011).

3 Lord Brabazon of Tara, *The Brabazon Story*, William Heinemann, London, UK 1956, p50.

4 ibid., p193.

5 Rose K., J. T. C. Brabazon, (1884-1964), *Oxford Dictionary of National Biography*, 2004-11, Oxford University Press, Oxford, UK, (on line edition, accessed 17 September 2013).

6 Furse A., *Wilfred Freeman. The genius behind allied survival and air supremacy 1939 to 1945*, 2000, Spellmount, Staplehurst, UK, p309.

7 Lord Brabazon of Tara, *The Brabazon Story,* William Heinemann, London, UK 1956, p205.

8 ibid., p207.

9 Phipp M., *The Brabazon Committee and British Airliners 1945-60*, 2007, Tempus Publishing, Stroud, UK, p16.

10 Colville J., *The Fringes of Power*, 2004, Weidenfeld and Nicolson, London, UK, p380.

11 Masefield P., Gunston B., *Flight Path*, 2002, Airlife, Shrewsbury, UK, Chapter 9 et seq.

12 Phipp M., *The Brabazon Committee and British Airliners 1945-60*, 2007, Tempus Publishing, Stroud, UK, p17.

13 Lords Brabazon and Sempill, Hansard, 17 November 1942, vol 125, cc 70-90.

14 Gunston B., *Fedden – the life of Sir Roy Fedden*, 1998, Rolls-Royce Heritage Trust, Historical Series No. 26, Derby, UK, p264.

15 ibid., p250 et seq.

16 AVIA 10/99, *Mission to America, the Fedden Report*, 1943, TNA

17 Gunston B., *Fedden – the life of Sir Roy Fedden*, 1998, Rolls-Royce Heritage Trust, Historical Series No 26, Derby, UK, p273.

18 ibid., p266.

19 Masefield P., Gunston B., *Flight Path*, 2002, Airlife, Shrewsbury, UK, p238 et seq.

20 ibid., p235.

21 AVIA 9/83, *The Fedden Mission to Germany*, TNA

22 Gunston B., *Fedden – the life of Sir Roy Fedden*, 1998, Rolls-Royce Heritage Trust, Historical Series No 26, Derby, UK, p288.

23 Sharp C. M., *D H the history of de Havilland*, 1982, Airlife, Shrewsbury, UK, p302.

24 AVIA 10/104, Clarkson R. M., Visit to Messerschmitt Plant at Oberammergau June 18th-25th 1945, TNA

25 Caygill P., *Sound Barrier. The rocky road to Mach 1.0+*, 2006, Pen and Sword Books, Barnsley, UK, p116.

26 DSIR 23/17962, Moakes J. K., Jones F. H., Note on accident to DE H. 108 No. 306, RAE Technical note No: structures 4, 1947, TNA

27 Caygill P., *Sound Barrier. The rocky road to Mach 1.0+*, 2006, Pen and Sword Books, Barnsley, UK, p117.

28 Rivas B., Bullen A, *John Derry, The story of Britain's first supersonic pilot*, 2008, Haynes Publishing, Yeovil, UK, p99 et seq.

29 Brown E. M., *Wings on my Sleeve,* 1978, Airlife, Shrewsbury, UK, p154 et seq.

30 ibid., p76,

31 ibid., p107 et seq.

32 Harvey-Bailey A., *Hives, The Quiet Tiger,* 1985, Rolls-Royce Heritage Trust, Historical Series No. 20, Derby, UK, p97.

33 Bray W., *The History of BOAC 1939 to 1974*, unpublished in-house history, BAA, p151.

Chapter 3: The engine

1 Beaty D., *The Story of Transatlantic Flight*, 2003, Airlife Publishing, Shrewsbury, UK, p218.

2 Hooker Sir S., *Not much of an engineer, an autobiography*, 1984, Airlife Publishing, Shrewsbury, UK, p82.

3 Lumsden A. S. C., *British Piston Aero-Engines and their Aircraft,* 1994, Airlife Publishing, Shrewsbury, UK, pp178 and 221.

4 Anderson D. F., Eberhardt S., *Understanding flight*, second edition, 2010, McGraw-Hill, New York, USA, p109 et seq.

5 Hooker Sir S., *Not much of an engineer, an autobiography,* 1984, Airlife Publishing, Shrewsbury, UK, p53 et seq.

6 Davies D. P., *Handling the Big Jets,* 1971, Civil Aviation Authority, London, UK, p15 et seq.

7 Gunston B., *The development of Jet and Turbine Aero Engines*, second edition, 1997, Patrick Stephens, Yeovil, UK, p10.

8 Various authors, *The Jet Engine*, Rolls-Royce Technical Publications, Derby, UK, 2005, p12.

9 quoted in Hamilton-Paterson J., *Empire of the Clouds*, 2010, Faber and Faber, London, UK, p58.

10 Hooker S, *Not much of an engineer*, Airlife, Shrewsbury, UK, 1984, p67.

11 Gunston B., *The development of Jet and Turbine Aero Engines*, second edition, 1997, Patrick Stephens, Yeovil, UK, p13.

12 Postan M. M., Hay D., Scott J. D., *Design and Development of Weapons Studies in*

Government and Industrial Organisation, 1964, HMSO, London, UK, p177.

13 Griffith A. A., *An aerodynamic theory of turbine design*, Report No. H.1111, July 1926, Royal Aircraft Establishment, Farnborough, UK

14 Postan M. M., Hay D., Scott J. D., *Design and Development of Weapons Studies in Government and Industrial Organisation*, 1964, HMSO, London, UK, p182.

15 *Flight International*, 2 January 1969, London, UK, p26.

16 Kay A. L., *Turbojet History and Development 1930-60*, Volume 1, 2007, The Crowood Press, Marlborough, UK, p13.

17 Whittle Sir F., *Jet, The Story of a Pioneer*, 1953, Frederick Muller, London, UK.

18 Golley J., *Genesis of the Jet, Frank Whittle and the Invention of the Jet Engine*, 1987, Airlife, Shrewsbury, UK.

19 Nahum, A., *Frank Whittle Invention of the jet,* 2004, Icon Books, Cambridge, UK.

20 Postan M. M., Hay D., Scott J. D., *Design and Development of Weapons Studies in Government and Industrial Organisation*, 1964, HMSO, London, UK

21 Bulman G. P., *An Account of Partnership - Industry, Government and the Aero Engine, The Memoirs of George Purvis Bulman*, Rolls-Royce Heritage Trust Historical Series No. 31, 2001, Derby, UK

22 Gunston B., *The development of Jet and Turbine Aero Engines*, 1997, Patrick Stephens Ltd, Yeovil, UK, p117.

23 Kay A. L., *Turbojet History and Development 1930-60*, Volume 1, 2007, The Crowood Press, Marlborough, UK, p11.

24 First James Clayton Lecture by Air Commodore F. Whittle, *Journal of Institute of Mechanical Engineers*, March 1946, p427.

25 Kay A. L., *Turbojet History and Development 1930-60*, Volume 1, 2007, The Crowood Press, Marlborough, UK, p24.

26 Whittle Sir F., *Jet, The Story of a Pioneer,* 1953, Frederick Muller, London, p32.

27 ibid., p34.

28 Bulman G. P., *An Account of Partnership - Industry, Government and the Aero Engine, The Memoirs of George Purvis Bulman*, Rolls-Royce Heritage Trust Historical Series, No. 31, 2001, Derby, UK, p309.

29 ibid., p311.

30 Gunston B., *The development of Jet and Turbine Aero Engines,* second edition, 1997, Patrick Stephens, Yeovil, UK, p123.

31 Postan M. M., Hay D., Scott J. D., *Design and Development of Weapons Studies in Government and Industrial Organisation*, HMSO, London, UK, 1964, p179.

32 Nahum, A., *Frank Whittle Invention of the jet*, 2004, Icon Books, Cambridge, UK, p30 et seq.

33 Postan M. M., Hay D., Scott J. D., *Design and Development of Weapons Studies in Government and Industrial Organisation*, HMSO, London, UK, 1964, p178.

34 ibid., p193.

35 Whittle Sir F., *Jet, The Story of a Pioneer*, 1953, Frederick Muller, London, pp75 and 102.

36 ibid., p89.

37 Kay A. L., *Turbojet History and Development 1930-60,* Volume 1, 2007, The Crowood Press, Marlborough, UK, p32.

38 Whittle Sir F., *Jet, The Story of a Pioneer*, 1953, Frederick Muller, London, p153.

39 Postan M. M., Hay D., Scott J. D., *Design and Development of Weapons Studies in Government and Industrial Organisation*, HMSO, London, UK, 1964, p214.

40 Hooker Sir S., *Not much of an engineer, an autobiography*, 1984, Airlife Publishing, Shrewsbury, UK, p74.

41 Bulman G. P., *An Account of Partnership-Industry, Government and the Aero Engine, The Memoirs of George Purvis Bulman*, Rolls-Royce Heritage Trust Historical Series No. 31, 2001, Derby, UK, p330.

42 Kay A. L., *Turbojet History and Development 1930-60*, Volume 1, 2007, The Crowood Press, Marlborough, UK, p18.

43 Hooker Sir S., *Not much of an engineer, an autobiography*, 1984, Airlife Publishing, Shrewsbury, UK, p26.

44 Golley J., *Genesis of the Jet, Frank Whittle and the Invention of the Jet Engine*, Airlife, Shrewsbury, UK, 1987, p149.

45 Furse A., *Wilfrid Freeman, The genius behind allied survival and air supremacy 1939 to 1945*, Spellmount, Staplehurst, UK, 2000, p262 et seq.

46 Postan M. M., Hay D., Scott J. D., *Design and Development of Weapons Studies in Government and Industrial Organisation*, HMSO, London, UK, 1964, p219.

47 Bulman G. P., *An Account of Partnership-Industry, Government and the Aero Engine, The Memoirs of George Purvis Bulman*, Rolls-Royce Heritage Trust Historical Series No. 31, 2001, Derby, UK, p332.

48 Hooker Sir S., *Not much of an engineer, an autobiography*, 1984, Airlife Publishing, Shrewsbury, UK, p98.

49 Postan M. M., Hay D., Scott J. D., *Design and Development of Weapons Studies in Government and Industrial Organisation*, HMSO, London, UK, 1964, p228 et seq.

50 Kay A. L., *Turbojet History and Development 1930-60*, Volume 1, 2007, The Crowood Press, Marlborough, UK, p41, et seq.

51 Whittle Sir F., *Jet, The Story of a Pioneer*, 1953, Frederick Muller, London, p286.

52 Kay A. L., *Turbojet History and Development 1930-60*, Volume 1, 2007, The Crowood Press, Marlborough, UK, p43, et seq.

53 Taylor D. R., *Boxkite to Jet – the remarkable career of Frank B. Halford*, 1999, Rolls-Royce Heritage Trust, Historical Series No. 28, Derby, UK, p110.

54 Bulman G. P., *An Account of Partnership-Industry, Government and the Aero Engine, The Memoirs of George Purvis Bulman*, Rolls-Royce Heritage Trust Historical Series No. 31, 2001, Derby, UK, p324.

55 Taylor D. R., *Boxkite to Jet – the remarkable career of Frank B. Halford*, 1999, Rolls-Royce Heritage Trust, Derby, UK, p113.

56 ibid., p114

57 Golley J., *Genesis of the Jet, Frank Whittle and the Invention of the Jet Engine*, Airlife, Shrewsbury, UK, 1987, p179.

58 Whittle Sir F., *Jet, The Story of a Pioneer*, 1953, Frederick Muller, London, p121.

59 Bulman G. P., *An Account of Partnership-Industry, Government and the Aero Engine, The Memoirs of George Purvis Bulman*, Rolls-Royce Heritage Trust Historical Series No. 31, 2001, Derby, UK, p319.

60 Taylor D. R., *Boxkite to Jet – the remarkable career of Frank B. Halford*, 1999, Rolls-Royce Heritage Trust, Historical Series No. 28, Derby, UK, p115.

61 Darling K., *De Havilland Comet*, 2005, The Crowood Press, Marlborough, UK, p20.

62 Whittle Sir F., *Jet, The Story of a Pioneer*, 1953, Frederick Muller, London, p247.

63 Taylor D. R., *Boxkite to Jet – the remarkable career of Frank B. Halford*, 1999, Rolls-Royce Heritage Trust, Historical Series No. 28, Derby, UK, p128.

64 Hooker Sir S., *Not much of an engineer, an autobiography*, 1984, Airlife Publishing, Shrewsbury, UK, p66.

65 ibid., Appendix II, p231.

66 Gunston B., *Fedden – the life of Sir Roy Fedden*, 1998, Rolls-Royce Heritage Trust, Historical Series No 26, Derby, UK, p239.

67 Kay A. L., *Turbojet History and Development 1930-60,* Volume 1, 2007, The Crowood Press, Marlborough, UK, p137 et seq.

68 ibid., 118 et seq.

69 ibid., 45 et seq.

70 ibid., 158 et seq.

71 Pugh P., *The Magic of a Name, The Rolls-Royce Story, Part II, The Power Behind the Jets*, Icon Books, Cambridge, UK, 2001, p14.

72 Darling K., *De Havilland Comet*, 2005, The Crowood Press, Marlborough, UK, p96

73 Davies D. P., *Handling the Big Jets*, 1971, Civil Aviation Authority, London, UK, p72.

74 Painter M., *The DH.106 Comet An illustrated History*, 2002, Air-Britain, Tunbridge Wells, UK, p80.

Chapter 4: Designing the airframe and its systems

1 Interim report no. 3 and final report: on the accident on 1st June 2009 to the Airbus A330-203 registered F-GZCP operated by Air France flight AF 447 Rio de Janeiro-Paris. Bureau d'Enquêtes et d'anlyses pour la sécurité de l'aviation civile, 29 July 2011 and 5 July 2012.

2 Darling K*., Hawker Typhoon, Tempest and Sea Fury*, 2003, The Crowood Press, Marlborough, UK, p22.

3 Caygill P., *Sound barrier. The rocky road to Mach 1.0+*, 2006, Pen and Sword, Barnsley, UK, p34.

4 Darling K*., Hawker Typhoon, Tempest and Sea Fury*, 2003, The Crowood Press, Marlborough, UK, p64.

5 Andrews, C. F., Morgan E. B., *Supermarine Aircraft since 1914*, 1987, Putnam, London, UK, p216.

6 Gunston B., *Faster than Sound. The story of supersonic flight*, 1992, Patrick Stephens, Yeovil, UK, p28.

7 See Gunston B., *Faster than Sound, The story of supersonic flight*, 1992, Patrick Stephens, Yeovil, UK, for a fuller discussion.

8 Caygill P., *Sound barrier. The rocky road to Mach 1.0+*, 2006, Pen and Sword, Barnsley, UK, p24.

9 Brown E., Miles M., *Gateway to supersonic flight*, 2012, Spellmount, Stroud, UK, p28 et seq.

10 Smith J. R., Kay A., *German Aircraft of the Second World War*, 1972, Putnam, London, UK, p431.

11 Gunston B., *Faster than Sound. The story of supersonic flight*, 1992, Patrick Stephens, Yeovil, UK, p61.

12 ibid., p38.

13 Smith J. R., Kay A., *German Aircraft of the Second World War*, 1972, Putnam, London, UK, p707.

14 DR11/112, Royal Aircraft Establishment Farnborough, Report on Comet Accident Investigation, Part 8, Possibility of Loss of Control, Ministry of Supply, 1954, TNA, p5.

15 Darling K, *De Havilland Comet*, 2005, The Crowood Press, Marlborough, UK, p88.

16 DR 1/39, de Havilland Aircraft Company, Type Record Volume 1 DH 106 Comet, 1951, Hatfield, UK, TNA, p9 et seq.

17 Gordon J. E., *Structures. Or why things don't fall down*, 1978, Penguin Books, London, UK, p257.

18 BT 220/118, Public Inquiry transcript, day 14, TNA, p 59.

19 AW 1/908, Comet wing fatigue, extracts from C.S.(A) meetings, BAA, p1.

20 BT 220/118, Public Inquiry transcript, day 14, TNA, p60.

21 ibid., p61.

22 Painter M., *The DH.106 Comet An illustrated History*, 2002, Air-Britain, Tunbridge Wells, UK, photograph p81 et seq.

23 Emmerson A. J., *Ageing Commuter Aeroplanes – Fatigue Evaluation and Control Methods*, International Conference on Ageing Aircraft and Structural Airworthiness, Washington, DC, USA, 1991, p368. (adsabs,havard,edu/full/1992TNASCP3160.367E, accessed 26 April 2012).

24 BT 220/118, Public Inquiry transcript, day 14, TNA, p62.

25 Type specification of the de Havilland Comet four turbojet airliner (type DH 106-10-01) for BOAC, issue No. 2 October 1951, de Havilland Aircraft Company Ltd., 1951, National Aerospace Library, Farnborough, UK.

26 Darling K, *De Havilland Comet*, 2005, The Crowood Press, Marlborough, UK, p90 et seq.

27 AVIA 6/22292, Royal Aircraft Establishment Farnborough, Report on Comet Accident Investigation, Part 2, Wreckage Investigation, 1954, Ministry of Supply, TNA, p11.

28 Gordon J. E., *Structures. Or why things don't fall down*, 1978, Penguin Books, London, UK, p336.

29 AVIA 6/22292, Royal Aircraft Establishment Farnborough, Report on Comet Accident Investigation, Part 2, Wreckage Investigation, Appendix 5, Air Conditioning and Pressurisation System G-ALYP, 1954, Ministry of Supply, TNA, p48.

30 Semmens P. W. B., Goldfinch A. J., *How steam locomotives really work*, 2000, Oxford University Press, Oxford, UK, p63.

31 Gordon J. E., *Structures. Or why things don't fall down*, 1978, Penguin Books, London, UK, p121.

32 Atkinson R. J., Winkworth W. J., Norris G. M., Behaviour of skin fatigue cracks at the corners of windows in a Comet 1 fuselage, 1962, Aeronautical Research Council Reports and Memoranda, Ministry of Aviation, HMSO, London, p1, (accessed online at <Naca.central.cranfield.ac.UK/reports/arc/rm/3248.pdf>).

33 Painter M., *The DH.106 Comet An illustrated History*, 2002, Air-Britain, Tunbridge Wells, UK, photograph p89.

34 ibid., photograph p120.

35 Dix E. H., 'ALCLAD' A new corrosion resistant aluminium product, NACA Technical Note 259, 1927, Washington, USA, (accessed on line from NASA Technical Reports Server (NTRS), 23 December 2012).

36 Alexander W., Street A., *Metals in the Service of Man*, Fifth Edition, Pelican Books, 1972, Penguin Books, Harmondsworth, UK, p190 et seq.

37 Atkinson R. J., Winkworth W. J., Norris G. M., Behaviour of skin fatigue cracks at the corners of windows in a Comet 1 fuselage, 1962, Aeronautical Research Council Reports and Memoranda, Ministry of Aviation, HMSO, London, p2, (accessed online at <Naca.central.cranfield.ac.UK/reports/arc/rm/3248.pdf>).

38 DR 1/45, Type Record for DH 106, volume 3, Structural Test Reports, Test report No. T.R. 106058 ADD 2, 08 February 49, test carried out on 02 December 1948, TNA

39 Moon Y. I., Bharatram G., Schimmels S. A., Venkayya V. B., A Vulnerability Map of a Commercial Aircraft, Structures Division, WL/FIBAD, Bldg. 45, Area B Wright Patterson AFB, Ohio 45433-7552, p4, (accessed on line <citeseerx.ist.psu.edu/viewdoc/download?doi=10.1.1.122>).

40 Principal Films, *Secret History: Comet Cover-up,* 2002, Channel Four, London, UK.

41 Cohen Lord, Farren, Sir W. S., Duncan W. J., Wheeler A. H., Report of the Court of Inquiry

into the Accidents to Comet G-ALYP on 10 January1954 and Comet G-ALYY on 8 April 1954, Ministry of Transport and Civil Aviation, 1955, HMSO, UK, p10.

42 Williams D., Strength of aeroplanes in relation to repeated loads, 1950, The Aeronautical Quarterly, The Royal Aeronautical Society, London, UK, vol 1, p291-304.

43 DR 1/45, de Havilland Aircraft Company, test report T.R. 106005 including photograph, 15 April 1947, TNA

44 DR 1/45, de Havilland Aircraft Company, Summary of tests on windscreen and cabin window panels, 09 June 52, TNA, p646.

45 BT 220/118, Public Inquiry transcript, day 14, TNA, p56.

46 Cohen Lord, Farren, Sir W. S., Duncan W. J., Wheeler A. H., Report of the Court of Inquiry into the Accidents to Comet G-ALYP on 10 January1954 and Comet G-ALYY on 8 April 1954, Ministry of Transport and Civil Aviation, 1955, HMSO, UK, p11.

47 Darling K, *De Havilland Comet*, 2005, The Crowood Press, Marlborough, UK, p23.

48 *Classic Airliner The Comet, Aeroplane*, November 2012, Kelsey Publishing Group, Cudham, UK, p18 et seq.

49 Darling K, *De Havilland Comet*, 2005, The Crowood Press, Marlborough, UK, p99.

50 Painter M., *The DH.106 Comet An illustrated History*, 2002, Air-Britain, Tunbridge Wells, UK, p9

51 Ziegler P, *Edward Heath,* 2010, Harper Press, London, UK, p54.

52 Walker T, *The First Jet Airliner: The Story of the De Havilland Comet*, Scoval Publishing, Newcastle upon Tyne, UK, 1999, p171 et seq.

53 Cocroft W. D., Thomas R. J. C. ed., Barnwell P. S., *Cold War Building for Nuclear Confrontation 1946-89*, 2003, English Heritage, Swindon, UK, p28.

Chapter 5: The Comet prototype takes shape

1 Painter M., *The DH.106 Comet An illustrated History*, 2002, Air-Britain, Tunbridge Wells, UK, photograph p75.

2 Principal Films, *Secret History: Comet Cover-up,* 2002, Channel Four, London, UK.

3 Skinner S., *British Airliner Prototypes since 1945*, 2008, Midland Publishing, Hinckley, UK, p21.

4 Holmes, H., *Avro The History of an Aircraft Company,* 2004, The Crowood Press, Marlborough, UK, p146.

5 Phipp M., *The Brabazon Committee and British Airliners 1945-60*, 2007, Tempus Publishing, Stroud, UK, p93.

6 Rawnsley C. F., Wright R., *Night Fighter*, 1957, London, UK.

7 Ramsden J. M., Wings of Change, August 1989, *Aeroplane Monthly*, Cudham, UK, p456.

8 Painter M., *The DH. 106 Comet An Illustrated History*, 2002, Air-Britain (Historians), Tunbridge Wells, UK, p77. (Painter says the Comet covered the 2,980 mile flight in 3 hours 23 minutes but presumably this was the time for one leg.)

9 Golley J., *John 'Cats-Eyes' Cunningham The Aviation Legend*, 1999, Airlife Publishing, Shrewsbury, UK, p203.

10 Painter M, *The DH. 106 Comet An Illustrated History*, 2002, Air-Britain (Historians), Tunbridge Wells, UK, p78.

11 ibid., p80.

12 ibid., p81.

13 ibid., p82

14 ibid., p83.

15 ibid., p83 et seq

Chapter 6: The production aircraft

1 de Havilland Sir Geoffrey, Sky Fever. The Autobiography of Sir Geoffrey de Havilland, 1961, Hamish Hamilton, London, UK, p177.

2 Povey H, Planning and Production Methods used in the Construction of the de Havilland Comet, 1951 (August), *de Haviland Gazette*, Supplement to No. 64, Hatfield, UK, p21 et seq.

3 Darling K, *De Havilland Comet*, 2005, The Crowood Press, Marlborough, UK, p24.

4 Povey H, Planning and Production Methods used in the Construction of the de Havilland Comet, 1951 (August), *de Haviland Gazette*, Supplement to No. 64, Hatfield, UK, p36.

5 ibid., p3, et seq.

6 ibid., p4, et seq.

7 ibid., p5.

8 ibid., p12.

9 ibid., p13 et seq.

10 DR 1/40, DH 106 Comet Type Record Volume 2, drawing dated April 1952, TNA, p477.

11 Povey H, Planning and Production Methods used in the Construction of the de Havilland Comet, 1951 (August), *de Haviland Gazette*, Supplement to No. 64, Hatfield, UK, p16.

12 ibid., p17 et seq.

13 ibid., p25.

14 ibid., p32.

Chapter 7: The airline the Comet would join

1 Penrose H, *Wings across the world. An Illustrated History of British Airways*, 1980, Cassell, London, UK, p107 et seq.

2 ibid., p109.

3 Robbins K., Lister, Philip Cunliffe, first earl of Swinton (1884-1972), *Oxford Dictionary of National Biography*, 2004-11, Oxford University Press, Oxford, UK, (on line edition, accessed 14 February 2011).

4 Furse A, *Wilfred Freeman, The genius behind Allied survival and air supremacy 1939 to 1945*, 1999, Spellmount, Staplehurst, UK, p80.

5 ibid., p103.

6 Bulman G. P., *An Account of Partnership - Industry, Government and the Aero Engine, The Memoirs of George Purvis Bulman*, Rolls-Royce Heritage Trust Historical Series No. 31, 2001, Derby, UK, p258.

7 Amery L. S., *My Political Life, Volume 3 The Unforgiving Years 1929-40*, 1955, Hutchinson, London, UK, p330.

8 Peden, G. C., Wood, Sir (Howard) Kingsley (1881-1943), *Dictionary of National Biography*, 2004-11, Oxford University Press, Oxford, UK, (on line edition, accessed 14 February 2011).

9 Penrose H, *Wings across the world. An Illustrated History of British Airways,* 1980, Cassell, London, UK, p103.

10 ibid., p110.

11 ibid., p116.

12 Bray W, *The History of BOAC 1939 to 1974,* unpublished in-house history, BAA, p1.

13 Penrose H, *Wings across the world. An Illustrated History of British Airways*, 1980, Cassell, London, UK, p111.

14 Bray W, *The History of BOAC 1939 to 1974*, unpublished in-house history, BAA, p9.

15 ibid., p15.

16 ibid., p13.

17 ibid., p14.

18 Penrose H, *Wings across the world. An Illustrated History of British Airways,* 1980, Cassell, London UK, p122.

19 Mcintyre I, Reith, John Charles Walsham, first Baron Reith (1889-1971) the first director-general of the BBC, 2004-11, *Oxford Dictionary of National Biography*, Oxford, UK, p7, (on line edition, accessed 21 April 2011,)

20 ibid., p9 et seq.

21 Bray W, The History of BOAC 1939 to 1974, unpublished in-house history, BAA, p4.

22 Penrose H, *Wings across the world. An Illustrated History of British Airways*, 1980, Cassell, London, UK, p105 et seq.

23 Beaty D., *The Story of Transatlantic Flight*, 2003, Airlife Publishing, Shrewsbury, UK, p133.

24 ibid., p145.

25 ibid., p235 et seq.

26 Cassidy B., *Flying Empires Short 'C' class Empire flying boats*, 2004, Queens Parade Press, Bath, UK, p207. (accessed on line 'Flying Empires', 26 April 2011).

27 Beaty D., *The Story of Transatlantic Flight,* Airlife, 2003, Shrewsbury, UK, p145.

28 ibid., p135.

29 Penrose H, *Wings across the world. An Illustrated History of British Airways*, 1980, Cassell, London, UK, p117.

30 Bray W, *The History of BOAC 1939 to 1974*, unpublished in-house history, BAA, p21.

31 Penrose H, *Wings across the world. An Illustrated History of British Airways*, 1980, Cassell, London, UK, p125.

32 Bray W, *The History of BOAC 1939 to 1974*, unpublished in-house history, BAA, p18.

33 ibid., p27.

34 Penrose H, *Wings across the world. An Illustrated History of British Airways*, 1980, Cassell, London, UK, p127.

35 Coster G, *Corsairville*, 2000, Viking, London, UK.

36 Taylor A. J. P., *Beaverbrook*, 1972, Hamish Hamilton, London, UK, p428 et seq.

37 Penrose H, *Wings across the world. An Illustrated History of British Airways,* 1980, Cassell, London, UK, p128.

38 Bray W, *The History of BOAC 1939 to 1974*, unpublished in-house history, BAA, p25.

39 ibid., p30.

40 Penrose H, *Wings across the world. An Illustrated History of British Airways*, 1980, Cassell, London, UK, p130.

41 Bray W, *The History of BOAC 1939 to 1974*, unpublished in-house history, BAA, p27.

42 Penrose H, *Wings across the world. An Illustrated History of British Airways*, 1980, Cassell, London, UK, p131.

43 Moran, Lord, *Winston Churchill The Struggle for Survival 1940-65*, 1966, Constable, London, UK, p78.

44 Bray W, *The History of BOAC 1939 to 1974*, unpublished in-house history, BAA, p28.

45 Churchill W. S., *The Second World War Volume 3, The Grand Alliance*, 1950, Cassel, London, UK, p568 (in Folio Edition 2002).

46 Moran Lord, *Winston Churchill The Struggle for Survival 1940-65*, 1966, Constable, London, UK, p23.

47 Beaty D., *The Story of Transatlantic Flight*, 2003, Airlife Publishing, Shrewsbury, UK, p160 et seq.

48 Bray W, *The History of BOAC 1939 to 1974*, unpublished in-house history, BAA, p36.

49 Penrose H, *Wings across the world. An Illustrated History of British Airways,* 1980, Cassell,

London, UK, p135 et seq.

50 Bray W, *The History of BOAC 1939 to 1974*, unpublished in-house history, BAA, p41.

51 Penrose H, *Wings across the world. An Illustrated History of British Airways*, 1980, Cassell, London, UK, p137.

52 *Bray W, The History of BOAC 1939 to 1974*, unpublished in-house history, BAA, p65.

53 ibid., p67.

54 ibid., p69.

55 Penrose H, *Wings across the world. An Illustrated History of British Airways*, 1980, Cassell, London, UK, p141.

56 ibid., p144.

57 Bray W, *The History of BOAC 1939 to 1974*, unpublished in-house history, BAA, p78.

58 ibid., p119 et seq.

59 Penrose H, *Wings across the world. An Illustrated History of British Airways*, 1980, Cassell, London, UK, p148.

60 Phipp M, *The Brabazon Committee and British Airliners 1945-60*, 2007, Tempus Publishing, Stroud, UK, p37.

61 Penrose H, *Wings across the world. An Illustrated History of British Airways*, 1980, Cassell, London, UK, p156.

62 Bray W, *The History of BOAC 1939 to 1974*, unpublished in-house history, BAA, p77.

63 Penrose H, *Wings across the world. An Illustrated History of British Airways*, 1980, Cassell, London, UK, p157.

64 Bramson A, *Master Airman, a Biography of Air Vice-Marshall Donald Bennet*, 1985, Airlife, Shrewsbury, UK, p127.

65 Penrose H, *Wings across the world. An Illustrated History of British Airways*, 1980, Cassell, London, UK, p159.

66 Phipp M., *The Brabazon Committee and British Airliners 1945-60*, 2007, Tempus, Stroud, UK, p65.

67 Beaty D., *The Story of Transatlantic Flight*, 2003, Airlife Publishing, Shrewsbury, UK, p218.

68 Penrose H, *Wings across the world. An Illustrated History of British Airways*, 1980, Cassell, London, UK, p166 et seq.

69 ibid., p169.

70 ibid., p168.

71 Phipp M, *The Brabazon Committee and British Airliners 1945-60,* 2007, Tempus Publishing, Stroud, UK, p53.

72 Bray W, The History of BOAC 1939 to 1974, unpublished in-house history, BAA, p208.

Chapter 8: Introduction into service

The best and most comprehensive account of the histories of individual Comets of all marks is in Martin Painter's excellent book on which this chapter draws heavily. The references that follow are just to allow the appropriate page to be found easily.

1 Painter M., *The DH. 106 Comet An illustrated History*, 2002, Air-Britain (Historians), Tunbridge Wells, UK, p87 et seq.

2 ibid., p40.

3 Davies R. E. G. Birtles P. J., *De Havilland Comet The World's First Jet Airliner*, 1999, Paladwr Press, McLean, Virginia, USA, p22.

4 *Flight Magazine*, Jet Air-routes, 01 May 1953, London, UK, p547.

5 Painter M., *The DH. 106 Comet An illustrated History*, 2002, Air-Britain, Tunbridge Wells, UK, p92 et seq.

6 ibid., p95 et seq.

7 ibid., p97 et seq.

8 ibid., p99 et seq.

9 ibid., p105 et seq.

10 ibid., p106 et seq.

11 ibid., p110 et seq.

12 ibid., p111 et seq.

13 ibid., p113 et seq.

14 ibid., p15

15 ibid., p116 et seq.

16 AVIA 6/22292, Royal Aircraft Establishment Farnborough, Report on Comet Accident Investigation, Part 10, Flight investigation on Comet G-ATNAV, TNA, p3 et seq.

17 Painter M., *The DH. 106 Comet An illustrated History*, 2002, Air-Britain (Historians), Tunbridge Wells, UK, p121 et seq.

18 ibid., p123 et seq.

19 ibid., p124 et seq.

20 ibid., p129.

21 ibid., p130 et seq.

22 ibid., p133 et seq.

23 ibid., p135 et seq.

24 ibid., p125 et seq.

25 ibid., p127 et seq.

Chapter 9: Passengers and crew

1 Beaty D, *The Naked Pilot The Human Factor in Aircraft Accidents*, 1995, Airlife Publishing, Shrewsbury, UK, p110 et seq.

2 P. R. W. D., Conversion to Comets, 1953 (1 May), *Flight Magazine*, London, UK, p535 et seq.

3 Principal Films, *Secret History: Comet Cover-up*, 2002, Chanel Four, London, UK

4 Davies D. P., *Handling the Big Jets*, 1971, Civil Aviation Authority, London, UK, p56 et seq.

5 RS 1/946, Campbell Orde A. C., *The introduction of the Comet into service*, BAA, p7 et seq.

6 Davies D. P., *Handling the Big Jets*, 1971, Civil Aviation Authority, London, UK, p83 et seq.

7 Bibel G., *Beyond the Black Box,* The Johns Hopkins University Press, Baltimore , USA, 2008, p134.

8 ibid., p140.

9 Davies D. P., *Handling the Big Jets*, 1971, Civil Aviation Authority, London, UK, p161 et seq.

10 Windebank K., personal communication about his father A. E. Windebank.

11 Anon, How Good is Good, 1952 (16 May), *Flight Magazine*, London, UK, p608 et seq.

12 Painter M., *The DH. 106 Comet An illustrated History*, 2002, Air-Britain (Historians), Tunbridge Wells, UK, p40.

13 *Flight Magazine,* 1953 (1 May), London, UK, p547.

14 M.A.S. Passenger's Point of View, 1952 (25 April), *Flight Magazine*, London, UK, p503 et seq.

15 C.B.B-W., Flight in the Comet, 1952, *Flight Magazine*, London, UK, p174.

16 H.A.T., Passenger Impressions in the Comet, 1952 (22 February), *The Aeroplane*, London, UK, p209 et seq.

Chapter 10: The crashes begin

1 BT 220/55, Report No. CA.147, DH. Comet 1 G-ALYZ, Ciampino Airport, Rome, 26 October 1952, Accidents Investigation Branch, Ministry of Civil Aviation, 1952, HMSO, London, TNA

2 AW/1/2430, BOAC Inquiry, Interrogation of FO Josling, 12 November 1952, BAA.

3 AW/1/2430 *The Daily Telegraph*, London, 27 October 1952, BAA.

4 AW/1/2430 *The Daily Telegraph*, London, 28 October 1952, BAA.

5 AW/1/2430 *Daily Express*, London, 5 November 1952, BAA.

6 AW/1/2430, BOAC Inquiry, Comet G-ALYZ Rome, 26 October 1952, Report of the Independent Committee of Inquiry, p10, Extract from statement of Mr E. T. Kelly, 29 October 1952, BAA.

7 BT 220/56, letter, P. G. Tweedie to Mr. Follows, secretary of BALPA, 26 January 1954, TNA.

8 BT 220/56, Accident at Rome, The response to the BALPA case, 1 April 1954, TNA, p15.

9 BT 220/56, Appendix A to BALPA case, Comet Flying Training Notes in force at the time of the Rome accident, TNA

10 Beaty D., *Cone of Silence*, 1959, Martin Secker and Warburg, London, UK,

11 AW/1/2430, BOAC Committee of Inquiry, Accident of Comet G-ALYZ, Rome, 26 October 1952, p3, BAA,

12 BT 220/56, Appendix C to BALPA case, BOAC Memorandum, takeoff technique in Comet aircraft, Rodley E., Fleet Manager Comets, circulated 26 to 31 October 1952, TNA.

13 AW/1/2430, BOAC Inquiry, Accident of Comet G-ALYZ, Rome, 26 October 1952, BAA, p4.

14 Golley J, *John 'Cats-eyes' Cunningham, the aviation legend*, Airlife, Shrewsbury, UK, p157.

15 Classic Airliner The Comet, *Aeroplane,* November 2012, Kelsey Publishing Group, Cudham, UK, p45.

16 BT 220/56, Statement by ARB, 'Comet' take off accidents 9 December 1953, appendix B to the first BALPA case submission, TNA.

17 Beaty D., *The Naked Pilot. The Human factor in Aircraft Accidents*, 1995, Airlife, Shrewsbury, UK, p155.

18 BT 220/67, letter, J E Scott, Hawker Siddeley Aviation, to Mr. Keith, Canadian Pacific Airlines, 30 March 1971, TNA

19 BT 220/69 Keel J. E. Memo to Permanent Secretary, 24 March 1953, TNA

20 BT 220/69, Pakistan Government Order Instituting the Inquiry into the crash of Comet CF-CUN, 4 March 1953, Appendix 23, Evidence of Group Captain J Cunningham, TNA, p6.

21 BT 220/69, Pakistan Government Order Instituting the inquiry into the crash of Comet CF-CUN, 4 March 1953, Section 14 Discussion of evidence, TNA, p2.

22 BT 220/69, Pakistan Government Order Instituting the Inquiry into the crash of Comet CF-CUN, 4 March 1953, Appendix 23, Evidence of Group Captain J Cunningham, TNA, p1,

23 BT 220/69, Pakistan Government Order Instituting the Inquiry into the crash of Comet CF-CUN, 4 March 1953, section 15, findings, TNA, p22.

24 Classic Airliner The Comet, *Aeroplane*, November 2012, Kelsey Publishing Group, Cudham, UK, p60.

25 Golley J, *John 'Cats-eyes' Cunningham, the aviation legend*, Airlife, Shrewsbury, UK, p158.

26 BT 220/67, letter from Nelson to Tweedie, 15 March 1953, TNA,

27 BT 220/67, D.H. Aero Dept/1179/DRN/106, 6 May 1953, TNA.

28 BT 220/56, Appendix B, 'Comet' take off accidents, Statement by the Air Registration Board, TNA.

29 Gunston B., *Nimrod the Centenarian aircraft*, 2009, Spellmount, Stround, UK, p42.

30 BT 220/67 Notes of a meeting to discuss angle of incidence indicator, 9 March 1953, TNA.

31 RS/1/8116, Notes of a meeting held at de Havillands between Bishop and BOAC representatives on 31 August 1953, BAA.

32 BT 256/4, Air Safety Board, Its Activities and Recommendations November 1946 to March
1954, item 51, Comet Aircraft - Take Off technique and Angle of Incidence, TNA.

33 RS/1/8116, letters, BAA.

34 Vaughan D., *The Challenger Launch decision,* 1996, The University of Chicago Press,
Chicago, USA, p38.

35 BT 220/56, letter from BALPA to Sir G. Jenkins, 8 January 54, TNA.

36 BT 220/56 Accident to Comet G-ALYZ Rome 26 October 1952, The case for reinvestigation,
presented by the British Air Line Pilots Association on behalf of Captain R. E. H. Foote, TNA.

37 BT 220/56 Majendie A. M. A., Comments on 'The case for reinvestigation', presented by the
British Air Line Pilots Association on behalf of Captain R. E. H. Foote, 23 February 1954,
TNA.

38 BT 220/56 letter from P. G. Tweedie CIA to BALPA, 26 May 1954, TNA.

39 BT 220/67 Joint IFALPA/de Havilland statement re accident to Comet 1A at Karachi 3 March
1953, TNA.

40 Principal Films, *Secret History: Comet Cover-up,* 2002, Channel Four, London, UK.

Chapter 11: Entebbe, Dakar and Calcutta

1 BT 218/31, Directorate of Civil Aviation East Africa, Accident report No.1, 1953, TNA.

2 BT 218/31, Directorate of Civil Aviation East Africa, Accident report No.1, 1953, Appendix
B, TNA.

3 BT 218/31, Directorate of Civil Aviation East Africa, Accident report No.1, 1953, Appendix
J, TNA.

4 AW/1/2428, BOAC Committee of Inquiry, 10 February 1953, BAA.

5 Painter M., *The DH. 106 Comet An illustrated History*, 2002, Air-Britain, Tunbridge Wells,
UK, p129.

6 Report of the Court Investigation on the Accident to COMET G-ALYV on 2 May 1953,
HMSO, London, UK, (copy of an Indian document, it can be accessed on the Federal Aviation
Administration's website).

7 BT 220/73 witness statement of Murari Mohon Roy, 15 May 1953, TNA.

8 BT 220/73 witness statement of Chandra Bidu Singh Ray, 15 May 1953, TNA.

9 Nelson T. R. Falling Stars, *Aeroplane Monthly*, Cudham, UK, October 1993, p18.

10 BT 220/73 witness statement of Captain C. J. Vlotman 15 May 1953, 23 May 1953, TNA.

11 Principal Films, *Secret History: Comet Cover-up*, 2002, Channel Four, London, UK.

12 Painter M., *The DH. 106 Comet An illustrated History*, 2002, Air-Britain, Tunbridge Wells,
UK, p106.

13 BT 220/73 Walker P. B., Ripley E. L., RAE First Summary Report on the accident to Comet
G-ALYV near Calcutta on 2 May 1953, TNA.

14 Darling K, *De Havilland Comet*, The Crowood Press, Marlborough UK, 2005, p68.

15 Gordon J. E., *Structures or why things don't fall down*, 1978, Penguin Books, London, UK,
p223 et seq.

Chapter 12: Disaster off Elba

1 Cohen, Lord, Farren W. S., Duncan W. J., Wheeler A. H., Report of the Court of Inquiry into
the Accidents to Comet G-ALYP on 10 January 1954 and Comet G-ALYY on 8 April 1954,

1955, HMSO, London, UK, p11.

2 Waterton W. A., Hewat T., *The Comet Riddle,* 1955, Frederick Muller, London, UK, p10.

3 Cohen, Lord, Farren W. S., Duncan W. J., Wheeler A. H., Report of the Court of Inquiry into the Accidents to Comet G-ALYP on 10 January 1954 and Comet G-ALYY on 8 April 1954, 1955, HMSO, London, UK, p13.

4 ibid., p14.

5 ibid., p12.

6 BT 220/96, witness statements, TNA.

7 BT 220/106, Day 2, Public Inquiry, transcript, TNA, p66 et seq.

8 BT 220/92, letter from Captain Brown to Inspector of Accidents and Search and Rescue Form R, TNA.

9 BT 220/92, Lombardi's statement 16 January 1954, TNA, p8.

10 PREM 11/802, TNA.

11 Nelson T.R., Falling Stars, *Aeroplane Monthly*, Cudham, UK, November 1993, p20 et seq.

12 ibid., p22.

13 ADM 116/6006, Salvage operations on Comet airliner G-ALYP which crashed off Elba, TNA.

14 BT 220/92, letter from Captain Brown to BOAC Operations Director, 11 January 1954, TNA.

15 ADM 116/6006, Salvage operations on Comet airliner G-ALYP which crashed off Elba, TNA, p39.

16 BT 220/107, Day 3, Public Inquiry, transcript, p11 et seq., TNA.

17 ibid., p17.

18 BT 220/96, Fornari's statement, TNA.

19 BT 220/101, Whittingham H. E., Stewart W. K., Medical report on the crash of Comet G-ALYP near Elba on 10 January 1954, 21 January 1954, TNA.

20 Penrose H, *Wings across the world. An Illustrated History of British Airways*, 1980, Cassell, London, UK, p103.

21 Masefield Sir P., Gunston B., *Flight Path,* 2002, Airlife, Shrewsbuy, UK, p70.

22 BT 220/101, letter from Brabazon to Lennox-Boyd dated 20 November 1954, TNA.

23 BT 220/101, Teare D., letter from Teare to Tweedie 05 March 1954, TNA.

24 Roth E. M., Rapid (explosive) decompression emergencies in pressure-suited subjects, The Lovelace Foundation, Natiomal Aeronautics and Space Administration, November 1968. (accessed 06 March 2012).

25 Segal E, Pizov R., Pulmonary complications of blast injury, PCCSU Article, 11 January 2007, The American College of Chest Physicians (accessed 06 March 2012).

26 RS/1/8337, Ramsden, Adjudication on the complaints made to the Broadcasting Standards Commission about the Channel Four 2 Comet Cover-up programme broadcast on 13 June 2002, reported by Ramsden, BAA, p6.

27 RS/1/8113, Memorandum from (BOAC) Passenger Relations Officer, Airways Terminal to Sales and Revenue Accountant, Brentford, dated 26 February 1954, BAA.

28 RS/1/8116, memo re cable from New York, dated 30 December 1954, BAA.

29 Principal Films, *Secret History: Comet Cover-up*, 2002, Channel Four, London, UK.

Chapter 13: The decision to resume flying

1 BT 220/110, Day 6, Public Inquiry, transcript, TNA, p67.

2 BT220/101, draft letter to Sir Miles Thomas, TNA.

3 BT220/110, Day 6, Public Inquiry, transcript, TNA, p68.

4 ibid., p68 et seq.

5 ibid., p70 et seq.

6 ibid., p72.

7 ibid., p73.

8 BT220/111, Day 7, Public Inquiry, transcript, TNA, p4.

9 ibid., p5.

10 ibid., p34.

11 ibid., p41.

12 BT 248/78, letter from Sir Miles Thomas to the Rt. Hon. A. T. Lennox-Boyd, 19 February 1954, TNA.

13 BT 248/78, letter from Lord Brabazon to A Lennox-Boyd, 24 February 1954, TNA.

14 BT 220/113, Day 9, Public Inquiry etc., transcript, TNA, p49.

15 BT 220/110, Day 6, Public Inquiry etc., transcript, TNA, p11 et seq.

16 BT 256/3, Minutes of the 60th meeting of the ASB, 2 March 1954, TNA.

17 BT 256/3, Minutes of the 60th meeting of the ASB, 2 March 1954, Appendix, TNA.

18 BT 220/109, Day 5 Public Inquiry etc., transcript, TNA, p19.

19 Principal Films, *Secret History: Comet Cover-up*, 2002, Channel Four, London, UK.

Chapter 14: The final disaster

1 Cohen, Lord, Farren W. S., Duncan W. J., Wheeler A. H., Report of the Court of Inquiry into the Accidents to Comet G-ALYP on 10 January 1954 and Comet G-ALYY on 8 April 1954, 1955, HMSO, London, UK, p44.

2 ibid., p44 et seq.

3 BT 220/108, Day 4 Public Inquiry etc., transcript, TNA, p54.

4 Cohen, Lord, Farren W. S., Duncan W. J., Wheeler A. H., Report of the Court of Inquiry into the Accidents to Comet G-ALYP on 10 January 1954 and Comet G-ALYY on 8 April 1954, 1955, HMSO, London, UK, p46.

5 BT 220/148 RN accounts of search, TNA.

6 TS 52/111, Reports on post-mortem examinations by Dr. Donald Teare on four of the five bodies recovered (from G-ALYY), TNA.

7 BT 220/148, reply to telegram from Piccard, TNA.

8 Moran Lord, *Winston Churchill The Struggle for Survival 1940-65*, 1966, Constable, London, UK, p542.

Chapter 15: The Royal Aircraft Establishment investigation starts

(The RAE report on the Comet crashes is included in several TNA files although not all of them are complete. AVIA 6/22292 does not mention part 12 on its contents page, AVIA 6/17623 mentions part 12 on its contents page but says that it is closed for 75 years but DR 11/112 contains part 12. AVIA 6/22292 omits the account of the decompression of the model cabin from part 11 but this is included in AVIA 6/17623. This file number has been used for the references below except for Part 12.)

1 Golley J, *Genesis of the Jet*, 1996, Airlife, Shrewsbury, UK, p76.

2 Masefield P. G., Hall, Sir Arnold Alexander (1915 to 2000), *Oxford Dictionary of National Biography*, Oxford University Press, Oxford, accessed 07 January 2012.

3 BT 220/108, Day 4, Public Inquiry, transcript, TNA, p41.

4 AVIA 13/1362, letter from Sir Miles Thomas to Sir Arnold Hall, 14 April 1954, TNA

5 DR 11/112, RAF Institute of Aviation Medicine, RAE Report on Comet Accident Investigation, Part 12, Note on the Medical aspects, 1954, TNA

6 AVIA 6/17623, RAE Report on Comet Accident Investigation, Part 11, Miscellaneous

Investigations, 1954, TNA, p17 et seq.

7 AVIA 13/1205, Note from Chemistry Department, Comet Accident Investigation, TNA, p4 et seq.

8 AVIA 6/17623, RAE Report on Comet Accident Investigation, Part 11, Miscellaneous Investigations, 1954, TNA, fig. 2.

9 DR 11/112, RAF Institute of Aviation Medicine, RAE Report on Comet Accident Investigation, Part 12, Note on the Medical aspects, 1954, TNA, p4.

10 ibid., p5.

11 AVIA 6/17623, RAE Report on Comet Accident Investigation, Part 11, Miscellaneous Investigations, 1954, TNA, p7 et seq.

Chapter 16: Examination of the wreckage

1 AVIA 6/17623, RAE Report on Comet Accident Investigation, Part 2, Wreckage investigation, Appendix 1, 1954, TNA, figs 46 and 47.

2 AVIA 6/17623, RAE Report on Comet Accident Investigation, Part 2, Wreckage investigation, 1954, TNA.

3 ibid., p5 et seq.

4 AVIA 6/17623, RAE Report on Comet Accident Investigation, Part 2, Wreckage investigation, Appendix 1, 1954, TNA, fig 2.

5 AVIA 6/17623, RAE Report on Comet Accident Investigation, Part 2, Wreckage investigation, 1954, TNA, p6.

6 BT 220/96, witness statements of Francesco Sano and Vasco Normellini, TNA

7 AVIA 6/17623, RAE Report on Comet Accident Investigation, Part 2, Wreckage investigation, 1954, TNA, p6 et seq.

8 AVIA 6/17623, RAE Report on Comet Accident Investigation, Part 2, Wreckage investigation, 1954, Appendix 1, 1954, TNA, p17.

9 AVIA 6/17623, RAE Report on Comet Accident Investigation, Part 2, Wreckage investigation, 1954, TNA, fig 5.

10 AVIA 6/17623, RAE Report on Comet Accident Investigation, Part 2, Wreckage investigation, 1954, Appendix 1, 1954, TNA, p18.

11 ibid., p16.

12 AVIA 6/17623, RAE Report on Comet Accident Investigation, Part 2, Wreckage investigation, 1954, TNA, p7.

13 AVIA 6/17623, RAE Report on Comet Accident Investigation, Part 2, Wreckage investigation, Appendix 1, 1954, TNA, p20.

14 ibid., fig 62.

15 ibid., p21.

16 AVIA 6/17623, RAE Report on Comet Accident Investigation, Part 2, Wreckage investigation, 1954, TNA, p9.

17 AVIA 6/17623, RAE Report on Comet Accident Investigation, Part 2, Wreckage investigation, Appendix 2, 1954, TNA, p26 et seq.

18 AVIA 6/17623, RAE Report on Comet Accident Investigation, Part 2, Wreckage investigation, Appendix 8, 1954, TNA, p65 et seq.

19 AVIA 6/17623, RAE Report on Comet Accident Investigation, Part 2, Wreckage investigation, Appendix 10, 1954, TNA, p82 et seq.

20 AVIA 6/17623, RAE Report on Comet Accident Investigation, Part 2, Wreckage investigation, Appendix 3, 1954, TNA, p29 et seq.

21 AVIA 6/17623, RAE Report on Comet Accident Investigation, Part 2, Wreckage investiga-

tion, Appendix 4, 1954, TNA, p44 et seq.

22 AVIA 6/17623, RAE Report on Comet Accident Investigation, Part 2, Wreckage investigation, Appendix 5, 1954, TNA, p48 et seq.

23 AVIA 6/17623, RAE Report on Comet Accident Investigation, Part 7, Possibility of excessive pressure in the cabin and fuel tanks, Appendix 4, 1954, TNA, p14 et seq.

24 AVIA 6/17623, RAE Report on Comet Accident Investigation, Part 2, Wreckage investigation, Appendix 6, 1954, TNA, p51 et seq.

25 Comet Accident Investigation Farnborough, 1954, Documentary Film Unit RAE Farnborough.

26 AVIA 6/17623, RAE Report on Comet Accident Investigation, Part 9, Free flight tests of dynamic models, Appendix 6, 1954, TNA, p4 et seq.

27 BT 220/84, de Havillands' report on YP's engines, TNA.

28 BT 220/83, Comet/Ghost hub shaft fatigue tests, de Havillands, 1954, TNA.

29 AVIA 6/17623, Report on Comet Accident Investigation, Part 11, Miscellaneous investigations, 1954, TNA, p3 et seq.

Chapter 17: The investigation continues

1 AVIA 6/17623, RAE Report on Comet Accident Investigation, Part 4, Fatigue tests on the tailplane, 1954, TNA

2 Gordon J. E., *Structures or why things don't fall down*, 1978, Penguin Books, London, UK, p71.

3 Taylor J., Design and Use of Counting Accelerometers, Aeronautical Research Council Reports and Memoranda No. 2812, HMSO, London, UK, 1954.

4 AVIA 6/17623, RAE Report on Comet Accident Investigation, Part 5, Static strength tests of the tail unit, 1954, TNA

5 AVIA 6/17623, RAE Report on Comet Accident Investigation, Part 6, Damage to outer wing tanks during refuelling, 1954, TNA

6 AVIA 6/17623, RAE Report on Comet Accident Investigation, Part 6, Damage to outer wing tanks during refuelling, Appendix 8, 1954, TNA

7 AVIA 6/17623, RAE Report on Comet Accident Investigation, Part 7, Possibility of excessive pressure in the cabin and fuel tanks, 1954, TNA

8 AVIA 6/17623, RAE Report on Comet Accident Investigation, Part 8, Possibility of loss of control, 1954, TNA

9 AVIA 6/17623, RAE Report on Comet Accident Investigation, Part 10, Flight investigations on Comet G-ATNAV, 1954, TNA

10 Quoted in Gordon J. E., *Structures, or why things don't fall down*, 1978, Penguin Books, London, p55.

Chapter 18: Fatigue testing of the fuselage and wings

1 Walker P. B., The Experimental Approach to aircraft Structural Research, The Fifteenth Wright Brothers Lecture, 1952, Journal of the Aeronautical Sciences, Vol 19, No. 5., p11 and Fig 19. Accessed on line 07 January 2013.

2 RS/1/ 8116, various letters August to October 1951, BAA.

3 BT 220/145, Memorandum from Walker to Tweedie dated 15 April 1954, TNA.

4 Walker P. B. Destructive energy in aircraft pressure cabins, Journal of the Royal Aeronautical Society, Vol. 54, April 1950.

5 Walker P. B., Pressure-cabin Fatigue: A Survey of the Problem and the Test Methods

Developed at RAE, 1956, *Aircraft Engineering*, Vol. 28 Iss: 1, p15.

6 AVIA 6/17623, RAE Report on Comet Accident Investigation, Part 3, Fatigue tests on the pressure cabin and wings, 1954, TNA

7 Walker P. B., Pressure-cabin Fatigue: A Survey of the Problem and the Test Methods Developed at RAE, 1956, *Aircraft Engineering,* Vol. 28 Iss: 1, p14 et seq.

8 Walker P. B., Estimation of the fatigue life of a transport aircraft, Journal of the Royal Aeronautical Society No., 514, Vol. 57, October 1953.

9 AVIA 6/17623, RAE Report on Comet Accident Investigation, Part 3, Fatigue tests on the pressure cabin and wings, Appendix 1, 1954, TNA, p12.

10 ibid., p13.

11 ibid., p15.

12 ibid., fig. 6.

13 de Havilland Sir G., *Sky Fever*, 1961 Hamish Hamilton, London, UK, p183.

14 Cohen, Lord, Farren W. S., Duncan W. J., Wheeler A. H., Report of the Court of Inquiry into the Accidents to Comet G-ALYP on 10 January 1954 and Comet G-ALYY on 8 April 1954, 1955, HMSO, London, UK, p18.

15 AVIA 6/17623, RAE Report on Comet Accident Investigation, Part 3, Fatigue tests on the pressure cabin and wings, 1954, TNA, p6.

16 AVIA 6/17623, RAE Report on Comet Accident Investigation, Part 3, Fatigue tests on the pressure cabin and wings, Appendix 1, 1954, TNA, p16 et seq.

17 AW 1/ 908 letter from MoS (L. Caygill) to BOAC dated 13 November 1951, BAA.

18 AW 1/908 BOAC internal memo from T. D. R. Carroll, 16 November 1953, BAA.

19 BT 220/93, diary (of operation to salvage Comet G-ALYP) – main items, TNA

20 AVIA 6/17623, RAE Report on Comet Accident Investigation, Part 2, Wreckage investigation, 1954, TNA, area 2, fig 4.

21 AVIA 6/17623, RAE Report on Comet Accident Investigation, Part 2, Wreckage investigation, Appendix 1, 1954, TNA, fig. 66.

22 ibid., fig. 68.

23 ibid., p21.

24 ibid., p22.

25 ibid., fig. 74.

26 ibid., fig. 75.

27 Cohen, Lord, Farren W. S., Duncan W. J., Wheeler A. H., Report of the Court of Inquiry into the Accidents to Comet G-ALYP on 10 January 1954 and Comet G-ALYY on 8 April 1954, 1955, HMSO, London, UK, p20.

28 AVIA 6/17623, RAE Report on Comet Accident Investigation, Part 2, Wreckage investigation, Appendix 1, 1954, TNA, fig. 77.

29 BT 220/93 letter from A. A. Hall to P. G. Tweedie dated 14 September 1954, TNA.

30 Yates D. M., *Turing's legacy. A history of computing at the National Physical Laboratory 1945-95*, 1997, The Science Museum, London, UK, p39.

Chapter 19: The Court of Inquiry

1 Wilberforce R., Cohen Lionel Leonard, *Oxford Dictionary of National Biography* (online edition) accessed 08 May 2012, Oxford University Press, Oxford, UK, 2004.

2 Whittle Sir F., *Jet, The Story of a Pioneer*, 1953, Frederick Muller, London, p306.

3 Morgan M, Farren etc, *Oxford Dictionary of National Biography* (online edition accessed 8 May 2012), Oxford University Press, Oxford, UK, 2004.

4 Anon, re Duncan William Jolly, University of Glasgow Archives Hub, (accessed 14 October 2011).

5 Anon, re Wheeler Allen Henry, RAF organisational history, (rafweb, accessed 14 October 2011).

6 BT 220/105, Public Inquiry, transcript, day 1, TNA, p3 et seq.

7 Cohen, Lord, Farren W. S., Duncan W. J., Wheeler A. H., Report of the Court of Inquiry into the Accidents to Comet G-ALYP on 10 January 1954 and Comet G-ALYY on 8 April 1954, 1955, HMSO, London, UK, p32.

Chapter 20: The hearings begin

1 BT 220/105, Public Inquiry, transcript, day 1, TNA, p5.

2 ibid., p5 et seq.

3 ibid., p8.

4 ibid., p43 et seq.

5 BT 220/106, Public Inquiry, transcript, day 2, TNA, p3 et seq.

6 ibid., p65 et seq.

7 BT 220/107, Public Inquiry, transcript, day 3, TNA, p11 et seq.

8 ibid., p17 et seq.

9 ibid., p18.

10 ibid., p21 et seq.

11 Roth E. M., Rapid (explosive) decompression emergencies in pressure-suited subjects, The Lovelace Foundation, National Aeronautics and Space Administration, November 1968. (accessed 6 March 2012).

12 Cohen, Lord, Farren W. S., Duncan W. J., Wheeler A. H., Report of the Court of Inquiry into the Accidents to Comet G-ALYP on 10 January 1954 and Comet G-ALYY on 8 April 1954, 1955, HMSO, London, UK, p14.

13 BT 220/110, Public Inquiry, transcript, day 6, TNA, p21.

14 BT 220/112, Public Inquiry, transcript, day 8, TNA, p22.

15 BT 220 /113, Public Inquiry, transcript, day 9, TNA, p45 et seq.

16 Waterton W. A., *The Quick and the Dead*, 1956, Frederick Mulller, London UK, p45.

17 BT 220 /113, Public Inquiry, transcript, day 9, TNA, p59.

18 ibid., p49.

19 ibid., p52.

20 BT 220/117, Public Inquiry, transcript, day 13, TNA, p49.

Chapter 21: The stress debate begins

1 BT 220/107, Public Inquiry, transcript, day 3, TNA, p27 et seq.

2 ibid., p45.

3 AVIA 6/17623, Report on Comet Accident Investigation, Part 2, Wreckage investigation, 1954, TNA, fig. 66.

4 BT 220/107, Public Inquiry, transcript, day 3, TNA, p49.

5 ibid., p51 et seq.

6 ibid., p58 et seq.

7 BT 220/108, Public Inquiry, transcript, day 4, TNA, p10.

8 AVIA 6/17623, Report on Comet Accident Investigation, Part 3, Fatigue tests on the pressure cabin and wings, Appendix 5, Fatigue tests on DTD 546 material, 1954, TNA, redrawn from fig 1, p40.

9 AVIA 6/17623, Report on Comet Accident Investigation, Part 3, Fatigue tests on the pressure cabin and wings, 1954, TNA, p8.

10 BT 220/108, Public Inquiry, transcript, day 4, TNA, p29.

11 Cohen, Lord, Farren W. S., Duncan W. J., Wheeler A. H., Report of the Court of Inquiry into the Accidents to Comet G-ALYP on 10 January 1954 and Comet G-ALYY on 8 April 1954, 1955, HMSO, London, UK, p27.

12 BT 220/108, Public Inquiry, transcript, day 4, TNA, p20.

13 AVIA 6/17623, Report on Comet Accident Investigation, Part 2, Wreckage investigation, Appendix 1, 1954, TNA, fig. 76.

14 ibid., fig. 77.

15 ibid., fig. 78.

16 BT 220/108, Public Inquiry, transcript, day 4, TNA, p22.

17 BT 220/112, Public Inquiry, transcript, day 8, TNA, p35.

18 ibid., p37.

19 ibid., p39

20 ibid., p40.

21 ibid., p61.

22 Shawcross H,, *Life Sentence*, Constable, London, UK, p119.

23 Beloff M., re Hartley Shawcross, *Oxford Dictionary of National Biography,* online edition accessed 19 October 2011.

24 Shawcross H., *Life Sentence*, Constable, London, UK, p228.

25 AVIA 6/17623, Report on Comet Accident Investigation, Part 7, Possibility of excessive pressure in the cabin and fuel tanks, Appendix 4, 1954, TNA, p13.

26 BT 220/113, Public Inquiry, transcript, day 9, TNA, p16.

27 DR 1/45, test report TR 106005, 15 April 1947, TNA

28 BT 220/113, Public Inquiry, transcript, day 9, TNA, p25.

29 ibid., p26 et seq.

30 ibid., p27.

31 Williams D., Strength of aeroplanes in relation to repeated loads, 1950, The Aeronautical Quarterly, The Royal Aeronautical Society, London, UK, vol 1, pp291 to 304.

32 BT 220/113, Public Inquiry, transcript, day 9, TNA, p35.

33 ibid., p38.

34 BT 220/114, Public Inquiry., transcript, day 10, TNA, p8.

35 ibid., p18.

36 ibid., p19.

37 Green A. E., Stress systems in isotropic and aeolotropic plates V, Proceedings of the Royal Society of London, Series A, Vol 184, No. 998, 1945, pp231-52,

38 BT 220/114, Public Inquiry, transcript, day 10, TNA, p21.

39 BT 220/121, Public Inquiry, transcript, day 17, TNA, p47.

Chapter 22: More Stress

1 Walker P. B., Fatigue of aircraft structures, Proceedings of the Royal Aeronautical Society, 1949, vol 53, pp763-96.

2 BT 220/108, Public Inquiry, transcript, day 4, TNA, p40.

3 BT 220/114, Public Inquiry, transcript, day 10, TNA, p50.

4 ibid., p52.

5 ibid., p53.

6 AVIA 6/17623, Report on Comet Accident Investigation, Part 3, Fatigue tests on the pressure cabin and wings, Appendix 5, 1954, TNA, fig. 1.

7 BT 220/114, Public Inquiry, transcript, day 10, TNA, p59.

8 BT 220/115, Public Inquiry, transcript, day 11, TNA, p42.

9 Walker P. B., The Experimental Approach to aircraft Structural Research, The Fifteenth Wright Brothers Lecture, 1952, Journal of the Aeronautical Sciences, Vol 19, No. 5, p18, (accessed on line 7 January 2013).

10 BT 220/114, Public Inquiry, transcript, day 10, TNA, p66.

11 ibid., p70.

12 ibid., p74.

13 Taylor J. publication not identified.

14 BT 220/115, Public Inquiry, transcript, day 11, TNA, p15.

15 ibid., p16.

16 Tye W., Summary of discussions at the full day meeting on fatigue, 27 March 1953, Proceedings of the Royal Aeronautical Society, 1953, p589.

17 BT 220/115, Public Inquiry, transcript, day 11, TNA, p22 et seq.

18 ibid., p27 et seq.

Chapter 23: Mr. Tye's doubts and Professor Murphy's certainties

1 BT 220/115, Public Inquiry, transcript, day 11, TNA, p45.

2 BT 220/116, Public Inquiry, transcript, day 12, TNA, p22.

3 ibid p21.

4 ibid., p28.

5 ibid., p30.

6 BT 220/117, Public Inquiry, transcript, day 13, TNA, p5.

7 ibid., p10.

8 ibid., p26.

9 AVIA 6/17623, Report on Comet Accident Investigation, Part 2, Wreckage Investigation, Appendix 1, 1954, TNA, fig. 76.

10 BT 220/117, Public Inquiry, transcript, day 13, TNA, p33.

11 Bibel G., *Beyond the Black Box The forensics of airplane crashes*, Johns Hopkins University Press, Baltimore, USA, 2008, p150 et seq.

12 BT 220/117, Public Inquiry, transcript, day 13, TNA, p31 et seq.

13 BT 220/118, Public Inquiry, transcript, day 14, TNA, p10.

14 ibid., p18.

15 AVIA 6/17623, Report on Comet Accident Investigation, Part 2, Wreckage Investigation, Appendix 1, 1954, TNA, fig. 75.

16 BT 220/118, Public Inquiry, transcript, day 14, TNA, p21.

17 ibid., p29 et seq.

18 BT 220/118, Public Inquiry, transcript, day 14, TNA, p32.

19 Withey P. A., Fatigue failure of the de Havilland Comet, Engineering Failure Analysis, UK, 1997, vol. 4, no. 2, pp147-54, p. 152.

20 Darling K., *de Havilland Comet*, 2003, The Crowood Press, Marlborough, UK, p24.

21 Ramsden J.M., Wings of Change, *Aeroplane Monthly*, Cudham, UK, September 1989, p521.

22 Atkinson R. J., Winkworth W. J. and Norris G. M., Behaviour of Skin Fatigue Cracks at the Corners of Windows in a Comet 1 Fuselage, Reports and Memoranda No. 3248, 1960, Ministry of Aviation, HMSO, London, UK, p7.

23 Gunn N. J. F., Fatigue cracking rates and residual strengths of eight aluminium sheet alloys, Royal Aircraft Establishment Technical report 64024, October 1964, table 1, p13, accessed on

line.
24 ibid., p11.
25 BT 220/118, Public Inquiry, transcript, day 14, TNA, p33 et seq.
26 ibid., p35.
27 ibid., p36.

Chapter 24: The de Havilland witnesses

1 BT 220/118, Public Inquiry, transcript, day 14, TNA, p55.
2 ibid., p59 et seq.
3 Joint Airworthiness Committee, paper 579, para 10.4, October 1952, (not accessed)
4 BT 220/119, Public Inquiry, transcript, day 15, TNA, p5.
5 ibid., p10.
6 ibid., p30.
7 ibid., p13.
8 DR 1/45, Test Report 106058 Add 5, TNA.
9 DR 1/45, Type Record for DH 106, volume 3, Structural Test Reports, Test report No. TR106058 Add 2, 8 February 1949, test carried out on 2 December 1948, TNA.
10 DR 1/45, Test report TR106108 Add 1, date of report 9 November 1948, TNA, p1.
11 BT 220/119, Public Inquiry, transcript, day 15, TNA, p23.
12 TS 52/114, Hall Sir A., A note on stress concentrations in a cylindrical structure with cut-outs, TNA
13 TS 52/95, Coles W. W., Handwritten calculations for Comet 1 fuselage cutouts, The de Havilland Aircraft Company Ltd., April 1947, TNA.
14 TS 52/95, Agreed statement re calculations of stress made a) by de Havillands in 1947 b) by Sir Arnold Hall in November 1954, TNA.
15 BT 220/119, Public Inquiry, transcript, day 15, TNA, p56.
16 Bishop R. E., Considerations in Designing the Comet, *The Aeroplane*, 2 May 1952, Kelsey Publishing Group, Cudham, Kent, UK pp514-23.
17 BT 220/119, Public Inquiry, transcript, day 15, TNA, p61.
18 BT 220/120, Public Inquiry, transcript, day 16, TNA, p17.
19 ibid., p22.
20 AVIA 6/17623, Report on Comet Accident Investigation, Part 2, Wreckage Investigation, Appendix 1, 1954, TNA, fig. 76.
21 BT 220/121, Public Inquiry, transcript, day 17, TNA, p40.
22 ibid., p44.
23 ibid., p47.
24 BT 220/108, Public Inquiry, transcript, day 4, TNA, p51.

Chapter 25: Mr. Jablonsky's Theory

1 BT 220/116, Public Inquiry, transcript, day 12, TNA, p33.
2 ibid., p35.
3 ibid., p42.
4 Cohen, Lord, Farren W. S., Duncan W. J., Wheeler A. H., Report of the Court of Inquiry into the Accidents to Comet G-ALYP on 10 January 1954 and Comet G-ALYY on 8 April 1954, 1955, HMSO, London, UK, p23.
5 BT 220/116, Public Inquiry, transcript, day 12, TNA, p58.
6 ibid., p54.

7 ibid., p61.
8 ibid., p71.
9 BT 220/113, Public Inquiry, transcript, day 9, TNA, p10.
10 BT 220/116, Public Inquiry, transcript, day 12, TNA, p72.
11 ibid., p71.
12 BT 220/120, Public Inquiry, transcript, day 16, TNA, p38.

Chapter 26: Last words
1 BT 220/123, Public Inquiry, transcript, day 19, TNA, p58.
2 BT 220/124, Public Inquiry, transcript, day 20, TNA, p6.
3 Cohen, Lord, Farren W. S., Duncan W. J., Wheeler A. H., Report of the Court of Inquiry into the Accidents to Comet G-ALYP on 10 January 1954 and Comet G-ALYY on 8 April 1954, 1955, Appendix VII, HMSO, London, UK, p41.
4 ibid., Appendix VIII, p42.

Chapter 27: The Commissioner's report
1 Comet crash findings, *The Times*, 12 February 1955, Digital Archive, accessed 10 August 2012, London, UK.
2 Cohen, Lord, Farren W. S., Duncan W. J., Wheeler A. H., Report of the Court of Inquiry into the Accidents to Comet G-ALYP on 10 January 1954 and Comet G-ALYY on 8 April 1954, 1955, HMSO, London, UK, p17. (The full report is on the US Federal Aviation Administration's website.)
3 ibid., p20.
4 ibid., p22.
5 ibid., p24.
6 ibid., p25.
7 ibid., p26.
8 DR 1/45 test TR 106005, date of test 15 April 1947, TNA
9 Cohen, Lord, Farren W. S., Duncan W. J., Wheeler A. H., Report of the Court of Inquiry into the Accidents to Comet G-ALYP on 10 January 1954 and Comet G-ALYY on 8 April 1954, 1955, HMSO, London, UK, p28.
10 ibid., p30.
11 ibid., p31.
12 ibid., p32.

Chapter 28: The aftermath
1 Atkinson R. J., Winkworth W. J. and Norris G. M., Behaviour of Skin Fatigue Cracks at the Corners of Windows in a Comet 1 Fuselage, Reports and Memoranda No. 3248, 1960, Ministry of Aviation, HMSO, London, UK, (accessed on line at <Naca.central.cranfield.ac.UK/reports/arc/rm/3248.pdf>. It is also on the Federal Aviation Administration's website.)
2 ibid., p2.
3 BT 220/80, Walker P. B., Static strength tests of a Comet 1 pressure cabin, Structures 196, Royal Aircraft Establishment, MoS, TNA.
4 BT 220/80, Note verbal of recovery No. 4/1956, TNA.
5 ADM 116/6006, Salvage Operations on Comet airliner G-ALYP which crashed off Elba, Plate 1 (redrawn by author), TNA.

6 BT 220/80 R. Warren, hand written file, TNA.

7 AVIA 6/17623, Report on Comet Accident Investigation, Part 2, Wreckage Investigation, Appendix 1, 1954, TNA, fig. 67.

8 Atkinson R. J., Winkworth W. J. and Norris G. M., Behaviour of Skin Fatigue Cracks at the Corners of Windows in a Comet 1 Fuselage, Reports and Memoranda No. 3248, 1960, Ministry of Aviation, HMSO, London, UK, p1, accessed on line at <Naca.central.cranfield.ac.UK/reports/arc/rm/3248.pdf>.

9 BT 220/80, letter from Walker to Tweedie dated 19 December 1956, TNA (see Appendix 4).

10 BT 220/80, letter from Tye to Walker dated 4 January 1957, TNA.

11 BT 220/80, letter from Hall to Walker dated 4 January 1957, TNA.

12 BT 220/80, letter from Walker to Hall dated 11 January 1957, TNA.

13 BT 220/80, letter from Hall to Walker dated 14 January 1957, TNA.

14 BT 220/80, letter from Bishop to Walker dated 19 March 1957, TNA.

15 Ramsden J. M., Wings of Change, *Aeroplane Monthly*, September 1989, p520.

16 RS/1/8337, BAA.

17 RS/1/8337, letter from Masefield to Lucking dated 6 October 1995, BAA.

18 RS/1/8337, letter from Tye to Lucking dated 4 January 1996, BAA.

Chapter 29: Consequences

1 Bray W, *The History of BOAC 1939 to 1974*, unpublished in-house history, British Airways, London, UK, BAA, p142.

2 AIR 2/13368, Comet programme, TNA

3 Bray W, *The History of BOAC 1939 to 1974*, unpublished in-house history, British Airways, London, UK, BAA, p214.

4 ibid., p223.

5 Cole L, *Vickers VC10*, The Crowood Press, Marlborough, UK, 2000, p113.

6 Painter M., *The DH. 106 Comet An illustrated History*, 2002, Air-Britain, Tunbridge Wells, UK, p356.

7 Pagnamenta P., Overy R., *All our working lives*, 1984, BBC, London, UKL, p63.

8 AIR 2/13368, letter from Sir James Helmore to Sir Herbert Brittain, dated 07 October 1954, TNA.

9 AIR 2/13368, Butler R. A., letter to Minister of Supply, 1 March 1955, TNA.

10 CAB 128/28, TNA, p6.

11 AIR 2/13368, Helmore J., minute to Minister, 11 October 1954, TNA.

12 AIR 2/13368, Air Council, The long range transport force – introduction of the Comet II, 26 November 1954, TNA, p2.

13 CAB 195/16, 15 October 1957, TNA, p202.

14 DR 33/107, Notes on Comet 2 for transport Command and Comet 3, TNA, drawing on first page.

15 Mansfield E. H., Neutral Holes in Plane Sheet: Reinforced Holes which are Elastically Equivalent to the Uncut Sheet, 1955, Aeronautical Research Council, Ministry of Supply, HMSO, London, UK

16 Walker P. B., Pressure-cabin fatigue: A Survey of the Problem and the Test Methods Developed at RAE, 1956, *Aircraft Engineering*, Vol. 28 Iss: 1, pp 11, 12.

17 Davies G. A. O., personal communication, 1 November 2012.

18 DR 33/107, Notes on Comet 2 for transport Command and Comet 3, TNA.

19 DR 6/47, Plan of C2, TNA.

20 DR 33/119, Atkinson R. J., letter from RAE to de Havillands, 16 October 1956, TNA.

21 DR 33/119, Notes of a discussion at the MoS 30 October 1958, TNA.

22 DR 33/119, Minutes of a meeting at the MoA,15 December 1960, TNA.

23 DR 33/119, Minutes of a meeting at the MoA, 2 January 1963, TNA, p2.

24 Painter M., *The DH. 106 Comet An illustrated History*, 2002, Air-Britain (Historians), Tunbridge Wells, UK, p357.

25 Campbell R. I., Wing Commander RAF (retired), personal communication, 16 August 2013.

26 Painter M., *The DH. 106 Comet An illustrated History*, 2002, Air-Britain (Historians), Tunbridge Wells, UK, p116 et seq.

27 ibid., p174 et seq.

28 Bray W, *The History of BOAC 1939 to 1974*, unpublished in-house history, British Airways, London, UK, BAA, p268.

29 Painter M., *The DH. 106 Comet An illustrated History,* 2002, Air-Britain (Historians), Tunbridge Wells, UK, p183 et seq.

30 Sharp C. M., *DH A History of de Havilland*, Airlife, Shrewsbury, UK, 1960, p357.

31 Painter M., *The DH. 106 Comet An illustrated History*, 2002, Air-Britain (Historians), Tunbridge Wells, UK, p23.

32 ibid., p216.

33 Sharp C. M., *DH A History of de Havilland*, Airlife, Shrewsbury, UK., 1960, p442.

34 Hayward K., *The British Aircraft Industry,* Manchester University Press, Manchester, UK, 1989, p73.

35 Pugh P., *The Magic of a Name, The Rolls-Royce Story, Part Two: The Power Behind the Jets*, 2001, Icon Books, Duxford, UK, p46, (quoted in).

36 Gunston, W., *The Plane Makers,* Basinghall Books, Birmingham, UK, 1980, p140.

37 Gardner C., *British Aircraft Corporation*, Batsford, London, UK, 1981, p22.

38 Sharp C. M., *DH A History of de Havilland*, Airlife, Shrewsbury, UK, 1960, p339.

39 Hayward K., *The British Aircraft Industry*, Manchester University Press, Manchester, UK, 1989, p79.

40 ibid., p80.

41 Hooker Sir S., *Not much of an engineer, an autobiography,* 1984, Airlife Publishing, Shrewsbury, UK, p179.

42 de Havilland Sir G., *Sky Fever*, 1961 Hamish Hamilton, London, UK, p192.

43 Walker P. B., Pressure-cabin Fatigue: A Survey of the Problem and the Test Methods Developed at RAE, 1956, *Aircraft Engineering*, Vol. 28 Iss: 1, p16 et seq.

44 Bibel G., *Beyond the black box. The forensics of airplane crashes*, 2008, The Johns Hopkins University Press, Baltimore, USA, p231.

45 ibid., p150.

46 ibid., p232.

47 Swift T., Damage tolerance in pressurized fuselages, 11th Platema Memorial Lecture, 1987, p1.

48 National Transportation Safety Board, Current Investigations, Southwest Airlines Flight 812, 1 April 2011, (accessed on line 18 September 2012)

49 Bibel G., *Beyond the black box. The forensics of airplane crashes*, 2008, The Johns Hopkins University Press, Baltimore, USA, p88.

Chapter 30: The reasons why

1 Gardner R., *From Bouncing Bombs to Concorde*, 2006, Sutton Publishing Limited, Stroud,

UK, p105.

2 Principal Films, *Secret History: Comet Cover-up*, 2002, Channel Four, London, UK

3 BT 220/120, Public Inquiry, transcript, day 16, TNA, p16.

4 BT 256/3, Minutes of the 60th meeting of the ASB, 2 March 1954.

5 BT 220/110, Public Inquiry, transcript, day 6, TNA, p21.

6 BT 220/80 Walker P. B., Static strength tests of a Comet 1 pressure cabin, Structures 196, Royal Aircraft Establishment, MoS, TNA.

7 Gunston B., *Nimrod the Centenarian aircraft*, 2009, Pen and Sword, Stroud, UK, p48.

8 Bibel G., *Beyond the black box. The forensics of airplane crashes*, 2008, The Johns Hopkins University Press, Baltimore, USA, table 4.1, p108.

9 AVIA 6/17623, RAE Report on Comet Accident Investigation, Part 5, Static strength tests of the tail unit, TNA.

10 DR 1/40, Type Record Vol. 2, TNA, p467.

11 BT 220/119, Public Inquiry, transcript, day 15, TNA, p61.

12 Walker P. B. Destructive energy in aircraft pressure cabins, Journal of the Royal Aeronautical Society, Vol. 54, April 1950.

13 BT 220/118, Public Inquiry, transcript, day 14, TNA, p57.

14 BT 220/115, Public Inquiry, transcript, day 11, TNA, p70.

15 BT 220/113, Public Inquiry, transcript, day 9, TNA, p34 et seq.

16 BT 220/114, Public Inquiry, transcript, day 10, TNA, p74.

17 BT 220/113, Public Inquiry, transcript, day 9, TNA p36.

18 Walker P. B., Estimation of the fatigue life of a transport aircraft, The Journal of the Royal Aeronautical Society, October 1953, vol. 57, p614.

19 BT 220/119, Public Inquiry, transcript, day 15, TNA, p21.

20 Cohen, Lord, Farren W. S., Duncan W. J., Wheeler A. H., Report of the Court of Inquiry into the Accidents to Comet G-ALYP on 10 January 1954 and Comet G-ALYY on 8 April 1954, 1955, HMSO, London, UK, p26.

21 BT 220/114, Public Inquiry, transcript, day 10, TNA, p20.

22 BT 220/119, Public Inquiry, transcript, day 15, TNA, p24.

23 Green A.E., Stress systems in isotropic and aeolotropic plates V, Proceedings of the Royal Society of London, Series A, Vol 184, No. 998, 1945, pp231-52,

24 BT 220/114, Public Inquiry, transcript, day 10, TNA, p21.

25 DR 1/45, Test Report 106005, 15 April 1947, TNA.

26 DR 1/45, Test report 106058 add 5,17 September 1953, TNA

27 BT 220/116, Public Inquiry, transcript, day 12, TNA, p22.

28 Timoshenko S., Goodier J. N., *Theory of elasticity,* second (international student) edition, 1951, McGraw-Hill, New York, USA, p78 et seq.

29 Williams D., Strength of aeroplanes in relation to repeated loads, 1950, The Aeronautical Quarterly, The Royal Aeronautical Society, London, UK, vol 1, p293 et seq.

30 Taylor J., The Investigation of Design Problems on Major Structural Components by means of Static Strain Measurements, Ministry of Supply, ARC, Reports and Memoranda 2129, November 1945, later published in March 1952.

31 BT 220/113, Public Inquiry, transcript, day 9, TNA, p22.

32 BT 220/112, Public Inquiry, transcript, day 8, TNA, p39.

33 Cohen, Lord, Farren W. S., Duncan W. J., Wheeler A. H., Report of the Court of Inquiry into the Accidents to Comet G-ALYP on 10 January 1954 and Comet G-ALYY on 8 April 1954, 1955, HMSO, London, UK, p11,

34 BT 220/118, Public Inquiry, transcript, day 14, TNA, p68.

35 ibid., p61.

36 BT 220/113, Public Inquiry, transcript, day 9, TNA, p39.

37 Heywood R. B., The Influence of Pre-Loading on the Fatigue Life of Aircraft Components and Structures, 1956, Aeronautical Research Council, Structures 182, HMSO, UK (accessed on line 18 January 2013 at Naca.central.cranfield.ac.uk/reports/arc/cp/0232.pdf)

38 Mansfield E. H., On the Design of a Row of Windows in a Pressurised Cylindrical Fuselage, 1963, Ministry of Supply R & M No. 3360, HMSO, London, UK (accessible online at aerade.cranfield,ac.UK)

39 Mansfield E. H., Neutral holes in Plane Sheet: Reinforced holes which are Elastically Equivalent to the Uncut Sheet, 1955, Ministry of Supply R & M No. 2815, HMSO, London, UK (accessible online at aerade.cranfield,ac.UK).

40 AVIA 6/17623, Report on Comet Accident Investigation, Part 3, Fatigue Tests on the Pressure Cabin and Wings, Appendix 3, p6, figs 3 and 4.

41 Atkinson R. J., Winkworth W. J. and Norris G. M., Behaviour of Skin Fatigue Cracks at the Corners of Windows in a Comet 1 Fuselage, Reports and Memoranda No. 3248, 1960, Ministry of Aviation, HMSO, London, UK, pp23, 24.

42 ibid., fig. 7, p17.

43 ibid, figs.14, 15.

44 AVIA 6/17623, Report on Comet Accident Investigation, Part 3, Fatigue Tests on the Pressure Cabin and Wings, Appendix 3, fig 8.

45 Atkinson R. J., Winkworth W. J. and Norris G. M., Behaviour of Skin Fatigue Cracks at the Corners of Windows in a Comet 1 Fuselage, Reports and Memoranda No. 3248, 1960, Ministry of Aviation, HMSO, London, UK, fig. 14, p23.

46 Povey H, Planning and Production Methods used in the Construction of the de havilland Comet, 1951 (August), de Havilland Gazette, Supplement to No. 64, Hatfield, UK, p13.

47 DR 11/111, Special Inspection Carried out on Comet MK. 1 Aircraft 10 February 1954, TNA, p2 et seq.

48 Atkinson R. J., Winkworth W. J. and Norris G. M., Behaviour of Skin Fatigue Cracks at the Corners of Windows in a Comet 1 Fuselage, Reports and Memoranda No. 3248, 1960, Ministry of Aviation, HMSO, London, UK, p3.

49 AVIA 6/17623, Report on Comet Accident Investigation, Part 3, Fatigue tests on the pressure cabin and wings, 1954, TNA, p6.

50 Atkinson R. J., Winkworth W. J. and Norris G. M., Behaviour of Skin Fatigue Cracks at the Corners of Windows in a Comet 1 Fuselage, Reports and Memoranda No. 3248, 1960, Ministry of Aviation, HMSO, London, UK ibid., p7.

51 ibid., fig7, p17.

52 Pilkey W. D., Pilkey D. F., Peterson's Stress Concentration Factors, Third Edition, 2008, John Wiley, Hoboken, USA, p240.

53 AVIA 6/17623, Report on Comet Accident Investigation, Part 3, Fatigue tests on the pressure cabin and wings, 1954, TNA, Appendix 1, p15.

54 Atkinson R. J., Winkworth W. J. and Norris G. M., Behaviour of Skin Fatigue Cracks at the Corners of Windows in a Comet 1 Fuselage, Reports and Memoranda No. 3248, 1960, Ministry of Aviation, HMSO, London, UK, fig. 21, p27.

55 DR 1/45, Test Report 106268, dated 10 August 1949, TNA.

56 Swift T., Damage tolerance in pressurized fuselages, 11th Platema Memorial Lecture, 1984, Fig. 6, p37, (accessed online).

57 ibid., p6 et seq.

58 BT 220/119, Public Inquiry, transcript, day 15, TNA, p61.

59 Postan M. M. in Postan M. M., Hay D., Scott J. D., Design and Development of Weapons, Studies in Government and Industrial Organisation, HMSO, London 1964, p29 et seq.

60 Barnett C., *The Audit of War*, Macmillan, London, UK, 1986, p210.

61 ibid., p149.

62 AVIA10/104, Report of British Mission to United States of America to study production methods, September to October 1942, TNA, p5 et seq.

63 Ramsden J. M. Wings of change, *Aeroplane Monthly*, Cudham, UK, September 1989, p525.

64 AVIA 9/83, The Fedden Mission to Germany, 1945, TNA

65 AVIA 10/411, Farren Mission to Germany, TNA, p9.

66 Waterton W. A., *The Quick and the Dead*, 1956, Frederick Muller, London, UK (reprinted in 2012 by Grub Street, London).

67 ibid., p243. (reprint p198).

68 Hamilton-Paterson J., *Empire of the Clouds*, 2010, Faber and Faber, London, UK, p175.

69 Fedden R., *Britain's Air Survival*, 1957, Cassell, London, UK,

70 ibid., p77.

71 ibid., p75.

72 ibid., p138.

73 Postan M. M. in Postan M. M., Hay D., Scott J. D., Design and Development of Weapons, Studies in Government and Industrial Organisation, HMSO, London, 1964, p31.

74 Ramsden J. M., R. E. Bishop de Havilland designer. An appreciation. *Aeroplane Monthly*, Cudham, UK, August 1989, p461.

75 Hooker Sir S., *Not much of an engineer*, Airlife, Shrewsbury UK, 2002, p82.

76 Russell Sir A., *A Span of Wings, An autobiography*, 1992, Airlife, Shrewsbury, UK, p5.

77 Postan M. M. in Postan M. M., Hay D., Scott J. D., Design and Development of Weapons, Studies in Government and Industrial Organisation, HMSO, London, 1964, p30.

78 Quoted in Forte A., *Prof, The Life of Frederick Lindemann*, 2003, Jonathan Cape, London, p74.

79 Fedden R., *Britain's Air Survival,* 1957, Cassell, London, UK, p3.

80 Whittle Sir F., *Jet, The Story of a Pioneer,* 1953, Frederick Muller, London, p94.

81 Waterton W. A., Hewat T., *The Comet Riddle*, 1955, Frederick Muller, London, UK, p25.

82 D. Rumsfeld "...there are known knowns; there are things we know we know. We also know there are known unknowns; that is to say we know there are some things we do not know. But there are also unknown unknowns – the ones we don't know we don't know."

83 RS/1/8337, Masefield P. G., letter to A.J . Lucking 6 October 1995, BAA.

84 Boyne W. J., *Beyond the Horizons - The Lockheed Story*, 1998, St. Martins Press, New York, USA, p211 et seq.

85 Bray W, *The History of BOAC 1939 to 1974*, unpublished in-house history, BAA, p158.

86 RS/1/8116, memo re cable from New York, dated 30 December 1954, BAA.

87 Quoted in Gardener R., *From Bouncing Bombs to Concorde, the authorised biography of aviation pioneer Sir George Edwards OM*, 2006, Sutton Publishing Limited, Stroud, UK, p140.

88 *Metal. How it works*, Miodownik M., BBC Four, first broadcast 2 April 2012.

89 Waterton W. A., *The Quick and the Dead*, 1956, Frederick Muller, London, UK, p232. (reprint p196)

Appendix 2: Hookers' comparison of the Merlin and Whittle's engine

1 Hooker Sir S., *Not much of an engineer,* Airlife, Shrewsbury, UK, 1984, appendix 2.

Appendix 3: Lord Brabazon's statement to the Court of Inquiry
1 BT 220/113, Public Inquiry transcript, day 9, TNA, p52 et seq.

Appendix 4: Walker's letter to Tweedie
1 BT 220/80, letter from Walker to Tweedie dated 19 December 56, TNA

Appendix 5: Stress, strain, cracks and cutouts. A summary
1 See also J. E., *Structures or why things don't fall down,* 1978, and *The New Science of Strong Materials*, 1968, Penguin Books, London, UK.
2 Neuber H., Theory of stress concentration for shear strained prismatical bodies with arbitrary non linear stress strain law, 1961, Journal of Applied Mechanics, pp544 to 550.
3 Inglis C. E., Stresses in a plate due the presence of cracks and sharp corners, paper read at the 54th session of the Institute of Naval Architects, 1913, (accessed on line).
4 AVIA 6/17623, Report on Comet Accident Investigation, Part 3, Fatigue tests on the pressure cabin and wings, Appendix 5, Fatigue tests on DTD546 material, 1954, NA, redrawn from fig 1, p40.
5 Gordon J. E., *Structures or why things don't fall down*, 1978, Penguin Books, London, UK, p119 et seq.
6 Redrawn from Ko W. L., Stress concentration around a small circular hole in the HiMAT composite plate, Ames Research Center, Edwards, California, USA, NASA. Technical Memorandum 86038, December 1985, p12, (accessed on line at www.nasa.gov/centers/dryden/pdf/88004main_H-1235.pdf., 21 August 2012).
7 Timoshenko S., Goodier J. N., *Theory of Elasticity*, second edition, international students' edition, 1951, McGraw-Hill, New York, USA, p78.
8 Green A. E., Stress systems in isotropic and aeolotropic plates V, Proceedings of the Royal Society of London, Series A, Vol 184, No. 998, 1945, pp231-52, p249.
9 Sobey A. J., Stress-Concentration Factors for rounded Rectangular Holes in Infinite Sheets, Aeronautical Research Council 3407, 1965, Ministry of Aviation, HMSO, London, UK (accessed on line at <aerade.cranfield,ac.UK/ara/arc/rm/3407.pdf>).

Appendix 6: Finite element analysis of the static stress levels in the vicinity of the cabin windows in the Comet 1 fuselage.
1 Pilkey W. D., Pilkey D. F., *Peterson's Stress Concentration Factors*, Third Edition, 2008, John Wiley, Hoboken, USA, chart 4.62b, p. 349.

Appendix 7: Comparison of the Comet 1 with the Airbus A318
1 Wikipedia, A318, accessed 1 February 2012.
2 Airbus.com
3 Painter M., *The DH.106 Comet An Illustrated History*, Air-Britain, Tunbridge Wells, UK, 2002, p15.
4 Type specification of the D H Comet four turbojet airliner (Type D.H. 106-10-01) for BOAC, Issue No. 2, October 1951, The de Havilland Aircraft Company, National Aerospace Library, Farnborough, UK
5 DR1/39, DH 106 Comet Type Record, Volume 1, TNA.

Appendix 8: The names of the people who lost their lives in the Comet crashes
1 BT 218/31, Directorate of Civil Aviation East Africa, Accident report No. 1, 1953, TNA.
2 BT 220/69, Pakistan Government Order Instituting the Inquiry into the crash of Comet CF-

CUN, 4 March 1953, TNA., p6.

3 BT 220/67, letter from UK High Commission, Karachi, to Viscount Swinton, dated 6 March 1953, TNA.

4 Report of the Court Investigation on the Accident to Comet G-ALYV on 2 May 1953, Appendix 2, HMSO, London, UK.

5 Report of the Court Investigation on the Accident to Comet G-ALYV on 2 May 1953, Appendix 3, HMSO, London, UK.

6 Cohen, Lord, Farren W. S., Duncan W. J., Wheeler A. H., Report of the Court of Inquiry into the Accidents to Comet G-ALYP on 10 January 1954 and Comet G-ALYY on 8 April 1954, 1955, HMSO, London, UK, p12.

7 BT 220/101, G-ALYP List of passengers and crew, TNA.

8 Cohen, Lord, Farren W. S., Duncan W. J., Wheeler A. H., Report of the Court of Inquiry into the Accidents to Comet G-ALYP on 10 January 1954 and Comet G-ALYY on 8 April 1954, 1955, HMSO, London, UK, p44.

9 *The Times*, 10 April 1954. London, UK.

Index

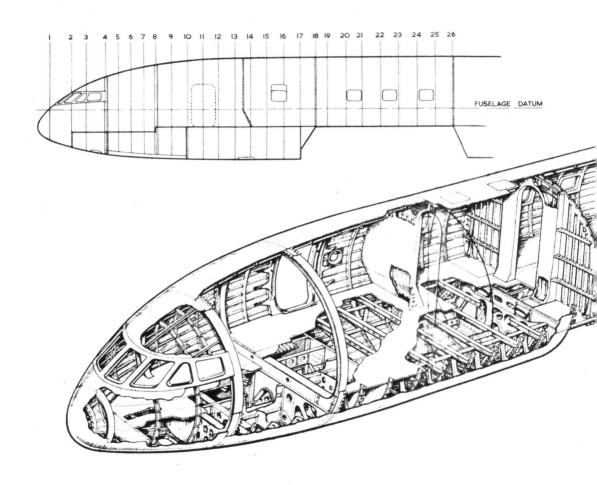

The internal structure of the Comet 1 fuselage, © *BAE SYSTEMS Heritage*

THE
NEW YOUTH
ARTS & CRAFTS
BOOK

ALAN DEARLING
HOWIE ARMSTRONG
ILLUSTRATIONS BY GUBBY

THE NEW YOUTH ARTS AND CRAFTS BOOK

First published in May 1996 by
Russell House Publishing Limited
38 Silver Street
Lyme Regis
Dorset DT7 3HS

© *Alan Dearling and Howard Armstrong*
Cartoons by Gubby

Diagrams by Gubby, Willy Langlands, Ian Hamilton, Jerry Neville and Alan Dearling
Design by Alan Dearling

British Library Catologuing-in-Publication Data:
A catalogue record for this book is available from the British Library.

ISBN 1-898924-75-9
Printed by Hobbs the Printers
Totton
Hants.

CONTENTS FOR THE *NEW YOUTH ARTS AND CRAFTS BOOK*

ACKNOWLEDGEMENTS

This is a new book, but it is also a development of the *Youth Arts and Craft Book* published in 1982. Over the intervening years, both of us have continued to work with young people in a diverse range of settings, including youth clubs, youth social work groups, playschemes, Travellers' sites and festivals, and, of course, in our families. Arts and crafts have been a part of this work, along with group work, individual work, residential projects, use of games and policy development work with both statutory and voluntary agencies. There is no way in which we can honestly remember to thank **all** the individuals, agencies and youth groups who have in some way contributed to this collection.

However, accepting our own limitations, we would like to offer especial thanks to certain groups and individuals. We'd particularly like to thank all the young people in Scotland and England who participated in our 'trial' sessions. Everyone, young and old alike, had lots of fun, even when not every aspect of our artistic endeavours went exactly to plan! Over the years we have also worked with a number of outstanding adult staff, notably, Kate, George, Linda, John, Donald, Charley, Gilly, Jack and others who were part of the original practical skills 'Roadshow' which took arts and games activities to youth and social work organisations throughout every region of Scotland. George Symington from Glasgow has contributed a 'guest' section on DJ culture and mixing for the Music section – thanks George! We'd also like to thank Bob Stead and Simon Jacquet for their contributions to the section on the creative use of Questionnaires, Russell House Publishing and Phil Bayliss (who proofed it!)

We are very grateful to Gubby for his patience with us while we have sent him a seemingly interminable flow of sections to illustrate. His humour and skill with the pen make this a much more enjoyable book to use. Whilst we were compiling the activities for the book, we consulted with a number of suppliers of arts and crafts materials and equipment. These are all listed in the Suppliers'section and many offer special discounts to youth organisations. We would especially like to thank Paul Crick and Rob Jones at Specialist Crafts, formerly Dryad; Tim Bean at NES Arnold; John Tiranti, even if we couldn't include that many of Tiranti's sculpting and casting materials; Sue Morse and friends at the London Emblem Company; Stuart Hails at Le Prevo Leathers and staff at the Big Top and Jugglemania.

Finally, our thanks to our families and friends for putting up with us while we've been searching out, testing (playing with) activities for yet another book.

Alan and Howie

KNOCK!
KNOCK!

I knew that I should never work with children or animals!

INTRODUCTION

The aim of this collection of arts and craft activities is to provide anyone who works or spends time with young people with activities which are:

- exciting
- creative
- lively
- practical
- and flexible.

Neither of us are artists or 'experts' in this field of work. We are like the majority of youth workers, playworkers and staff involved in social education – we are more than willing to have a go, and participate in arts activities with young people. Most of the activities included do not require 'specialist' tutor skills, but many do require preparation, planning and careful consideration of appropriateness for particular groups, ages, abilities and, of great importance, safety.

The examples we have included of what goes wrong, as well as the descriptions of 'how-to-do' various activities should seem familiar. They are taken from the daily lives of adults working with young people, not the pages of Craft Encyclopaedias. Most importantly, we have tried to stress the importance of adopting a flexible approach to activities which encourage individual young people to develop their personal style and interests. There is no adherence to a curriculum involved in this collection, even though art teachers may well find useful information and ideas; rather it is designed as a hands-on guide to successful participation in the fullest range of arts activities possible.

Who is it for?

In each section, we have tried to give a certain amount of information, both about how to approach a particular activity (the gathering together and preparation of tools and materials) and the running of the activity session in different settings, with varying types and ages of young person. It can be very different operating a papier mache session with eight year olds in a Junior Youth Club in rural Sussex, to organising the same activity with a Youth Treatment group on the outskirts of Glasgow. Although this is stating the obvious, many books which are presently available to those working with young people, do not always take account of the pitfalls which can occur in organising an arts activity with 'real' kids. You try hot air ballooning in a Force 10 gale, or hot enamelling with a bunch of amateur tattoo artists!

We have also tried to remain flexible in our presentation of the various arts and activities mentioned. What is suitable for silk-screen printing as a style, i.e. hard, factual information on how to build a screen and stencil, is not required in the presentation music-related work. Music is such a broad area that a thick book would be needed to cover the scope of the subject, as it might be applied to working with young people. So, we have tried to indicate how we, and some of our colleagues in a variety of UK work situations, have used music-related activities as a creative tool.

Within this approach then, the information offered in this book will vary, depending upon the subject under discussion. For some, we have offered only 'tasters', giving a few ideas for how a particular activity may be incorporated into a youth programme. Scraperboard, building bogies and circus skills are pretty typical of this pared-down presentation. On the other hand, the sections on video, papier mache and murals all offer a wealth of knowledge on some of the most popular youth activities.

All about 'doing'

The anecdotal style of the book, we think, makes the subjects come alive. Arts and crafts are hardly a 'book' subject; they are about 'doing'. We hope that this comes over in the descriptions of each activity as they might be used in your club, play centre, festival or organisation. What we and our colleagues have done wrong, as well as correctly, will help you to plan some new arts and crafts sessions with the young people in your area.

The main thing about arts and crafts is that they can be used to introduce young people to a wide range of new skills, yet at the same time can be fun to be involved in. If you are at all like us, you will find that in using arts activities, you will also be enjoying the satisfaction of being able to produce articles which you would not have thought possible. This element of 'success' is crucial to building up the self-image of many youngsters, and it is the key to using the arts and crafts activities described in this book, positively.

Getting prepared

For each activity, we have tried to offer:
- how-to-do-it information;
- information on what can be produced and how it might be used;
- details of materials, tools and often suppliers;
- an idea about space, time, safety and staffing considerations;
- commentary on working with young people of differing ages and abilities and backgrounds;
- problems, pitfalls and how to avoid them.

It is impossible to make suggestions which can be applied to all the situations in which you will be working. Some youngsters will need an especially high level of support in attempting many of the activities – we think here of people with learning difficulties or impairments with whom we have worked. For them, you will probably have to adapt our directions to suit individual requirements. In other instances, it may be particularly necessary to keep a weather-eye open to dangers which may become apparent as you are organising a particular session. For instance, the woodworking skills needed for making a bogie may be imaginatively transformed by your youth group, ending with you being nailed into the resources cupboard!

As you can see from the style of the book, it is about getting involved. Young people you are involved in spending time with will frequently show you artwork or crafts they have experimented with, as well as vice versa. As a reader/user, you can be involved too. If you find any mistakes in the text, or you would like to tell us about the arts and crafts which you use with your youth group, do contact us through Russell House Publishing.

Both of us still do get involved with practical skills training, often in the form of a travelling 'Roadshow', demonstrating a selection of arts, crafts, games and group work sequences – if your organisation would like details, let us know. We hope that you enjoy using this book!

Alan and Howie.

ORGANISATION OF MATERIALS

If arts and crafts activities are to be a regular feature of your work with young people, then it is pretty obvious that some thought has to be given to the way you organise and store the necessary materials. Simply chucking everything into one corner of a room is not to be recommended!

For those lucky enough to have a workshop with storage facilities there should be no real problem; others may have to make special arrangements, like building cupboards, storage boxes, etc.. We have used a lot of the plastic storage boxes, which stack neatly into one another and are easy to label. Material that is well stored is easy to organise and use and means that people don't have to spend ages looking for the scissors which were with the comics which were thrown in a box which was put...?

Messy or dangerous materials (paints, adhesives, chemicals, modelling knives, turps, etc.) should be carefully stored and kept under lock and key if you think that necessary. Other things can be grouped together for storage, e.g. paper and cardboard, crayons, pens and pencils, findings for jewellery making, enamelling and leatherwork, printing materials, etc.. As well as organising your material carefully, you will have to consider the security of materials and tools. Especially vulnerable are photographic and video equipment, bicycles and some 'popular' arts materials such as mouldable candle wax. Youth premises are notorious for having vast quantities of items 'walking'. Padlocks and locked cupboards are a virtual necessity.

Things like Scrap Boxes and Dressing up Boxes are useful to have around, as they keep things tidy and can offer valuable inspiration to bored kids.

Scrap Box

Many of the arts and crafts which you are likely to use with groups depend on a ready supply of suitable materials. Often these materials are commonplace and easily obtainable for free, or next to nothing. Having a good supply, readily available, makes sense, not just from the economic point of view, but because you will never be short of ideas or a suitable activity if you have a wide selection of 'bits and bobs' available.

Your should consider collecting:

> Wallpaper; milk bottle tops; newspaper; colour supplements and magazines; egg cartons; milk cartons; yoghurt cartons; match sticks; ice lolly sticks; wood offcuts; corks; matchboxes; tins; buttons; shells; string; pebbles; wine bottles; coat hangers; boxes; washing up liquid bottles; soap; wool; fabric; eggshells; silver paper; old posters; and comics.

Virtually anything can be collected (as long as it doesn't go off or smell) and young people can easily be involved in gathering and searching for material. You could, for example, consider organising a trip to the beach to collect shells and small and interesting looking pieces of driftwood. It can also be worthwhile contacting local businesses for 'end-runs' that they don't need. Wooden offcuts, ceramic tiles, wallpaper, newsprint and printing ink can often be obtained in this way.

Bear in mind that shops you give custom to are likely to be sympathetic to an occasional request for materials. For example, the thin plastic bags used in corner shops are perfect for making 'delta' kites (if you get a pile of new bags you can use a template to cut out masses of kite shapes at one go.

Dressing Up Box

Any kind of clothing – shoes, hats, dresses, trousers, feather boas, skirts, scarves, waistcoats – can be chucked in the Dressing Up Box. These items can be gathered by young people themselves, or you may be able to get hold of a good selection of interesting clothing at the local jumble sale or charity shop. This can be used to hilarious effect at special occasions such as parties, open days, etc.. 'Dressing up' complements other activities like face painting, drama, and role play particularly well. And, after all that effort, it would be a great pity not to record the event for posterity, wouldn't it? Still photographs, or video films can be great fun to shoot when everyone is dressed and made up. A good time can be guaranteed at the subsequent viewing session!

Foraging

Autumn is an excellent time for collecting materials out of doors. Vibrantly coloured leaves are a must and it is easy to find a range of different sized cones which can, for example, be sprayed lightly with gold or silver paint to use in Christmas displays and decorations. We've also mentioned a number of activities which require 'found materials', such as: stone painting; eco costumes; flowercraft; and certain types of collage work.

AIRBRUSHES

A lot of commercial artwork, especially where it is produced for advertisements features the use of an airbrush. Futuristic landscape artists like Giger, famous for the 'Alien' film sets, and many poster and rock cover designers, work almost entirely with very fine airbrushes. Likewise, airbrush work features in most car and motor-bike customising – you know the sort of thing – featuring three dimensional figures and scenes. The airbrush is also a very popular tool with modelmakers, animators and cartoonists. Airbrush painting particularly appeals to young people, because, in the right hands an airbrush can be used to produce immaculately textured results of near 3-D quality, and photographic look-alikes. In youth group work, it is probably only appropriate for the adolescent age range and then only in very small groups, or for individual, supervised art work. A skilled supervisor is pretty much a necessity, because of the delicacy of the work and patience required from the potential students.

The main trouble is that the airbrush itself is:
- relatively expensive;
- requires a good deal of patience, and
- can be easily wrecked.

So, if you are thinking of buying one or two airbrushes for your youth group work, you have been warned! Make sure that a reasonably watchful eye is kept on the equipment.

The basic principle of the airbrush is used in a very simple piece of equipment called a 'diffuser'. This utilises the fact that air pressure can be used to extract paint out of a paint and blow a spray of paint onto another surface. A diffuser costs very little and can produce some interesting, simple textures onto a surface. However, it does take quite a lot of puff and the results are a bit uncontrollable.

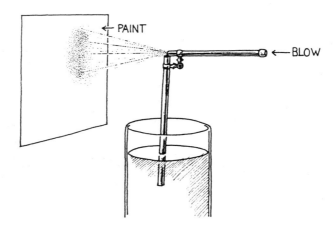

Proper airbrushes are a development on the aerosol paint can, and come in an almost bewildering range of styles and types. The old adage, 'you pays your money and takes your choice' is very apt. The more you pay, the more control the artist will have over the range of possible effects. The degree of control over the paintflow and airflow is usually managed by pressing a finger lever on the top of the airbrush using a single or double action. The button may move forwards, backwards and downwards. Unfortunately, the greater the level of independent control, the harder the airbrush is to learn to use!

The second area of expense is buying the source of the air, which will propel the paint through the instrument. A small compressor from a well known airbrush manufacturer such as DeVilbliss costs about the same as twenty disposable cans of air. For larger scale work, such as car-customising, a larger compressor will be required. If your youth group develops a great interest or aptitude for airbrush work, it will be necessary to have a compressor which includes a pressure gauge and a moisture filter. Without these sophistications, the flow of air will always be slightly variable, which will make very intricate, fine line work impossible.

The 'medium' used – the proper word for the type of ink or paint being sprayed, can be fed through the airbrush by gravity, or from underneath using suction. However, with all airbrushes it is best for young people to learn how to use the airbrush using a relatively light medium such as ink, starting with a dark colour so as to easily judge results. Whenever a new colour is introduced it is necessary to empty the airbrush and completely clean it. This helps to prevent the nozzle becoming clogged up; a frequent and often frustrating experience for younger airbrush artist. Later on, as people develop a mastery of the instrument, thicker paints can be used, but these may require passing through a filter to remove lumps.

A few hints

To get young airbrush users started, it is important that they practice some basic techniques. The airbrush has a different 'feel' to any other art instrument they are likely to have used.

1. It is vital to start and stop the airbrush while on the move, otherwise you will end up with uneven, splodges of paint.
2. To produce a fine line, the nozzle of the airbrush will be almost touching the paper and the brush must be moved quite quickly, but smoothly, above the surface. The pressure on the button must also be decreased which is quite hard to do without a lot of perseverance and practice!
3. To produce an even tone of ink across a wider area, the airbrush should be held further from the paper, usually about six inches, and more air and ink must be fed through.
4. Much airbrush work depends on adding a number of layers of colour. This builds up an image and creates the impression of shape and depth, which is so characteristic of airbrush work. Being 'slow and careful' are basic requirements of this type of art work.
5. Masking is another basic feature of airbrushing. Pre-cut or shaped card is the simplest form of mask, but masking film is the most accurate form. It is cut to shape, usually using a surgical scalpel. The film is then stuck lightly onto the surface being sprayed. Masking film is clear, and therefore, with care, can be cut 'in situ' whilst stuck over the surface.

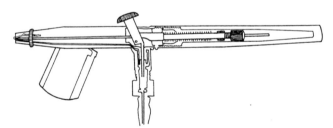

Overall, the airbrush has its merits, but is probably a risky extravagance for most youth groups, unless there is a skilled tutor and one or more highly motivated pupils. The benefits can include some very polished mural work for a building or complex design work on vehicles, leather jackets, denims or whatever.

BADGE MAKING

Most young people enjoy wearing badges. They are often used to stress individuality, identification with styles and cultures, as well as and sporting and music groups. Helping young people to design and make their own badges makes the process even more personal. In this section we look briefly at some of the ways in which you can organise a badge-making session with a small group of youngsters.

Tin Badges

Metal button badges of various sizes from 25mm to 77mm, round or square in shape, can be made using a badge-making machine. These machines are heavy duty presses, which are used to bend a thin clear sheet of plastic film over a drawing, cartoon, pre-printed picture or whatever and attach that permanently onto a metal badge, to which a pin is attached at the rear. A number of companies including Enterprise Products, Badge-a-Minit and the London Emblem Company (see Suppliers' Addresses at end of book) can supply the equipment:

- a circular cutter for cutting out the artwork
- the badge-making machine
- components
- pre-printed artwork.

Badges are cheap to make and when used in group-work or for fundraising can provide a popular and profitable activity, even with very young groups. The badge machines are relatively expensive, with robust models like those from London Emblem costing upwards of £250 – quite a large, capital outlay.

Getting youngsters started can often be the most difficult stage in any artistic endeavour, so, plan what you are going to try and produce and have the necessary materials prepared. You'll need plenty of paper, circles of paper already cut out, pencils, rubbers and a variety of felt pens, including some fine-tipped black pens.

If you are lucky, your group will be full of ideas for the badges and raring to go. If not, you'll have to motivate them. For instance, provide copies of old cartoon books and comics for copying or even tracing. London Emblem and others also produce pre-printed sheets of artwork, ranging from wildlife pics through to Drugs Awareness captions.

If your youthful artists are designing their own artwork, you must remember to tell them that they should not draw too close to the edge of the paper circles, otherwise their masterpiece will be curled up round the edge or back of the badge.
Another dodge is to prepare some samples of cartoons drawn simply on A4 sheets of paper spaced out for cutting into circular badge shapes. These sheets can then be photocopied and this then supplies a re-useable resource for groups. The individual line drawings can be coloured, modified and personalised with names, story-balloons etc.. For younger groups, just get them to produce brightly coloured doodles to which staff can add clearly printed names. These make surprisingly professional looking badges. After the artwork has been completed, each badge can be produced in less than a minute on the more sophisticated machines.

Other ideas for what to put on badges are fairly obvious. Names, slogans, pop groups, football teams are typical examples. London Emblem have also been marketing Berol Cromar paints along with their badge/keyring/magnet and mirror backs. This paint stays liquid under the seal of the plastic cover sheet of the badge. The result is a coloured painting which can be squeezed and which can change effect.

Our experience has shown that it is best to have only older, perhaps fourteen plus, young people actually operating the badge machine. This saves on wastage and ensures that the badge machine remains operational for as long as possible! Whilst they are not difficult to operate, each badge requires a sequence of operations and getting used to that sequence needs a bit of practice, which can prove expensive!

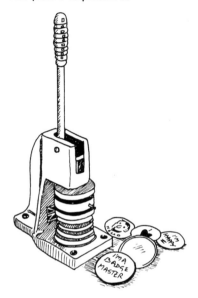

The badge-making machine can always be used to help pay for itself at fairs, festivals, open-days, carnivals, fetes and fundraising events. The machine can also be used for semi-commercial work producing runs of badges for sports teams, community groups etc., especially if you commission good quality art work.

Wooden Badges

Before we discovered the electric fret saw, 'Shaper Saw', or similar make, we used to use a coping saw for cutting out shapes from thin plywood. Although it is not the quickest way to make a badge, some unusual and striking results can be obtained. The method involves drawing a simple shape on the wood, cutting this out with the saw, cleaning it up with a fine file or sandpaper, then painting and varnishing the shape, finishing it off with a badge pin at the back of the wood. Such wondrous items as bright yellow Teddy bears, menacing Dennis's, Power Rangers and Oor Wullie's (a Scottish character) can be manufactured without too much difficulty.

The two main skills involved are:
      (a) cutting out the wooden shape using an electric fret or coping saw, and
      (b) painting a design on the badge.

These skills can easily be mastered by most young people aged about ten to twelve years or over. Part of the attraction of this kind of badge making is that the creative element is very high, but it does require a fair investment of time and commitment from the participants to produce the finished article.

We hear you asking, how dangerous is all this sawing?, we hear you asking. The answer is hardly at all. The Shaper Saw does tend to break blades quite quickly and it takes some getting used to pushing the wood into the blade, rather than the other way round. But despite being noisy and a little frightening at first because of the vibrations, we've never seen anyone hurt themselves. A coping saw is slower, perhaps more fiddly, but easier to control.

Wooden badge making itself is most likely to appeal to those who are already acquainted with arts and crafts activities and who can concentrate for a good half hour or longer on one activity. It is best treated as a small group activity, with one 'instructor' to every four or five young people.

How to do it
Materials and other requirements:
A workshop is virtually essential for wooden badge making, involving as it does, wood cutting, paint, glue etc.. Minimum requirements are as follows:
- Vice
- Plywood
- Tracing paper, pencils and comics
- Electric fret saw or coping saw(s) and spare blades, sandpaper
- Enamel paints and brushes, poster colour pens or acrylic paints
- Glue and varnish
- Badge/brooch pins

Specialist Crafts of Leicester stock just about anything you could require for this activity, except the plywood.

STEP 1: prepare space and materials.
Create sufficient space for yourself and the young people in the workshop area, and then lay out tools and materials, checking that vices and coping saws are properly set up.

STEP 2: brief the group.
Make sure the young people know what's involved by showing them examples of wooden badges, and briefly outlining the processes to be involved.

STEP 3: choose and cut out your shapes.
Unless anyone is particularly good at freehand drawing, designs should be transferred from comics to a piece of plywood, either by careful copying or by using tracing paper and carbon. Encourage young people to choose a shape which does not have complicated contours and is therefore easy to cut out. Shapes should be traced towards the edge of the plywood, so that they can be easily cut out.

The coping saw or Shaper Saw should be handled gently, so that the thin blade does not break. When the blade needs to be withdrawn from the wood, the sawing motion should be continued and the blade 'reversed' back the way it came. Once shapes have been cut out, any rough edges should be sandpapered.

STEP 4: paint your shape.
This can be done using tins of enamel paint and fine brushes, making sure that the paint is well stirred before use. Painting can be done freehand, or following the traced image. The painting process is critical to the whole sequence, as it is on this that the final appearance of the badge will depend. Young people should be given every encouragement at this stage to ensure that the badge shape is well painted. Helpful hints can include using only one or two 'blocks' of colour so that a contrasting effect is obtained. If enamel paints are too fiddly or slow in drying, use acrylic paints or permanent poster pens, such as the Posca range from Mitsubishi. A permanent black fine liner pen is useful for finishing off the outlines.

STEP 5: turn it into a badge.
Once the enamel paint has dried (up to three-quarters of an hour), a badge pin can be glued on, and the shape varnished to provide a protective coat. With poster pens, you can move quickly to this stage.

Staffing
Although some artistic ability can be an advantage to those intending to run a wooden badge making session, it is in no way essential. The process of tracing out shapes and designs is adequate and gives good results. The cutting out of shapes requires little more than patience and a respect for the tools being used.

It is, however, crucial that the staff member is confident in passing on badge making skills to the young people. To this end, it is important to be fully acquainted with the tools, materials and skills required; this can easily be acquired by doing a 'dry run' and making badges, possibly with other members of staff. This is a useful way of ironing out any potential difficulties relating to premises, tools or materials.

Other Badges
Badges can be made in many different ways. You can, for example, use self-hardening modelling clays (like Das, Newclay or Darwi Roc) to make badge shapes which can be painted and varnished. Tiranti's, Specialist Crafts and Arnold's all offer a range of useful products. Oven-hardening Fimo is another useful product. it comes in a good range of colours, which can be blended and mixed in unusual ways. Once baked and varnished the results are very professional. A badge pin can be added to any of these creations.

Shapes can also be cut out using pastry cutters or a craft knife. You can even (believe it or not) make badges out of an extra hard biscuit mix! Once they have been baked in the oven or even in a microwave oven (using staged cooking times; often five minutes on medium – stand; five minutes medium – stand; one minute medium – stand; one minute on low power. They can be painted and finished as above.

Plain copper shapes (used for hot enamelling, not microwaving!) can be decorated using an engraving drill, or by burnishing with a blow torch. A coat of varnish and a badge pin should be used to finish. (see Hot Enamelling section)

BAKING AND COOKING

As well as having 'survived' a variety of youth projects which have included cooking as one of their activities, we have occasionally dabbled in the kitchen ourselves! However, don't be put off, as the comments and suggestions in this section come from more able folk than ourselves. Pilton Youth Programme in Edinburgh, West Sussex Youth and Community Service and a number of our colleagues from around the UK all provided us with useful material. While it is not exactly the youth work equivalent of Mrs Beeton's, we hope that it will provide a useful starting point for groups who want to use baking and cooking as an activity with young people.

In this section we have tried to offer something of an idealised set of ground-rules. We realise that you may have to battle with problems like lack of space, resources and money. Hopefully though, you can move towards these safety standards, even if they are unattainable in the short term. The recipes, which form the bulk of the section are mostly nice and simple, and should offer some unusual alternatives for the young people you are working with.

In the Kitchen

If you are going to work with a group of between six and eight in number, the kitchen should be large enough to allow young people to spread themselves about, without adding danger to the activity. For this reason, it is vital that the space is left uncluttered. Working with this size of group, an extra large oven is really essential, if everyone is to be fully involved. Similarly, bowls, trays, measuring jugs, pans, scales etc. should be large sized. Often in youth work, it is the paid or volunteer member of staff who provides equipment, so you will have to adopt an adaptable and flexible approach to 'making-do'.

In social education groups, and in some of the drop-in centres and playcentres, the provision of meals is crucial to the identity of the groups. Meals and their preparation, in such circumstances, take on an important role as a central part of the group provision, rather than a peripheral activity. The 'main meal' experience can provide a very useful platform for relationship building, and used supportively, it is a good shared activity which encourages co-operation between adult and youth group members. It is worth remembering that if you use cooking as a regular part of your youth programme, it is likely that you will suffer far less hassle when you go for camping and self-catering residential holidays. The same equally applies in the family home, where the adult members are fed up being unpaid galley slaves!

Group rules

Safety and cleanliness are central to this activity. To help ensure that the activity does not turn into a health and safety nightmare, it is worth agreeing certain basic rules, such as:

- everyone should wash hands and dry them thoroughly on a clean towel before starting;
- everyone should take a share in food preparation, cooking and washing up;
- there should be no poking of fingers into food, pies etc., while in preparation;
- once cooked, the food should be divided up fairly;
- cultural and religious traditions must be considered(for instance, many young people will come from families which do not eat meat; most Muslims and Jews do not eat pork; many Muslims fast during the daylight hours of the Ramadan; Hindus do not eat beef – many are vegetarian; many Jews do not eat dairy products and meat at the same meal);
- have a first aid kit handy and try to organise some first aid lessons for staff and young people;
- a fire blanket and appropriate fire extinguishers are important for safety in the kitchen in case of fire;
- once a cooker is on, it should not be left unsupervised;
- be aware that matches, scalding water and hot containers can all cause serious injuries.

The Main Meal

In quite a number of youth projects, children come straight to the facilities from school and may stay on quite late into the evening. At holiday times and weekends, they may be present for the whole day. For this reason it is important that children get a wholesome meal. Regrettably, there are also many children known to youth workers who are poorly provided for in the way of food. A diet solely of fish and chips is hardly a stimulating, balanced guide to healthful living! In offering the opportunity to prepare and eat a main meal, a youth programme can:

- offer children the opportunity to acquire new skills, in the areas of food preparation, cooking, and diet;
- provide the meal as an exercise in mutual co-operation between members of the group;
- provide a 'social learning' experience, in sitting down as a group and eating a meal together.

To quote the Pilton Youth Programme: "We have found it to be frustrating, chaotic and sometimes onerous. However, it can also be productive, pleasant and cohesive for the group. At any rate, a meal is always prepared and leftovers are a rarity. It is, nevertheless, hard work to organise."

With those cautionary words, it is hopefully a model which other workers will want to copy. In the setting up facilities such as drop-in coffee bars, where there are multi-cultural groups, it affords the opportunity for youngsters to engage in a down-to-earth experiment with their own culinary traditions. A West Indian coffee bar in Acton called NOCTA used to run disco evenings (called 'Sounds') where goat curry was the staple food. The other staple additive – the 'herb' was mostly prevented from being put into this Rastafarian dish!

Try to give the young people as much responsibility as they can handle. It is worth getting suggestions for menus from the young people themselves. Pilton use a loose-leaf folder as a group cook book, which is kept handy for easy reference. With groups in fairly deprived areas, it is best to avoid being too ambitious or too experimental. Spaghetti with too many 'raj' vegetables (Pilton term to describe disliked items such as: peppers, celery, garlic, courgettes etc.) was a disaster. On the other hand, spaghetti along with a simple sauce (mince, onions, tomatoes, mushrooms) has proved a great success. Needless to say, it is usually lots of fun to watch it being eaten! As prejudices are broken down, the menu can become more ambitious.

A number of groups in the social education field have used 'going out for a meal' as an enjoyable, shared experience towards the end of a group's life. Alternatively, this can always be adapted to a 'cook-in' at the centre. Pilton used the concept of a 'Chinese evening' with the 14 to 16 year old group – they are now quite expert at stir-frying in a wok and eating with chopsticks!

Baking and Snacks
Youth clubs from the Junior variety upwards, can concoct quick snacks and baked items at little expense. Care may be needed using hot ovens and some workers would suggest avoiding recipes involving frying. Most young people like to produce items which look nice, e.g. coloured sweets and fancy biscuits, but the speed of production is also of primary importance. Pilton's favourite for instant gratification is popping corn. It's great value and the kids love making it. You can make either sweet popcorn using a small amount of golden syrup to sweeten it, or season the corn with salt. It takes only a few minutes to make – but it gets eaten just as quickly, so you may need a shift system at the stove.

Always use recipes when working with young people, and prepare for a cooking session by making sure that you have the necessary ingredients and cooking implements to hand. A stock of the 'basics' such as flour, sugar, dried fruits, spices etc., is useful; fresh items such as eggs and milk can be bought on the day. There are plenty of simple recipes in most cookery books, but we would suggest a few well tried and tested favourites which are worth looking for in the books:

simple biscuits; flapjacks; chocolate cookies; chocolate crispies; peppermint creams, ginger bread.

With a number of baking recipes, it may be worth starting with pre-prepared packet kits. They are available in the cake section of all supermarkets. These are useful with low ability groups and give almost guaranteed results. If your group is organising fetes, gala days or the like, baked goods can be sold to the visitors to raise some funds. Finally, we offer a few recipe ideas of our own. We have tried to move away from 'traditional' British recipes, and offer instead some simple snacks which may be slightly unfamiliar, but use familiar ingredients.

Snack recipes for children and young people

French Toast
Quick, tasty, easy to make and relatively hassle free! Mix two tablespoons of milk with one large egg, a small amount of sugar, salt (and pepper and herbs according to preference). This mix produces enough for about three slices of bread, about enough for a snack tea for one person.

Cut the slices of bread into two, or into fingers, then dip them into the egg mix. Meantime, heat a mix of one ounce of butter with a tablespoon of oil in a frying pan. As soon as the oil starts to 'foam', put as many pieces of soaked bread into the pan as are required (or will fit!). When the bread is brown on the underside, turn over and when that side is also brown, serve while hot. Obviously, when frying with hot oil, an extra amount of care must be taken in the cooking area.

Cheese steaks
These are quick to prepare and are tasty. The following recipe produces enough for between one and two young people, depending upon their appetites. Whisk one egg until frothy, then add to a quarter pound of cottage or cream cheese, one big tablespoon of self-raising flour and half a teaspoon of salt and sugar. Mix well.

In a frying pan, heat two tablespoons of butter with one tablespoon of oil. When it begins to bubble, add a tablespoon of the cheese mix and fry on each side until nicely browned all over. Serve hot.

Swiss eggs
This produces enough for a snack for four. Pre-heat the oven at gas mark 5 or 375° f (190° c). Spread a thick layer of butter over the bottom of an oven proof dish. Cover this with thin slices of Edam, Gouda or Mozzarella cheese. Carefully break eight eggs and pour them one at a time onto the cheese. Add ten ounces of single cream and sprinkle with salt, pepper, nutmeg and your choice of herbs. Sprinkle grated cheese over the top. Bake for ten minutes, then place under a very hot grill to brown. This is an unusual egg and cheese dish.

Bacon cakes

You need a mincer for this recipe! Take any odds and ends of bacon, the end of a bacon joint or gammon steak and mince it until it's quite fine. Mix up a packet of sage and onion stuffing with the required amount of boiling water. When it cools a bit, mix in the shredded bacon. Mould the mixture into flattish rissoles, dust with flour and fry in shallow oil in a frying pan for four minutes per side, until golden brown. Most youngsters love these served with a healthful mountain of baked beans.

Basic cakes

Cakes are easy to divide up, and quite easy to prepare and cook. Extra ingredients such as sultanas and fruit peel can be add if required. Heat up the oven to 350° f (180° c). In a bowl, mix three and a half ounces of margarine or butter with the same quantity of sugar, beat in two eggs and sieve in five ounces of self-raising flour. Add about one or two dessertspoons full of milk and mix well. The mix should be put into a well greased baking tin or poured into individual paper baking cases. A tempting cake will be ready in between 15 and 20 minutes, depending upon the size of the cake(s) and the particular oven.

BOGIES

This is one of those activities which are part of street culture. Young people build and play with 'bogies', 'box-carts' or 'go-carts' on estates, derelict sites, etc. without much help from adults. However, that is not an argument for avoiding the use of this activity with youth groups, rather it is meant as a memory jogger for professionals who are getting forgetful of their own youth.

Since a box-cart is built from available resources, it fits into the area of junk or found art, which is mentioned elsewhere in this book. No two carts are identical and that, indeed, is part of the charm and attraction for young people. The bogie is seen as a scaled-down version of the car by many youngsters, and as long as this does not lead directly to staff encouraging auto-crime, it can be a pleasant, lively exercise, building and then racing the carts. As a group activity it has different stages.

1.   *Planning and foraging for materials.* This includes assembling the required tools for the job (probably screwdrivers; saw; spanners; drill; sandpaper; nails; screws; two-and-a-half inch bolts; paint and the necessary wood and pram wheels with axles).

2.   *Building.* This is a good activity to be done using volunteers and perhaps even parents. Some 'DIY' type help can be very useful at this stage – a trawl of your volunteers or local parents will usually uncover the necessary skills. With this kind of help the building process is fairly straightforward. The basic design we offer here can be tailor-made to suit your own group's preferences.

3.   *Finishing.* If possible, allow time to paint/varnish/decorate the vehicles. Personalising/customising is fun! When building the carts, a decision should be taken, early

on, as to whether the finished items belong to the individual builders or the establishment. Our advice is that it is better to encourage a wee bit of private ownership (and pride) in the creation of these mini-vehicles.

4.　　　*Racing.* Young people will quickly organise their own fantasy world around their carts. This can be encouraged, if you wish, by using events, races, downhill trials or team competitions as part of the activity.

Overall, the activity will probably be most acceptable to the younger age group. *As with adventure playgrounds, workers might be advised to check insurance liability, in case of mishaps.* We have seen carts used by youth organisations as part of their contribution to community events, such as fetes, carnivals and gala days. This is worth a thought, as a different style of contribution to the local neighbourhood. With children over twelve, the fascination with engines, motor-bikes, cars etc. is likely to have taken over. If you are working with this older age group and want further advice on motor vehicle projects with young people, contact the National Youth Agency, 17-23 Albion Street, Leicester LE1 6GD.

Materials required

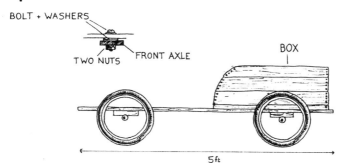

The baseboard should be prepared to the approximate dimensions in the diagram. Be flexible about this, because it has to fit the youngsters **you** are working with. The cut out front sections ensure that the front axle has freedom of movement, to enable tight turns to be made.

NEW YOUTH ARTS & CRAFT

The front axle is bolted to the front frame, the rear axle is preferably screwed to the base plate. The box section, with front removed should be bolted to the base plate. It will take a lot of pressure! Make sure that any sharp bolts and screws are cut/filed/covered, before embarking into the world of racing. The hand held rope loop is an additional form of steering, which uses the feet as well as the hands. With more elaborate carts, we have seen steering wheels and turning gear fitted and also braking devices. Brakes are usually pads attached to pivoted 2 x 1 inch wood, which can be swung onto the rubber of the rear wheels. We haven't seen them being very effective. One design which **was** very impressive was built by two thirteen year olds. This used rear motor cycle wheels, on the back of a cart, utilising hub brakes and cables. The front wheels were from the old Moulton/RSW 16 cycles. The eventual product was rather in the style of U.S. of A. chopper-bogies. All it lacked was the high-level handle-bars!

BRAIDING AND PLAITING

We'd like to thank Tanya and Kirsty down in Lyme Regis for their help with this section. Since then, Alan, despite nine fingers and three thumbs, has made his first couple of friendship bracelets, so it can't be that difficult! Braiding and plaiting, especially, around hair have become incredibly popular. At first it was a 'crusty' fashion only copied by the envious or faithful, but it has since blossomed and grown into a popular hobby and a mainstream fashion accessory. Go almost anywhere on holiday, and you'll probably encounter a youthful entrepreneur or three, sitting on a rug plaiting other people's hair for anything up to a tenner a time. Who said crafts can't be profitable? As a youth activity, it is possible to accomplish reasonable results with youngsters from about ten upwards, but expect a few knots and the occasional naughty words as threads get 'dropped'!

Plaiting and braiding threads of cotton around hair, attached to hair, or to make items such as chokers, headbands and friendship bracelets is relatively easy to learn. The basis of the craft is the simple weaving technique which links the single or double strands of cotton thread together. These can stand alone, as in bracelets, or can be intertwined around a person's hair.

Friendship bracelets

To start off, choose three colours for the bracelet, then you need to measure one thread around a suitable wrist. Double this length and then add four or five inches to allow for the tying off at one end and any fiddly bits. Measure the other two coloured threads against the first and cut to a similar length. The very process of plaiting naturally shortens the overall length of the threads.

We have found that cup hooks screwed into a wall or plastic hooks with suction pads are useful to assist the process of plaiting. Now take each of the three threads and double them over so that loop at the top is over a separate hook (see next diagram).

¾" MAX ← → ← ¾" MAX →

LEFT   CENTRE RIGHT

Next comes the first encounter with simple plaiting. Using the pair of threads to the right of central pair, fold them over and under the central pair. Repeat this with the left hand pair, wrapping the pair over and under the central pair. The braider (person doing the braiding) must try to keep all three pairs of threads tensioned and get a plaiting-rhythm going.

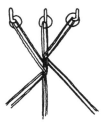

To finish off, tie a knot at the end of the plaiting, about two inches from the end of the loose threads. Similarly, tie a knot below the loop at the top of the plaiting at the other end of the bracelet. By pulling the knot through the loop, the bracelet has a natural fastener.

Hair braiding

The simplest and much less permanent way to add a hair braid to someone's hair is to use the above method to make a length of braiding, then to use the loop to tie it to the hair. However, it's not the proper method! With younger children it may be best to check out whether parents mind having their kids with braids before you embark on the following, since it can be a bit fiddly to take apart. Some schools are also distinctly 'iffy' about pupils with hair braids in their classes.

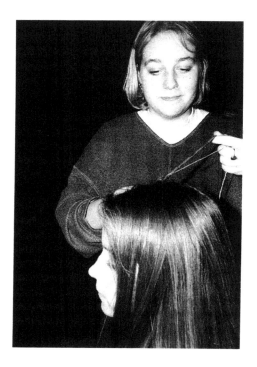

Unlike in the bracelet example, hair braiding (rather naturally) requires someone acting as braider and a second person as model. The model should be sitting at a lower level than the braider – it's easier to work this way. The stages for the method we want to describe are as follows, but, hair braiding lends itself to experimentation. There are no single right and wrong ways, and all sorts of unusual results are obtainable. Our method, based (we hope accurately) on what Tanya showed us, works as follows, with instructions aimed at the braider:

1. Plait the model's hair, (using the same technique as described in the bracelet example) separating a length of hair into three bunched strands.
2. Tie off the plait at the bottom with a piece of thread.
3. The braider may, with the model's permission, use a pair of scissors to tidy up any split ends sticking out of the plaited hair. Otherwise these stick out of the braided hair.
4. Take two or three lengths of thread all cut to similar lengths. Usually, at least twice the length of the hair plait.
5. We'd suggest tying these together neatly at one end.
6. Getting started with the braiding is the most difficult bit, because you are trying to keep the braids and the plait away from the rest of the hair. Here we go! Choosing one colour thread and starting at the top of the hair plait nearest to the scalp, wind that thread around the plait for between one quarter to one half inches worth of turns. Make sure that the other one or two threads are held taut together with the hair plait and under the thread being twisted round the hair plait.
7. Continue to repeat the process with the second and third colours of threads until you begin to run out of thread towards the bottom of the plait.
8. Knot the threads together and neatly cut off any loose ends of cotton.

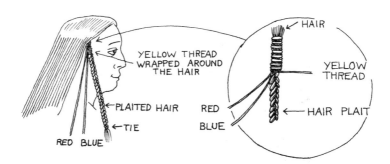

For an addition to simple hair braiding, add a criss cross pattern around the hair plait, by tying one or two threads together, and then wind them tightly around the hair plait and the original braiding in two, overlapping spirals. Finish the pattern by tying off neatly at the bottom.

A further interesting, but obvious variant, is to take three single or double stranded lengths of thread and plait them around the entire length of the hair, working in the same way from top to bottom.

BUBBLES

Blowing bubbles holds a fascination for children, but have you ever watched the poor souls trying to make bubbles with washing up liquid? Right – it doesn't work at all well.

We don't know why British washing up liquid doesn't blow good bubbles – nor do we have any evidence of an anti-fun conspiracy on the part of detergent manufacturers! Although it sounds utterly ludicrous, the only way to make good bubbles is to use *American* washing up liquid. Luckily, suppliers like The Big Top in Glasgow (see Suppliers Guide) import the stuff, so all you need to do is buy it off the shelf. Inevitably it's expensive, but if you avoid using it for washing up dishes it will keep you in bubbles for a fair length of time!

The good news is that bubble making has been transformed by the arrival of 'bubble wands.' Even better, they cost a fraction of the cost of a big bottle of 'Joy' or 'Dawn' (the American stuff you need to get hold of).

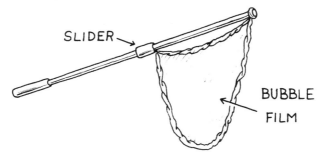

The bubble wand is a pole and slider arrangement. Two loops of fabric are connected to the end of the pole and to the slider. From this simple contraption, gigantic bubbles can be made to appear – it's a magical and addictive process.

Bubble Solution

First you need to make up some bubble solution. Follow these directions carefully (Howie didn't first time around and discovered that warm water kills the solution!)

- Measure 10 cups of water (and one or two extra cups on a hot, dry day) into a clean bucket followed by one cup of Joy or Dawn. We recommend that you add three or four tablespoons of glycerine at this stage to make the bubbles more durable (now you know how TV 'bubble magicians' do their tricks – lots of glycerine!)
- Stir the mixture very gently to avoid frothing it, and leave it to settle.

Precautions

Gigantic bubbles produce copious amounts of slippery liquid, particularly around the solution buckets, so avoid smooth surfaces like worn pavements, metal grilles and covers etc.. Wash away spillages with clean water when you're finished.

This is an outdoor activity which should be kept well away from roads to avoid distracting drivers. Bear in mind that children like to chase bubbles to burst them so make sure that your downwind playing area is safe. In any event, anything above a light breeze will make bubble blowing difficult so you may have to find a sheltered spot.

Remember that these detergents are powerful – excessive contact can do horrible things to your skin – make sure that children rinse their hands often, so have plenty of clean water nearby. Have some disposable gloves with you for children with sensitive skin or allergies and for the staff member on bubble duty! Avoid suds in the eyes.

Gigantic Bubbles

Make sure you have a bubble wand for each person, unless you want to referee arguments about who gets them first! If you can, provide a solution bucket for every four or five people. There is a simple technique for using the wand and this should be demonstrated to the group. You can pick it up yourself by following these instructions.

- Skim away any froth from the surface of the solution – froth stops bubbles from forming properly on the wand.
- Make sure that the fabric loops of the wand aren't tangled and move the slider to the bottom of the wand, i.e. all the fabric hangs from the end of the wand.
- Now immerse the loops in the solution and leave the soaking for a few seconds. make sure that all of the fabric is coated with solution but do **not** stir!
- Raise the wand until the loops are out of the solution, but keep the wand over the bucket to catch the drips. Open the loops a little by pulling the slider and look for a film of solution between the loops. If it's not there, soak the fabric in the solution again for a few seconds.
- This is the bit that needs some hand/eye co-ordination! Blow a gigantic bubble by pulling the slider along the wand towards you – as you wave the wand to create enough draught to form the bubble – then almost immediately push the slider back to the end of the wand to close off the bubble.

If you leave the wand 'open' for too long, you'll create a long sausage shaped bubble – fun, but they don't last very long. With practice, you'll learn how to control the size and shape of the bubbles by varying the distance you pull the slider towards you, how quickly you wave the wand, and when you close it. During your session, keep the wands and buckets 'froth free' for best effect. You can get several bubbles from each 'dipping.'

Other Bubbles

You can easily find smaller scale bubble blowing 'gizmos' in toy shops and department stores (often sold as part of a kit). These can be fun to use to make, e.g. different shapes, masses of tiny bubbles etc.. We didn't find any of them particularly easy to use – they are typically made of plastic and the solution sometimes doesn't adhere to them too well.

Clearly, the manufacturers of the bubble wand knew what they were doing when they used a fabric loop! If you can incorporate a covering of fabric or cloth tape on your bubble blowing implements you will achieve outstanding results. Big Al found a fabric and wire coat hanger in a junk shop and it works a treat – as long as you pull it out to a circular or oval shape! The tricky bit is removing the kink where the wires twist together; you may need to use pliers for this.

In fact, many 'found' objects can be used to make bubbles. Remember that you'll need to find a suitably shaped container for your gizmos, e.g. a large dish or frying pan for the coat hanger. Baking trays come in handy for items like:

- Plastic 'six pack' can holders.
- Two straws and a loop – thread a piece of string through two straws and tie off to make a squarish frame. Dip in the solution, carefully lift it out and pull it towards you to make the bubble. The knack is in flipping the frame to close off the bubble.
- Kiddie's fishing net frame.

You can blow loads of bubbles into the baking tray itself to create interesting effects. Do this using a straw which is first dipped in the solution (to create a film on the end). Now hold the tip of the straw just above the bubble solution and blow a bubble directly onto the solution. Blow it to a fair old size if you can and then carefully withdraw the straw and repeat the process as often as you like.

The most impressive bubble blowing feat we've heard of (at a Fair Play for Children in Scotland annual event) is life sized bubbles. Unfortunately we did not see this demonstrated, but we are assured that it works very well. To try it for yourself, apart from plenty of bubble solution, you will need a large tyre (lorry or tractor) and a Hula Hoop. The tyre is sliced in two laterally to make two containers for the bubble solution (although you may only want to use one of them.) The Hula Hoop should be covered in fabric or cloth tape, and is placed into the solution in the tyre and allowed to soak for a minute.

A volunteer can now stand in the middle of the tyre and be encased in a bubble created by a couple of people lifting the hoop out of the solution and over the volunteer's head to create a bubble. Again the knack is in how you flip the hoop to close off the bubble.

CALLIGRAPHY

This is the 'proper' name for the art of handwriting and lettering. Calligraphy is the technique used for creating italicised and script lettering. Many of us probably saw it for the first time when looking at old manuscripts and books now preserved in museums. As a creative art form for use with young people, you need to inject fun into the activity. For instance, with a younger group you might suggest that they design a 'Treasure map'. With an older group it could be design a 'Handbill,' 'Certificate' or 'Poster'.

The materials needed for calligraphy are cheap which is a bonus. To begin, all that is needed are a small selection of pens with different widths of nibs, paper, ink, and some way of creating lined paper. The pens are principally sold in three forms:
1. A pen holder with a selection of broad lettering nibs, and reservoirs which fit on the back of the nibs to provide enough ink for a few letters at a time.
2. A fountain pen, again with a range of interchangeable nibs.
3. Single nib width italic felt pens.

A number of manufacturers make these pens and you will probably find a range of each kind in your local art shop. Strangely, perhaps, calligraphy materials are one of the art materials which can be obtained from almost all art suppliers! The very largest interchangeable nibs are about one inch wide and from personal experience can take a little practice to get used to. The ink channel is so large that there is definite tendency for the ink to spill out in unwanted blobs – not a good recipe for providing young people with a successful artistic experience. William Mitchell, Dryad (Specialist Crafts), Gillot, Pentel, Shaeffer and Nikko are among the main manufacturers of pens for squared, left-oblique, italic and poster nibs. The best inks are permanent, waterproof and non-clogging. Black is still the most popular colour, but inks are available in crimson, emerald and other striking, bold colours.

Getting started
You'll definitely need one of the cheap sets of sample alphabets or calligraphy books, which offer both instruction and examples to copy if you are going to really get to grips with the range of calligraphic possibilities. To keep the lettering straight it is usually best to use a grid sheet underneath the lettering parchment/paper, or to lightly pencil rule lines with three elements:

$$\text{\textit{This is a sample}}$$

These offer guides for where the tops and bottoms of most letters should be placed. The difficulty for young people, especially, is to have the patience to spend time practising each letter. The most important aspects of calligraphic lettering are:
*   to hold the pen at a 45 degree angle on both vertical and horizontal strokes(both strokes should be equally wide);
*   to consider how tall and wide each letter should be relative to its alphabetic companions;
*   to learn how many individual nib strokes are required for each letter. For instance, many calligraphic masters would argue that a capital 'S' is constructed from three strokes:

Our illustrator and cartoonist, Gubby, writes all his letters to us in calligraphic form, so here we've let him loose with a bit of space to offer examples of how he constructs one particular style of script. With upper case on its own, there is no real problem with spacing between letters. When using lower case lettering, there should always be enough space to avoid the upstrokes of letters (called ascenders) colliding with the downstrokes (called descenders).

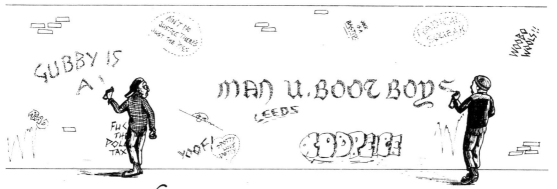

Calligraphy, I must explain,
    is a damn fine thing to do;
'Cos when Xmas or a birthday comes,
    & granny sends to you,
some bright green socks or a horrid tie,
    that makes you want to spew,

You write her back to thank her
    & say how do you do,
In a cursive script that's beautiful,
    & regular & true,
Then she will barely note the fact,
    that she got nowt from you!!
So now you see, this script can help,
    when pounds & pence are few!

Gubby

Many young people will not be tempted to get involved with calligraphy, purely because it smacks of school and being told to 'improve handwriting'. For those who do try it out, making letters into art forms and experimenting with inventing new styles of lettering can be fun and can even earn the proficient calligrapher a few spare pounds, helping design things such as certificates and posters.

CANDLE MAKING

Wax is a versatile material (witness Madame Tussaud's!) which can be used to make an incredible range of differently shaped, textured and coloured candles. At its simplest, the craft involves melting wax, dyeing it, pouring it into a mould and allowing it to set. It is important to prepare your work area well, as wax can be unbelievably messy – a few minutes spent covering working surfaces and the floor with old newspapers is time well spent. Wax is well nigh impossible to remove from carpets – plush youth centres beware! And, without putting you off, overheated wax can ignite, just like cooking fat – so, always heat wax and stearin very, very slowly!

Apart from slabs of paraffin wax (the cheapest way of buying it) or pellets of wax (easier to use), you will need:

- Stearin (helps the wax set, intensifies colours, and makes it easier to remove from moulds).
- Candle dye (disc form is easiest to use).
- Candle wicks (of varying length and thickness).
- Wicking or knitting needle.
- Skewers.
- Kitchen thermometer.
- Double boiler (or two saucepans – one to fit inside t'other. It should be either an old pan, or one which will be kept for use with wax). A thermostatically electric wax pot is also available but costs £80+.
- White spirit or turpentine.
- Blowtorch (optional).
- Moulds.
- Vybar, used instead of stearin when using flexible moulds.
- Bucket of sand (to make sand candles)
- Wax perfume or fragrance discs(optional).
- There are also non-heated options for younger children using coloured beeswax sheets, a new mouldable, coloured candle wax, or candle sand.

If your budget stretches to it, you can buy bags of wax ready mixed with stearin. This is certainly easier to use, but you will pay a premium. Flexiwax is a specially blended wax for use with flexible moulds. All the above and more are available through Specialist Crafts.

As we've already mentioned, wax can burn very fiercely, so care is needed when melting it down. A double boiler is safest, but you can use a saucepan sitting in another pan of boiling water. One Scottish I.T. worker we know (who shall remain nameless!) confided that he heats the wax directly in a saucepan, as this greatly speeds up the process. His inference was that the danger from burning wax was substantially less than that from a bunch of impatient, frustrated I.T. kids! If you do not mind using this method (we cannot recommend it) a thermometer can be used to keep a check on the temperature. Smoking wax is the danger signal to look out for. In case of fire, have a tight fitting lid to hand – this will take care of the problem more quickly and safely than a fire blanket or wet dish cloth. For most purposes, the wax should be heated to between 57 – 92 degrees C, (see maker's instructions) depending on the specific wax type and the strength of the mould, although sand candles may need hotter wax.

Method: Tapers, Moulded Candles, Layered Candles

Slabs of wax should be broken up into chunks for melting. Try wrapping it up in an old sheet and setting someone loose on it with a hammer – that usually does the trick! Approximately 10% stearin should be added to the wax – this should be heated up separately along with the dye and the perfume, if required, before mixing with the wax.

Simple candles, or tapers, are easily made by repeatedly dipping a wick into a deep container of dyed wax. The wax should be allowed to harden between dips (doesn't take long) and should be pulled taut after the first dipping. Interesting effects can be obtained by dipping in different colours. Once the candle has set it can be scooped back with a hot spoon to expose multi-coloured layers. Remember to use a thick or thin wick, depending on whether you want to dip a thick or thin candle! This can be a time-consuming process, and you may want to start your group off with something that produces a quicker result, by using commercial or 'found' moulds like milk cartons, yoghurt tubs, plastic balls, empty eggshells, wine bottles, etc.

These moulds should be cleaned before use and the inside treated with silicone spray or washing up liquid to help the candle slide out of the mould easily. The candle can be wicked before or after the wax is poured. Commercial moulds tend to be designed to be wicked beforehand (i.e. they are provided with a hole to take the wick) so it is just as well to prepare them this way. Knot the wick (selecting the correct thickness of wick) and pass it through the hole in the bottom of the mould, tying it to a skewer placed across the other (open) end of the mould.

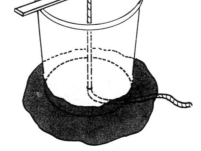

Plastic Mould

The wick should be arranged centrally in the mould and should be quite taut; the knot at the bottom should be sealed with Blu-tak or candle sealing compound.

The molten wax can now be poured smoothly down the centre of the mould; the mould should then be tapped gently to release air bubbles. The candle should be left in a cool place to set, or if you want a quicker result it can be immersed in water (taking care to match the depth of water with the depth of wax in the mould), or put in a fridge. The quicker you cool the candle, the more difficult it will be to remove from the mould; you will also get a frosty effect on the surface due to thermal cracking. You can get rid of this by first dipping the candle in very hot water and then cold to glaze the surface. Alternatively, the surface can be rubbed with white spirit or heated gently with a blowtorch. Because wax contracts as it cools, a well is formed in the centre of the candle which will need topping up – poke holes in the surface crust to provide a 'key' and carefully pour in the new layer of wax. A candle should only be removed from its mould once it is perfectly cold and set hard. Remember to cut off the wick knot first and then to trim it down to a quarter inch. Polish with a pair of old tights for a high-gloss finish.

Wicking a candle after it has set is relatively easy, and is recommended for most found moulds as they are often fragile. A hole needs to be bored in the candle once it has been removed from the mould. A heated wicking needle, knitting needle or skewer can be used for this. The inventive among you can try attaching a knitting needle or similar to an electric drill – this greatly speeds up the process. (This **may** be dangerous. Ed.). Alternatively, you can insert a metal wire when the wax is still soft and remove it once the candle has set. The wick should be pre-waxed by dipping, inserted into the hole, sealed with a blowlamp at the top and bottom, and trimmed. We'd suggest keeping the blowtorch in adult hands, unless you are sure of your young people.

When using found moulds like bottles, light bulbs, eggshells, etc. you will have to carefully break the mould once the candle has set hard. The 'dipping' technique can be used to colour part of your candle and you may find that some commercial moulds are designed with this in mind.

A variation on this kind of candle is to make it with different coloured layers. Each layer should be allowed to set a little before poking holes in it to form an anchor and pouring in the next layer. It is possible to produce diagonal layers by supporting the mould so that it is set at an angle. The angle can be changed between pourings to produce even weirder results!

Chunk or Carved Candles

So called because these candles use chunks of pre-dyed wax which are bonded together with fresh wax and then carved back to produce a rock-like effect. First of all break up a block of pre-dyed wax into small chunks and put into a prepared mould or other suitable receptacle (e.g. pint or half pint tankard). Now pour in hot wax of a contrasting colour and allow to set. Once set, the candle can be wicked and carved back with a craft knife to expose the original chunks or cross-sections of contrasting colours. You may like the rough effect created by carving but you can smooth it out by using a blowtorch or dipping the candle into white wax for five seconds.

Sand Candles

These got their name because (yes! you've guessed it) sand is used as a mould for the wax. Making a candle in this way bonds sand to the outside of it creating a nicely textured terra cotta effect. The sand you use should be damp (but not too damp as the result will be a poor coating of sand on the candle) and should be put in a bucket or other suitable container. The next step is to make a mould by pushing a suitably shaped object e.g. bowl or block of wood into the sand to create a recess. The recess itself can be indented with e.g. a spoon or small block of wood to create surface patterns. Hot wax can now be poured into the recess to create the candle; you may wish to experiment a few times to get the effect that you want, as a thicker coat of sand can be formed by using hotter wax or drier sand.

Once the candle has set it can be removed from the sand and wicked. The sand should be trimmed back to an even thickness with a craft knife – vivid patterns can be made by cutting through the sand crust to create coloured 'windows' in the candle. Also, the top of a rectangular candle can be pared down to create a conical shape if desired – use a craft knife and an old electric iron (set at warm) to smooth the wax.

If you want to try something spectacular, make three identical moulds in the sand and link them with channels. This will create three linked candles suitable for use as a table centrepiece. Small sand candles set relatively quickly and can usually be completed within one, two to three hour session. Another advantage of these candles is that once they have burned down the sandholder which is left can simply be topped up with fresh wax and re-wicked.

Other Candles and Waxy Ideas

Balloon Candles: fill a small balloon with cold water and tie the neck. Dip it carefully into hot wax several times to build up layers, taking great care not to let the balloon touch the bottom of the pan (it will burst if you do and may propel hot wax all over the place). Once enough layers have been built up for it to remain rigid, carefully cut the top off it, pour out the water and remove the balloon. The wax holder thus created can now be filled up with hot wax, a little at a time, swilling it around until it sets. Once all the wax has set the balloon candle can be wicked, sealed and trimmed.

Ice Candles: put a ready made commercial candle into a mould and pack with ice. Pour in hot wax to create a cratered, cave-like effect.

Candle Modelling: warm wax is nice to handle and can easily be modelled and sculpted into unusual shapes.

Decoration: plain candles that you make can be decorated in many different ways. They can be carved with craft knives or painted with acrylic paint or hot coloured wax. You can apply transfers to them or indent the surface repeatedly with a hard object to create a pattern. Chunks of discarded wax or strips of modelling wax can be glued onto them, and the artists among you can use modelling wax to create intricate patterns or artificial flowers to attach to the candles.

Face Masks: pour hot wax onto a large plate or tray and allow to become cool and pliable. It can then be peeled off and carefully placed over someone's face, care being taken to leave a breathing hole and to smooth in all the details. Once removed it can be hardened in cold water and painted.

Gory Hands: the wax specialists at Dundee's Clubbie assured us that you get a realistic gory effect if you drip warm multi-coloured wax onto your hands and arms. This was apparently an accidental discovery (we are not surprised!) which seems to have a lot of potential, particularly for those interested in making horror videos. The idea of meeting a pair of gory hands **and** a painted wax face mask on a dark night hardly bears thinking about!

Shell Candles: these are some of the nicest effects we have seen. If you are unable to collect large shells at your local beach, you can buy them from suppliers. You will need shells with a deep, wide opening so that you can pour the wax in easily. A large opening also means that they will shed a good amount of light. Conch and bonnet shells are particularly suitable.

If your chosen shell will not stand upright of its own accord, fix some modelling clay under the base. As with any other 'stand alone' candles, you should really place them on a saucer when burning to avoid spillages on your favourite table!

Shell candles must be wicked before pouring the wax. Hang a wick of correct length and thickness from a rod or pencil placed over the top of the shell. Use a thin wick for openings of up to one inch, medium for up to three inches and thick for openings larger than this. Make sure the wick is hanging straight down and gently pour the wax in until it is almost at the top of the shell. Finally (once the wax has set) remove the rod and trim the wick.

Beeswax sheet candles: These are used cold, by hand-wrapping around a wick in tightly formed cylinder shape. They come in 40 cm x 20 cm sheets in a range of colours. Ideal for younger groups.

Mouldable candles: This is rather like making candles out of plasticine! The trays of mouldable wax can be cut from the container with a knife and then moulded by hand. It is safe, easy to use and requires no stearin, dyes or melting. It comes in six basic colours which can be mixed.
Candle sand: This is not the same as Sand candles! Candle sand is simple for any age group to use. The sand is poured in any thickness into a suitable container, then a wick is inserted and the candle can be lit. It also floats, which can give stunning effects with the silver, gold and purple star mixes. Not cheap, but fun and definitely less messy!

Candle making is an excellent activity to use with small groups (4 or 5 at a time) of young people for several reasons. If you plan properly, some candles can be completed within one session, enabling them to be taken home immediately. Candles are always useful and can be used straight away, while the process of making and decorating them allows for individual creativity and experimentation. Although it is a good all year round activity, candles become 'extra-special' if made in the autumn leading up to Christmas and New Year. They make good Christmas gifts or first-footing presents, and generally add to the festive atmosphere.

CARDS, CALENDARS AND CARTOONS (including Stencilling)

Cards

Young people are often keen to produce designs for cards, notelets, calendars and all manner of greetings missives. These may be linked to special occasions, and especially the festive seasons celebrated by different religions. There are many different techniques which can be applied, some of which are covered elsewhere in this book. For instance, lino and screen printing, collage, airbrush techniques and photography can all be used to make interesting designs for cards. When working in monochrome – black and white – designs can easily be enlarged, reduced or multiply copied on a photocopier. This can be an impressive way for kids both to show off their own developing skills and to obtain good results for relatively little labour.

Design

In the collage section we mention cutting and pasting photos. A professional looking greeting card can be produced by pasting a photo onto card on its own, or with a 'bubble' or some other sort of caption. This can be very effective and is easily produced using only card, photo images, scissors, paper and glue. Old cards can be recycled this way. The more environmentally-conscious, or perhaps miserly, will use this technique to return a Christmas robin to Great Aunt Jane!

Young groups still enjoy making cards which abound with glitter and all things silver and gold. Pilton Youth Programme recommend the purchase of quite expensive gold and silver pens which are oil based as: "Well worth the trouble and expense". Posca pens by Mitsubishi are the best we've encountered and come in a vibrant range of colours as well as metallic finishes. Specialist Crafts market Edding metallic markers and the Zig professional marker range, which can be refilled. Paper, glue, glitter and coloured sheets of tissue come in useful in this method of card or calendar design.

Drawing and painting are still, happily, popular with youngsters. The youth worker may be required to brainstorm a few ideas to determine suitable subjects. This can then avoid the constant flowing chorus of youthful voices saying: "What shall we draw?" Tracing is another way in which accurate representations can be realised. It is not 'cheating' in the way youngsters see it – graphic artists do it all the time! The ideas described in the rubbings section could also be considered for pasting up onto card. As with collage, a drawback of some glues is that as artwork dries out, bubbles tend to form and in extreme cases, central heating can cause almost total destruction of home produced artwork. If you can afford it, and provide a well ventilated area, 3M's Spraymount range is very reliable, and Pritt-type stick glue is non-toxic and fairly effective.

Lettering

It can be a good idea to encourage young people to produce lettering, often referred to as *typography* on a computer. They might either use a word processing package such as Word 6, or a design application like Corel Draw; also there are a number of CD packages offering literally thousands of different type founts and clip art. The danger lies less in their use, but in the potential to overload the computer's memory. For instance, the words 'Happy Birthday' look very different in different typefaces:

HAPPY BIRTHDAY   HAPPY BIRTHDAY   Happy Birthday

Happy Birthday   HAPPY BIRTHDAY

Most young people will have had some experience of using different type styles at school o home and experimenting with lettering can be a very creative exercise. An alternative, is to use sheets of *dry transfer lettering* such as those manufactured by Letraset or Edding. To use these it is necessary to draw a light pencil line on the paper. The letters are then lined up with their base against the pencil line. Rounded letters tend to be slightly larger, therefore line up with the lower curve just below the pencil line. Once the lettering is finished, tell the budding graphic artists to carefully and lightly, rub out the pencil line. When trying to make photos into cards, a good dodge for lettering, which has been used by youth groups trying to produce cards for fund-raising, is as follows. Letraset, as above, onto the clear film directly over the paper. The result will give accurate, professional, white lettering contrasting against a darker background. One last comment (for the moment) on the use of dry transfer lettering: the spacing between letters **can** be proportionally worked out. With youth groups, especially under-twelves, this normally gives untidy results. An easier answer is to line up each letter as close as possible to its predecessor, whilst still leaving a very minimal amount of space.

Other forms of lettering which can be considered include:

1.   stencilled letters;
2.   cut-out letters from magazines and newspapers;
3.   italic or handwritten (calligraphic) headings.

Stencils: these are OK for use with youngsters, although since it's a slow process it may use up the kids' patience rather quickly. If you buy stencils you will often be offered a stencil brush which can be used with water colour/poster paint. The stencil must be held firmly onto the paper of card, otherwise an untidy image is produced. Really, for hand producing cards, it is a bit laborious. One useful dodge for work with younger groups is to use special stencils with prepared messages, such as 'Thank You' or 'Happy Christmas' already cut out as a complete image.

Stencil sheets of single letters are more suitable for producing lettering onto T-shirts etc., used in conjunction with fabric pens made by reputable firms such as Dylon, Berol and Pebeo. A quick look through the Arnolds' and Specialist Crafts' catalogues will provide plenty of ideas.

If you are feeling very masochistic, you might follow our example and occasionally make your own stencils, with lettering already spaced and perhaps included within an overall design. To do this, use at least 120gsm paper and preferably heavier weight card. Mark out the design as accurately as possible, then cut out sections of the letters with a designer's knife/scalpel. When used for calendars or T-shirts, this can, if you are careful, produce a good primitive lettering style which can be repeated a number of times. It's still time consuming, but less than stencilling individual letters. Only older young people will have the skill and patience to use this technique, but younger children would be able to use stencils already prepared for them. For use on cards, unless they are quite big, or require only a few letters, this lettering system will be too fiddly. Yet another word of warning! Watch out when you are cutting out the letters, otherwise you will be left with rather odd letters, for instance, a big round hole, as opposed to an 'O'.

Cut out letters: since blackmail letters and later punk rock became cults, youngsters have enjoyed experimenting with their own forms of typographical layout. The idea is simple. Collect various printed material. (If you are planning for a group, think ahead and ask them to bring old newspapers and magazines on a specific day). Individual letters and words can then be cut and pasted onto the card or paper. It if is a 'one-off' design, youngsters can, in this way, add colour to their artwork. If it is for photocopying, it is safer to stick to black letters. Some photocopiers dislike particular colours and they are reproduced in a very faint form.

Calligraphic headings: you might like to refer to our short calligraphy section for more technical advice on this form of lettering. Some young people will welcome the opportunity of sitting down and painstakingly writing headings and lettering by hand. As a youth worker, the job is to encourage, and offer alternatives to youngsters who do not have this skill, or perhaps confidence. Plenty of useful books on calligraphy are usually available from the local library. In Lothian Region in Scotland, one of our staff team at the Longniddry Youth Centre successfully used calligraphy as the basis for a popular and well attended group.

Cartoons

Cartoon animation work with youth groups is covered elsewhere, but popular cartoon characters can be copied by a lot of youngsters, if you have done your homework and brought along a goodly stock of cartoon books. Depending upon the age group, Hagar, Simpsons, Viz, Beavis and Butthead, Flintstones, Peanuts; Asterix; Tom and Jerry; Marvel Comix (Superman etc.); the Brooms etc., should add a bit of inspiration to a drawing session. From experience, it would seem quite useful to pull tables together and attempt to give a stock of books and felt pens, paper and tracing paper to each small group. This makes the session easier to supervise.

There is sometimes a temptation for talented members of staff to end up doing all the designs for youngsters. This is hardly the purpose of the exercise, though it's a good idea to involve members of staff in this activity who have a genuine interest and are willing to get fully involved. You may also find that some of the youngsters you are working with are able to invent and develop their own cartoon characters and story lines. Using cartoons in this way can lead to the development of cartoon strips and even little books. Our artist, Gubby, started this way and has produced a number of irreverent little A5 cartoon books.

NEW YOUTH ARTS & CRAFT

Using cartoons to illustrate cards, a personalised bubble caption can radically alter a cartoon into a personal message. So, when Bart from the Simpsons starts to say rude things about **you** in a Christmas card from a hulking sixteen year old, you will know you've made it! If you still make the effort and facilitate the activity to take place, there is a good chance that you may be able to mobilise a range of hidden talents in your youth group. If you find yourself as a youth worker with a number of talented cartoonists, this may be very useful if you plan to start a youth magazine or similar. (see magazines, zines and publications section) The organisation of a competition or a non-competitive show/display could also be a way to generate increased enthusiasm for the activity.

Calendars

Not a lot needs to be said about these. There are (at least) three ways of producing calendars which are accessible to youngsters:

1.	The simplest is to produce a design on a card and glue or tape a pre-printed calendar block on to the bottom of the card.
2.	This involves drawing out the months of the year by hand into month-by-month sheets. These could also be the printed sheets from a calendar block, pasted onto separate sheets for each month. Seasonal photos, cartoons or some such item could complete the presentation.
3.	Another method is to draw out a wall calendar for the whole year. Rather a mammoth task, but we have seen A3 or A2 size versions constructed by youthful artists. In one case, a youngster produced a calendar based on the theme of Tolkien's 'Lord of the Rings', dragons and all!

CARNIVALS, FESTIVALS AND PERFORMANCE ARTS

We honestly weren't sure what to call this section. For youth clubs, playschemes, community groups and the like, performance arts and street arts have become a form of celebration. These activities may be organised for friends and parents or may be part of a community event such as a festival, fete, street party or carnival. One of the most noticeable developments of the late 1980s and 1990s has been the proliferation of such participation events, whether they are 'traditional', as in the local church fete, multi-cultural, such as the Notting Hill Carnival and its many offshoots, or counter-cultural such as the Tree Fayre and the Rainbow Circle camps and workshops. What is true of them all is that they can provide a unifying influence on communities in the planning and organisation of such events. They also offer the opportunity to present 'arts activities' to audiences who might normally run for cover to try and avoid anything 'cultural' or 'arty'.

Working with young people, the key aspects of **performance arts** are that they provide opportunities for:
- learning new skills;
- gaining confidence to perform in front of other people;
- participation by the audience;
- interaction with other people;
- having fun.

A number of the activities featured in this book can have a part to play in performance arts. Along with obvious ones such as circus skills, there are bubbles, masks, papier mâché, face painting and make-up, puppets, kites, film and video making, and murals which may also have an important part to play in any arts or community event. They are also easy to transfer from the confines of the playscheme or community centre out into the street or the local playing field.

In the individual sections of the book dealing with these subjects, we have tried to make it clear which activities require skilled instruction and lots of practise, such as juggling and unicycling, and are therefore, best tackled with young people in workshop sessions. Others such as face-painting, murals, hair braiding and video-making can produce attractive results without a long learning curve. And, most importantly, every one has fun!

Carnivals, festivals and street events

Nearly all youth-related organisations are likely at some time to participate in street celebrations and community events. Some may build a float on the back of a lorry or trailer, others will design and dress walking displays. The reasons for taking part can include:

- gaining publicity for the group and good public relations;
- the chance for winning prizes;
- a co-operative undertaking involving adults and young people working together;
- raising money for charities or the organisation itself;
- making a contribution to the community;
- practically learning arts and performance skills.

Design of floats

Young people can be encouraged to help with, or entirely design a float, or a costume. An event may have a theme or entrants may be invited to produce the most colourful, humorous or dramatic display. When designing a float, for instance it is important to consider all of the following:

- safety for those taking part and those watching, and, potentially insurance;
- cost and ease of construction;
- how many people need to fit on the float and what they will be doing;
- what type of vehicle is carrying the design/people and its overall dimensions;
- types of materials to be used;
- need for power for music/sounds.

As a general rule, the materials used may depend on whether the float is to be used only once or at a number of events. For instance, in the south-west of England there is a bustling carnival season each autumn, with floats sometimes appearing at three or four venues in different towns each week. Hardboard and plywood can make useful frames for float designs and are often covered with stretched cloth which is painted in a similar way to theatre stage 'flats'. Cardboard and strong paper are easier for children to work with, but can rip easily on the back of a moving vehicle. For costumes and floats, there are three stages of preparation:

1.   design
2.   manufacture
3.   assembly (onto the vehicle, on the day or soon before).

Many of the most successful floats combine strong visual images, constructed into imaginative and unusual shapes. Some employ movement such as a mobile dragon's head at the front. Slogans on the float can offer humour, whilst the people on the float should be colourfully dressed and present an active spectacle to their street audience. The themes of many floats use songs, music and dance as a major part of the moving presentation. Among many unusual floats we have seen were: Sinderella (we'll leave that to your imagination!); The Batgirls; The Sounds of Music and How the West was Lost. Frequently, the images and actions portrayed on the float are enhanced by walking participants in an array of costumes. The carnival streetwalkers will often employ circus skills: clowning, juggling, stilt-walking, uni-cycling, to increase their visual impact. If you are briefing walking performers or those on floats, it is important to tell them that they must continue to 'act' all the time they are in a procession. Masks, as described in the special section of the book, have a special place in fiestas, carnivals and community arts, and this even spills over into street demonstrations and protest. Television has broadcast many images of larger than life world leaders involved in anti-road rallies and protests against the Criminal Justice Act.

Multi-cultural
In recent years, carnivals have taken on a much more international dimension which can make them a useful part of multi-cultural education for children and young people. For example, in Alan's current area of Lyme Regis in Dorset, the annual summer Street Party organised by Ayvin from the Fuego South American shop, always features music, dance and artists from a variety of cultures – Caribbean, South America, Africa etc.. Percussion is particularly popular with street audiences, and steel drums, bongos, bodhrans, mancalas, tablas, whistles and rattles can bring a carnival or street event to life.

Walkabout performers

Increasingly, there are more anarchic walkabout acts, which often can abuse as well as amuse audiences. How far this is relevant to *your* youth work depends a great deal on your politics and the views of your organisation. Typical examples include dressing up as police, penguins, escaped convicts, a troupe of Scottish bagpipe players, aliens, or an entire squadron of red arrows' pilots, pushing wheel-barrow planes in earthbound aerobatics! Confrontation can be part of the act, and young people like dressing up as outcast sub-cultural groups like Hell's Angels or Punks. Unusual behaviour and quirky dress like gay police, walking hand in hand, complete with handbags over their shoulders are typical ploys of walkabout, street performance. This is very much the territory where carnival crosses over into street theatre.

Planning and safety

For the organisers of most events there are a number of things to consider:

*   To start with, publicity is important.
*   A good show with no audience, isn't much good! Think of ways which will give the local media the chance to 'tell a good story' about your event.
*   Try and get bunting, flags and banners erected around the route or event site.
*   Seek permission from the police for the route you intend to use. You may also need to work closely with the local council and other public authorities.
*   It is wise to take out public liability insurance.
*   Check the safety of the vehicles and constructions on floats. You don't want either performers or spectators to get injured.
*   Look out for temporary or permanent obstructions and inconveniences like: wind, rain, tight bends, low bridges and erratic drivers.
*   Heat can also pose a problem for performers on very hot days, especially where they are wearing heavy costumes, masks or big heads.
*   Have adequate first aid assistance on hand.
*   Try not to block access to shops for any longer than necessary.
*   Brief participants and vehicle drivers in particular. Tell them that patience and good humour are vital to make the event a great success.
*   If the police require co-operation, try to be as helpful as possible.

CIRCUS SKILLS

Historically and culturally it may be argued that most circus skills are popular developments from the traditional skills of the magic men – the shamans. These were the people in a tribe who conjured up spirits and whose stock skills were magic, acrobatics and the skills of the fakirs, such as levitation, sword swallowing and sitting on a bed of nails. The 'fools' of the medieval court often employed juggling and clowning skills. Nowadays, the UK's newer Travellers are among the most recent group to continue in the tradition of the ancient buskers and showmen using juggling, street music, fire-eating and occasional buffoonery. What has made them, and many European anarchic circus acts such as Archaos, Royale de Luxe, Malabar and Generik Vapeur particularly exciting for young audiences, is the confrontational nature of many of the acts. This type of circus uses no animals and the performers bring street skills and values of skateboarding, motor cycling, punk and rave cultures, radical theatre, loud music and pyrotechnics along with the more usual skills of acrobatics, clowning and juggling.

This book does not allow the space for a full scale introduction to circus and juggling skills. Dave Finnegan's 'The Complete Juggler' is about the most practical guide to juggling and

the associated skills required for balancing, diablos, plate and ball spinning, and using devil sticks. In the same Butterfinger's series is Sebastian Hoher's 'Unicycling from beginner to expert'. A good book on circus skills with youth and community groups is Reg Bolton's 'Circus in a Suitcase'. His book is particularly good on clowning and community participation. He also offers the following **checklist for street circus/busking**:

- Don't obstruct the street or sidewalk.
- Don't block access to shops, which would turn the shopkeeper's goodwill into bad.
- Be sure the ground is safe for stilts and unicycles – not wet or slippery.
- Don't plan an acrobatic *rolling* sequence, unless you have a mat or grass.
- Don't use bouncy juggling balls unless you're an excellent juggler.
- Take a length of bunting for the front row of the audience to hold, if it is necessary to keep them back (from the performance area).
- Don't take a lot of loose props, and keep an eye on those you have. The public is generally kind to street performers, but you should avoid providing the temptation to steal your gear.

One of our advisors who runs a London-based juggling shop and teaches circus skills, confided with us, "Juggling is basically a very boring activity." However, it is still a skill which is not too hard to learn at a basic level, and children and young people seem to love both its repetition and the almost infinite variety of items which can be juggled or manipulated: balls, beanbags, rings, clubs, cigar boxes, scarves etc.. Special juggling scarves are particularly suitable to learn with because they fall more slowly through the air than balls. As Dave Finnegan says:

"Another characteristic of juggling is its rhythmic, almost mystical nature. It can have the same calming effects on your spirit as playing or listening to good music. For many, juggling is a form of meditation, of integrating mind, body and spirit."

It sounds pretty good to us!

Having attended a couple of circus skills workshops ourselves and quizzed the instructors, we'd like to emphasise that juggling and circus related skills are not like a lot of the other arts activities described in this book. They do take a good deal of practice to become proficient, and they cannot be learned in one practice session by adults, who can then teach them or pass them on to groups of young people. We would recommend that nearly all circus skills are best learned in workshops run by experienced practitioners. Young people often learn more quickly than adults, and learning by 'seeing and doing' is the most effective way to learn.

In the last couple of years the use of devil sticks, two sticks held in either hand and used for tossing and flipping a centre-stick have, together with the use of diablos and plate-spinning, greatly increased in popularity alongside juggling.

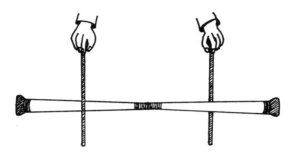

Many young street performers now mix juggling with the use of diablo spinning and throwing and devil sticks, and may even combine this with:
- unicycling
- stilt walking
- clowning
- acrobatics.

Putting on a show

Whilst it is easy to accomplish basic moves, the juggling arts, acrobatics and balancing take practise and more practise to achieve real skill which can be used to entertain an audience. From Aikido, performers may learn to 'stay with the experience' – the more you practise, the better the focus of attention. Showmanship is also something which has to be learned. For young people, it is worth getting them used to thinking in terms of:

- how they are dressed and made up;
- what they say;
- how they move;
- how they can involve an audience;
- good links to use between sequences and stunts;
- the development of their own personal, unique style of presentation.

For playschemes and similar, a 'circus' performance for families, friends and other members of the very localised community can form a good focus for an event. There can be lots of different types of performance including BMX/mountain bike riding, dance and skateboarding and roller or blade skating. Plate-spinning and diablo manipulation are easier to learn up to a rudimentary level for a lot of young people than juggling, and offer a useful introduction to circus skills. Use of a 'Play-go' which is a bit like a pedal skateboard, can be a good way to learn the balancing skills and co-ordination necessary to ride a unicycle. Combined in a show with a compere, music, acrobatics and plenty of colourful costumes, lack of highly developed skills don't matter much. Enthusiasm and energy count for a lot!

There are also a lot of myths and secrets surrounding circus skills; for instance, many young people can learn to stilt walk in under two hours! If you are stumped for contacts in the circus/juggling worlds, you could try to get help from the people listed in the suppliers' section at the end of the book. As well as supplying circus and other equipment (such as training videos, books, earthballs and parachutes) to buy and hire, often at discount prices they also have a lot of experience in running kids' workshops and circus shows.

COLLAGE, MOSAICS AND MARBLING

Actually, this section is quite 'arty', with a number of suggested methods for using art techniques which are best suited to a setting which is at least somewhat structured. Otherwise, it is perhaps only too easy to picture the scene of flying shreds of paper wafting not so delicately through the space of the temporary craft room. After the section on collage, there are sections on mosaic and marbling, which will provide a starting point for enterprising adults who wish to brighten up the premises where youth work is carried out, or perhaps add some new, youth art work to the local neighbourhood.

Collage

For most youth groups, there are two distinct memories of collage. One involves the primary school technique which sounds like,

> "One group should paint a background scene onto a large sheet of paper or wallpaper. The main group work must work individually to paint/colour/draw objects, people, animals etc. which can be pasted onto the background."

The second, and oft-prepared collage is a scissors and paste job. This turns sections of colour supplements and similar into a mass of dissected images which can then be re-positioned and pasted to form a new work of art. The process can be carried out individually or as a group activity, and no artistic skill as such is required. Usually the more bizarre the collage is, the more successful the image. A Dali-montage or surrealist images can be constructed in this way by even the most uncompromising GBH specialist! It is also particularly successful and enjoyable with younger groups, aged between eight and twelve.

Collage, almost by definition, is concerned with turning discards and disposables into art forms. A base onto which items can be attached must first be prepared. The question, is it to be permanent or disposable?, should be asked early on since it affects what sort of materials to consider using. If participants are new to collage work it is best to start with fairly small designs first. As mentioned in our section on organising and gathering materials, it is important to amass a collection of 'FOUND OBJECTS'. The list below might give a guide to the sort of things which can be used:

> corrugated paper, bottle tops, old posters, sacking, rice, string and rope, milk bottle tops, watch parts, colour supplements, pop newspapers, women's papers, pasta shapes, tissues, photos, herbs, cellophane, coffee beans, dried leaves, seeds and pods, feathers, fabric/cloth, sequins, and film negatives.

Some of the items will give a two-dimensional image, similar to the wall displays used in a number of popular restaurants and pubs, where montages of photos, posters, stamps and bank notes and now a common decoration. These are the easiest form of collage and if used directly onto a wall, they can be varnished into a permanent state. In the club or centre it can prove an impressive and professional form of decoration. The youth club in Tranent, East Lothian has an entire stairwell adorned in this fashion. It has a hallucinatory effect on the eye, but at the same time is stunning. One word of warning: you may, as a youth 'leader' find yourself out of favour with mums and dads, when the youngsters practice their new found skills on the bedroom at home! Some of the images produced by youthful collagers may be discriminatory, so it is important to prepare for a bit of lively social education on images, stereotyping and why they might be hurtful to others.

Three-dimensional collages rely on the sense of form and texture which can be achieved using this medium. It is not a subject which should be learned or taught. Experimentation will show the range of art forms which can be produced. However, when organising this sort of group, enthusiasm may have to be generated. One way of doing this is through the employment of the old teaching adage of 'structure'. Suggest themes for the exercise, i.e. advertising, people, animals, or alternatively stress contrast, texture or impact.

With regard to adhesives, one almost feels hesitant to make recommendations given the current anxiety concerning solvent abuse. However, here are a few types of adhesives which have been used effectively. Which you choose will depend upon both the nature of the materials used (some glues can only adhere to paper) and where the end product is to be a temporary or permanent creation.

> Cow gum; Berol Marvin medium and other PVA adhesives (polyvinyl acetate adhesive); Spray mount (various); Pritt stick and Evostick have all been successfully used in different circumstances. NES Arnold, Galt and Specialist Crafts all market a good range.

Application can be made using a knife, brush, aerosol, a piece of card, or, as will probably occur, fingers (!). Be careful, since some of the adhesives are dangerous to inhale in a confined space – so, window open!

Other techniques which might be combined into collages or murals are offered below:

Mosaics

The simplest mosaics are made using gummed paper shapes which are stuck onto sheets of paper in imaginative combinations. There are also various sets of tessellated shapes made of card or wood which schools use for maths teaching. These offer a variety of shapes and colours which can be joined together to make mosaic style patterns and pictures. Galt's offer a useful range of these.

When starting with a new group, especially with younger children or people with learning difficulties, it is important to show some examples of what sort of thing might be produced. Mosaics are easier to understand by looking and doing, than through description. A simple exercise involves each participant having their own sheet of card, at least A4 in size. Get them to cut or tear up lots of pieces of different coloured papers. Old wrapping paper, sweet papers, metallic foils or newspaper can all be effective. Using wallpaper paste, or slightly diluted PVA adhesive, these shapes can be stuck either adjacent to one another, or in slightly overlapping sequence. Using lots of varied types of paper can produce nice textural effects. Once the picture is completed, a further coat of PVA will give it a shiny, varnish-like finish.

Specialist Crafts and others market colour beads, which are small plastic beads that come in a nice variety of colours and which can be pressed into place on peg-boards to form mosaic pictures. These are popular with younger groups, up to about thirteen and with therapeutic groups of various kinds.

Traditional mosaics do not use overlapping pieces. The designs tend to be geometric and are part of Indian, Greek and Roman cultures. It is still possible to purchase from Specialist Crafts, the glass enamel and glass pieces, known as 'Smalti', which can be cut to shape using a special set of nippers. Bonded with tile cement and tidied up with a palette knife, squeegee and sponge, this is all (apart from a lot of patience) that is required to produce either authentic or modern mosaics.

Marbling techniques

There are a variety of techniques which can be used to produce unusual marbling techniques on paper, fabric or other surfaces.

1.   *Wet paper.* Wet a sheet of colour supplement thoroughly, crush it into a ball and squeeze hard. Open and place on a newspaper to dry. The result is a cracked image. A similar result can be achieved by crushing paper while dry and then running water over the surface. Coloured tissue papers are worth experimenting with if you have some funds for materials. The colours run and when glued together, the sheets can combine elements of collage and origami.

2.   *Oil in Water/Marbling. Method One.* We found this technique popular with youth groups of most ages, though it may have been over-used in some schools. Using a tray of water about an inch deep as a base, add different quantities of oil paint which has been diluted with a small quantity of oil thinners. Stir or splash the water around (not too vigorously!) and when the pattern on the surface of the water is interesting, place a sheet of white or coloured paper onto the surface. It takes only a few seconds and unusual, almost psychedelic results abound. If you are using a smooth surface card or cartridge paper, you can try floating pools of water directly on the surface of the card and then adding the oils. By rocking the card, swirling patterns of colour can be achieved. The end result is similar, but **feels** slightly more like an act of creation as opposed to spontaneous luck!

3.   *Oil in Water/Marbling. Method Two.* This process enables multi-coloured images to be made on plain paper or fabric. It can be used for collage work, wall displays, fabric design, end papers for hand made books, or pasted onto greetings cards. Marbling relies on the fact that oil and water don't mix and is a quick way of making highly individual designs without the necessity of being artistically gifted.

All these collage techniques have been used with people with learning difficulties and young people of all ages. The end products are both unusual and professional looking, and do not require any degree of technical or artistic skills, which makes them ideal in a wide range of settings.

Most of the necessary materials can be prepared in advance, leaving you free to nurture the kids' creative talents!

You will need:

> A shallow container like a photographic dish, or the kind of tray butchers use.
> Artist's oil paints, or specialist fashion marbling colours, seaweed colours or
> > Marblin inks.
> Oil thinners/turpentine/white spirit if using oil colours.
> Things to stir with, particularly a marbling comb.
> Small jars or pots.
> Old newspapers.
> Sheets of plain paper (as long as it's not too soft, thin or porous) that are
> > slightly smaller than the container.
> A packet of powdered gelatine size, or marbling ground.

Prepare the size by mixing one dessertspoon of gelatine with a little boiling water in the container, or the ground following the instructions. Mix well and make up to the quantity required with cold water. Ideally, the container should be about three-quarters full and be allowed to stand until it reaches room temperature.

Oil colours are prepared by mixing a small amount of each colour with turps, oil thinners or white spirit in a separate pot. These should be well stirred until they reach a runny ~onsistency. Special marbling inks and colours are pre-mixed to the correct consistencies.

The size and colours must now be tested to obtain a good match. Before using any colours, use some strips of newspaper to break the surface tension in the container of size. Then, drop a spot of each colour onto the surface and spread out till each is one or two inches across. If the droplets spread out too much, the paint is too thin, and vice versa. If the droplets stay at the bottom, then the size needs thinning, and if they expand and then contract, it should be allowed to stand a little longer to reach room temperature.

COMPUTERS, VIDEO-GAMES AND RADIO-CONTROLLED MODELS

Lots of things electrical with plenty of likelihood of blowing-up or going wrong have crept into the repertoire of work with young people. Computers, in particular, have had a dramatic effect on almost everyone's lives in the past ten years. Video games machines were really a forerunner of the multi-megabyte powered computers. In both cases though, they have provided an entertaining source of fun and a means of improving dexterity. The computer has taken this a stage further with the development of software with a high educational value.

Computers

The current generation of multimedia machines, with their capacity to run e.g. interactive encyclopaedias such as Encarta and complex games, have brought the computer into many living rooms. An impressively powerful computer can now be purchased for well under £1,000, although you will have to pay a little more for a complete multimedia machine, which includes full sound, music and video capabilities.

Youth workers, teachers, social workers and the like mostly now take for granted the computer's capacity to act as a word processor, saving time and effort in re-drafting letters and reports; as a data-base for keeping records; and an accountancy package for monitoring finances. It can also be a valuable learning tool for work with young people. Computer obsolescence has become less of a problem, as most new machines are easily upgradeable.

Powerful new software packages have transformed the capability of home computers over the past decade. As long as you can afford the software, you can have a 'home office' (this software is often bundled free with new computers), digital recording and mixing capability, graphic and design studio or desktop publishing outfit.

Some of the most useful software to use in creative work with young people is of the graphics/desktop publishing type. Commercially obtainable images on disk (called 'clip art') can be combined with photographic images, animation and video to produce unique results. The processes involved offer endless possibilities, and of course you can manipulate the images as much as you like with specialist software.

Hand held 'scanners' are very cheap and enable you to introduce line art and greyscale or colour photographs. You can edit these images pixel by pixel (dot by dot) on screen. However, unless you have access to a 1,000 dpi (dots per inch) printer the output quality of line art and photographs will be degraded.

We strongly recommend that you use computers in this kind of creative way with young people. Other specialist software programmes can be used to create sound mixing facilities or to publish newsletters, magazines and fanzines. You'll find that several graphics programmes, e.g. Corel Draw, include founts (type styles) which kids love to use.

Many programmes allow you to stretch and otherwise manipulate text to produce special effects. We especially liked the 'Banner' software which is very easy to use and can produce some very fine poster designs.

Available Software

The following list comprises the types of games software currently available:

- Quizzes and competition programs ranging from hangman to trivial pursuits.
- Decision-making games and role playing adventures, which may involve a sequence of puzzle solving, similar to the 'Crystal Maze' on the TV.
- Personal assessment programs on behaviour and attitudes. Aggression, drugs, alcohol and crime are all covered by specialist programs.
- Computer versions of commercial games such as Scrabble, Monopoly and chess.
- 'Intelligent' action games based on settings such as wars, sports and activities such as flying, driving etc..
- Simulations which try to recreate a real situation where choices can be made which affect outcomes.
- Learning programs which teach keyboard, computing, language, literacy, numeracy and music skills.
- Questionnaires on a variety of subjects.
- Virtual reality games which put the players in the centre of 3-D action, sometimes using headsets.

This list is not a comprehensive one, but it does highlight the usefulness of the computer in working with young people.

Video Games

'Dedicated' video games machines remain very popular with today's youth. As these machines can *only* play games you need to give careful consideration to forking out £300 or £400 for the most powerful versions. The received wisdom is that a good computer is better value, as it will run leading edge games and is upgradeable.

The ubiquitous Sega MegaDrive was selling for around £100 in early 1996; it is enormously popular, there is an excellent range of software available and a healthy second hand market. Interactive CD machines, or CDi's, were around £400 and competing directly with multimedia computers. The Sony Playstation was the newest machine around. Costing around £300 the graphics quality is excellent, but it still does not win out over a decent PC or Mac.

It is still the case that many games are not well enough designed to retain their interest value beyond the first few playings. Some are of little use at all. Others, however, can be ideal group work tools providing the basis for thought-provoking discussions and valuable insights into how individuals think. Some of the specialist organisations listed in the

Supplier's Guide may be able to help you with advice and information on the most up-to-date programs and where to obtain material which most nearly meets your particular needs.

Radio-Controlled Models

Planes, boats, cars and tanks are just part of a growing range of model transport which is appealing both to the eye and the brain. But, they can be expensive and their popularity may be short-lived relative to the financial outlay. Where we have been involved with the use of these vehicles, the regular availability of space for the activity has been a necessity. When no accessible indoor space is available, or outdoor for planes, tanks etc., the activity tended to fall flat.

The nature of the activity requires both money and a reasonable technical dexterity. The best models require attention on a regular basis and this puts the activity into the fifteen plus age range – much older than might be thought at first. To control a vehicle, both a transmitter and receiver are required and these control the direction and speed of movement. Beware models with only limited direction controls, like left movement only!

If you are keen to get involved try to get the assistance of local model shops and contact any local clubs. Finally, there is a high risk of damage, both to your equipment, and in the case of planes, to other people's property. So, make sure you have organised adequate insurance cover before embarking on maiden flights, voyages, journeys etc..

COSTUMES AND DRESSING UP

Trying on clothes and make-believe play acting are a very natural part of children's development and are especially used in nursery and primary school education. In addition to theatrical productions; parties, carnivals and street events provide ideal opportunities for wearing costumes and fancy dress. In youth clubs, discos and dances can also be organised to include a fancy dress 'theme'.

The actual range of potential costumes is limitless and your eventual creation can include elements such as face painting, masks or the eco-costumes described in the Eco-Activities section. In the meantime, we offer one costume example which is a perennial favourite for Halloween and Trick or Treating.

Witches, vampires and ghouls are ever popular dressing up characters. Their costumes are readily made using available materials. Black and white are very much the colours of the night, plus perhaps a little bit of fresh blood substitute!

For an easy to construct witch's hat:
- To construct this you, or the youngsters you work, with will need two sheets of thickish black paper.
- Use one sheet to construct a cone, by twisting the paper into a funnel shape. When the open end of the cone will fit over the intended wearer's head, tape it together from inside, flatten out the wide end and cut to make a circle.
- Use the second sheet to construct the brim of the hat. A compass or two round plates or saucepan lids can be used for measuring the inside and the outside of the brim. Draw a cross in the inner circle and then cut along each line from the centre and bend the four triangles back to the circle. These can then be glued together with the cone.
- Black and red wool cut about 18inches-two feet (45 to 60 cm) long can make great hair which can be attached with tape to the inside of the hat.

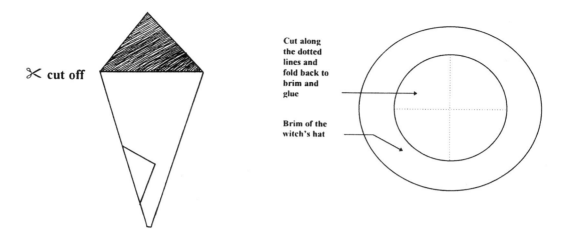

- An old bin liner, with openings for arms and head looks great as a modern punk-witch cape!
- Silver and gold stars, moons, frogs, bats or spiders can be cut out of coloured paper and stuck to the hat or cape to finish off the costume.
- Face painting or a grotesque mask will complete the ensemble.

Vampires can also be made from bin liners. Cut the bag so that the bottom of the bat cape is ragged, and as wide as the outstretched arms of the wearer. Black trousers, shoes and plenty of gaudy face paints make a fearsome creature of the night. Underneath the cape, if this area is showing, a white shirt can add a useful contrast to the black exterior.

A useful idea is to create a **clothes resource box.** This can be assembled from jumble sales, donations and charity shops. In it you will quickly accumulate items which can be cut up, modified and generally cannibalised in a creative and imaginative way. Hats, shoes and jackets are especially useful for dressing up, as are belts and scarves. An old bathing hat is ideal to form a bald head, or the basis for a fabulous wig.

For play groups and nursery groups, where pretend play is particularly important, the NES Arnold catalogue offers a range of dressing up clothes. They have specifically developed a range of clothes from Africa, Asia, China and Japan, and a second range of workers' clothes including outfits for a male nurse, police, chef and ambulance driver.

CYCLING

Most youngsters in the ten to sixteen age range own or have access to a bicycle. Many have learned, at their own or their parents' expense, a little about cycle maintenance. What we are suggesting is using a range of experiences which will harness or resuscitate some of the natural enthusiasm and interest in cycles.

In groups we have worked with, **bicycle maintenance** was first introduced because the kids' bikes were in a thoroughly deplorable state of repair. Unlike working on cars or motor cycles, only a few tools are required to do basic work. Complex work on gears is another story, and another set of tools!
The range is approximately:

> a set of five open ended spanners (Whitworth, or more usually metric depending on the make(s) of the bike(s)); a quarter and eighth of an inch tipped screwdrivers, plus a Phillips-type; an Allen (hex) key set, now used for many handlebars and seat bolts; puncture repair outfit and three tyre levers; cone spanner; pliers; hammer; and for chain and wheel jobs - link extractor and spoke spanner. Extra large size spanners become necessary when working on the steering nuts. A large adjustable spanner is an alternative. You will also need oil; SAE30 is better than the household type. Dry lubricants such as Superspray are good for chains, as are Bike Lube and Bike Eze; and grease for bearing maintenance jobs, and sometimes petrol, if you have to soak a chain etc..

We are not going to offer a how-to-do-it selection of repairs for bicycles. 'Richard's New Bicycle Book' by Richard Ballantine (Pan 1990) is a good resource for any youth group and its members. To complete our comments on maintenance – it is a good idea if you avoid becoming the youth-working, bicycle repair person for the area. The reasons, we hope, are obvious! Certainly show kids how to carry out tasks, but don't do all the work for them. Finally, we know of a couple of youth centres which have successfully operated bicycle repair services to raise money. This might be accomplished by first teaching a small group of youngsters how to repair their own bikes and then letting them offer the service. In the cases we know of, one centre offered the service to any members of the youth centre. The other put up notices in local shop windows, and used the community newspaper and local radio station to advertise the service. One might have a few qualms about the morality of competing with local traders, but in many cases these days, bicycle shops sell bikes and are more than happy to let someone else carry out repairs.

Repairing bikes with youngsters is a good activity to develop relationships between workers and kids. Building a 'bitsa' bike has been a regular activity run by Charley Mathers in Dundee. He says,

> "A good conclusion is the intrepid mechanic riding off into the sunset (sigh) or, on the other hand, botched up jobs hold the consequence of a long walk back, skinned knees or worse. Also make sure you have enough tools - it is unnecessarily frustrating to end up with a fight over essential tools."

Building bicycles to use and sell is another activity which has provided both skill-learning and money for some youth group members. Based on an ethos close to the Friends of the Earth cause, kids have been encouraged to put a halt to the built-in obsolescence, and philosophy of disposability of broken or faulty items. Often one bike can be made, or retrieved, from the parts of two useless bikes. This does not have to cost vast sums of money, and some centres, including Ferry Road in Dundee, have stockpiled bicycles which can later be cannibalised to build working models for use or sale. Odd-shaped bikes, fixed-

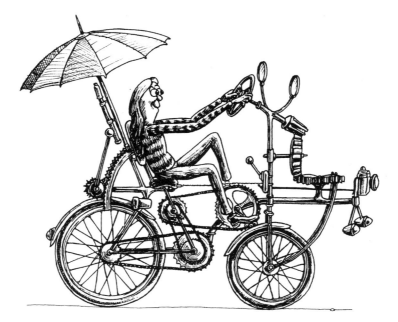

wheel bikes and bikes with unusual gear ratios have been made this way, as have tandems and bikes with trailers etc.. A close acquaintance with the police bike pound, the rubbish tip and the local scrap-dealers can come in useful if you are contemplating this aspect recycling!

From Dundee (again) we learned that using tandems can be an aid to learning to ride a bike, with the youngster as a passenger. Not falling off provides a boost to confidence and encourages the pupil to have a go solo. The disadvantages of tandems are that it is hard to obtain spares and that they are **lethal** in the hands of two inexperienced riders.

Safety
These days, with increasingly busy traffic, it is very important that young people get involved in at least basic cycle proficiency training. This involves learning the rules of the road, basic Highway Code, attentiveness, and through practise, an ability to stay out of trouble. Wearing a cycle helmet is also now a basic necessity. The national Cycling Proficiency scheme may be pleased to offer a course at your centre. In some areas of the UK there is the 'Bike Mate' scheme which matches learners with experienced riders.

Insurance should also be investigated. The bike itself should be covered and, if possible the riders and their potential to cause damage to others.

Other activities
Other activities involving bicycles which we have helped organise include:

Sponsored cycle rides
To do this you need a lot of people acting as marshals en route. You are also required to notify the police of your plans. In most cases they will be pleased to help, but be sensible about the roads you are using. A sponsored cycle is probably best suited to areas outside of towns, but it may be that a local park or sports centre could be used for an event, even in a large urban area. This would not provide such an interesting route, but it would ease the

dangers on the road. Other points which we would suggest as ground rules are:

- Take the names of, and perhaps allocate numbers to all of those taking part.
- Check and fix (if possible) all the bikes going on the event. They must be roadworthy.
- Consider the insistence on use of safety helmets. These are increasingly becoming a necessity in urban areas and on main roads.
- Depending on the route, ensure that everyone is old enough and a sufficiently competent cyclist to complete the course.
- Choose a course which offers a challenge, but is not too demanding for the relatively inexperienced cyclists taking part.
- Have marshals' vans involved in the event, equipped with tools and first aid equipment. These could perhaps be situated in the middle and at the rear of those taking part. They can attend to any roadside problems and ferry bikes and cyclists back to the home base as necessary.
- When starting the cycle run, stagger the starters and tell them that it is not a race. We found it useful to let the fastest cyclists go first. Although this makes the event a bit longer, it reduces the amount of overtaking.
- Encourage riders to have their own drink bottles, but if, for instance, the event is fifteen miles long, have a stop for drinks at the half-way stage.
- Make sure that the route is clearly marked with direction arrows, and have difficult points attended by marshals. By this strategy you should lose fewer participants!
- The final home base should again offer some refreshment and each cyclist's name should be checked off the list.

Using the above tips and adding some of your own, say, having some staff cyclists out on the course to cut down on dangerous antics, the day should be an enjoyable, safe and profitable one.

Customising

This is not a good idea for Wayne's new twenty-one gear mountain bike, but it can be applied to the aged relic. Organising a paint-in is a good fun activity and can also breathe new life into elderly machinery. The use of an air-brush spray may be especially useful, also coloured tapes, transfers, metallic foil etc. can all add to the personal touch. Unlike the car though, we wouldn't suggest a fur seat cover unless your youngsters want very soggy backsides!

Treasure Hunt/Scavenger Hunt

As some readers will realise, in both the 'New Youth Games Book' and 'World Youth Games', written by us, we have tried to describe a whole range of games and events which can be used with youth groups of varying ages. What we are offering below are two simple events which are ideal to adapt to cycle events. Since they do not relate solely to the speed at which different competitors can cycle, we think that they are useful to consider when planning cycle-related activities. It is also well worth your while looking at Alan Smith's book on 'Creative Outdoor Work with Young People' which has lots of useful orienteering-type ideas.

Treasure Hunt: Here are two ways of organising a treasure hunt which is easy enough for most organisers to consider using.
1.   This involves supplying each contestant with a sheet of clues. These can be descriptions of buildings in the local area, of objects like trees, seats, railings, bus shelters

etc.. The clues can be made as difficult, or easy, as the event calls for. With young groups, say up to twelve, you should avoid clues which are too cryptic. For instance, clues to the local church might be:

UNDER THE TALL TOWER, or
THE TALLEST BUILDING, or
FOR WHOM THE BELL TOLLS, etc..

At the intended site, leave a piece of card, perhaps with a 'letter' (i.e. **D**) on it. This ensures that contestants must go to all sites, rather than just naming them. If you want to add an extra element: when contestants have found all the letters they might have to make the letters into a word or phrase. Don't try this with groups whose literacy is poor and whom it might embarrass. Unfortunately, since the clues may get stolen it may be better to use an alternative method, described next.

2.   Give participants a map of the local area with some of the details removed (i.e. street names, villages). On it, mark circled numbers or letters at points where the participants must name what they see at that particular point. The question sheet may ask questions such as, "When was the building built?" Or, "Who is the Director of this organisation?"

Scavenger Hunt
We have included a version of the following in the Eco-section of this book, but it can easily be adapted for cyclists. We believe this is an old scouting game. Each participant is given a list of articles to find and bring back. Thought should be given to likely sources, otherwise it may just be a matter of cycling home and back. The sort of objects to be scavenged might include a clothes peg; a pine cone; a nail; a particular flower; a photo of a pop group; a sea shell etc.. You should make use of available local resources, so in a town the objects might include a hamburger wrapper; an empty bottle etc.. Each youngster involved will need a good, safe shoulder bag, or preferably a saddle bag or panniers. And for this reason, keep the size of the objects small.

The use of bicycles makes these events more fun and in all types of hunts, the accent should be on participating. Bikes speed things up and can make the event into something of a local history or natural history course, where historical buildings and the natural environment are used as answers to the clues. But don't forget to stress 'safety first' to the kids taking part.

Trials, BMX and Mountain Bikes
Obstacle courses and/or trials courses are good fun and can be easily set up on a small piece of ground. See-saw planks, greasy planks, ducking under barriers are all feasible

adaptations of the popular motor-cycle TV programme 'Kick Start'. British Moto Cross (BMX) organise trials events and the use of special sturdy bicycles. Local cycle dealers may be happy to sponsor events, perhaps relishing the thought of all the rough treatment these bikes have to go through! The mountain bike is really an adult version of the BMX, plus lots of gears. It has brought a lot of fun to cycling by opening up off-road routes through the countryside. Be warned, though, that not all footpaths and bridleways are legal for cycles. With youth groups, make sure permission to ride over private land has been obtained in advance. The large types of mountain bikes, coupled with the wide, straight handle bars makes them very stable. They are also durable and can carry reasonable loads for successful long distance touring.

After you have organised one of the above events, it is likely that the youngsters will ask for more. The trick is then to try and get them organising future competitions. They will prove far more devious than you!

Youth Hostels

We don't wish to write a essay on youth hostels, but it is worth remembering that they are especially suited for youngsters who are on cycling tours or just away on bikes for the weekend. Some leaders have organised very successful cycling holidays with small groups of youngsters. It is worth planning short orienteering/map reading exercises prior to embarking on a long trip. Another spin-off is that through cycling to hostels, youngsters are treated with favour by many smaller hostels. Learning the rules allows the youngsters to understand how all the Youth Hostels Association (YHA) hostels work and they can then plan their own tours. They have over 5,000 hostels in 64 countries. Their HQ is at Trevelyan House, 8 St Stephen's Hill, St Alban's, Herts. AL1 2DY.

Sponsored Events

Cycle events can raise money for charities and equipment. Most of the activities listed in this section can be adapted for sponsored fundraising. Safety, insurance and matching the event to different age groups and abilities are important aspects of the organiser's role.

DÉCOUPAGE

Literally translating from the French, this means, "cutting out, or carving out." This is only a part of what découpage art work is. It was a very popular pastime with Victorian ladies and in the last ten years, or so, has enjoyed a period of rediscovery. For youth or community work, it is a useful activity which allows people who are not very good at drawing to produce decorated items which can look stunning and highly professional. In many senses it is a development of collage work, described earlier in this book. It essentially involves:

- cutting out pictures, patterns and drawings, or using transfer or stick on decals (pictures of flowers, animals, birds etc.);
- arranging these in an interesting way on a base picture or object;
- gluing them in place using either ordinary glue, or if attempting to obtain a 3-D image, using silicone solution;
- spray fixing;
- varnishing.

The diverse range of available objects and materials which can be used for découpage make it an ideal activity for youth groups. It is cheap and flexible and as an art form can produce varied and pleasing results. As with a number of art activities it is useful to adopt a 'Blue Peter' style approach at the beginning, by showing examples of découpage and explaining the process to the participants,

"Here's something I produced in the lunch-hour...."

You know the type of thing!

With a youth group you need a good variety of both things to **cut out**, and items to be **stuck on.** To start off a group you'll need plenty of newspaper covered tables, and:

- a selection of facsimile Victorian decals/pictures, wrapping paper designs, coloured and black and white pictures (colour supplements, advertising materials, music and sports pictures etc.);
- scissors and sharp craft knives (handle with care!);
- paints for preparing some surfaces to take découpage images;
- adhesives, possibly including silicone, for producing flat and raised images;
- spray fixative for sealing;
- varnish(es) for completing the object.

For instance, one member of the group may want to decorate an old junk tray, another a flower vase, and a third is intent on attacking a waste bin. The process is the same for each person:

 – choose a selection of appropriate pictures/images to cut out or transfer/stick on;
 – carefully undertake any cutting required;
 – prepare (clean/paint/sand down) the object or surface which will receive the images;
 – test out the possible positions for the pictures. Blu-tak or similar can be useful for this purpose;
 – glue the cut-out images into place;
 – spray fix if necessary;
 – apply a first coat of varnish, allow to dry, lightly sand, then apply the next coat. Most items look their best with three or four coats minimum.

 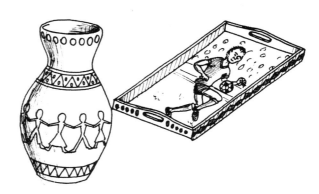

A few tips:

1.   To finish off an object properly will require more than one session because of the varnishing. Explain this at the outset and plan for the follow-up.

2.   An increasingly varied selection of paints, adhesives and cheap Victorian decals are becoming available. Specialist Crafts market a small range of 3-D découpage kits.

3.   Don't be afraid of encouraging young people to experiment. There are no rules, and anything can be stuck to the finished object. The NES Arnold catalogue includes a glittering array of sequins, chenille, feathers, jewels, pompoms and glitter. The glitter can always be added to the layers of varnish.

4.		Try using spray paint through patterned items, such as doilies, tights or stencils to produce imaginative backdrops for the cut outs.
5.		With younger groups, it is best to use pre-prepared shapes and relatively blunt scissors for cutting out. Older children may be safe using craft knives – but they are very sharp and make potentially lethal weapons!
6.		PVA adhesive, when slightly diluted, can be used to paint objects to give them a sheen quite similar to varnish.

DRAWING AND VARIATIONS

Many of the young people we worked with have had their creative instincts effectively removed or suppressed by experiences at home or school. Few have any regular access to materials which can encourage and develop their creative talents. If you are serious about using arts and crafts in your work with young people, then it makes sense to allow them access to materials with which they can test out ideas and fulfil some of their creative aspirations, even if this is just designing a gang logo or a football crest. The short piece on 'Spray Can Art' in the Murals section offers such street ideas.

Painting, drawing and their variations provide tremendous scope for individual experimentation and fulfilment. While painting may need some specialised materials and workspace, drawing materials can be used anywhere. So, why not try leaving out spare paper and pencils, felt pens, crayons, charcoal etc., and see what happens! Keep your fingers crossed that it is not a collection of obscenities on the walls! Having comics and magazines around can be useful to help stimulate flagging imaginations. See the Badge making section for related ideas.

What we call 'Drawing games' are also worth considering. Using what we call the **'Egg Head'** game is a good way of getting non-artists to draw. In this activity we usually photocopy a variety of heads/egg shapes:

Sometimes we start participants off with a few simple additions to aid their imagination:

The idea is to let the young people create their own characters. Perhaps only some of them will look like you!

Another fun idea is to play a visual version of the old paper and pencil game, Consequences. We have heard the game called **'People'** and **'Figures'**. First you need to prepare a strip of paper by folding it into a concertina shape of six parts for: head; upper body; waist; thighs; knees, ankles and feet. We've found it best to prepare the linking lines which go over the fold lines. This ensures that the body all joins together.

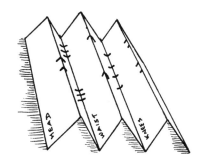

The game sequence involves each person adding a drawing of one part of the person in turn. It is much more fun if other participants do not see the drawing until the end. The first person draws a head – as weird as they like, and then folds it over so that the next person can only see the space where they can add a drawing of the upper body. This process is then repeated for each part of the body. The final creation can often be extremely strange, if at times a bit sexist.

It can also be worth experimenting with making your own **stencils** out of paper or card, to be used with paint or felt-tip pens. A number of firms also manufacture wooden or plastic stencils in the shapes such as animals, letters etc.. Specialist Crafts sell stencil card which is good for making accurate stencils which can be used to produce patterns for stencilling on walls or onto pictures. The Galt catalogue offers some nice stencils for Christmas cards and drawing. In the Lino Printing section, we have suggested a number of simple printing techniques.

Most people will have seen **pin and thread designs**, using coloured thread wound round panel pins hammered into a piece of wood or chip board which has been painted black. Abstract designs can be made by placing pins round the edge of the board with a few in the centre and experimenting with different loops and twists. Alternatively, patterns and designs for flowers, stars or ships can be achieved with a little practice.

Pens and drawing aids
Amongst our favourites are the poster paint pens in the Uni-POSCA range. These pens come with different size tips and dispense a bright solid paint colour onto just about any sort of surface you come up with. We've used them on wood, metal and paper. In fact these days the range of different drawing mediums for work with young people is enormous. Each offers a new dimension for learning and experimentation. It includes:
* pencils, coloured pencils and water colour pencils;
* wax and oil crayons;
* charcoal;

- pastels, oil pastels(the Filia range are very good) and conté crayons;
- marker pens, felt pens and pens for overhead projection transparencies;
- drawing pens such as the Edding 1800 pens and those by Rotring, Ceramicron and Mecanorma, used for accurate technical drawings and fine illustrative work, like Gubby's cartoons!
- and, see the Airbrush section at the beginning of the book.

A **pantograph** is another cheap piece of equipment which makes drawing accessible to all. The pin on the device is used to trace out the lines of a drawing, design or photograph while a pencil is drawing out the design on a larger scale. It is less automatic than its sounds and is actually quite creative. We have used the pantograph to draw a correctly proportioned outline of a 'face' or 'object', then carried on freehand. Youngsters can learn something about the scale, positioning and proportions of humans, animals and other objects. Some of the commercially available 'drawing games' are also worth considering for use with youth groups. The **Spirograph** range of drawing toys use geometric shapes for creative design and they do enable youngsters who do not see themselves as being artistic, to produce interesting and accomplished pictures.

ECO ACTIVITIES
There are a whole range of both indoor and outdoor crafts and activities which can be organised using natural environments and 'found' materials. Some of these overlap with other sections of this book such as mask making and jewellery. Others sit squarely at the intersection between activities and games playing, but since we are writing *this* book at the moment, rather than another volume on games playing, we are happy to include them here!

The leaf slide show
To organise this outdoor activity you need to have pre-prepared a set of fold-over cards, allowing one for each participant in your group.

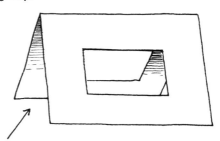

insert leaf between the flaps

The activity is a good one for using while out on a walk in the woods or on an outdoor expedition. To start with, you ask everyone to find an interesting or unusual leaf. Once they have all done so, hand out one fold-over card each, and ask each person to place their leaf in between the two sheets of card so that an interesting part of the leaf is trapped between the two holes. Then, get everyone to form up in a circle and look through their 'slide viewers' at the leaves using the sky (hopefully, sun) as a light source. Everyone is likely to be surprised at the complexity and beauty of the leaves. In turn, get the group members to pass on the slides to the next person in the circle, so that everyone has the opportunity to scrutinise each leaf. It's an enjoyable and educational way to spend a quarter of an hour in the country and works with any age or ability group.

Wide Games

These were first developed by the Scouting movement as a means of using the potential of wide open spaces for recreation. Recently, the Play movement has begun to sing the praises of these activities, especially with big groups of youngsters. Both of us attended a very enjoyable two-day Play Convention held in Perth, organised by 'Fair Play for Children in Scotland'. The Wide Games sessions were organised by Martin Rothero, who stressed that the natural resources of a woodland or beach can be effectively utilised to:

- provide good entertainment and exercise;
- get young people to make creative, positive use of the environment;
- develop their own activity and games ideas;
- work effectively in teams and develop personal initiative.

Traditional games/activities such as a **Scavenger Hunt** (see also Cycling section), are effectively a Wide Game. Participants are usually provided, individually or in pairs, with a list of objects to find. The organiser should spend some preparation time making sure that it is a 'possible' list and that obtaining the items do not involve, trespass, danger or destruction of living things. A typical Scavenger Hunt might involve participants in a half hour search for:

● something sharp ● a pine cone ● an oak leaf ●a feather ● something beautiful ● 3 pieces of human litter ● a piece of bark ● some sheep's wool ● an acorn ● a conker ● a fern leaf ● a sycamore seed.

Each participant or pair is given a bag to put their findings in, and is told exactly what geographical boundaries to work within. A recognisable call or whistle should be used to get everyone to re-group at the end of the activity, since not everyone can be relied upon to (a) have a watch, and (b) use it!

After the hunt, the organiser should praise the participants for their 'finds', make any comments on unusual discoveries, and ask about what else searchers found or saw while they were engaged in the hunt. This activity is successful with groups from about nine or ten upwards, but may not be suitable for participants with movement difficulties.

Conkers and Acorns

At the end of Martin's Wide Game session, which had involved in a good deal of running about in a couple of search and capture games, he invited the two groups of seven or eight to invent their own Wide Game. And so, 'Conkers and Acorns' was born; a simple, eco activity based on tag. To start, a playing area was defined, in this case a hockey pitch. The two goals were declared as the home bases. At the beginning of the game, each individual on one team received three conkers each, and the opposing team members were each given three acorns. These were either held in the hand or put into a convenient pocket. Each base houses a stock of more acorns or conkers, say 24 for an eight player team.

Then, the following rules apply:
  – the game lasts until the organiser blows a whistle;
  – only home team members can visit their own home base;
  – the aim of the game is for individual players to tag opposing team players, thereby winning one acorn or conker;
  – there is no re-tagging after a tag by another player;
  – when a player runs out of their personal stock of three seeds, they can make <u>one</u> visit to their home base to replenish their stock (back up to three);
  – the winning team is the one which has the most seed trophies captured from their opponents when the whistle blows.

NEW YOUTH ARTS & CRAFT

A couple of points to consider. One: if there are lots of acorns or conkers lying about, it offers admirable opportunities for cheating! This can be averted by marking the seeds for the game with a spot of paint. Two: Try and divide up the teams in such a way as to make the ages, sizes and running abilities reasonably equal. And, if you are reasonably lucky, your reward as organiser, will be a bunch of exhausted but happy young people!

Eco costumes

Young people like dressing up and making unusual costumes and headgear. The 'found' resources of a wood or field can provide for some very interesting and imaginative creations. Say, for instance, that you set a task for a youth group of making a hat or crown, these can then be complemented by a later group making a cloak or costume to go with it.

The leaves, twigs, bark, berries etc. required for a costume can all be scavenged in the opening minutes of the session, and then, back in a workshop area, provide enough paper, card, scissors, glue, staplers, coloured papers, pens and anything else you think is appropriate to enable the construction of some unusual apparel. One result from a workshop session for training leaders can be seen in the accompanying photo. This activity can take a bit of time. We'd suggest that you allow about 1-1½ hours.

Your friend the tree!

This is an interesting sensory, eco activity which involves dividing your youth group up into pairs. It works with just about any age group, but needs to take place in a safe, reasonably flat wooded area, preferably with a variety of different tree types. The pairs take it in turns to be blindfolded, twirled around (safely), and then led up to a tree. The blindfolded person is encouraged to get-to-know their tree, giving it a hug, possibly even a kiss! After two or three minutes, the leader gently guides their partner back to a position away from the tree, gives them another twirl for disorienting, good measure, and then invites them to try and locate their own, friendly neighbourhood tree. Surprisingly, most people do find the tree they hugged, or, whatever! Then, it's the turn of the partners to swap roles and the leader becomes the led.

A pleasant, gentle way of getting young people to develop their awareness of what is growing around them.

EGG-MOBILES

These strange devices were directly a result of a BBC Television programme, in which teams designed a small, model vehicle which was capable of transporting an egg. Hence, our mate, Tony Watson's name for them – EGG-MOBILES! It's neither expensive nor difficult to organise as an activity, but you do need to plan ahead and ensure that all the materials are available. We reckon that it is best organised in quite a long session, perhaps about two hours long, with up to five groups operating concurrently, with three youngsters in each. The best age for the activity is twelve plus, and it is a good mixed ability and/or mixed age group task. Normally, the event is organised on a competitive basis, but it can be modified to be simply a co-operative, fun exercise.

The aim

Each group is given the same task to complete. You can vary the goal, but in our example the basic aim is to build an egg-mobile from the materials provided, which will propel itself over an agreed, or longest distance across a gym or similar floor. You can choose whether this also entails setting a new travelling time record, as recorded on a stop-watch.

The materials

The main requirement is that each group gets exactly the same components from which to build their egg-mobile. The following list gives an indication of the sorts of things required. These are all obtainable from Specialist Crafts, but there are also a good range of CDT accessories in the NES Arnold and Galt catalogues.

1. Standard length rubber bands (reasonably strong).
2. Model wheels, wood or plastic.
3. Balsa wood, or light weight bamboo canes.
4. Adhesive, masking tape and string.
5. Steel axles.
6. Piano wire.
7. A modelling-knife/scalpel for cutting, and possibly a small hacksaw.
8. An egg, or similar, to be conveyed.

A typical mobile may look like:

The triangular shape tends to run in a more stable way than its four-wheeled counterpart, but **don't** tell the kids **that,** or show them the above drawing!

Other competitions/activities

We don't want to duplicate the material from CDT modelling and construction projects, or our mate, Alan Smith's book, 'Creative Outdoor Work with Young People'. There are lots of examples of things to design and build, which can be turned into group work/team activity projects. Getting more ambitious, the outdoor environment does offer the chance to plan lots of 'now get out of this-style' or 'Crystal Maze' exercises, which combine brain and a bit of brawn to find a solution. Raft-building and racing, and constructing tree houses are two possibilities, along with town trails and social history projects, all of which can get young people studying their local area and its community.

FACE PAINTING AND MAKE-UP

Arm most teenage groups with a supply of face paints and within minutes you are sure to have a good selection of Draculas, Clowns, Witches, American Indians, and Animals. With a little skill and a knowledge of the available products and their application, this enthusiasm can be used as the basis for a whole range of arts activities particularly in the performance arts arena. Make-up is sexually stereotyped as a female domain, but the basics of making up a face are very similar whether it is for face painting, beauty or stage productions.

Face painting

Face painting has proved popular with many youth groups, large and small and of varying ages. It requires relatively little in the way of equipment and is an easily supervised activity.

There are quite a range of face paints to choose between for use with young people. Some people are allergic to make-up of any kind, so it is important to use paints or crayons which have been well tested. Ideally, young people with sensitive skins won't ask to be face painted, but that's not the real world! Instead, have on hand, water, soap and skin cleaning lotion. Also it is a good idea to have other, equally fun activities available just in case some members cannot participate in a face painting session.

Although it is possible for each person to paint their own face, this requires a mirror for each person, well beyond the resources of most youth clubs, unless you are running beauty classes. It is just as simple, and arguably a lot more fun, to divide the group up into pairs, with each person taking it in turn to decorate their partner's face. Adults should be on hand to offer general advice, keep an eye on the face paints and how they are being used, and (we hope) get involved in the spirit of the activity, as active participants!

Apart from when using paint crayons, each face painter will need a small piece of sponge for applying large areas of colour and a couple of paint brushes, one of which should be quite fine. With younger children, it is best if paint/colour is kept away from the eyes and hair, but with older young people, they can be encouraged to experiment more (i.e. painting arms, legs and body), and with attention to detail around the eyes and mouth. It is always best to apply the large areas of base colour first, then to add in the detail.

Face painting is a useful part of circus, carnival, street performance and drama and theatre activities. Running a face painting stall at a fete or show can provide both fun and useful funds. *Make-up sessions* run on a regular basis in a youth club, or as a workshop at an activity day or weekend, are almost always very popular with girls and young women. They may also be combined with related activities such as hairdressing and hair braiding.

Types of face paints: *Options include:*	
Face paint crayons:	quite expensive, easy to use, non-toxic, but hard to use to create strong colours or cover large areas. Some are hard to remove.
Left over make-up:	cheap, but a limited range of colours. Tends to be viewed as the province of girls and women, and therefore will not be used by boys or young men.
Stage make up:	often referred to as greasepaint, it is either oil-based or water soluble. A good range of colours are available, it is easy to apply with sponge or brushes, but it is relatively expensive. For youth group use, water-based are probably the best. Grimas, Aquacolour and Snazaroo are well known makes.
Baby lotion plus powder paint:	50:50 mix; easy to use, good range of colours, some colours are hard to remove and they may dry out the skin.

The Alan part of Howie and Alan, spent about five years of his late school and college days working part time and full time in West Sussex theatres, including the prestigious Chichester Festival Theatre. Primarily, he was involved with set design, lighting and sound, but inevitably a bit of make-up work was involved. The rest of this section is based on that work, and material from the Grimas book 'Make-up for profession or Hobby' (Grimas, 1992) and Mary Quant 'Quant on Make-up' (Century Hutchinson, 1986).

Base colour

Since the skin is a delicate canvas for painting, care should be taken that make-up will not cause harm. Ideally, anyone applying make-up or face paint should wash their face first. Acid-balanced cleansing bars or liquids are the kindest to the skin and help to preserve the skin's natural oils. When using make-up which will be worn for any length of time, it is best to apply a moisturiser. This protects the skin and helps to provide a stable surface for the foundation. The best type to use depends on the person's skin – dry, oily, normal, allergic etc..

In face painting, cake make-up (which is oil based) is used as the foundation. The colour(s) used depends on the required effect. Foundation for make-up is usually liquid or past and is best applied with a slightly damp sponge. Remember to apply to the neck as well as the face. Colours for the base and the detail can be tested on the back of the hand and later washed off.

Applying the detail

Face: Rouge for cheekbones and temples can be applied with a brush, as can water-based paints for the creating effects such as animal and clown faces. Brushes in two or three thicknesses will be needed for applying water-based colours. Blending of a number of colours together is very important in make-up. Some effects require subtlety, some boldness!

Modelling the face using rouge can achieve the effects of changing the shape of the face

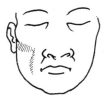

| LONGER /
NARROWER | SHORTER /
BROADER | NO
CHANGE |

The 'rules', such as they, are for make-up and face painting are contradictory. Blending one colour into the next, using a subtle touch, is the basis for good make-up technique. In face painting, stark lines and vivid colours help to present a powerful image. Similarly, on stage, make-up is used for strengthening or changing features and this can be achieved to even greater effect when using a base of latex, but that *is* beyond the scope of this section!

Once the foundation is settled, then use a light coating of powder, including a little around the eyes. Then carefully remove the excess with a powder brush. Proper 'fixing powder' is also available, which ensures that make-up stays put.

Eyebrows
In face painting, and in ordinary make-up, building up or disguising the eyebrows is an important part of the whole design. To strengthen or re-shape the eyebrows it is possible to use small, stiff brushes, eyebrow pencils or a mascara brush. Often, more than one colour, including rouge, is used and blended for striking effects. For stage work or for elaborate face painting, eyebrow plastic may be used to block out the eyebrows. Camouflage make-up can also be used for this purpose and for masking skin discolorations.

One of the tricks of applying make-up successfully, is to use a spatula to pick up small amounts of colour, which are then applied with a brush or cotton wool buds. It is also an advantage to have a good range of brushes available for use with different colours and uses.

Eyes
False eye lashes come in natural or bright colours, even gold, rainbow and red! They require cutting to size and applying carefully with a special adhesive to the lid of the eye. If the recipient isn't used to having them applied, it can take a few attempts. The eyelash is usually applied from the inside of the eye first, moving outwards, pressing lightly into place close to the rim of the eye lid. Eye liner is used to disguise the join and if a 'natural' look is required, the false eyelash and the real lashes are blended together and shaped.

Next comes the artistic bit, colouring and shaping the eyes. The eyes are an expressive feature and putting a light colour on the eyelids with a darker colour in the fold above the lid accentuates the eye, as does the use of eye liners, which can be applied with a brush or pencil.

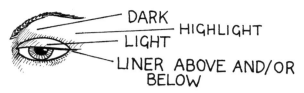

DARK
HIGHLIGHT
LIGHT
LINER ABOVE AND/OR BELOW

For bolder effects, eye liner can be obtained in primary colours, white and black and with a pearlised effect. A highlight can be added to great effect on the highest point of the brow bone. As with other aspects of face make-up, either blend colours for a natural effect, or emphasise the contrasts for strong, powerful effects. To prevent powder falling on to the cheeks, place a piece of tissue below the eye being worked on. Finally, apply mascara of whatever shade and colour seems appropriate.

Lips

A tiny amount of foundation applied with the finger to the lips, provides a firm base for lip colouring. Nearly all professional make-up artists use a lip pencil and then a lip brush for shaping and colouring the lips. The pencil is used to produce a clear, crisp outline and the brush to provide a uniform colour. Lip gloss is used to achieve a shiny effect and sealant. Fixing powder will prevent the lip colour quickly deteriorating.

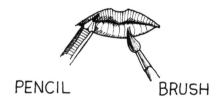

PENCIL   BRUSH

Special effects

For *colouring hair*, applying water-based colour with an old toothbrush is about the easiest method. Once colours are established, the hair can be modelled and fixed in place using a strong-hold, hair spray. *Beards, false eyebrows and moustaches* can be made from crepe wool, cut to size and fixed in place using spirit gum. Special *face glitter* creates a good party look and can be applied with fingers, brush or sponge.

Body painting uses a lot of paint but is extremely impressive in parades and carnivals. A technique which has limited uses, but which is nonetheless fun, is to paint feet using water-based paints, possibly creating mock shoes or little people on the toes.

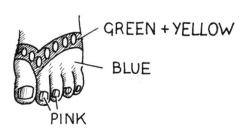

GREEN + YELLOW

BLUE

PINK

For artists, *tattoos* can be painted on or designs painted on the face. Transfers are also available. In recent years, football and rugby colours have been painted on faces; flags, animals and flowers are all popular. Finishing touches like colouring hands, arms and legs may complete the effect; likewise *nail varnish,* which now comes in an amazing range of colours.

Removing make-up

The make-up described in this section is a mixture of oil and water-based products. To carefully remove make-up, especially if you are working with a group of youngsters, you will need:

- cleansing lotion/cream;
- make-up removal oil;
- spirit gum remover;
- wool pads and cotton buds;
- eye make-up remover.

Skin cream is usually applied afterwards to offset any effects of the make-up.

Designs for face painting

Face painting and make-up sessions are the ideal opportunity for young people to display their own individual flair and imagination. We do not advocate a slavish paint-the-face-by-numbers approach. Instead, as a workshop leader, encourage both the artist and the model to experiment, to take risks and to learn for themselves how different materials work, blend, rub of, cover each other, etc.. Working with young people whose base skin colour may vary from very pale to very dark requires, particularly for make-up rather than face painting sessions, a good range of foundation colours which correspond as nearly as possible to the natural skin colour.

Possible ideas for face painting include:

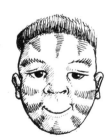

CLOWN   WITCH   WEREWOLF   PUNK.

Obviously, for a number of occasions, face painting needs finishing off with wigs, hats and suitably bright or appropriate costumes.

FLOWERCRAFT

We guess that almost everyone has groaned either inwardly, or outwardly, at the very thought of pressing leaves and flowers. We have been among them! However, having been introduced to the craft activity of pressing flowers, it does have a number of things to commend it:

* it's cheap – flowers and leaves are plentiful;
* it's easy to achieve interesting and pleasing results;
* if you don't have , or can't afford a proper press, an old phone directory will do the job, since the paper is absorbent and the book is heavy enough to flatten out the flowers.

To collect, press and display dried, pressed flowers will require two or three sessions, so it works best with young people who do not demand instant results.

Collecting specimens

This is best done when it is relatively dry, otherwise dampness will ruin the items during the drying process, when they will go mouldy. Direct your young people to collect specimens which do not belong to someone else (in other words, are growing wild, or cultivated by you or your organisation); offer an interesting range of colours and textures, and importantly, do not destroy the only examples of rare flowers and foliage.

To preserve freshness, collect the specimens in airtight plastic bags or use a simple type of travelling press.

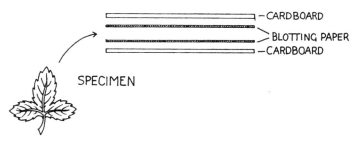

Bind these sandwiches together with a couple of elastic bands. The quicker the specimens are dried, the more effective the final pressed version is likely to be. Use small nail scissors for snipping off the flower heads, leaves, buds, stems and grasses. With some flowers, the multitude of petals make them hard to press into a two dimensional form. With these it is often best to dismantle the separate petals and dry them individually.

Try to help your group choose what they collect by considering:

* is it very fleshy and succulent? (these do not dry out well);
* is it relatively dry already? (best for pressing);
* is it a suitable size, shape and colour for the intended picture?

It may help if your group has a small guide book to wild and cultivated flowers. (The Observer's series are good, as are those from Collins and the Treasure Press).
The following are recommended for pressing:

☐ snowdrop ☐ daffodil ☐ heather ☐ anemone ☐ primula ☐ alyssum ☐ buttercup
☐ wild pansy ☐ dog rose ☐ elderflower ☐ daisy ☐ coltsfoot ☐ primrose
☐ celandine ☐ cow parsley ☐ hydrangea ☐ montbretia ☐ rose ☐ larkspur
☐ lobelia ☐ gypsophila ☐ forget me not ☐ rock rose

Ferns, leaves, seed pods and even seaweeds (if well washed) all make interesting materials for pressing.

Pressing
A small pair of nail scissors and tweezers are necessities. Many flowers and leaves are best divided up before pressing. Later they can be re-assembled in an abundant variety of ways. As we've already said, an old telephone directory can be used for pressing or you can make or buy a version of the travelling press which includes plywood panels and wing nuts to exert the best even pressure on the drying samples. A nine-inch square press is about the optimum size. The telephone book or blotting paper can be re-used almost endlessly.

Most plants take up to six weeks to become fully dry and ready for mounting on card or any other surface.

Presentation
Sticking flowers to a surface is a collage-type activity. The aim is to present a new picture which offers a unique blend of textures, shapes and colours. It can be worth discussing with young people, how symmetry and patterns can be made from the different parts of the flowers. Choosing appropriate types of surface to mount the flower parts on will also influence the effectiveness of the overall design. Contrasting colours or subtle blending of tones can both produce good results.

To attach the individual pieces of leaf and flower to the mount, it is often adequate to use a slightly damp finger to transport them about. Then use a little latex (or similar) glue to affix each piece in place. We've also used cow gum, dispensed from the end of a cocktail stick! The design aspect is always harder to teach. As with many other craft activities, it is best to encourage imagination and individuality, rather than copying any particular style. Pressed flowers are very suitable for book marks, simple greetings cards and calendars. Paper plates can make an attractive mount for a dried flower picture.

For a more 'polished' finish, some young people like to turn their creation into a proper framed picture. Oval frames are often particularly suitable. It is worth suggesting to the young people that they should spend some time considering the options for mounting material. A piece of silk stretched over a wooden backing may make the most appropriate background for a lot of flower creations. Alternatively, gluing leaves and flowers onto wood or even a stone can be finished off with two or three coats of clear polyurethane varnish, which will bind the picture into place.

Specialist Crafts and many other firms supply a good range of different sizes and qualities of flower presses.

HANDMADE PAPER

This definitely falls into the category of environmentally friendly youth activities, as you can easily recycle newsprint or office paper. For finer quality results you can now buy newspaper pulp from your arts and craft supplier, who will also sell you a starter kit if you don't want to make up your own paper making frame.

This can be a fairly messy activity, so you don't want to do it in the living room! Ideally you need access to a large kitchen sink, and you should have plenty of old newspaper handy to put on the floor and to mop up spillages.

Equipment Needed

You'll need the following pieces of equipment, most of which you can make up yourself or find easily at home, school, club etc..

• *Paper making frame.* This should be relatively small – A4 (297mm X 210mm) or A5 size is ideal. You will need to make up two identically sized frames out of one-inch wood. The bottom frame should be covered with a fine synthetic mesh and stretched tight. Alternatively you can use a fine metal mesh. The upper frame is left empty and serves to contain the paper pulp solution while the water drains away.

• *Pulp:* newsprint or office paper torn into small pieces.
• *Aquapel size.* This makes the paper stronger and resistant to waterbased colour medium. Mix in the proportion of 2% Aquapel to 98% water, and use this mixture to soak the pulp or paper in.
• *Small decorative pieces* like flower petals, small seeds, threads etc. can be used in the mixture for effect.
• *Paper making dye* or food dye if you want coloured paper. Tea, coffee or scent can be used if you want smelly paper!
• *Buckets* to mix the pulp in.
• *An electric whisk* or blender.
• *A washing up basin* or sink large enough to take the size of frame you are using.
• *A number of tea towels* or similar for drying the paper between. The material and weave of the cloths you use will give your paper different texture effects.
• *A pair of strong pressing boards* to squeeze the water out of the paper (or you can buy a pressing frame for a few pounds).

Method
Remember that you will need several sets of equipment if you are working with a group.

1. Fill a bucket with pulp or paper and leave it to soak in water. Paper should be soaked for a couple of hours or overnight. Pulp need only be soaked for half an hour or so.
2. Now take a handful of the mixture and squeeze out most of the water. Put these balls of pulp in the blender and add some fresh water. Blend the mixture for four or five minutes, adding more water if needed, until it is the consistency of thin porridge.
3. Put the pulp mixture in the basin and add one and a half times this amount of warm water. Mix together with any colour, scent or decorative effects.
4. Now arrange your frame so that the gauze is in the middle with the open frame on top. Hold the frame firmly and immerse it in the pulp. Lift it slowly out, making sure you keep it level, and allow the water to drain away before putting the frame down.
5. When you lift off the top half of the frame you will be left with a sheet of (wet!) paper lying on the gauze. Tip the paper carefully onto a tea towel on a pressing board and cover it with another tea towel. Repeat the process until you have a stack of sheets, each separated by a tea towel. Place the second pressing board on top and squash it gently but firmly to squeeze out all of the water. This can be quite messy so it's a good idea to lay the pressing boards on newspapers to soak up the water.
6. Finally, peel off each sheet of paper, keeping it on a drying cloth, and lay them out on newspaper until thoroughly dried. You can speed up the drying process by using a hairdryer.

Once you have dried the sheets of paper, they can be used for many other arts and crafts purposes. Simply painting or drawing on them with charcoal, for instance, can produce an attractive finished product. Found materials like feathers, shells, fabric etc. can also be used to good effect and will blend in well with the natural appearance of the paper. Greetings cards and calendars are also worth considering. You may well find that your young people end up writing to their 'special' friends using the handmade paper!

HOT AIR BALLOONS
Making and flying hot air balloons is an exciting project for any group aged eleven upwards. The balloons you make with your group are very realistic. They will fly, and differ only in scale and sophistication from the continent-jumping record-breakers we've seen in recent years.

Your group will need a moderate amount of patience to work with the tissue paper used to construct the balloon, but the effort is well worthwhile.

To build one balloon you will need:

- 17 sheets of tissue paper in two colours 20 x 30 inches.
- Cream adhesive or Pritt stick adhesive.
- Stiff wire about 70 inches long (strong garden wire).
- Cotton wool roll.
- Methylated spirit.
- Sellotape.
- Scissors.
- Pliers and wire cutters.
- A large table and plenty of space.

Method

1. Open out the tissue paper, fold in half lengthways and build two piles, each one consisting of eight sheets of alternate colours (fig. 1)

2. Keeping the piles as neat as possible, cut away the shaded areas shown (fig. 2). Keep your offcuts in case patches are required later. Pile 1 will form the top half of your balloon and pile 2 the bottom.

3. Now open out the sheets and stick them together to form eight panels. Glue in one thin continuous line and if possible keep the pieces separate until dry (fig. 3). Half inch overlap should be sufficient and it is important to keep the edges parallel.

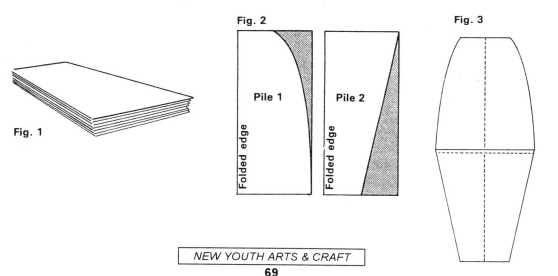

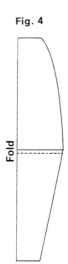

Fig. 4

Fold

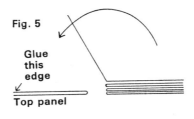

Fig. 5

Glue
this
edge

Top panel

Fig. 6

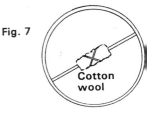

Fig. 7

Cotton
wool

4.   Fold each panel in half lengthways and build a pile remembering to alternate the colours (fig. 4)

5.   The top panel is placed as shown and the top edge glued in the same way as before. Fold the upper part of panel 2 over and glue as shown. Fold the next part of panel 2 over and glue ready to take the upper part of panel 3 (fig. 5). Care must be taken to separate the two halves of each panel to prevent them from sticking. When all the panels have been stuck the first and last edges can be glued together.

6.   Gently open out your balloon. Two people make this easier. Hold the balloon by the seam which runs round the centre of the balloon and shake the bottom half down into the top with the balloon upside down (fig. 6).

7.   Cut the remaining sheet of tissue paper to the largest octagon possible and stick this to the inside of the top of the balloon. This is the most difficult part. Try gluing two panels at a time and work round the hole.

8.   All that now remains to be done is to make a circle of wire with a cross-piece and wrap about 2 foot of cotton wool around it, tying it on tightly with light wire (fig. 7). Make sure the cotton wool is kept well away from the circle and cannot slide.

9.   Fix the circle in place to the base of the balloon with many small pieces of sellotape and your balloon is ready to fly. (If there are any holes or tears they should now be patched). About a cupful of meths is plenty. Pour this onto the wick just before ignition. Alternatively, a piece of solid firelighter can be used instead of cotton wool and meths.

Read the following notes carefully before attempting to fly your balloon, and always make sure that young people are properly supervised.

•   Hot air balloons can only be flown safely on windless days.

•   If the countryside is very dry there may be some danger, e.g. if the entire balloon catches fire during the launch and drops to the ground.

•   Choose launch sites carefully and make sure that the breeze won't take the balloon anywhere it could cause damage.

•   Once the balloon is safely airborne, it won't come down until the fuel runs out. However, the wick will remain hot and could smoulder. Always have several containers of water handy to ensure that any fire hazard on take-off or landing is dealt with swiftly.

Launching

Make sure the balloon is held, fully opened out, by the middle seam with one person holding the top and with the base a couple of feet from the ground. Light the wick and wait for the balloon to fill with hot air by which time it can be safely held at the base. When the balloon starts to lift you can let go. It helps to walk with the breeze if there is any.

Good Luck!

HOT ENAMELLING

This is always a popular activity with young people, probably because professional looking results are easily obtained. We reckon that it is best used with the thirteen and over age group. Enamels are derived from powdered, coloured glass. The whole process of firing this at high temperature in a kiln to produce a glossy finish seems to have a magical quality which appeals to kids.

Starter kits are readily obtainable, and are relatively inexpensive. However, you still require a kiln. In the past we have made much use of a simple kiln (essentially a hot-plate with lid) which has a limited heat output. This makes it difficult to fire millefiori (patterned glass beads) or to achieve a scrolled effect. If you intend enamelling to be a long-term activity for your youth group it may be worthwhile investing in a more expensive kiln with higher heat output, and possibly a regulator to prevent the risk of the heating wires burning out. We liked using the simple kiln, though, and found it especially useful for soldering badge findings directly onto finished copper shapes (much quicker than glue). Unfortunately, we have had difficulty in recent years to trace suppliers for this kind of kiln. The more expensive kilns, the enamels, tools and copper blanks are all available from Specialist Crafts.

To get started you'll need the following **equipment:**

* Kiln (high output ones start at around £220).
* Enamels – available in opaque and transparent (and sometimes translucent and opalescent) powdered forms. Millefiori, enamel lumps and threads.
* Shaker jars (for enamel powder).
* Trivet (if using front-loading kiln).
* Spatula.
* Sandpaper.
* Enamelling oil and brush (helps the firing process but is not essential).
* Descaling liquid (helps prevent copper oxidising in kiln).
* Copper shapes and jewellers findings, including leather thong for pendants (jewellers findings are things like earring clips, rings, and badge pins which are glued or soldered to the completed enamel shape).
* Asbestos or other heat resistant board.

In health and safety terms, the Department for Education have pointed out that most jewellery enamels contain a certain level of toxic metals. However, it is perfectly safe to do hot enamelling work with older children, providing there is adequate supervision. When using powdered enamel it is recommended that masks are worn when sifting powder, and that young people should be advised that the powder is dangerous if it comes into contact with eyes or mouth.

Copper shapes suitable for badges, pendants, rings, etc. are easily obtainable, although you can cut your own from copper sheeting. The copper needs to be prepared for accepting the enamel powder by sanding it to a smooth finish with a fine grade sandpaper and applying a thin coat of enamelling oil if required. Descaling liquid can also be applied at this stage to the reverse side of the shape. Now the powder can be sprinkled onto the shape to provide a thin even coat. Placing the shapes on the sheets of newspaper will help when it comes to clearing up. This is the first of two coats, and should be the same colour, or lighter, than the final one. The shape can now be placed in the kiln with a spatula and fired until the surface has a shiny, wavy appearance. This only takes a minute or two, and the shape should then be removed and laid on a sheet of asbestos to cool.

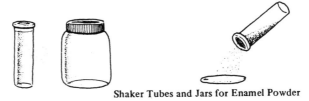

Shaker Tubes and Jars for Enamel Powder

Now comes the exciting bit when you can create your own individual design. You must first prepare the shape with a second coat of enamelling powder, using a thin coat of oil again, if you like. The simplest method is to make your design or initials by removing some of the powder with a fine brush (as long as the colour underneath is a contrasting one). When fired, the design will stand out due to the contrasting colours. Second coats should be fired until the surface is smooth and glossy. If any objects to be fired are not flat, or have sloping surfaces, Tramil Gum can be used to affix the enamel to the surface ready for firing.

Once allowed to cool, findings – badge pins etc. (to transform the shape into a badge, ring, earring, etc.) can be glued or soldered on. Epoxy Resin two-part glue sets in about ten minutes and is very strong; Super Glue is quicker, but slightly less permanent. When soldering, the back of the shape must be sanded down until smooth and shiny, or the solder will not take. 'Jump rings' are very useful in making pendants. Once the little ring has been twisted through the hole at the top of the shape you'll find that it can be laced easily with leather thong and will sit nicely round the neck.

Enamel lumps and coloured threads are always popular ways of decorating shapes, and are simply laid on top of the second coat before it is put in the kiln for firing. In the kiln they will melt flat to form part of the smooth glossy surface. Young people love using the threads to spell out their initials! Millefiori can also be used to good effect but you need a good kiln if they are to melt down properly.

Simple combinations of different colours can be effective at the second coat stage and these can, when melted, be scrolled with a pointed implement to produce a swirled effect. There are several other enamelling methods (e.g. champleve, cloisonne, pique-a-jour) which demand jewellery-making skills or specially prepared materials, but can produce exciting results for those prepared to persevere.

There isn't much that can go wrong with the simpler forms of hot enamelling, and it is therefore worth trying this activity out with most older youth groups. Articles made can be used as presents, or even offered for sale at open days to swell your coffers.

Try to limit the numbers participating in enamelling sessions to about four to six young people per facilitator, and make sure you have an adequate amount of working space. Kilns get very hot indeed and can take a long time to cool down; make sure that the kids are aware of this. Asbestos gloves or a fire blanket can be used if you need to move the kiln during use or after the session.

INSTANT ANIMATION

You'll probably remember flicker books which used occasionally to be given away free by children's comics and breakfast cereal manufacturers. Well, stop being lazy, and invent your own instant version of a cinema great! A flicker book uses exactly the same technique as a cartoon animation.

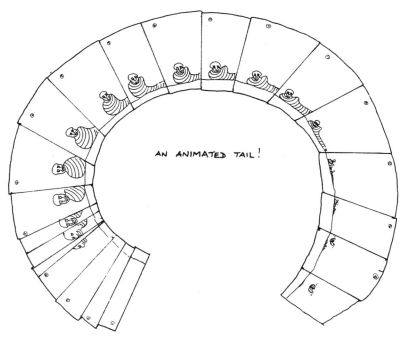

AN ANIMATED TAIL!

To make a piece of instant animation you'll need to obtain or cut out about 30 equally sized pieces of lightweight card (about 120gsm, for the technically minded!) Index cards are good and you can at least be sure that they are exactly equal in size. These should then be numbered in the left hand corner so you and the other artists keep them in sequence order.

Now, draw a line somewhere in the middle of each card and start drawing a simple cartoon sequence for your flicker books, using the right hand side of your book for the drawings. Keep the line drawings simple. With a group of youngsters it's a good idea to have lots of source cartoon materials available and pencils and tracing paper. Try though, to encourage some original drawings to come out of a session. Since it doesn't require too high a skill level, just patience repeating the drawings, you don't need to be a great artist to achieve a pleasing bit of dynamic action. You can get different effects by making the cartoon animation move in very small or larger gradations of movement.

Once the set of drawings is complete, tape the bundle together holding them tightly in the middle and binding them round the left hand edge.

JEWELLERY

This craft can utilise the products of several techniques outlined in other sections of this book. For example, polished pebbles can be used to make earrings, pendants and rings. Similarly, you can use brightly painted papier maché beads and shapes as raw material for these items and necklaces as well.

In most cases you will want to use jewellers' 'findings' to help you make finished articles quickly and easily. These are the mountings used to make rings, brooches, earrings, cufflinks and even bracelets. Findings are typically made of base metal but can also be obtained with various qualities of silver and gold finishes. A vast range can be obtained from a number of specialist suppliers. You will need an epoxy resin adhesive to fix your chosen materials to the mounts.

If your budget will stretch to it, Manchester Minerals provide a vast array of jewellers' findings including ones made of solid silver and gold. Their design range is extensive and includes complex and popular designs such as butterflies, flowers, teddy bears and dolphins. Excellent results can be obtained almost instantly using these findings, and of course they are perfect when working with younger children or those with a very limited concentration span.

We suggest that you start off by getting hold of some findings to give you ideas about the kinds of material you might want to use with them. For example, you may want to glue some millefiori enamel straight on to earring mounts; silk threads and small feathers or down are also suitable to decorate earrings. With the current gender bending trends of the 1990s, including cross dressing, jewellery making (and wearing!) is no longer a predominantly female pastime. Acid, new age and rave cultures have contributed to create demand for all kinds of weird and wonderful brooches, pins and other adornments. There is often much cachet and street credibility to be gained if these artefacts are home made, particularly from found materials.

Encourage the young people you are working with to explore the possibilities of particular materials and to experiment with non-traditional designs. The following sections outline a few key techniques, and we begin with one of the newer materials now available which can be manipulated easily into striking designs.

Fimo Modelling Material

This is a versatile clay type of material which is fired in an ordinary kitchen oven to harden it. It is available in three dozen different colours, and they can be mixed together to create any specific colour you want. Fimo is renowned for its brilliant colour intensity, and of course this means that there is no need to paint the material once you have made your piece of jewellery.

Its uses include:

- beads for necklaces;
- modelled birds, animals, cartoon or human figures;
- brooches, pendants, badges and earrings;
- 3-D badges and pictures;
- braiding or marbling to produce spectacular effects, including millefiori.

Fimo produce a very helpful leaflet which demonstrates how you can make various designs very easily indeed. All in all this is an amazingly versatile material which is very easy to use.

As full instructions and ideas are included in every pack, we will not go in to detail here. However, there are one or two safety rules which need to be borne in mind:

- As with many craft activities you should not eat, drink or smoke in the activity area.
- Fimo is not suitable for use with children under eight.

- Hands should be washed after using the material.
- Fimo needs to be hardened in the oven at an exact temperature. As harmful gases can be produced if this temperature is exceeded, we recommend using an oven thermometer.

Pebble Pendants

You can use pebbles you have polished yourself (see section in this book) or bought from a supplier such as Fred Aldous or Manchester Minerals. There is a specific jewellery mount called a 'bell cap' which you will need to obtain, and you need to select your pebble carefully so that the bell cap will fit.

Before you glue the cap to the pebble using epoxy resin, fit the cap to the pebble by pressing it on to the stone. A pair of jewellers' pliers are handy for this job – these are long nosed pliers which are obtainable with one round and one flat end, or with both ends round or flat. If you are working with a range of different materials, you will probably want one of each – otherwise go for the one flat/one round version.

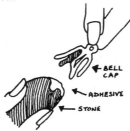

Once you have glued the cap to the pebble you will need to leave it to set. Of course with pebble pendants, and with rings, you can't simply put them down on a table, because the finding is likely to fall off. What you need is a pot of sand or salt – then simply push your item into it to hold it in an upright position.

Pebble pendants can be completed using a jump ring and metal chain or leather thong.

Pebble Rings and Bracelets

Most rings and bracelets use a flat 'pad' type of mount. Unfortunately this means you will probably not be able to use pebbles you have polished yourself, because one side of the pebble needs to be perfectly flat to make good contact with the pad. However, these 'cabochon cut' stones can be bought fairly inexpensively from your supplier. It is then simply a matter of choosing (for bracelets) stones of similar, or complementary colour, and gluing them on.

You can obtain linked bracelets onto which you can hang a number of bell capped pebbles – and of course you will be able to use your own pebbles with these. Take care when sticking the caps to the pebbles that the ring on the cap faces the same way as the display face of the stone. Now when you put the jump ring on the cap and fix it to the necklace, all the pebbles will hang facing the right way.

Do remember that jewellery comes in for exceptionally hard use, so when you are gluing items together follow the manufacturer's instructions and allow the glue to set for the recommended time before wearing the jewellery.

Silver and Copper Wire

Simple pendants and rings can be made very easily with copper or silver wire. Generally, any metal you will be working with needs to be annealed (softened) before you start to make your piece. Do this by holding the metal with tongs and heating it with a blowlamp until it is a dull red colour; then plunge it into cold water. Rub the metal with wet and dry sandpaper to brighten it up again. The metal soon hardens up again, so you may need to anneal it a few times as you work. 16-18 gauge wire is best for this kind of work.

If you need to straighten out the wire, place one end in a vice and grip the other end with flat nosed pliers – if the pliers have teeth, cover them with cloth tape or sticking plaster so that they don't mark the metal. To provide a good grip for the pliers, make a small right angled bend at the end of the wire – now give a few steady pulls on the wire to straighten it out.

To make a simple pendant, take a length of wire about six to eight inches long, and make a small loop in one end using round nosed pliers. To do this, grip the end of the wire towards the end of the jaws of the pliers and bend it around to form a small circle. Next, change the grip on the pliers (see diagram) and bend the circle back to centre it. Now move to the other end of the wire and make another small loop (but don't centre it this time).

This little loop forms the beginning of the winding, circular shape you are going to make. Start coiling the wire by using your fingers to push it round the loop, and as the coil gets larger hold it firmly with flat nosed pliers. Finally, twist the original loop by 90° so that the pendant will lie properly when you thread a chain or thong through the loop.

A square shaped pendant can be made by using flat nosed pliers to make 90° turns in the wire. An interesting effect can be obtained with either pendant by flattening the wire. Young people love doing this, as it involves bashing the wire with a flat headed hammer against a metal block or anvil!

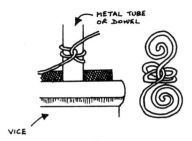

A coiled ring can be made in similar fashion by using an 8 inch length of wire and winding it twice around a suitably sized metal tube or dowel (which will need to be held upright in a vice). Now cross the ends of the wire to secure the ring. File the ends of the wire smooth (cut to adjust the length of the wire at this stage if required). Next, the two ends of the wire can be shaped into circles or squares . Again, the wire can be flattened with a hammer for effect.

Drop Earrings

These earrings can be made using headpins or eyepins and your own selection of beads. A pendant bead, or other item, can be hung from the loop of the eyepin if desired.

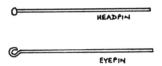

First you should thread your selection of beads onto the headpin, taking care that the hole in the bottom bead is sufficiently small for it not to fall off. Now, if you need to, cut the pin to adjust the length, leaving around 8mm at the top to form into a loop (see 'Copper Wire' above). Make sure that the loop is centred over the beads. The dropper is finished by opening the loop on an earfitting (several kinds are available for pierced and non-pierced ears) and attaching it to the dropper loop.

To start off an eyepin, open the loop by gently twisting it sideways with pliers. Hang a pendant bead from the loop and close it up with pliers. Now add your selection of beads and finish off in the same way as for a headpin.

Simpler drop earrings can be made by attaching a pendant bead directly to an earfitting without using a pin.

Shell Jewellery

Seaside shells can be used to make attractive earrings, pendants and badges. Many shells have a natural 'drop' shape and are perfect for earrings and pendants – you need do little more than fix a bell cap to them before attaching to the earring findings or to a jump ring and chain or leather thong.

Another technique is to use a flat badge finding and glue a selection of matching small shells to this to give a very attractive effect. Flower shapes can be built up easily using tiny shells. Often, you'll be able to glue a small shell, or pearl, in the centre of a larger shell to form a 'jewel.' Finally, don't discard broken shells, as they can often be used as a pendant – simply sand away any rough edges, and if there is not a natural hole to thread your chain or thong through, use a bell cap mount.

KITES

Kites have a long and respectable history, reputedly originating in China more than a few years B.C.! The Chinese, in fact, successfully developed man-lifting kites which they used as military lookouts, and Koreans and Japanese developed fighting kites – the line near the kites was coated with glue and powdered glass, the aim being to cut your opponent's line.

Kite flying has undergone a considerable revival in recent years, while hang-gliding (a derivative of the Chinese man-lifting kite) has achieved cult status. Simple kites are quite easy to make out of basic materials and can fly remarkably well. Instructions are given at the end of the section. Kites are probably best used with your youth group on residential trips or outings to the country, as turbulence created in towns by buildings and traffic makes them difficult to fly and extricate from roofs, chimneys, and the like! Similarly, kites will not fly well in forested areas. Ideal places include flat fields, the windward side of a hill, or near the sea or lake. You should not (for obvious reasons) fly one in a thunderstorm (remember good old Benjamin Franklin's experiment!). Overhead power cables are absolutely lethal and you must *always* check for them carefully before launching kites – especially in country areas where there may only be a single cable visible.

Preparing and Launching

Most kites have a bridle which attaches the kite to the line; this hold the kite at a specific 'angle of attack' – a high angle for normal wind conditions, and a lower angle for strong winds (see diagram). Make sure that this angle is correct before flying, by doing a couple of trial launches and then making the necessary adjustments to the bridle. You should find (with the notable exception of the sled kite, which you can fly at a very high angle) that the best angle of attack is between 30 and 35 degrees from the horizontal. **Always,** before launching, check the balance of the kite by throwing it gently up in the wind – if the kite keels over to one side, you will have to add weight to balance it.

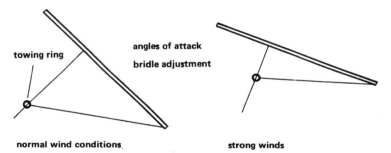

towing ring

angles of attack

bridle adjustment

normal wind conditions   **strong winds**

If the wind isn't too strong and you are using a kite reel (advisable for good control) you can gain height by 'winching' the kite. What you do is to launch the kite by throwing it up in the air; now allow the line to run slack until the kite almost drops to the ground, and then reel in quickly so that the kite soars up. Repeat this process (see diagram) until the kite is as high as you want, or it reaches a height where there is more wind.

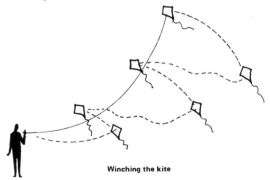

Winching the kite

You can also launch the kite with a helper by unrolling about 20 yards of line and getting her to hold the kite high about her head. As the helper launches the kite you should move backwards until it begins to rise and then slowly let out more line. Once the kite has reached a good height you can use the winching technique to make it drop and soar.

Landing the Kite

In moderate wind conditions it isn't too difficult to land the kite; reel it in slowly and steadily until it is just a few yards away, then let the line go slack to bring the kite slowly to the ground. If there is a lot of tension on the line, you can ease it by walking towards the kite while reeling it in. In high winds, extra care is needed as the kite can suddenly plunge to the ground. Ideally, ask someone to help you by walking out along the line towards the kite, pulling the line down at the same time. Once they are about 30 yards away and holding the line to take tension off your end of it, walk towards them while reeling in; repeat the process until the kite is safely down.

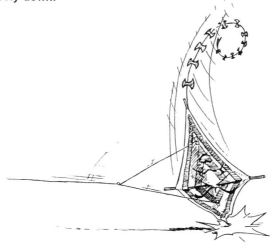

Materials and Construction

We have found that choice of materials and accuracy of construction are immensely important in creating a machine that will actually fly! We therefore include only two kite designs in this section which we found to be simple to make and virtually guaranteed to fly.

COVER MATERIAL	EASE OF USE	SUITABLE FRAME	ADHESIVE METHOD	WEIGHT	FLYING LINE
Light paper	Good	Thin stick Rice straw	White glue Sticky tape	Very light	Sewing thread
Heavy paper	Good	Cane Bamboo Rattan	Wood glue Strong glue Sticky tape	Light	Sewing thread
Silk or Cotton	Moderate	Thin stick Rattan	Fabric glue Reinforcing tape	Light	Linen
Synthetic fabric	Moderate	Bamboo Deal Light alloy Polypropelene	Sewing Sticky tape	Light to heavy	Fishing line
Nylon or Plastic film	Poor	Stick Synthetic tubing	Plastic adhesive tape	Light to heavy	Nylon
Polyethylene film	Very good	Stick Light alloy Synthetic tubing Fibre-glass	Sticky tape Cloth tape Heat application	Light to heavy	Nylon

By all means attempt to build other kinds of kite, but remember that the designs may be complex, calling for great accuracy, relatively sophisticated construction techniques, and an awful lot of patience. Most youth groups will probably relish the experience of flying kites rather than making them, so try to keep it simple. Remember that kites can be decorated and personalised – this is an enjoyable activity and helps the kites look attractive in the sky.

For those who **do** want to experiment, this Materials and Construction Chart will be useful.

Generally, a light and flexible kite will perform will in a light wind; attempt to launch it in a strong wind and it is likely to be damaged and torn.

A heavy kite, made from strong materials and able to support strong wind pressure without twisting its shape, will fly well in bad weather. In a light wind it will not even get off the ground! As a rule of thumb, flat kites should fly well in light winds, while 'bowed' kites perform well in moderate winds, and cellular kites in strong winds.

On a kite flying expedition it makes sense to take a selection of different kinds of kite, so that you have at least one or two which will fly irrespective of the wind conditions you meet.

Tails
The main purpose of a tail is to create drag and thus provide directional stability. A tail also helps reduce the side to side 'snaking' motion that often occurs. The tail should add as little extra weight to the kite as possible – remember it's the drag factor that is important. In flight, the tail should fly gracefully in the wind, counterbalancing the movement of the kite, without adding any backlash.

The length of the tail should be adjusted to suit wind speed (larger tail for high winds) but will usually be between five and seven times the length of the kite. **Do** have a few trial attempts with tails of different lengths.

Tails are always needed on flat kits.

Winding Bobbin
While not as useful as a kite reel, a winding bobbin is a reasonable substitute, and very easy to make (see diagram).

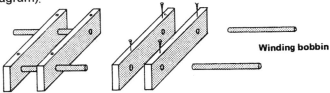

Winding bobbin

How to make a Simple Kite
This kite flies well in moderate to high winds.

You will need:
- Two spars of square section soft or hard wood
  - one of 36 inches x .25 inch
  - one of 32 inches x .25 inch.
- Lightweight cloth or crepe or tissue paper 36 inches x 36 inches.
- Line (25 kg breaking strain minimum – stronger for high winds).
- Glue and towing ring (curtain ring, washer or similar).

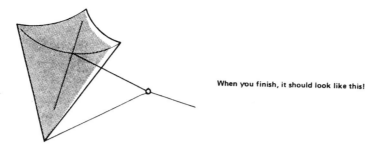

When you finish, it should look like this!

Using the long spar as the spine of the kite, tie the short spar to the spine six inches from the top to form a cross. Now notch the ends of the spars and tie line round the frame (Diagram 1).

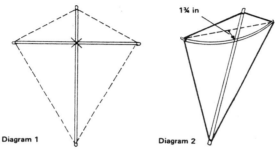

1¾ in

Diagram 1   Diagram 2

Cut out the cover, allowing enough of a hem to turn it over frame, and glue it down. Next, tie a line tightly along the cross-spar to bow the kite. There should be roughly 1.75 inches clearance between the line and the spine (Diagram 2).

Now strengthen two bridle points on the cover, approximately 6 inches from the top and 2 inches from the bottom of the kite. This can be done with paper reinforcing circles (paper kites), or with cloth tape or material on other kites. Pierce a hole in the strengthened part of the kite and tie the bridle ring around the spar behind. The string should be a total length of approximately 84 inches, and should be looped once through the towing ring. If you adjust the bridle so that the top part of it is roughly 36 inches long and the bottom part 48 inches, then the kite will be set at the correct angle of attack for normal wind conditions (Diagram 3). Finally, attach the line to the towing ring. The ring will remain in position as you tighten the line and bridle. Prepare to launch! A tail can be added to this kite to increase its stability. It should be made of a very light material, roughly five times the length of the kite itself.

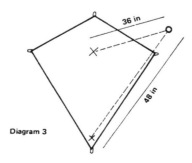

36 in

48 in

Diagram 3

Sled Kites

This kite is a recent design and came from experiments for improving parachutes. You can see the similarity to parachutes used by sky-divers. It flies well in all winds, although you may have to add twin tails for stability in strong winds.

You will need:
- Two spars of square section soft or hard wood 36 inches x .25 inch.
- 200 gauge polythene or PVC 40 inches x 40 inches.
- Fishing line.
- Strong adhesive tape.
- Metal eyelets.
- Towing ring.

Carefully cut the cover and air vents; then reinforce the bridle points with adhesive tape and metal eyelets.

Now lay the spars on the cover and fix them firmly with adhesive tape. Fix a piece of line to the bridle points as shown, laying it out round the kite to achieve the correct length.

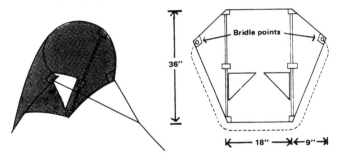

Finally, fix a towing ring at the centre of the bridle. The kite is now complete and can be attached to the flying line. Note that sled kites can fly well at an angle of attack of 50-60 degrees to the horizontal. As with any kite, if you are not happy with its balance or angle of attack in flight, make some adjustments till you get it right. It will be worth the effort!

Note that the proportions of these kites can be scaled up or down as required to make kites of different sizes – make sure to alter the bridle in line with the new dimensions.

Finally, avoid flying kites within two miles of an airport (it's actually against the law) or at high altitudes. Kites made with certain materials can show up on radar screens causing all sorts of difficulties for air traffic controllers, not to mention very real risks to the flying public.

LEATHERWORK AND PYROGRAPHY

Leather is a flexible resource for making lots of items which kids like and use, whether it is a studded dog collar for the boy or girl-friend, or bags, belts, pouches, wristbands, pendants, hairslides, pet collars and clothes, to name but a few items. Scrap leather is inexpensive and can be used to make mosaics in the form of a wallhanging, or to embellish a garment. Some leathers can be tooled or stamped with a design. You can also dye it, paint it, or stud it. Articles are usually made by cutting out shapes and joining them by gluing, stitching, thonging or riveting.

A number of leather suppliers will supply clearance, cut lengths of leather and specify their suitability for different uses. For instance, at the time of writing this at the beginning of 1996, it was possible to obtain ten belt lengths, ¾ inch wide, 3mm thick and between 432 inches and 53 inches long cost £110 per unit. It's not an activity for people who feel strongly about working with and wearing animal skins. But, virtually no suppliers in the leather trade use skins from animals killed for their skins – it is a by product of the meat industry. Some synthetic alternatives to leather and suede are available – you will need to enquire locally. Financially, leatherwork lends itself as a fundraising activity, whereby the group can help their organisation raise funds, or at very least cover most of the costs.

A fair number of fiddly bits of equipment are necessary to do some jobs properly, especially when dealing with rivets. It is possible to improvise in some cases, but you will end up with a fairly high level of wastage of eyelets, rivets, press studs etc.. Hand, hammered tools are inevitably more fiddly to use than more solid machines with special dies for applying rivets, eyelets and press studs. In the old phrase, *"You pays your money and takes your chance."*

If you want to test out the demand for leatherwork among young people you are working with, you should consider buying kits. These are useful, as you are provided with a basic pattern that can be used many times over. Because most of the leather cutting and preparation has been done for you, you can do without many of the tools until such time as the demand merits buying them. Remember, though, that kits will not keep people occupied for long as they can be completed very quickly. Since there are a number of knives involved in many leatherwork processes, it is important to match the leather projects to the age, ability and potential for aggressive behaviour levels of your young people. A reasonably comprehensive list of materials and equipment is as follows:

> Vegetable tanned leather: firm, easily tooled or stamped with a design.
> Chrome tanned leather: soft and supple - ideal for pouches, bags
>   and mosaic work.
> Leather thonging and needles
> Stanley knife
> Leather scissors with a serrated bottom for cutting
> Steel rule - for making straight cuts
> Awl - to score lines for cutting
> Revolving punch for holes
> Oblong punch for belts
> Thonging punch

Stitching punch
Stitch groover
Stitch marker
Press stud tool set, plus press studs
Riveting tool set, plus rivets
Eyelet tool set, plus eyelets
Sail-Eyelet/Grommet setter
Modelling tool
Swivel knife for leather carving
Wooden or (if you can afford it) a Rawhide mallet
An Edge Shave for rounding edges, and if your group get very keen a
        Safety beveller for bevelling and skiving edges (tapering thinner to
        join together)
Strap cutter - for cutting belt widths
Non-adjustable Groover – for decorating or deeply scoring leather
        (e.g. to fold)
Embossing tool and die stamps (highly recommended).

For supplies, and advice on leatherwork projects, both of the following operate nationally.
Stuart Hails from Le Prevo Leathers is especially helpful.
S. Glassner, 476 Kingston Rd, Raynes Park, London SW20 8DX.
Le Prevo Leathers, Blackfriars, Stowell St, Newcastle upon Tyne NE1 4XN.

Specialist Crafts also offer a limited range of leatherwork tools and leather.

Decorating Leather

The grain side of vegetable tanned leather is suitable for decorative work once it has been
moistened with a damp sponge. Very effective designs can be produced using the various
embossing tools available. These merely stamp the leather with a little design (e.g. a small
star). Repeated use of one or more embossing tools can quickly build up a pleasing pattern.
To finish, the leather can be stained if required, and polished. Particularly popular with
young people is the embossing of letters and names on to key rings, fobs, belts, and the
like. You need a whole set of alphabet embossing tools.

Intricate hand embossing takes a little more skill. As before, the leather should be
moistened, and then a design is drawn or traced onto it. This design should be carefully
gone over with an awl or modelling tool to produce an indentation, and then scored with a
swivel knife (a neat little tool that allows you to safely make intricate cuts or scores). The

design is now put into relief by stamping the areas between the lines with a smooth stamp and mallet. Again, the leather can be dyed and polished to finish.

Leather is best dyed by brushing the dye onto the leather using a tightly rolled cloth. This helps to avoid streaking. The dyes used are very powerful, and rubber gloves (and an apron to protect clothes) should be worn for protection.

Pendants
Use thick scraps of vegetable tanned leather for this. Draw a pendant shape directly on the leather and then trace it out with an awl. The shape can now be cut out using a leather knife or shears.

Make a design on the shape (you can, if you like, do this before you cut it out) by:

burning	–	use an electric pen/electric embossing tool
embossing	–	use embossing punches
tooling	–	use a modelling tool and swivel knife

The pendant is finished off by bevelling the edges, punching a hole in the top and threading with leather thong.

Wrist Bands
Fearsome looking specimens are easily made by cutting out and decorating with rivets, studs and eyelets. The edges can be holed with a thonging punch, and then thonged to effect. The easiest way of fixing them to the wrist is by using a press-stud arrangement or providing holes so that the wristband can be laced with leather thong: we would stress that it is possible to make more subtly designed wristbands by embossing or tooling the leather! Le Prevo Leathers recommend finishing off the wrist band with Resolene or Carnauba Creme.

Hint – watch your stocks of rivets and studs as an inevitable spin-off of this activity is the exciting 'decorate your denim or leather jacket syndrome'. Alternatively, you can just order more studs.

Belts
Heavy leather belts suitable for tooling and dyeing can be made from thick, vegetable tanned leather. Start off by selecting a suitable buckle, and cut a strip of leather to fit the inner width of the buckle. (Use a scrapcutter or knife and steel rule). The leather strip should be a foot longer than the waist measurement. A stitch groover can be used to cut decorative grooves along the edges of the belt, and one end should be cut to a curved shape. Make sure that the other (buckle) end is cut square and then trim off the corners. A slot for the buckle prong should be cut, starting approximately 1¼ inches from the buckle end of the belt. An oblong punch and mallet should be used to cut out the slot, although you can cheat (and save money on an oblong punch) by punching two holes roughly 1¼ inches apart and then cutting out a slot between them. The slot should be wide enough for the prong to more about freely. With the buckle in place and the leather doubled over to hold it, mark out four rivet holes (for the two rivets that will fix the buckle) and then punch them out (with a hollow or rotary punch). five or six punch holes should be made out at 1 inch intervals, starting about 3 inches from the shaped end. With a safety beveller, bevel all the edges on both sides of the belt. The belt can now be tooled, and dyed if required, and only needs to be riveted at the buckle end to finish it off.

A belt made in this way will not only look good (especially if it is well tooled) but will be extremely hard wearing and as good as any expensive shop-bought product.

Suede can be used to make belts too, although the finished product will not be as tough and durable as a leather belt. This is compensated by the ease of working with the material, and the possibility of using appliqué techniques to decorate it. The main differences from the method shown above are as follows:

Allow twice the width of suede as the inner width of the buckle you are using, as the suede has to be doubled for strength; otherwise all measurements are identical. Working on the reverse side of the suede, make a line centrally along the length of the strip and apply a fabric adhesive to the whole of the reverse side. Now turn each side of the belt over to meet at the central line and press flat. Trim one end to a diagonal point and make sure that the other end is square. Appliqué shapes can now be made out of thin scraps of leather or suede, and can be ironed flat on the reverse side with a hottish iron. The shapes can be made a simple or complicated as you like (squares, circles, crescents, butterflies, etc.) and should be arranged to form a pleasing pattern before being lightly glued onto the belt. The professionals use double sided sellotape for this purpose, which avoids splashes of glue marking the suede.

A sewing machine equipped with a leather work needle can be used to fix the shapes properly - advisable because the stitching itself will strengthen the belt. The diagonal point should also be stitched to finish, and eyelets should be used to reinforce the belt holes.

Chamois Shoulder Bag
Originally the skin of the mountain antelope of that name, chamois now commonly refers to the softer side of a sheep or lamb skin. It is very soft and supple leather which is easily worked. You will need one chamois skin, at least 20 by 16 inches.

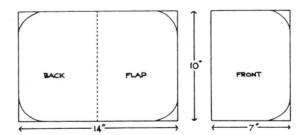

Following the diagram make a template from a paper pattern. As all the curves need to be identical, use only one template to cut out the shapes as shown - one large piece for the back and flap, and one piece for the front. Using the remaining chamois, make up a strip about 4 feet long by 1¼ inches. This forms the gusset between front and back sections and 'runs on' to form the strap. You will have to join pieces together by gluing and stitching to make up the 4 foot length. Now, at half inch intervals, punch holes along both edges of the strip and around the edges of the other pieces. These holes are to accommodate thonging to join the gusset to the front and back sections and to give a decorative effect to the front of the bag and the strap. Various thonging stitches can be used, but the single whipstitch is easy to do, and decorative (see diagram).

Sewing and thonging stitches.

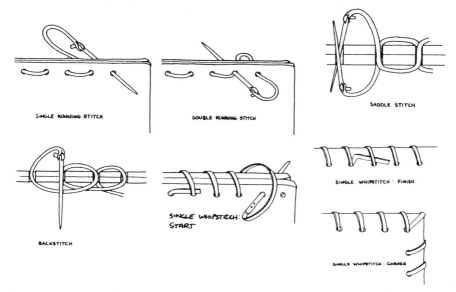

SINGLE RUNNING STITCH

DOUBLE RUNNING STITCH

SADDLE STITCH

BACKSTITCH

SINGLE WHIPSTITCH: START

SINGLE WHIPSTITCH: FINISH

SINGLE WHIPSTITCH: CORNER

Use this stitch to join the gusset to the front and back sections, continuing the thonging along the edges of the strap and the front flap. You can use commercially available leather or suede thonging, or make up your own from chamois if you have any left. The bag is finished off by punching a couple of holes about an inch apart at the front of the bag, just below the flap - thread a few strips of chamois through the holes and knot losely for effect.

Other leather items worth tackling are belt pouches and, if you have the finances, and are happy that your youngsters have the ability, waistcoats. Pouches can be made out of leather or suede and decorated by tooling or appliqué. Pouch fastenings can be made with press-studs or Velcro. Waistcoats are best made from a soft suede leather or chamois. Simply buy a waistcoat pattern, or copy an existing one, and use offcuts to decorate the finished article.

It is worth trying to find a source of cheap leather offcuts - try any small leather goods manufacturer. Such offcuts can be used for appliqué work, and to make small items like pendants and wristbands. It is also possible to make patches from offcuts. They can then be glued and stitched onto fabric backing and used to make bags, purses, waistcoats, etc.. Big frames and handles are available from craft shops, and this provides a useful shortcut to good quality results.

Pyrography
This is the art of pokerwork, often applied to leather and wood, which burns a design permanently into place. Specialist Crafts offer quite a good range of Pyrography irons and machines for pokerwork and wood and leather offcuts, but a more specialist source for irons and wood and leather items is:
Janik Eneterprises, Brickfield Lane, Denbigh Rd, Ruthin, Clwyd LL15 2TN.

This activity is only suitable for young people who you feel are safe with the equivalent of a soldering iron, which the pyrograph tool essentially is. The best pyrograph tools incorporate a variable heat setting and can be fitted with a whole range of tips, brands and wires to achieve a variety of effects. These include decorative shapes, numbers and letters, which can be used to decorate a belt, a purse or a wooden clock or box. Janik stock a useful array of wooden pencil boxes, money boxes, egg cups, door plaques and badge shapes.

To produce a pyrography design, the artist can either draw freehand with the iron, stamp out patterns, or following a pencil design or tracing. Celtic art designs are particularly popular using this medium, but do require quite a high level of proficiency with the tool. Our own experience has shown that it is often difficult for young people to produce evenly burned imprints on the leather or wood surfaces. They can end up in tears and tantrums! This is an interesting, complementary craft to the more usual leatherwork techniques, nonetheless.

LINO AND BLOCK PRINTING

Although it is a very simple way of producing printed images, excellent results can be achieved by using this method. You can make multi-coloured prints in one go, for example, without the complication of register boards and other paraphernalia. Linoprints can be used to decorate cards and calendars or to make magazine covers, or prints suitable for framing. Because of the nature of the tools involved and the relative difficulty of manipulating them without amputating fingers, it is best to limit this activity to two or three young people working with one instructor. The cutting tools employ very sharp blades so we would not recommend it as an activity with primary school age children.

To organise a lino printing session you will need:

- Pieces of lino – available from craftshops, NES Arnold, or Specialist Crafts. It can be bought in a lino roll (4.5 mm thick) for economic cutting or in a variety of pre-cut sizes, in either 4.5 mm or 3.2 mm thickness.
- Lino cutting tools – these use sharp steel blades mounted in wooden handles, so exercise care in use.
- Consider the purchase of small G-clamps, or, bench hooks, which are like a drawing board with raised edges, used to keep the lino block in place, enabling the use of both hands for cutting.
- Ink tray or plate glass slab.
- Small rubber roller (with handle).
- Tubes of oil or water based printing ink. Alternatives are using specially formulated blockmix with powder paints, or special oil based printers' inks.
- Soft (unsized) paper or card for printing – e.g., Japanese type or Quickprint special paper, or smooth matt surfaced paper.
- White spirit for cleaning.
- Aprons.

Although the lino can be used as it is, you will find it easier to print with if you mount it on a block of wood. Water based inks are easier to clean than oil based, but many of the inks give less impressive results.

Lino and block printing involves gouging out sections of lino to leave a design in relief which can then be inked and used to print on paper or card.

Preparation

You must first draw your design onto the lino, remembering that the print you get will be a

reverse image. For this reason it is probably best to suggest to your youth group that they should avoid lettering until they gain enough skill to cut them out in reverse. Tracing can be used to make the initial design, transferring this to the lino by using carbon paper (placed carbon side down on the lino with the tracing placed **upside down** on top of it). If the design is difficult to see on the lino, cover it with a thin coat of white poster paint before the design is drawn. This makes the design easier to see when cutting out. When all the cutting and gouging has been done, the poster paint can be washed off and the lino dried before moving on to the print stage.

Remember, too, that you can achieve a positive or negative image depending on how you cut the lino. For example, if you want to print a star shape, you can simply gouge this shape out of the lino and print it. You will get a **negative** image with the star shape being formed by the ink surrounding it. If, however, you gouge away all the lino **except** the star shape, the resulting print will be **positive**, i.e. only the star shape will be inked onto the paper.

Printing

Prepare a print area for your group on a sturdy table or workbench, by spreading out some old newspapers. Then squeeze a couple of inches of ink from a tube onto a glass slab or tray and roll it out to form a thin layer. The lino block is inked by running over it several times with a roller. Now, encourage the printmakers to make a few test prints on some waste papers, applying even pressure with the hand across the inked area, or ideally, by using a second un-inked roller, or, better still by using a special printing press. Each print requires the block to be re-inked. It will take 2 or 3 test prints before the block will print evenly. Final prints (several hundred) can now be made from a lino block.

Burnishing is another method that can be used to produce lino prints. Ink the block as above and lay it face up with the printing paper carefully laid on top of it. Now, using a smooth implement like a wooden spoon, and taking care not to move the paper, rub through the paper onto the design underneath to produce a print. If you are using thin paper, you'll have to cover it with a thicker sheet as well, as the colour will otherwise come through the thin paper to be nicely smudged by the wooden spoon! Burnishing will produce very good quality prints and can also be used to tidy up imperfect prints created by the pressure method. The quality of a print can be checked by carefully turning up the corners, one at a time, and having a 'peek'. If you are not happy with the quality, replace the paper and tidy it up with local burnishing.

Multi-coloured prints

Prints of many colours are easily produced by the lino printing method. This will be most successful where the design has several discreet elements which can be inked separately. Instead of using a roller to ink the block, this method requires the use of inking 'dollies' to dab the ink on. These are simply small wads of cloth wrapped in cotton wool. Cotton buds work very well for this purpose. However, if you have a large expanse of block to ink with one colour, you should still be able to use the dollies for smaller areas. Any ink which spills over onto other print areas (or the background) can be wiped off with a rag and white spirit. Once the block has been inked up with the required colours you can proceed to make prints in the normal way. Outstanding results can be produced with this method, and it is well worth spending some time experimenting with it.

Other things to try

You can experiment with other materials to 'cut' such as vinyl tiles, hardboard, rubber blocks, different woods, etc.. In fact, almost any kind of thin, close-textured board can be cut to make printing blocks. New linoleum cuts much better than old, but you can make old lino easier to cut by warming it up before use.

It is possible to etch lino using caustic soda (this substance is corrosive, so great care should be taken when handling it. Only for use by older, responsible youth groups!). Make up a saturated solution by adding caustic soda crystals to a jar of cold water until no more crystals will dissolve. Stir it with a piece of wood using protective gloves. As heat will have to build up during this process, allow the solution to cool and then add a teaspoon of meths (this helps it spread on the lino). Now prepare the lino by cleaning it with meths. You can section off areas that you want etched by using plasticine – the caustic soda solution can then be carefully poured into the well that is created. It is also possible to paint the solution directly onto the lino. The solution should be left on for at least two hours before washing it off. The dissolved lino can be removed by brushing it off under running water to leave an interesting, granulated surface. Other interesting effects can be made by scoring the lino or indenting it with nails.

Using poster paint (the consistency of thin cream) it is possible to make prints from found objects like bits of wood, metal, leaves, etc.. Some vegetables (onion, cabbage, artichoke) sliced in half make good prints and you can also carve a design into a cut potato.

LEAF PRINT

HALF POTATO

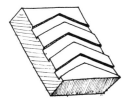
WOOD BLOCK

MAGAZINES, ZINES AND PUBLICATIONS

Many people who ultimately become full time writers, poets and musicians started off penning a few words for their humble school or youth club magazine. From there they may have progressed, or was it regressed (?), to running their own zines or fanzines; perhaps even dabbled in something more commercial. Anyway, self publishing, small scale newspapers, promo leaflets and all sorts of printed weirdness happily continue to exist. The wonderful world of publications run-off on a photocopier and stapled together is very much the domain of youth groups. Here we'll have a go at trying to tell you why its rather beneficial to the health of young people, and a bit or two about how to do it!

Encouraging youthful publications without taking them over, or acting as the Big Brother or Sister Censor, is one problem area. Another is balancing on the tightrope between encouraging young people to write what they want, and remembering that writing may also be sexist, racist or highly critical of, for instance, the people who pay for a youth project or manage it! Having said that, a youth-produced newspaper or zine can:

- help increase literacy skills;
- provide a forum for young people amongst themselves and in the wider community;
- offer an opportunity for co-operative work;
- provide a chance for young people to express themselves;
- assist young people to understand a bit about how the media works.

Before getting started

For the adults involved, it is worth sorting out what resources are, or might be made available. These may help you decide what you produce. Likewise, the age of the young people you are working with will be a factor, as should be their own personal interests and preferences. At the very lowest level, you may just produce a 'Wall Newspaper' which can be ideal for younger groups. Individual children write their own articles, produce quizzes, poems and jokes and then the whole thing is pasted up on a wall inside the building, together with any photos and drawings. This sort of thing is ideal for playschemes and the like and is much used in primary education.

With older groups, the dramatic increase in the availability of personal computers and of photocopiers, means that many of the older methods of producing short run magazines such as duplicating and even typewriting are now nearly defunct. There is also more likelihood that the local council or college, and even some large community schools may have an offset-litho printing machine. This is 'proper printing' and is used for most professionally produced books. You also need to have paper for producing the master copy of each page and paper for printing the copies for distribution. The complete list of possible resources might include:

- one or more places to work from (for writing, artwork, collation etc.)
- computer and printer
- paper
- photocopier or printing machinery
- pens
- drawing equipment for artwork, illustrations and cartoons
- polaroid camera for instant photos
- a black and white darkroom (see photography section of this book)

- a drawing table/light box for planning and designing pages
- a stapler or other way of binding.

A good way to begin

Planning *what* your group wants to produce and perhaps *why* it wants to produce something, and *who* is for it is for, is as good a way to start as any other. After this, you need to consider whether it is going to be sold or given away free, and then have a look at what funds are available. You may also want to see if there any friendly local specialists who would be willing to advise on:
- how to use the computer and related software programs
- writing and reporting
- photography
- design and layout of publications.

It is then down to thinking about who will be doing what, and what should go into each issue. As we hinted at the beginning of this section, a lot depends upon how much risk-taking you want to engage in. Youth work itself is about risk-taking within boundaries. Kids will always test the boundaries. It is the reason why some of the most innovative arts work takes place in the voluntary sector, where the workers are particularly keen to allow young people to have access to the skills, materials and means of production which allow them to produce interesting publications.

Alan, out of the Alan and Howie writing team, has been especially involved in these types of ventures. He has helped young people and adults in over a dozen youth clubs and communities in England and Scotland to start club magazines, punk fanzines, rock and counter-culture zines and 'alternative' community newspapers. His own checkered career spans involvement in the infamous *International Times* magazine at the end of the '60s, through *Sound of the Westway*, (a 1977 Punk Fanzine produced from an Acton youth centre) and described by Julie Burchill in *NME* as, " *In my day it was Fanta orange and Gary Glitter - now it is Government sponsored chaos.*" More recently he helped produce *A Time to Travel? An introduction to Britain's newer Travellers* with Travellers themselves. Now, at the time of putting this book together, he is being threatened with a High Court defamation suit by a lady who identifies herself as being a gigantic dinosaur described in his local spoof newspaper, *SubLyme News!*

The contents

The answers to the questions about who it is for, and why it is being produced, should give a fairly clear set of answers regarding what type of things that should go in. If the aim is to publicise the programme in a youth club, it probably won't be appropriate to have a long article by a fourteen year old girl on why eating meat is murder. However, in another type of publication this might be exactly the right thing. For a lot of first time youth club-type zines, the following is a fair list of 'possible' contents:

- interviews
- news reporting
- sports news
- favourite hobbies and recreations
- reports on what has been happening in and around the club
- future events, trips etc.
- things to do and make
- music and gig reviews
- poems
- crosswords, quizzes, word games and competitions
- cartoons and jokes
- drawings and photos
- letters
- recipes
- surveys and questionnaires
- reports from members' committee and management committee.

For more experimental and adventurous zines, young people are more than likely to make their own agenda for the contents. This may include articles on anything from Green issues to pieces about Raves, House, Grunge, Sex and Sexuality, Politics - areas such as the Criminal Justice Act, Paganism, Spiritual Things, Drugs, Festivals, Gatherings and Demos. For instance, Piglet in Swordfish catalogue #1 says:

"'If you're not outraged, you're not paying attention.' Ever noticed all the shite things going on in the world? Wars....exploitation....eco-destruction....Listen, things are worse than you can possibly imagine. We are all the victims - of the Media, of the System, of ££$$$££. Criminal Justice? ACT!"

(for lots of samples of Youthful Indignation and Creation, contact Swordfish for their catalogue of comix, zines, books, ethnic things, underground music +++ more: PO Box 26, Crawley, W.Sussex, RH11 7YS.)

NEW YOUTH ARTS & CRAFT

The tasks

Some of the best zines and similar are run by very small groups of dedicated folk. The Levellers' mates produce the very interesting *On the Fiddle,* and the dub-reggae-house outfit, Zion Train, produce some well weird observations on life in their own highly polished *The Wobbler.* All of these and all other publications require most of the same tasks to be fulfilled:

- interviewing and reporting
- other writing
- research and note-taking
- photography
- illustrations and cartoons
- editorial tasks
- keying/typing
- graphic design/type fount design
- printing
- collating and binding
- selling/publicity/distribution.

The list clearly shows that either a few people have got to do a lot, or otherwise the tasks have got to be shared out with the aim of getting as many people involved as possible. In youth work, the latter model may be more appropriate for the official youth centre or school production, but as with supporting young musical groups, it is important to back young people in doing their own thing. The division of tasks also begs the question, who takes ultimate responsibility for what goes in and what doesn't? From this question it seems important to look at the power relationship of young people to adults in the process of production and need or otherwise for an overall editor or editorial board. A cautionary word: remember it is the writer, publisher and printer who can be held liable if you create some enemies who want to spend a lot of their money on taking you for a day or two out in the courts!

A few hints

Type styles: The size of type (this is called 11 point Arial) and the style of type fount **(this is called Renfrew!)** can be very important in making a publication, accessible, interesting, easy to read, and interesting or innovative. Handwriting, bits cut out of old newspapers, and graffiti art might all be considered as ways of enhancing a page of type. It is also worth looking at whether to justify type or not - this means whether to make the right hand edge of the type appear ragged (unjustified) or even (justified).

Layout: How the page is put together involves making decisions about how many columns of type are used, where to use illustrations and photos etc..

Photos: Unless you have access to a scanner (a kind of photocopier in reverse, which can scan illustrations and photos into a computer for editing) or a process camera (which turns an ordinary photo into a screened image made up of lots of little dots) you'll probably have to make do with sticking a photo on a photocopier an making the best of things. Black and white images and photos with lots of contrast work the best.

Desk top publishing programs for computers: DTP programs *can* make the job of producing an interesting page design easier, however, they can take some learning and may even inhibit more natural and creative forms of expression using a good old pen, scalpel and a can of spray mount or similar. Sometimes, it is just faster, more fun and simpler to take columns of type and headings and cut and paste them onto a page together with illustrations to make up a page of what is often referred to as CRC - camera ready copy.

At the time of writing, *Word* and *Word Perfect,* are two of the most popular word processing programs (for setting and managing type). More elaborate organisation of page designs can be handled by programs such as *Pagemaker, Quarkxpress* and *Ventura.* The learning curve can be a bit slow and fraught, but on the other hand, young people could learn skills along the way that help them in jobs in the future.

MASKS

Behind every mask is an actor trying get out! For young people this is often very true. A mask provides the security through which that person may show their 'real' selves, or it provides a facade to hide behind. Masks are best made with a purpose in mind, such as for a:

- pageant or procession
- drama activities
- dance groups
- street parties or other celebration.

Masks also present a challenge to adults when they are working with young people. Wearing a mask can unleash unusual behaviour – sometimes leaving even the mask wearer confused afterwards. Once any problems of this sort have been sorted out, it is important for the wearers to learn to move with the mask, using basic theatrical techniques.

Masks can be bought, but are often quite expensive. The rest of this section offers the cheaper (and fun) alternative of mask making. This can take minutes, hours or even days to make. Masks can be constructed out of a wide range of materials. For many youth groups cost is important, so, using what is available or easily obtainable may prove vital. In street carnivals, a mask can end up as a very complex, elaborate structure. A dragon's head might form the front of a long, cavorting chain of participants weaving down the road in a street parade.

Paper and card

Most primary age school children have made simple masks from brown paper/wrapping paper or old cereal cartons. Indeed, in the past, the cereal manufacturers have often provided pre-printed masks on the back of the packet for cutting out – anything from pirates to turtles to Power Rangers!

At its simplest, collect together some paper bags which are large enough to fit loosely over the heads of the youngsters you are working with, then mark the outside to show where the eyes, nose and mouth will be. These are then ready for the young people to take off, paint and decorate.

Using thin card, plus scissors, sellotape, a stapler, paper and paint or coloured pens, an interesting array of masks can be constructed. Imagination, a little ingenuity and a spark of talent are all that are required. By folding, bending, curling, cutting and sticking, a very impressive mask can be made. With young people it is often best to suggest a subject or theme for their mask-making. It might be an animal, monster or cartoon character.

Thicker, corrugated card may also be useful for building bigger 'Heads'. This can be accomplished by creating a cardboard cylinder. Onto this may be added (for instance):
- streamers of paper or wool for hair;
- an egg box section for a nose;
- holes for eyes and mouth;
- additional card or felt for a hat.

Once painted it can make a super mask for a carnival procession.

Plaster of Paris

Face masks can be made using wax (see Candle Making section) or with Plaster of Paris or Mod-Roc gauze, as favoured by our colleagues at Panmure House in Edinburgh. First of all you have to persuade someone to use their own face as the model for the mask. The unlucky person must cover their hair with a bathing cap, put on a smock to protect clothing and then have petroleum jelly (vaseline) applied to their face, including eyebrows, and lashes. The plaster gauze is cut into one inch wide strips, dipped in warm water, one strip at a time, and wrung out gently. The strips are then carefully applied to the face of the reclining model. The entire face, except the nostrils should be covered with three layers of gauze. Alternatively, you can leave the eyes clear. Allow the plaster to set for about ten minutes and then carefully remove from the face if set.

Once the mask has dried, the edges should be trimmed with scissors and re-inforced with strips of gauze folded over the rim. Eyeholes can now be cut and the nostril holes filled in. To model the mask further, it can be built up with modelling wax, newspaper, papier mâché, wood, wire etc., and then covered with a further two layers of plaster gauze. The completed mask is finished off with poster paint and a coat of shellac varnish. This can be a really exciting activity for kids, and most groups will have a lot of fun. However, do make sure that a hole is left in the mask for breathing and closely supervise the whole activity.

For even more life-like masks of real young people, you can take the mask made in the manner described above and use it for making a new mask. This time, the <u>inside</u> of the original mask is coated with vaseline, then Plaster of Paris or papier mâché strips are applied in layers to the inside of the mould. Three or four layers are applied and after they have hardened, the new mask can be eased off from its mould. This second generation mask should be really like the original face and can be gently sanded, generally tidied up and painted to produce a very sophisticated life-mask. These masks require an elastic ribbon to be attached around the back to hold them onto the wearer's head.

Papier Mâché

The section on Papier Mâché describes in a lot more detail the different techniques both to make and to use the medium. Here we offer some ideas for producing masks using this very flexible material.

Balloon mould

A very simple balloon shaped mask can be made by blowing up a balloon, coating it with baby lotion or vaseline, and then further coating it with paper strips, using the layering method described in the Papier Mâché section. Using alternate strips of newspaper and plain paper makes it easier to see how many layers have been applied. Once the mould has set, the bottom edge can be cut and trimmed to produce an open ended, egg-shaped mask.

Plasticine moulds

These offer a more sophisticated option to the balloon mould. To start, mask makers should draw on a sheet of paper the size of mask they require. This template is then placed on a piece of board, On top of this outline, a 3-D mask is made out of plasticine. This acts as a mould for making a mask using the basic papier mâché layering technique, starting with a vaseline coating and building up about four layers of paper strips.

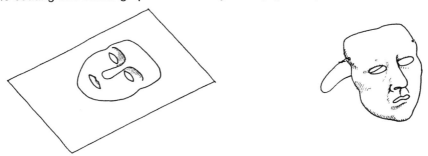

As with the other masks, it can be painted and decorated in any way the maker decides. This also requires an elastic tie around the back to keep it in place.

Wire frames

Using chicken wire, bent, shaped and secured together in the shape of the required head is a good way of making large, Big Head masks. You've probably seen some of these in street parades. Both wire netting and galvanised rust resistant wire are available from both Specialist Crafts and NES Arnold. When cutting and bending the chicken wire to form the head, make sure that there are no sharp ends left sticking inwards or outwards. For ears, nose, eyes and mouth and possibly hat/hair, add on smaller wire structures and attach them with lighter wire or string.

Because these heads are more complex, and take a lot longer to build, they are a more suitable project for adolescent groups who enjoy art activities. Alternatively, the wire structures can be assembled by adults and the young people can work on the layering with papier mâché strips in three or four layers. They can also decorate the heads with paint and possibly a final coat of PVA glue to give it a polished finish.

Obviously, the range of head mask types is virtually limitless; aliens, animals, monsters, gods and nursery rhyme characters are all popular subjects. In India, big headed devils are paraded around the streets for the Diwalli festival, and are eventually burned to destroy evil, in an equivalent of the UK's bonfire night celebration.

Because Big Heads are hot and unwieldy to wear, it is a good idea to:
* put in at least one extra ventilation slot into the head;
* attach shoulder pads and straps to the inside of the head to harness the head to the wearer's body, to aid both comfort and stability.

MOBILES

Mobile making is an excellent activity for youth groups, as good results can be obtained very quickly. Mobiles are hanging art forms – the dangling elements move around when air circulates, so it is best to hang them in a draught. Each mobile requires one or more wood or wire support rods from which the individual elements dangle on strong thread. The completed mobile is usually fixed to the ceiling with wire and a small hook. Wire coat hangers, bamboo or green sticks are very suitable for the rods, and sewing thread or fishing line make ideal line for suspending the materials. For affixing the items dangling from the rods, quick drying glues can prove useful, but are dangerous for young children to use.

The fascination of mobiles lies in the perfect balance between the different elements – this keeps the supporting rod(s) horizontal. There are two ways to achieve this when making your mobile. The first is to suspend your support rods from something handy – without fixing them permanently – and balance the whole thing as you add the individual elements. There are a number of ways to organise the mobiles, all of which should aim to achieve a balanced structure:

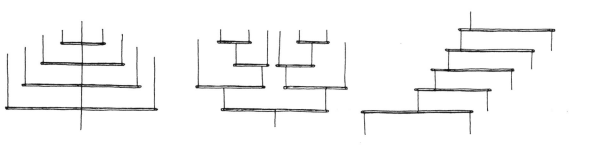

Cutting coloured, decorated card into circular patterns can look effective, as it creates a spiral:

And mobiles which spin round like propellers, using hot air are easy to make and effective.

↑
Hot air

Alternatively, you can encourage young people to make the mobile just as they fancy, later adding counterweights (Blu tack, lead fishing shot, etc.) to balance the whole thing out. Elements can be of different weights and can hang at different distances from the support rod. The side with most weight on it should be placed on the shorter end of the rod.

Virtually, anything from Airfix models to glass beads, can be used to make up the individual elements of your mobile. Suggest trying materials like stiff paper, cardboard, coloured plastic, tinfoil, milk bottle tops, coins, etc.. Some mobiles, like those made of shiny bottle tops or coloured transparent plastic, are particularly striking because they reflect or alter natural light. Other mobiles are successful because they are based on a particular theme, e.g., aeroplanes, birds, geometric or abstract shapes, motor cars, etc..

A guaranteed favourite with youth groups are mobiles which spell out an individual's name, football team, or slogan. Larger letters should be cut out from card, and arranged on the mobile in an interesting way.

For youth groups or a class of youngsters, it is a good idea to turn mobile-making into a group work activity, with four or five participants, individually or in pairs, making objects to hang from the rods. The balancing of the objects may prove a bit tricky, but it pays to encourage a bit of patience and suggest that the mobiles are tested. This can be done by hanging the rods over the edge of a table, which will help to determine where to fix the objects in place. Use a 'blob' of glue to finally fix each element in place, once it is balanced.

Another idea is to make a mobile using the jigsaw principle where the individual elements fit together to form a whole.

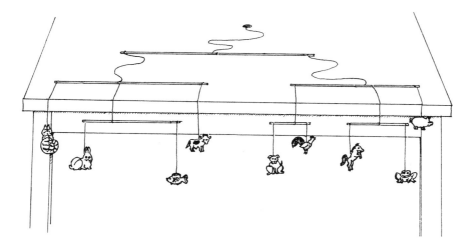

Musical mobiles are easily made out of items which make a noise when struck, e.g., tin, bamboo, shells, metal piping, etc.. The objects should be hung in such a way that they strike together when there is a draught. One way of doing this is to suspend the objects on a small circle of wire which has a heavier object hanging in the centre.

MODEL MAKING AND FANTASY FIGURES

Most parents think that children should have a go at building kits: constructing cars, aircraft, dinosaurs and the like. We suspect that adults try to force the pace too fast, and so end up doing most of the gluing and building themselves, while their offspring slouch in accustomed position on the sofa watching the box! Our experience is that model making of all kinds can be successful in youth groups, providing that the adults involved avoid inflicting the model making on the youngsters involved.

Actually, the range of potential model-building kits covers a very wide range, from:
* Airfix-type plastic models, predominantly of transport, through to the top of the range radio controlled model aircraft, boats and land vehicles.
* Plaster cast kits using clay or resin to produce chess pieces, small animals etc.. These often require some sort of baking or kiln firing. Alec Tiranti Ltd are amongst the most specialist suppliers of clay and all types of modelling materials.
* Air-drying modelling materials for producing models, playing figures etc.. Amongst a number of makes; Modair (in bright colours), Crayola Model Magic, Claykos and Modelight are all recommended for youth work purposes.
* Wooden kits for building prehistoric animals, and other animals and figures which slot together.
* Construction, Craft and Design Technology materials. For younger children, most components are made in plastic. Tomy's Popoids, Cleversticks, Jovo and Duplo are typical examples, but the range is immense. For older young people, about eleven plus, there are now large stocks of just about anything which can be used for modelling and construction purposes, including wood, plastic and metal parts, springs, propellers, gears, motors, pulleys etc.. NES Arnold and Specialist Crafts both stock extensive stocks of such materials. The Egg Mobile section in this book is one example of a simple CDT project.
* Matchstick modelling kits for building anything from galleons to houses and Romany vardos.

- Lego, Technics and other plastic construction kits which can be used to build static and moving models of all manner of types of buildings and vehicles.
- Battery and mechanically powered plastic figures such as Tomy's Zoids.
- Figures and three dimensional settings for Fantasy and Role Playing games such as 'Dungeons and Dragons'.
- Stonecraft models of castles.
- Traditional model making for train sets, doll's houses and Scalextric-type slot car racing.

One of the youth projects we worked closely with was the Pilton Youth Programme (PYP) in Edinburgh. They found that plastic model kits are, " ...unpredictably successful" with the young people they work with. Big stores often sell these model making kits at greatly reduced prices when they have become no longer fashionable, e.g. Star Wars, Batman, Power Rangers, Superman, Zoids, etc.. They made sure that kids who have no experience with models should be started off with simple kits which have only a few large parts and don't need glue (for sticking or sniffing!). Try to avoid models which are especially tricky and finicky to build. There are quite a lot which don't require any gluing, and it is surprising in more deprived areas how many youngsters have never had the opportunity to play with the ever popular Duplo and Lego sets. In Acton in West London, the youth centre advertised in the local press for Lego and Scalextric, and from what it obtained was able to create a resource which lasted three centres for a good few years.

PYP found that model making can be particularly good as a group activity which encourages co-operation and concentration. They usually have between four and eight young people and two to three adults working together around a large table. Most simple models can be assembled in one session, leaving the next session free for painting the models with enamel paint, and applying transfers. A great feeling of accomplishment can be achieved by taking a smartly painted model home to be admired.

Many of the modern models of robots and similar are capable of movement, powered either by wind-up, clockwork motors or battery motors. We especially enjoyed the Tomy Zoid models of mechanised prehistoric fighting machines. These are lots of fun for all concerned - and especially suitable for youth groups of different ages and abilities since they're made up in a whole variety of sizes and numbers of parts. Models can also be used as playing pieces for certain board games or can be used in fantasy or 'war' games. Although commercially available kits can be used to make, e.g. dragons, it is possible obtain moulds and make your own pieces; out of plaster of paris for example. Chess moulds in particular are available in many different styles. If your young people have an artistic bent, you should consider using clay to model with. Young people are often inhibited by the creative task of making something recognisable out of a shapeless lump of clay, so it does help if there is an adult around who can provide some kind of artistic inspiration and technical help. Clay models can be painted and varnished when dry to good effect.

Apart from making figures for war, fantasy, and role playing games such as 'Dungeons and Dragons', great fun can also be had in making up boards or scenarios for some games. Again, commercial models can be used, or individually modelled, clay ones. Three dimensional landscapes can be formed using papier mâché or clay to provide the perfect background for your models.

In most towns, because of adult interest one suspects, there is a 'Games Shop' of some sort. A model section will almost certainly exist and it is likely that the person running such an emporium will be an enthusiast. Likewise, many craft shops stock an interesting, but not cheap, range of craft kits. One of the tricks is to try and find a way to keep costs down. In Essex, we were able to link one youth club where we worked, together with the local, radio-controlled aircraft club. At weekends, members from the club joined the adults flying elaborate, and often very expensive aircraft for miles across the common at the north end of town. Very usefully, we have found that approaches to such committed individuals have, on occasions, provided us 'staff' for youth groups!

MURALS AND SPRAY CAN ART

At some point in time graffiti takes on a level of social acceptability and becomes a mural. The Pilton Youth Programme in Edinburgh tried to set up a measure of diversion for graffiti, by pinning up large rolls of paper on a wall of their centre. This was then used as a Graffiti Wall. They suggest providing water-based felt pens and trying to obtain large rolls of paper from printing and newspaper firms. To quote them,

"This won't be the answer to young people expressing themselves through spontaneous decoration of your walls, but it may help."

In that particular centre, three or four large strips of paper covered the entire length of a wall. The paper was changed each week. The week's product resembled a veritable battlefield of art work. Social comments on politicians, religion, and fine drawings of sexual organs rub shoulders or wall space with debates of the greatness of opposing football teams, rock stars etc.. This sort of creativity is probably worth encouraging, and as long as not too many pens are available at the same time and an adult is nearby, say, running another activity in the same room, no further supervision is required. If there is a spate of particular interest from the youth group concerned, the activity can be quickly transformed into the type of group mural work described in the rest of this section.

NEW YOUTH ARTS & CRAFT

For mural painters and planners we have a few tips from experience. One technique which makes high quality mural painting accessible to non-artists is to use an **epidiascope**. This strangely named object works roughly like a projector. However, it will project a full colour image of objects or flat images directly onto a wall or surface. The image can then be drawn over, thus ensuring an accurate representation. Some of the strongest images using this technique which we have seen were in Mark Hall Youth Club in Harlow, where polarised (negative black and white) images of Rock Heroes were transferred onto walls from the Melody Maker etc.. If you can't find an epidiascope, an **overhead projector** can be usefully employed to project images drawn on the clear film of OHP transparencies, up to a larger size across walls. Both are easier to use on indoor sites rather than out of doors.

Planning and drawing out a mural using **grid lines** is a useful method to ensure that a mural looks good and follows a design which has previously been planned on paper. It is also important to try and produce murals which harmonise with their permanent or semi-permanent setting. Working with young people in a large-scale arts activity like a mural involves a number of processes. Adults need to be involved in some of the decision making, but it is very important that young people are also encouraged to participate in each stage of the process.

The **stages** are likely to include:
- Deciding on a site for the mural – consultation with owners of potential spaces, the council and other members of the community are all part of this stage.
- What to paint – ideas for designs, themes and rough scale drawings, and then a decision making procedure.
- Obtaining the necessary materials, emulsion paints, brushes, cement filler, wire brush, masonry sealer etc..
- If using the grid line system, transfer the images onto an emulsioned wall or board surface using chalk or charcoal.
- Organise the painting of the mural.
- If it is to become quite a permanent mural, varnish the mural with yacht varnish.

Using grid lines
This really isn't complicated and young people quickly get used to the process. The mural organiser needs to produce a sheet or set of sheets which are a scaled down version of the actual mural site. For instance:

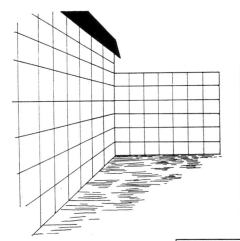

This can be replicated on two sheets of paper:

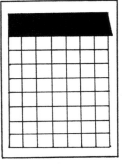
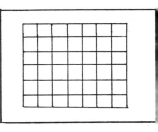

If the organiser photocopies the grid sheets for all the potential designers, they can all have a go at producing a design for the mural which will fit the designated site. The best ideas can possibly be incorporated into the final design, and the outlines can be chalked up on the wall(s).

Safety is of great importance and it is best if younger painters only work on the ground level, whilst older painters can use sturdy chairs, tables and step ladders to mark-up and paint the mural.

Ideas for designs

Both of us have attended the last couple of Glastonbury Festivals at Pilton in Somerset. There we have witnessed some of the most creative murals (and indeed performance arts) which exist anywhere in the UK. In 1995, a huge hoarding was built, undercoated and painted with the greens of Farmer Eavis's fields and the blue of the sky above. Old and young festival goers were then invited to join the bustling queue to add a small painting of themselves to the ever developing mural. To the right of the main area, a practise area was set up where the budding painters could obtain their brush, some paints and practise their own addition to the Festival Masterpiece. After five days of the festival, the end product was quite stunning. Perhaps forty thousand little figures had been added, dancing, singing, jumping, skipping and even flying across the giant wooden canvas. A truly participative mural! Alan now has a dream plan to produce a similar mural along the seafront at Lyme Regis during their Carnival week....

One useful tip: the Glastonbury mural painters used allocated painting zones, so that each painter was always working in an identifiable space (A – J or somesuch). On a smaller, more individual scale, this can provide a good model for young people to 'draw themselves into' a mural at a playscheme or youth club. One way we have organised this is to get young people to work in pairs, each drawing with chalk around the outline of their partner. Each artist then paints in the details of their own figure, individualising clothes, face, hair etc.. Other possible themes could be the town; the countryside; planets; sports; geometric patterns, or the circus.

Spray Can Art
Environmentalists have formed groups to combat the spread of this form of graffiti, but it has equally excited many modern art collectors and typographers who have found it a creative source of inspiration. Like it or loathe it, youthful artists have found spray can art a source of considerable fun. In the United States, the Metropolitan Transportation Authority's rolling stock was transformed into an enormous moving comic strip. Meanwhile, in the UK and Europe, the craze has spread and the culture of 'bombing' walls, buildings and transport has been ignorant of geographical boundaries.

Style has a lot to do with different forms of spray can work. UK street artists and wall writers have developed their own personal ways of making art statements. Often they are political and social comments; a form of challenge to local communities, the police and the authorities. Many of these artists are among the most alienated of the local youth population.

Some councils have reacted positively to the 'problem' of aerosol art. Grants have been made to groups of young artists to enable them to paint walls, underpasses, tunnels, bus shelters etc. – legally! Youth clubs in areas such as Ladbroke Grove in Brixton, Covent Garden, and Wolverhampton benefited in this way both from money and from the incentive to produce public art for their own communities. Users of this book can make their own decisions whether to experiment with the artistic streetculture of the 'Wildstyle' lettering of the spray can painters. For some youngsters you know or work with, it may be just the form of self-expression they need – to paint and tag their own wall.

MUSIC

This is not going to offer an encyclopaedic set of Guinness facts for the music world. Instead we would like to offer something of a 'brain-storming' approach to lots of music related activities which youth organisations could be offering for their youngsters. We have been involved in a number of these schemes ourselves and through that involvement, we have met a number of individuals who have been offering music as a means of developing youngsters' lives. We have always been more involved with 'popular' music and its connection with young people, so this section reflects that, rather than the tradition of formal musical tuition. In music, especially in its popular forms, there is a culture, counter-culture and sub-culture. Identification with the 'Rave' culture, or with rock personalities, the bands, and their styles of dress and behaviour, is a natural way in which many young people find a self-identity. Being a truant, an offender and unemployed are minor considerations relative to being a 'punk', 'skin', 'rasta', 'rude boy' or whatever. The choice of style may then include an aggressive rejection of society's standards, yet it is the fashion, or sub-cultural group, which gives youngsters their identity in the peer groups which they most inhabit. So, enough of this intellectualising.....how can we involve young people in contemporary music? What supports can youth facilities offer to youngsters to develop their skills and interest in that music?

We hope that the rest of this section give a few practical ideas. They are certainly not the only techniques which can be employed; however, they represent some of the initiatives which have been tried by various workers in a variety of UK settings.

Experiencing Live Music

Whether young people want to perform themselves, or not, it is almost always an exciting experience to see live music. Young people in the youth club context may be unable to afford the concert prices charged at many rock venues. Historically, this was a contributory factor in 1976 to the Punk boom, which led to many more gigs being established, even if they only lasted for a few years. It recreated the sort of pub and club rock scene which had previously existed in the rock n' roll heyday of the late-1950s and to a lesser extent the late 1960s psychedelic phase of British Rock. The point of the example is that without such small local venues, the music scene becomes a fantasised and distanced attraction which is OK as a means of diversion from reality, but has about as much real meaning as the mythical dodo. One punk, Derek Gibb, in a youth club in London wrote in an early fanzine, 'Sound of the Westway':

"When you are bored out of your mind on the dole with nothing to do, escapism has no meaning. Who wants their already depressed state of mind further stagnated by half-hour moog solos? This is where the appeal of Punk Rock lies; music to get you off your arse. Have you noticed how hippies at concerts just sit there bobbing their heads? Well, we don't. We pogo; we jump about. A dance of true expression from the heart. Who wants to wait three years for a shitty triple LP which is stale and boring and costs £12.00? Who wants to queue 12 hours for a £8/£12 ticket to see a band of raving posers that look like ants in an airplane hanger? I don't want to be made to sit down and then clap politely at the end."

Derek's indictment rings uncannily true of what came after punk as well as what went before. It was not until the rise of DJ and Rave culture in the late 1980s that the collective imagination of young people across the land was once again fired up in this way. Regrettably, the power of the Top 20 and disco managed to dissipate much of the raw energy and replace it with the harmless placebo 'escapist entertainment'. The positive side of this is where dancing, rap and bits of impromptu singing became creative and can be encouraged. At least through 'scratching' and rap the disco scene became more of a participation event. Just watch out for all those ghetto-blasters balancing on shoulders of hip-hop dancers in your local High Street. Perhaps at this point we should stop since it's getting very BOF-ish (you may not find **that** in a dictionary – ask the kids!).

Ways round the financial problem of how expensive music has become which we have used are to:
- organise gigs for young people through the youth and community service facilities;
- establish lively and relevant music tuition;
- provide practice areas;
- obtain free tickets for local music events.

Organising Gigs

It doesn't need to be as tame and tedious as it may first sound. Many fine bands have started their careers playing in youth clubs. Our own youth-working lives already span using an unknown band, 'Steampacket', which included Rod Stewart and Long John Baldry, a second-string synthesiser band which cleared a youth club dance – they were called Tubeway Army, featuring Gary Numan! Members of the Stranglers have helped out at one youth club Alan used to run; Misty in Roots members were regular artists and members at another club, and Pete Brown, who wrote most of the Cream's greatest hits donated the old Cream PA to a central London youth project.

More recently we have received help from the Levellers, Zion Train and Tofu Love Frogs. Big name bands all start on the circuit and most were, in their time, associated with youth facilities. So, don't despise two chord wonders, allow them the chance to play; organise events and perhaps establish a booking/gig system with other facilities in your area. This is a mechanism which the kids can then run themselves, with a bit of support. Often, difficulties arise through inappropriate staffing of concerts, gigs and dances. Heavy bouncers too often provide heavy scenes. It is best to run gigs with closed, or semi-closed access, building on known relationships between staff and users, rather than putting up centres as targets for inter-area gang fights. Having offered that advice, there are a number of examples of community arts facilities which offer cheap, varied, alternative media events for all who want to attend. It is also sometimes possible to make deals with commercial facilities to provide cut-price entry to clubs and venues for youth organisation members, or even to use their facilities to promote young performers, whether as mixers or muscians.

The organisation of local music festivals through the youth and community service is also a real possibility. For instance, Essex Community Education Service have been instrumental in organising events for their home grown talent and also full blown music festivals. Some of the early Rock Against Racism, Anti-Nazi League and Anti-Apartheid Movement gigs were partnership events with local youth service personnel. These proved ideal vehicles for many workers concerned with breaking down black/white prejudices, but the political base of the undertaking has been seen by some local authorities as impossible to support. Another area where change has occurred is in the yearly Arts Events run by many local authority services. With the rise in local festivals and carnivals, some of these events have been moved in the direction of reflecting young people's musical interests. A number of newer arts events are now featuring rock, folk, reggae, hip-hop, and all the off-shoots. In Scotland, estates like Craigmillar and Westerhailes have their own full time staff promoting festival events, and these have provided exciting venues in which young local bands can rub shoulders with established performers. As we comment later in this section, Rock Workshops and the like are allowing young people access to professional musicians and equipment.

Many of these workshops have promoted events which are often of a fundraising nature. The re-birth of the CND movement has also provided the impetus for a number of concerts raising money for local groups. There have also been attempts from sections of the young Labour Movement to become involved in promoting rock events. The Socialist Action for Youth group, based in London, have tried this type of show, on occasions combining it with other events such as conference and theatre programmes. Extending the use of music in drama productions is also a venture possible for many youth groups. Modern musicals such as 'The Rocky Horror Show', 'Jesus Christ Superstar' and 'Elvis' have quite wide appeal and can be adapted for youth club productions. In other cases, young bands have written their own music scores for stage shows. The Christmas Panto is still a medium for fun and variety and one which can include modern music **and** unite the local community, especially where a suitable theme is taken on board. In West Sussex, the eccentric star-gazer, Patrick Moore joins in the local Christmas show each year.

There are also literally thousands of traditional music groups and bands around the UK. Brass bands, marching bands, folk groups, youth orchestras, madrigals, choirs, jazz bands – all may find a home base, rehearsal space or performance area in the youth or community centre. They are very often the starting point where young people learn some appreciation of music and the basics of formal music knowledge.

Going to Music Shows

As mentioned before, it may be the cost of admission which prevents many youngsters from going to see live music. Where this is the case, contact with the local and national radio and television network may produce free tickets. The BBC Radio Ticket Unit is at Broadcasting House, London, W1A 1AA. This is especially useful for groups based in the major towns. Contacting the ever growing number of local radio stations can often result in an invite to the studio or, where radio stations are recording shows they have to obtain a sympathetic, appreciative audience, so they may actually welcome your enquiry. They will **not** love you if you arrive at their recording of Ossian for Clyde Folk, with a mini-bus full of Exploited fans!

As a caring, sympathetic, youth or social worker (you may remember the type!) it is sometimes possible to appeal to an impresario's finer instincts and get some cheap or free tickets for shows they are producing. Being the way of the world, you normally have to give something in return. The best and most possible return favour can be some publicity for either their show, generosity, or both.

The other major possibility for workers to assist youngsters in getting to see music, rests on the kids having some money, but no transport. Many older adolescents hitch right round the country, but for many, the provision of a mini-bus to a music festival or event is a godsend. If properly organised (by you!), this event can be a part of your youth work or group work programme, giving as it does an enjoyable shared activity. Because it is away from premises, workers must check out their legal responsibilities for accidents, etc., but it can be a good possibility.

DJ Culture

This section has been contributed by George Symington from Glasgow, who was actively involved in the DJ and Club scene for some years.

1988 saw the genesis of a new style of electronic dance music which evolved via the welding of black disco, funk and electro to white synth and industrial styles, e.g. Kraftwerk. Initially produced in Detroit and Chicago, it was mostly ignored in the US and reached Britain via DJ's holidaying in Ibiza, who upon getting the message, converted the clientele of clubs like London's Shoom and Manchester's Hacienda.

Starting off as a deeply cliquey and underground phenomenon it rapidly mushroomed (!) and has by now largely crushed the dominance of traditional rock music in the hearts, minds and feet of youth today. Dance music, splintering into a myriad of evolving factions – house, techno, garage, trance, acid, trip/hip hop and jungle – *is* the soundtrack to the 1990s and the coming of the next millennium.

Created and programmed primarily by computers, samplers and synthesisers, and characterised, according to the CJA (Criminal Justice Act) by, "a succession of repetitive beats", it is mostly heard via DJs but is also played live. The archetypal 'gig' has been superseded by massive, often illegal 'raves' – now mostly killed off by the CJA and its criminalisation of youth culture – and mainly now by thousands of clubs, some of which are a massive commercial/corporate phenomena, e.g. Liverpool's Cream. A typical teenager's weekend night out now consists of going clubbing/raving/drugging and dancing all night in an ecstatic, trance inducing tribal ritual. Hard to encourage in youth organisations, but ignored as a cultural pheomenon by the Youth Service, at its peril!

This is the first musical/cultural phenomenon to ignite the mass imagination of youth and as such its importance cannot be overemphasised. Quite simply, like the name of the club, it's 'AWOL' – a way of life. Club/dance culture is now an industry, with its own music, language, art and fashion; a subculture, that while initially demonised, has by now inevitably been sanitised, commercialised – some might even say sterilised – by regulation and assimilation, both economically and politically. So much so that there is a growing feeling of cynicism amongst the 'old school' against the hype and conformity of the mainstream clubs. A 'DIY' ethic is picking up momentum again – some of our best nights ever were held in a local youth club, believe it or not! So keeping the original vibe alive and underground has to be the way forward – getting back to our roots. Get on it!

The average teenager now dreams of being a DJ rather than a guitar hero – the DJ is the heart of the matter – the link between the studios and the club dancefloor, playing music which is often made in small bedroom studios with a minimal amount of equipment – this DIY ethic again mirrors the punk ethos – anyone could make music. The price of the equipment needed has fallen to levels whereby it is realistic to produce electronic music at home – and this democratisation of the creative process is responsible for the spread of the 'virus'! Hundreds of independent 12"s are released each week. The availability of such equipment is crucially important to young people, and any youth club which has a set-up will act as a magnet to kids desperate to get involved. A basic set-up for a youth club would consist of the following items (at 1996 prices):

2 X Stanton or similar cartridges, e.g. 500 ALs, £50.
2 X turntables with speed controls, £300.
1 X mixer (to mix the sounds from the decks), £200.
1 X amplifier, £200.
1 X double cassette deck/4 track cassette, £100.
2 X speakers (*heavy* duty!), £200.
1 X CD player, £100.
1 X drum machine, £100 – £1,000.
Slipmats, headphones, microphone, leads, £50.

All of the above can be bought for around £1,000 – £1,200.

Turntables
The only *serious* contender for turntable techniques is Technics' mighty SL1200. This is the industry standard and it performs perfectly for the DJ. These now cost almost £400 each. However Richer Sounds Ltd. have a good compromise in the Ariston 1600 at £150 each, which is quite serviceable. Other cheap copies of Technics decks are rubbish and are to be avoided at all costs. Cartridges will add an extra £50 per pair – Stanton's 500AL is standard for heavy duty mixing use.

Mixers
Mixers cost from £100 – £500 upwards depending on facilities offered, i.e. equaliser, samplers (very useful), number of channels available, etc.. Buy the best you can afford – Vesrax, Numark, Gemini and KAM are good quality.

Amplifiers
Ideally you'll need a heavy duty Mosfet power amp, the bigger the better, but 100 watts RMS will do for starters. An ordinary hi-fi amp will do if funds cannot stretch. Maplins do kit amps at low cost if you are an electronics wizard.

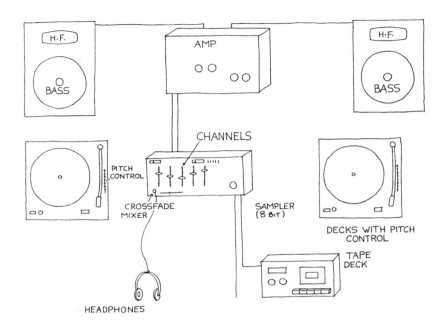

H.F. = TWEETER

DJ SET UP

Speakers
These must match the power rating of the amplifier. Quality doesn't come cheap but will *save* on blown tweeter and bass cones. Again these can be assembled from kit form at a great discount. Firms such as Maplin and Wilmslow Audio can supply them. A good speaker for dance music is the Cerwin Vega but there are loads to choose from. Look in DJ magazines each month for models and stockists of equipment.

Tape
A four track recorder enables overdubbing and more elaborate and creative mixing techniques. Otherwise a double cassette is useful for copying tapes. Or buy two single cassette decks and link them up.

Studio Equipment
For more serious creative composing, further equipment is essential. A basic set-up should include:
Amiga/Atari computer with Cubase or similar *sequencing* software. The Amiga 300/600 range of computers can also be used to good effect with programmes such as Octamed v5. PCs and Macs with large hard drives are of course preferable, but expensive. This will be the workhorse of the 'MIDI' studio (see below).

Other equipment includes:
Sampler, e.g. Akai S1000, £1,000.
Drum Machine e.g. Roland 909/808.
Workstation – a keyboard *combining* sampler, drum machine, synthesiser and sequencer in one package – a sort of electronic one man band. Models by Korg, Yamaha and Roland are

excellent and start at around £1,000 – very good value for money – whole tracks can be put together using just one keyboard. An excellent buy.

Synthesisers – Roland, Korg, Yamaha etc., not forgetting the vital Roland TB303 bassline (*the* acid machine). The Novations 'Basstation' – a Roland 303 clone is excellent and the Roland S1X101 keyboard is like gold dust. A lot of equipment can be purchased secondhand – look in magazines like 'Future Music'.

These items are linked by *MIDI – Musical Instrument Digital Interface* – a system by which instruments can be linked and 'slaved' together to communicate intelligently, controlled by the computer and its sequencing software. Music composed can be saved on hard disks (large, one gigabyte drives are needed ideally, as sampling is memory intensive). Or you can record onto DAT (digital audio tape) or cassette, 4 track or reel to reel. In order to link these instruments a 6/12 channel mixing desk is needed – these cost around £300 – £500. It is possible to save a lot of money by using special CDs/CD ROMS which are simply a collection of *samples* of keyboards, drum machines and all other instruments. These sounds can them be sampled and used without buying the instruments! They are advertised in 'Future Music' – a good publication for general information on electronic music, midi and computing.

Studios

A studio can be set up for well under £5,000 if you look around. Buy second hand and *your* kids could be pressing up their own 12 inch singles. You could start up a label, hundreds already have, anything's possible! There is bound to be a wealth of knowledge and experience to tap into, use it, ask the kids, they are the experts! Nothing is more guaranteed to ignite the kids' interest and imagination than the possibility of making their own music. You'll have a waiting list to join in the party. Well, it beats table tennis!

Club Nights, Discos and Raves

1990s youth are into club/dance culture – it's a way of life/dedicated lifestyle. The young people of today are increasingly sophisticated. The traditional youth club 'disco' with a crappy old console and a couple of light boxes just *won't* hack it anymore. You'll need a decent PA, size dependent on hall size, anything from 500 to 5,000 watts will be required. Then all you need are two decks, a mixer, some DJs and the party is pumping! You'll need a good vantage point for the DJs and a solid platform/table for the decks and mixer. Add some smoke, strobes, moonflowers, Optokinetiks projectors (oilwheels etc.), slide projectors, ultra-violet light and fluorescent banners and you have *all* the ingredients (well, almost!) for a party. All this stuff can be hired at a cost of £200 upwards. The more spent on production, the better the show, although imagination and technique are priceless. Get the artists involved in painting banners, designing flyers and tickets, and general decoration of the hall. Keep it loud, dark and smoky and you won't go far wrong!

Lighting is crucial to create mood and reflect the energies of the evening. We used to project onto white nylon sheets using slide projectors and Optokinetiks 250s. You can get excellent slides from computers and videos – use an exposure of less than 1/15 sec for video to avoid lines/scanning on the slide.

Banners/Decor

It is easy to design and produce your own banners using old sheets, canvas etc.. Fluorescent paint can be bought in one litre bottles at about £5 each. Basic colours like orange, red, yellow, green and black will get you started. An Episcope can be used to trace designs. These banners look great under UV lights.

White gauze or nylon (fireproofed) is ideal for projecting slides onto. Use the opportunity to design a logo for your club or group, and consider organising banner painting workshops. Graffiti techniques are popular – use spray paints, UV if possible.

Club Nights
No doubt you'll have queues of aspiring DJs wanting to impress the crowd with their mixing skills. Audition them first! 'Name' DJs can command exorbitant fees – £100 is nothing for a big name. But several hundred tickets at £3 or £4 can pay for a good night – you could even *make* money – plenty do! So, running a regular club night can do wonders for your bank balance and credibility! You'll learn from the kids – they can teach you the techniques and give you the ideas and the energy and enthusiasm you'll need to make things happen.

You'll need to organise your night properly and carefully – you'll need tickets, security, a cashier, a drinks bar, cloakroom and last but *not* least, a *chill-out* area where people can rest and cool and calm down. It's vital to have water on tap to prevent **heat-stroke** – kids have died due to the combined effects of over exertion, over sweating and dehydration. *Water consumption* should be limited to a *maximum* of one pint per hour – too much water CAN KILL – be careful. You'll need stewards to supervise things and keep a watchful eye on the proceedings – softly, softly is the best approach!

Drugs
Drugs are obviously an issue and are in fact inextricably involved with the dance music scene – especially Ecstasy, which is the substance blamed for recent well publicised deaths. Fundamentally, these deaths have been caused by *heat-stroke* which is why a *chill-out room* is *vital*. Street credible information on the various drugs should be on hand. The 'Peanut Pete' leaflets and books produced by Manchester's Lifeline Project are the best around. Remember kids – *just say know!*

DJ-ing
The black art of DJ-ing is a skill requiring thousands of hours of practice and the application of a variety of techniques. Basically, these overpaid record changers (!) mix two records so that the transition from one to another is fluent and mellifluous, i.e. a seamless transition from one track to the next. This involves synchronising the speed of each record using the pitch control on the turntable so that the BPM. (beats per minute) of each track are *identical*. The DJ then manipulates the record manually using headphones so that they synchronise the bass drums (downbeats) or snares (offbeats) in such a way that when record A is mixed via the cross fader into record B, the beats merge into each other without colliding and clashing horribly.

This is a difficult skill to acquire and takes endless practice. Other techniques such as scratching, cutting, transforming etc. are beyond our scope. But a good DJ responds to the crowd, judges the atmosphere and sequences the tunes so that the crowd is taken on a musical journey par excellence. In the last two years, Alan and Howie have attended a number of club sessions at the Glastonbury Festival, in between selling their books! Orbital and Billy Nasty were particularly impressive making mixing a real 'art and music form'. DJ-ing as an art and technique started off in the gay discos and black ghettos where HipHop DJs evolved the basic techniques still used to-day. So that now, many young people might argue that the DJ, and not Eric Clapton, is God!

Thanks, once again, to George, for this valuable and interesting contribution!
(Alan and Howie)

From our experience we'd add:
- What times to operate? How does this relate to local requirements of transport and neighbours' complaints?
- Do you have any staff who have good first aid experience?
- Although it may sound 'old fashioned', it can be a good idea to provide spot prizes and competitions during a club session. We recently saw a DJ who did wonderful Rolf Harris impersonations, miming to his eccentric record. Then he got youngsters up on stage doing their versions! It was memorable! Bizarre or fancy dress can also be subject to prizes.

Helping the Budding Musician

Running music workshop activities in a club or centre is one step towards provision of a range of facilities for the young musician. Using the talents of staff who might already be working with you is one way of providing the inputs for the workshop. Another method is to contact local bands, individual musicians and perhaps any musicians' collectives which operate locally. Ask them if they would be willing to help either run a 'one-off' activity, or help staff a permanent facility linking in to your centre or youth group. There is nothing quite so exciting for budding young musicians as to meet and be coached by the professionals.

If you are thinking of running such a facility you will have to make a space available. Ideally this should include a degree of sound-proofing and be equipped with a PA. It should also be secure. The range of instruments which you provide is likely to be limited by money, but often secondhand instruments and PA can be bought to start off such a project without too great an expenditure. Again, local musicians may even be persuaded to give or lend pieces of equipment. From musician friends, we have been told that it is not the best course of action to try and teach all youngsters acoustic guitar. Although a good teaching instrument it doesn't always fire the imagination. This returns to the question of sound-proofing: it may be **drums, organ, or electric guitar** which your kids want to learn. In London at one centre we know, they lined the walls of their basement room with layers of egg boxes. (Make sure they are adequately fire proofed!). It wasn't perfect, but it provided some protection for, and from, the neighbours! So, if you can, amass a collection of instruments which young people can try. Link the lessons into seeing bands and listening to tapes and records of different styles. The music list in the Questionnaires' section of this book may be useful in those sorts of programmes. They certainly seemed popular in music groups both ourselves and colleagues have run.

Making a bit of a jump, we would now like to suggest some ways you may be able to help the individual or group of youngsters who wish to perform or record. Some of this information comes from our own experience; other ideas we have gleaned from the very helpful information packs from the BBC Grapevine Series and the old Interaction Make-it-Yourself project.

Rehearsal Space

Often youth centres and similar are quite isolated from complaining humanity. Perhaps you can follow the example of many clubs and make available rooms for youth groups to practice in. Another suggestion is to find a suitably remote school building and then pressure the local education department to make rooms available for young musicians to practice in. This will bring you, inevitably, into close contact with caretakers/janitors and their rules and regulations, but it is worth the hassle if you can enable kids to practice.

Rough recordings and live demos

A number of youth organisations have built up their own collection of recording gear. This ranges in complexity from a cassette recorder attached to a couple of mikes, through porta-studios, to eight track mixing desks with DAT recording gear and all the mikes etc., that go with such apparatus. Groups generally do not have access to anything beyond a basic cassette deck and usually really appreciate the opportunity to get even a rough recording of their sound. It helps them and it is a learning experience in itself. The sound balance of groups is normally drastically improved from a competitive, wall-of-sound, approach to a discernible 'mix' by the rigours of recording a group's range of instruments/voices/sounds. Digital technology, combined with falling equipment prices have put high quality recording within reach of many more groups. See the section on DJ Culture (above) for details of both disco and studio equipment.

It may be worth considering the purchase of such equipment on an area basis as a shared resource, or for your own centre to act as that resource, if you wish to cater for, or promote special music facilities. In our experience, it is possible to get keen engineers to build mixing facilities for the cost of components. Your local college, university, or electronics firm may well be worth a visit. It is worth briefing yourself on what you are trying to do before attacking these institutions, otherwise you may neither help yourselves or those who might come after you. We even know of a youth club studio that offers training courses:

> The Basement Studio
> Sefton Park Youth Centre
> Ashley Down Road
> Bristol BS7 9BG

The next stage of development for many groups is actually going into the studio. This can be an expensive and potentially hazardous business. Here are some of the tips offered by the Interaction Make-it-Yourself Handbook.

> "The music should be thoroughly rehearsed before going into a studio. Remember that recording demands more accuracy than performance.
> The cost per hour of a recording studio is generally related to the number of tracks the studio has. As you might expect, the more tracks, the greater the cost. The number of tracks - 4, 8, 16 or 32 is a measure of the number of elements the group's sound can be divided into .....most Make it Yourself groups, and many commercial groups, opt for the cheaper 4 track studios."

Without going through the full range of information offered by the Beeb and Interaction, the following points are worth making to groups about to part with their money.

- Know what you want to be recorded, how many hours are necessary and whether a final mix is to be achieved in one session at a studio.
- Are you willing to buy the master tape (for about £35) or will you want to rent it? Work this out with the studio in advance.
- How many cassette or CD copies of the recording are required?
- Suggestions for where to find out the cost of studios and equipment supplies may be found in a number of music reference books, which may be available in the local library. The Showcase International Music Book, 12 Felix Avenue, London N8 9TL is about the best source, listing recording studios and services.

Cutting Discs and Merchandising

The range of small circulation records and cassettes on sale has vastly multiplied in recent years. Groups with a product that they think there is local support for, may well consider paying for the production of 500 copies of a 12 inch single, cassette or CD out of their own pockets. It is not unknown for youth clubs and similar to launch into this area of small scale business themselves. It is unlikely to make anyone rich, but it's good fun and groups can use the process as a springboard to bigger things. If you, individual artist, or groups using your facilities are considering producing their own record or tape, keep the following in mind:

- It is worth demanding test copies, even if it costs extra. It is also worth checking the quality of the eventual product, whether it is to be CD, cassette or vinyl.
- Make sure you have (a) a written order (dated) and (b) a delivery note for all parts that go to make up the product: box, cover art, labels and recording. And (c) a firm delivery date. Because most small orders are competing with big orders, this may require some hassling.

The production of small run cassettes is becoming increasingly popular. On a limited scale this can be done on a domestic level linking cassette machines together and making 'same speed' or 'double-speed' copies. The time this takes make it unsatisfactory for long runs. For more than, say, fifty copies you will require the services of a fast cassette copying service. This can provide copies of your tape onto cassette on fast speed, multi-copying machines. This is quite cheap and is being much utilised by groups who, for example wish to sell 30 minutes of their music to the public cheaply. It's also very useful for groups looking for gigs who want to promote their act to promoters. Labels can be easily printed or photocopied and pasted onto card for insertion into the cassette box. Tape-to-tape duplicating facilities require payment for a master tape for their fast copier, plus a cost per tape for the fast copying. A number of firms offer this service – a substantial list is available in the Recording Services section of the Showcase International Music Book.

Labels and Sleeves

Some processing plants supply blank labels on discs free – all do it quite cheaply. A cheap label or sticker can then be added by the group themselves. Most printers can do this using the group's artwork. If the group want a commercial label, especially if it requires more than one colour, expect it to cost quite a lot of money. It hardly seems worthwhile for a small run, and it may be worth concentrating more effort on the cover sleeve. Remember to ask the pressing plant to put different coloured stickers on the A and B side of a disc or cassette, or at least one sticker on side A to help your identification for labelling.

The sleeves can be made cheaply by groups using photocopied wrap-around sheets of paper, stapled cards etc.. It requires a lot of unpaid work, however, and it is not always much cheaper than getting the whole sleeve commercially made. Get your group of youngsters to look at the range of independent sleeves for singles at the local record store. This will probably give them a number of ideas for their own article.

Distribution and Promotion

To sell music products to the trade, you may go directly to record shops. They will require a 50% mark-up. Many will ask for sale or return deals. Try to avoid this. The majority of records are likely to be sold either through distributors, who require anything up to 75% mark-up on the price you charge, or through direct selling to friends at gigs. The growth of small labels has created certain distributors' networks dealing mostly with small-run music. There's obviously quite a lot of overlap between record companies and record distributors. Many, unfortunately go bust rather quickly! Rather like the practice it takes to make a musician, there is quite a lot of research work required to find the best distribution deal. Again, the Showcase book, or the White Book, PO Box 55, Staines, Middlesex TW18 4UG contain lots of suggestions.

To promote records it is necessary to spend some money on postage and letters to accompany free copies of records to be sent to the music press and radio stations. The local press may also be worth contacting. Some groups just want to sell their recording; others use a small circulation tape/record/CD to try to obtain a recording contract, so make sure you know what the aims of the group are. John Peel and Andy Kershaw remain two of the gurus of the British Music Scene when it comes to promoting indie music and young bands. They may be worth sending a copy to, but don't be too optimistic; they literally receive thousands of tapes, CDs and records each month. The satellite TV channels now have a number of 24 hour music channels, so this is an additional route to potential airplay. Local radio is probably a better bet for many aspiring musicians.

Managers and Contracts

A word or two of warning. Getting a manager or contract for a group is not the end of all problems; it can often be the beginning of major difficulties. A record deal is useless, unless it gives musicians enough money to play. Managers who don't work throughout the British Isles are unlikely to assist a band who wants to go professional. London is still one of the centres of the musical universe. Likewise, signing a contract which ties a band to a management firm for two or three years in return for the guaranteed production of a couple of singles may not be worthwhile. Contracts of this kind usually bind all the individual members of the group, so if a member leaves, they are still under contract - not a pleasant situation. The only real answer is to see a solicitor. Community Law and Advice Centres may be able to help, but contract law connected with the record business is quite a specialist area.

Discos

Finally, one cannot complete a section on 'music' without at least reference to more traditional discos, and their world of records, equipment and style. Most Junior Youth Clubs still make use of a simple disco set up, a pile of records, CDs and tapes, a couple of coloured lights and a constant stream of would be DJs. For many youth organisations these are the only 'busy' nights. Large sums of money can be made - over £200 a night even in the youth market from promoting a successful disco. If you are hiring a disco outfit from outside of the club, even semi-professionals start at about £50 per night and for the top outfits, £200 – £400 is a more realistic sum. You are paying for the quality of the music equipment, the professionalism of the DJ, the selection of music and the time and travel costs. Running a good disco can take more planning than is usually credited.

A well run disco in the world of fast-changing fashions can satisfy one group of youngsters and start tribal warfare from another section of kids. So, either a balance is struck between the factions, or a 'theme' for an evening should be hit on. Neither will you please all your constituency of youth so, over time, various permutations will have to be tried. It is a minefield for the entrepreneur since what works once, isn't necessarily a repeat success. The question of staffing-bouncer-door control, raised earlier in this section in connection with organising gigs, is worth bearing in mind. It is likely to be crucial in respect of your being allowed by management committees to continue running discos.

It may be useful to consider building or buying a disco as an area resource. Some areas have a number of units, which are then centrally stored and serviced. Trying out as a DJ, or disco dancing could be used as an arts activity – both involve a 'performance' of a kind. Majorettes dancing groups are an offshoot of this activity.

Discos do not have a single identity and for ethnic minorities, a disco, or sound, is a means of publicising individual identity. To a lesser extent, the nature of discos should be encouraged to have a local, cultural identity, apart from purely reflecting the music which makes the Top 20.

PAPIER MÂCHÉ

When we originally tried to find out about the different ways of using papier mâché, we used our mate Nick to get his hands messy, working with a number of youth groups around Renfrewshire. On one note he wrote to us he said: "A s versitile as an egg" . We are not sure whether this is symptomatic of a brain disorder, or an acute statement on the flexible use of papier mâché! Since then we have also been shown other methods and this section is an up-to-date amalgam of our ideas on the subject. It is also worth looking at our section on 'Masks', which makes considerable use of papier mâché. Anyway, down to business.

Papier mâché was traditionally a craft technique used for making coach panels (the horse-drawn variety!) In more recent times it has proved popular in schools, youth clubs, arts and drama groups, and for carnivals and street performers. It is fun with all age groups, but young children seem to particularly love it. Two quite simple techniques are used, depending upon the type of article which is being made. Sometimes a combination of the two methods is employed giving the benefits of both techniques. The range of items which can be made is wide, encompassing puppet heads, chess pieces, masks, ornaments and candle-stick holders right through to an eight foot tall mummy! This last objet d'art graced the lawn outside a friend's house; a strange sight indeed on an open-plan, middle-class housing estate in conservative West Sussex!

Given this sort of variety, papier mâché is a useful part of your arts and crafts armoury. It is also very cheap, wonderfully messy and appeals to youngsters' baser instincts. The only drawback that we have found is the need for planning when using the 'moulding' method; the mâché takes at least 24 hours to reach the required consistency. For the purpose of this section, we offer a description of the two basic methods, plus a very limited reference to the methods of making specific articles. Once you, and the members of your youth group have mastered the two methods, the imaginations and needs of your particular group should determine what is made. So, for instance, if you are planning to produce a play, the use of papier mâché masks might well offer an added dimension to the staging. In the professional and amateur theatre this has been successfully utilised in productions as diverse as 'A Midsummer Night's Dream' and 'Equus'. Both masks and false heads can be made in this way, using chicken wire as a base for the structure and then adding layers of paper, followed by moulded mâché.

And so, on to the principal techniques, and the materials required.

Materials
We had different recommendations on what to use in the way of materials, especially the glues. Depending on who you listen to, a combination of the following are needed:

- Wallpaper paste (without fungicide); flour and water paste; Interior Polyfilla; Polycell regular; white PVA glue thinned down with a little water; latex adhesives for sticking some paper; card and fabrics; quick drying, clear adhesive for some jobs; and spray adhesive which is great for sticking paper to paper and card, but must be used in an open space or specially constructed spray booth (the vapour is unpleasant and harmful).
- A large quantity of newspapers; better quality paper makes stronger products; but is obviously more expensive. Magazines are unsuitable. Kitchen roll paper is useful for quickly building up work and tissue paper or paper handkerchiefs are good for producing a smooth, top layer.

- Art Maché is a new material which is obtainable from both Specialist Crafts and NES Arnold. We haven't tried it, but Arnold's say of it,"Instant papier mâché – but so much cleaner and easier than the conventional method."
- A variety of cardboard is good to build up basic structures.
- Two buckets; one of which should be galvanised to withstand heating. One bucket; plus a very large saucepan works well.
- Water.
- Half inch wire mesh (chicken wire) and garden wire.
- Moulds for particular objects - i.e. wooden and cardboard boxes; dishes; bowls.
- For finishing papier mâché objects you will need things like card; white emulsion paint - water based; brushes; acrylic and other coloured paints and spray paints; enamel paints; varnish; masking tape; a craft knife and a heavier weight Stanley knife or similar; scissors; etc..
- The usual drawing equipment: pens, felt tips, pencils, rulers etc..

Layering Method

With the method, the first thing to do is prepare the paste. For example, to prepare flour and water paste mix flour with cold water, stir into thin past and add one tablespoon of salt per half pound of flour. Gently heat this mixture up in a pan. As the paste begins to thicken; add more warm water. When the paste is both quite thick and translucent it is ready for use. Some people recommend using boiling water with the flour to achieve the same results.

Polyfilla and wallpaper adhesives will give instructions with them but don't be afraid to experiment with varying densities of paste.

It is worth preparing a quantity of paper strips or squares in advance. Depending on the size and shape of the article being made, vary the size of the paper squares or strips. One to two inch squares of strips are the sort of size likely to be required. You will need both a bowl/bucket of water and one of paste, ready to be put into service. You also need to make sure that the mould is coated to help prevent sticking. Again, a variety of techniques are recommended. With smooth surfaces, which are not porous; such as a balloon, or a china bowl, cooking oil or Vaseline should be rubbed over the surface to prevent it from sticking. When using boxes and other porous objects, the use of dry or wet sheets of newspaper, without the addition of adhesive, to the inside of the mould is suggested. A final note on this subject concerns the use of moulds which are airtight. The vacuum which is formed can be repaired using the layering technique described below.

Having prepared all the necessary ingredients, dip the strips of newspaper one at a time into a bucket of cold water, then coat the surface with adhesive. Layer the pieces on to the mould one overlapping the next, until an entire covering has been made. Allow to dry and then repeat the process. Approximately six layers are necessary to provide a strong surface. With items such as bowls it is a good idea to make the base of the vessel thicker than the sides. If time is limited, there are two ways in which the drying process can be speeded up.

1. Use Interior Polyfilla. Rapid setting results from use of this medium, but it is less permanent.
2. Having squeezed out any air bubbles in the strips, starting from the middle and working outwards, put the object, (bowl or whatever) into a pre-heated, medium low oven at 250 degrees and bake on a greased tray for 5 to 10 minutes. Using this technique it is not necessary to allow drying time in between the six layers.

A useful method for ensuring a smooth edge to your bowl, or similar item, is as follows:

Once the bowl has been fired in the oven attach more strips, working them over the lip from the inside outwards. Re-bake the bowl in the oven and when cooled, gently sand to a smooth finish.

The layering method can be used with cloth initially instead of paper, particularly when working with wire frames. These can be wound over the frame, followed by coatings of papier mâché. A firm frame is a necessity; otherwise all the hard work and effort will be wasted.

Moulding or Pulp Method

This is the method which most workers will remember from their own messy childhood.

Once again; a bowl of paste is made up. The suggestions for the mix are very varied. Newspapers; fabric conditioner; whiting or ground chalk; wallpaper paste; linseed oil and PVA adhesive are used together in one typical recipe. The youngsters you are working with will just love this next bit! The paper for making the mâché is torn in small shreds and put into another bowl, into which boiling water is poured. The paper at this stage should be wet, rather than soggy. Add more water later as it becomes absorbed. Once the pulp is beginning to form, squeeze out excess water with your hands. This could also be done using a pair of old tights to sieve out the water. When this has been accomplished, add paste and stir well. The stirring is really rather nasty (from an adult standpoint), if done with hands. (Not that all youth type persons would agree!) Two ways around this are: either to use rubber gloves, or to make up a primitive form of whisk. One design for this entails bending up two coathangers thus.

The beaten mixture of water, paper and paste will become an unpleasant looking mix with the texture of modelling clay. Some users of pulp maché suggest boiling the mix; as described above in a galvanised bucket. When it has been strained, the pulp is allowed to cool and them emptied out onto a small pile of dry newspapers. It is then ready for use. The addition of a small quantity of wintergreen makes the mixture less foul smelling. Both pulp and paste can be stored in a refrigerator and used over a short period (when making pulp it improves if left overnight before use).

What do you do with this grey, soggy mess; you are probably asking yourself? Kids being kids, the paper equivalent of mud pies will already be winging their way through your local air space! More constructively, the pulp is a wonderfully cheap alternative to clay. Therefore, if you want to make a candle holder out of a bottle first paste strips of paper onto the bottle, then add the moulded lumps of pulp.

Make sure that the papier mâché is separated by a gap from the candle wax.

Bead and Bangle making

Rather a different use of papier mâché is its use in making beads. A three foot string of beads can be made in about half an hour, though this does not take into account the lacquering. Both use the layering method, but on a miniature scale of the bowl making technique. Wetted and pasted strips are wrapped around either a tin (for bangles) or a crochet hook or knitting needle (for beads). They are squeezed to get rid of excess moisture. With the bangle, leave it dry while still around the tin; in a warm place. Once it is dry, ease off the tin, sand smooth and then layer with tissue paper to the required thickness. The beads are shaped by squeezing with the fingers, firstly while on the hook or needle, then while loose. If speed is important, they should be baked in an oven, lightly sanded, then lacquered. Lacquering is done most easily by threading the beads on a string then dipping into a cup of lacquer. Coloured nail varnishes and enamel paints are alternatives for producing lively, colourful results.

Whether it is a papier mâché model of an enormous ginger cat; or the bangles just described; smoothing, painting and varnishing will help to make an inanimate object spring to life. The important things to remember are:

1. Make sure the model is completely dry.
2. Smooth off the surfaces of the model completely with sandpaper.
3. Undercoat models with white emulsion paint.
4. The choice of top coat paint depends a bit on the cost of the paint, size of the model, etc.. With small models, enamel paint and lacquer are good mediums. Big models are more cheaply covered with poster paints and then lacquered as necessary
5. Nail varnish is good as a paint cover on small jewellery items made with papier mâché.

PEBBLE POLISHING

With a simple tumble-polisher machine (under £50) you can make good quality pebble jewellery similar to that found in many tourist shops in sunny Scotland! Pebbles are easily collected from beaches and this can provide a useful focus for an expedition or trip to the seaside. Avoid collecting sandstone, flaky shale, slate or pitted or cracked pebbles. You'll find that there are at least three grade of pebbles – soft, medium and hard. At some point these have to be separated out, as they cannot be tumbled together. It is possibly best to do the sorting back at base. Don't spend too much time trying to spot attractive pebbles on the beach – often dull, uninteresting pebbles will polish much better anyway. Try to collect a range of different shapes of between a quarter and a half an inch; this helps the grinding process as the small stones grind into the hollows of the larger ones. Remember too that beaches yield lots of other interesting items for a scrapbox – shells, for example, or small weathered pieces of wood which can be mounted to create abstract sculpture.

Apart from a tumbler and pebbles, you'll need grinding grit (silicon carbide), polishing powder (cerium oxide or tin oxide), jewellery findings, (e.g. bell caps for necklaces, ready-made brooches and rings, neck chains or leather thongs, jump rings) and a small penknife and steel file to test the hard pebble. If it can't be scratched by knife or file, it's a hard pebble. If the only the steel file scratches it – medium. If the knife does then it's soft. Manchester Minerals and Specialist Crafts supply 'Rough Rock' packs in 1 to 1½ lb quantities of either agate or quartz stones. These are pre-sorted for size and hardness, which is useful for beginners to lapidary (the posh name for this type of gemstone craft)!

Grinding and Polishing

Hard pebbles will polish up the best. Manchest Minerals stock a range of tumblers up to industrial sizes. Specialist Crafts offer a good basic machine. Follow the tumbler manufacturer's recommendations regarding the kind of grinding grit to use, but if in doubt, start off with No. 80 Silicon Carbide grit. For a small (1½ lb barrel) tumbler you'll need about 100 pebbles and a heaped tablespoon of grit. Double check the pebbles to make sure that none of them is pitted or cracked and load them into the barrel until it is almost three-quarters full. Shake the barrel to settle the pebbles and sprinkle the grit over them. Now add water until it just covers the pebbles and put the lid on, making sure that it makes a good seal. (For example, no grit trapped under the lid). Wipe the barrel to check for leaks. Place it on the tumbler and switch on the motor.

The tumbler will create some noise in use so it should be sited where it will cause minimum disturbance. Every 24 hours the motor should be switched off, the barrel removed and the pebbles checked. This is necessary to release any gases that may have formed and to see how the pebbles are progressing. Wash a few of them and examine – they should feel noticeably smoother. Now replace them and switch on again. It will take between three and six days for hard pebbles to be ground reasonably smooth. Once this stage has been reached the pebbles can be removed and washed in a colander. The waste in the barrel should be thrown away into a dustbin as it blocks sinks easily, and the barrel itself should be washed out.

Before the next stage begins, any pebble that is blemished, pitted or cracked, should be set aside (reasonable specimens can be added to the next batch of pebbles to be coarse ground). Repeat the operation as for coarse grinding, but this time using a fine grit. After five or six days the pebbles should be ready for polishing and should look smooth, lacking only the final shine. After washing, you can test for readiness by rubbing one for a few minutes with polish and a smooth felt cloth. If you can spot any pinpricks or cracks, you will have to continue with the fine grind.

The pebbles should be handled very carefully at this stage and returned to the clean barrel. After sprinkling on the correct amount of polishing powder, the pebbles should be just covered with water, and the tumbler switched on. If it sounds like the pebbles are tumbling unevenly, a small amount of wallpaper paste can be added to promote smoother running. Again, inspect the barrel daily – the polishing stage is complete when there is no improvement on the previous day's progress and the pebbles look just as shiny dry as they do wet.

It will be abundantly clear from the above, to the critical reader, (i.e. harassed youth worker) that tumble polishing is a very time consuming process. However, the time spent working with the equipment is minimal, a daily check usually being all that is necessary. The craft has obvious possibilities for groups that only meet once a week – the tumbler can be left to do most of the work between sessions and with any luck each stage will be completed within a week.

When the polished pebbles are ready they can be easily made into attractive pieces of jewellery using Araldite, Epoxy Resin or Superglue adhesive and jewellers' findings. Exercising the imagination can produce other ideas, for example, they can be used to decorate various boxes or to embellish a key ring or fob. Making a bead curtain might just be feasible and we have seen polished pebbles used to make a 'gem tree' (using silver coloured wire and small metal leaves available from craft shops).

PHOTOGRAPHY

This is an activity which, over a period of time, **all** youth groups will have engaged in to some extent. Whether it is a quick snap, or a studied portrait, there is something magical about the photographic process. A myth, however, seems to have grown up around photography; a myth which implies that photography is a complicated operation. We **are** confident that it is a myth because we have both made extensive use of photography in our work with youth groups. It is a flexible activity since it can be used:
- to record youth group activities;
- as a 'one-off' session;
- as a preparation for a week(end) away or residential experience;
- as a planned course in photography.

In this section we would like to offer examples for photography sessions suitable for any of the above contexts. Before that, we would like to offer a few comments on the basic equipment you may require, given different types of groups, ages, etc..

The equipment

In 'one-off' sessions, we have worked with both cameras and black and white darkroom equipment. The same applies to a planned course, of say, six two-hour sessions. With the holiday outing or trip to a particular event, the camera alone will probably suffice as the 'equipment', unless you are considering its use as an introduction to photography. In this case, it is likely that you will avail yourself of the cheap colour printing service which (at the latest price, 1996) will cost anything between about £3.00 and £8.00 for developing and printing 36 colour prints. With the cost of the film, this can give a print cost of less than 20 pence. We have found the Radio Times Film Service pretty reliable, PO Box 5, Eastleigh,

Hants SO53 3XW. At the time of writing in March 1996, their 27 exposure Agfa colour print film costs £2.75 including 5 x 3½ inch prints.

With most youth groups who have not been let loose on cameras previously, it is best to get them to use a simple but versatile viewfinder camera such as the Olympus range, which usually have automatic metering. (This bit of technical phraseology means that it corrects the amount of light entering the lens to suit the conditions). Many cheaper viewfinder cameras have too great a capacity for producing blurred images. The reason for this is twofold. The lenses used will not focus on subjects much closer than six feet and the shutter speed is fixed – but at a speed too slow to prevent user shakes. Finally, the lens is made of cheap plastic instead of optical glass, and even the pressure on the shutter release button may cause blurring! So, beware the cheap pocket camera unless you have tested it and found it satisfactory! One we have tried, and that is not bad for the money is the Halina Panoramic. It wouldn't win any photographic awards, but its format, producing super wide angle prints, is both fun and especially useful for sweeping land and seascapes.

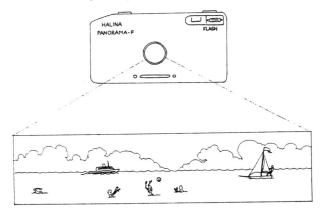

For universality, make sure that the camera you are using is a 35 mm. This is the size of the film. It is the easiest size for processing and is now the standard for much amateur and professional work. The 110 size is awkward and disc film impossible if you are working with domestic darkroom equipment. 120 roll film can produce superb results, but it is more expensive, and it is harder to work with when developing.

For youngsters who are gong to be shown basic camera techniques, you will need a camera with interchangeable lenses. It is best to stick to 35 mm format. Your local camera shop may be willing to do 'deals'. This might include the provision of good second-hand equipment. Cameras have come down in price in the past 25 years. In 'real' terms this means that a good quality single lens reflex (SLR) camera (one where you view the subject directly through the lens) will now cost less than a tenth, in real terms, of a similar camera in 1970. Many reputable makes of SLR exist. Nikon, Pentax, Minolta, Mamiya, Canon and Olympus are all worth looking at, and these firms provide cameras with both manual and automatic functioning for under £150. For teaching purposes, it is ideal if you have available a wide angle and a telephoto, or equivalent zoom lens to fit the SLR camera body. The need for extra lenses comes as a matter of teaching necessity.

In the darkroom you will need printing paper (basic, is grade 2 Ilfospeed glossy or equivalent), different developer for prints and negatives, and fixer (Hypam or equivalent).

Jessops of Leicester are very competitive and their own brand materials are good quality. They also offer an efficient mail order service for nearly anything you'll need, including the equipment listed below:

1 x double spiral 35 mm developing tank
1 x measuring cylinder
1 x thermometer (photographic range)
1 x force washing rubber tube
1 x enlarger, and spare bulb
1 x safelight and spare bulb
3 x chemical trays
3 x pairs of print tongs
1 x rubber tongs.

In the darkroom, or close by, you will also need a washing line with plastic clothes pegs to hang prints and negatives from, and a sink with a plug and overflow, in which to wash prints.

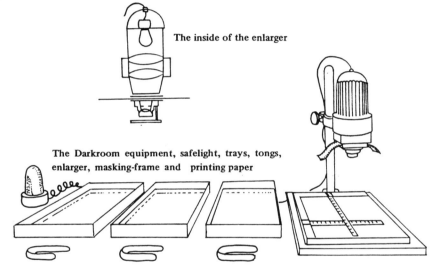

The inside of the enlarger

The Darkroom equipment, safelight, trays, tongs, enlarger, masking-frame and printing paper

A 'One-off' photographic experience

Imagine the standard issue school building, social work department or youth/community centre. Perhaps it is not a pretty 'imagining', but there are some small compensations. Among them are the availability of space for a makeshift darkroom. You need transport to get you and most of the equipment listed in the equipment section to your place of meeting. The Zenith enlarger is useful, in that it is a suitcase design, which can be moved to any site. Before offering your services, check that:

- There is a completely dark room, with enough space in which to erect one long table, or ideally two smaller, rigid surfaces.
- There is access to electric power in this room.
- The use of a sink with water supply and overflow is available, in or near the 'darkroom'.

Having ascertained that the above potentially exists, you can establish a temporary darkroom in a matter of a quarter of an hour. Do this **before** you are due to meet your group. The only additional equipment needed for the session, are the following: Camera(s); film – Black and White FP4 (for example); a hair-drier.

So, there you are perhaps, with an unfamiliar youth group, introduced as the 'photography expert'. All it requires is a fair degree of practice to ensure that you have the skills which give you, as the self-styled, 'flying' photography teacher, a bit of self-confidence.

Exactly how to do much of what is explained in this section is included in the section on a planned photography course. What is detailed here is a fun experience, geared to proving that photography is neither an inordinately long process or a complicated one. Try it with a group of about five. It can also be used as 'session one' with adults or youth groups who have come to do photography in eight (approximately) two-hour chunks. The exercise requires at least one-and-a-quarter hours and preferably two hours. As the group arrives, take their photos. This will probably be using flash. Introduce yourself alongside this and pass the camera around.

The 'how' a camera works should be subordinated to pre-setting the camera and getting the youngsters to feel and use the equipment. With the Olympus camera, or similar, this is a quick and painless exercise. We have also used a camera on a tripod with a cable-release attached on a 'blower' set-up. This allows for group members to take photos of themselves. Shooting a 36 exposure film in this manner will take about ten minutes to a quarter of an hour. At this point, you disappear into the darkroom and load the film into the tank, or you can use a purpose made changing bag, and load the film in a normal room. That **should** take about one to two minutes. Having previously mixed the developer/stop bath solution (if used) and fixer (all at the correct dilutions and temperature), process the film and wash it, explaining the stages of the process. This will take a maximum of fifteen minutes, if using a high concentration of fixer and a force-washer. You then take the roll of negatives from the tank, show the group and gently dry them with rubber tongs. Finally, for this stage, you hang up the film, and speed up the drying with the expedient use of a hair-drier, trying not to blow too much dust onto the soft surface of the film.

After half an hour you have a dry film. Cut it into lengths of six exposures, and explain the use of the enlarger and the three trays of chemicals in the darkroom. As is likely, the darkroom is small, so perhaps only take two or three youngsters in at a time. You can operate a shuttle system, where each youngster chooses two or three negatives which they would like a print of. They can then use the enlarger to print them. Again, it's quick and easy. If you are working well, it takes about one-and-a-half minutes, or two minutes per print, and even faster if you are stream feeding two or three prints through the chemical trays. Using Ilfospeed, resin-coated paper, only a short, three or four minute wash is required, before the paper can be hung up to dry. Drying takes approximately half an hour, but this can be reduced to three minutes or less, with a quick wave of the trusty hair-drier! In all, you can get a group of five or six youngsters each with two or three photos to take home in a very short period of time. If well handled, the group will be able to have a good shared experience, and prints which they can take away. All in the space of between an hour-and-a-half and two hours.

Using the camera – preparation for the group event or trip away

Some technical aspects of the camera need not concern youngsters. Others can be simply explained. Often, photography is treated as though the information is especially complicated. It is **not**. Even when showing twelve and thirteen year olds the basic workings of an SLR 35 mm camera, simple examples can make the process an easy one. In explaining how to take photos, it is mostly practice which determines an individual's ability to 'compose' a good photo. Getting a photo which is in focus and correctly exposed relies on simple rules which can be learned. The tips we use in explaining 'how a camera works' run roughly as follows:

SHUTTER SPEED. What are you trying to photograph? If the subject or you are moving, you require a faster shutter speed to freeze the action. An SLR or any other camera can be held at 1/60th of a second, but it is safer to use 1/125th of a second to prevent camera shake. To stop the movement of people walking, 1/125th is usually enough. For cars and people running, 1/250 - 1/1000th of a second should be used. A useful bit of information regarding camera angle: if you shoot 'head-on' with the subject coming towards you, this slows down the movement. Taking photos from the side if they are very fast-moving, for instance, in a motor-cycle race, is difficult unless your camera has a very fast shutter speed. If you want to take a shot from the side, use the 'panning' technique. This entails moving the camera in the direction the subject is travelling, keeping the subject in the viewfinder. The shutter speed should be fast enough, say 1/250th of a second, to stop blur from your movement. The panning should then stop the movement of the subject. The end product will be a shot of the subject in sharp relief with a blurred background – that's how so many sports photos convey a sense of action and movement!

APERTURE. This is the device which allows the user of a camera to restrict or increase the amount of light passing through the lens. Because of the calibration in f-numbers and the name 'aperture', many youngsters' eyes glaze over when you try to explain its use. As in the next diagram, each change in aperture allows exactly half or double the amount of light to pass through the lens as its neighbour. The 'f' numbers underneath or above the lens are the standard scale on all cameras. The largest numbers give the smallest amount of light exposure; the small numbers allow in the greatest amount of light.

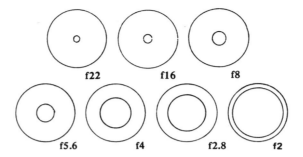

f22   f16   f8

f5.6   f4   f2.8   f2

Depth of field and composition

The balance between the amount of light allowed in to hit the sensitive surface of the film by the shutter speed, and that allowed in by the aperture control, give the total **EXPOSURE**, i.e. the amount of light forming the image.

The reason you wish to alter the aperture in taking photos is to alter the **DEPTH OF FIELD** in a photo. Depth of field is basically another way of describing the amount of the photo which is going to be in focus. How this works, we have found is best explained (especially with kids) in two stages. First, remind youngsters of a simple experiment which they have probably tried on themselves as young children. It works particularly well with those who wear glasses normally. Taking off any glasses, clench a hand, making a small pinhole space through the fingers. Look through this. The world should appear a sharper place to see! This can help explain how you use aperture controls. As a rule, the smaller the hole, the sharper (more in focus) the image. With SLR cameras, the lens can be detached from the body of the camera, so that you can show youngsters the effect of opening and closing the aperture control. (If your camera has an automatic switch, make sure that it is in the manual position, otherwise the demonstration will not work).

The actual depth of field is related to the distance away from the subject and the type of lens you use. Briefly, the longer the lens - standard is about 50 mm - the less depth of field is available to the user. Therefore, a wide angle lens, say 28 mm, will offer the greatest depth of field. In the diagram below the depth of field is charted, using different apertures. When explaining this subject, remember that there is a greater depth **beyond** the subject than in front of it.

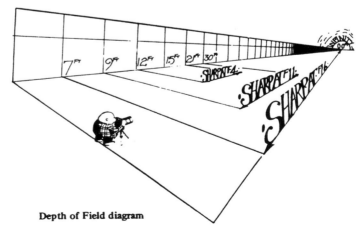

Depth of Field diagram

The use of an exposure meter, either in-built to the camera, or used separately is a great aid. You should be able to use the information on speed and aperture as a guide to settings. Basically, the film speed is set on the meter, then the meter is aimed at the subject. (Close metering – taking the meter to the subject is recommended for accurate readings). A range of options which will each give the same overall exposure are then obtained. The choice you or your group make should be based on **(1) the nature of the subject**, and **(2) the type of photography you wish to obtain**. This second variable brings one on to questions about composition. Finishing the subject – depth of field – it is useful to experiment with different apertures to achieve very different pictures. For example, using f16, the picture will generally all be in focus, useful for landscapes and large groups etc.. At f2 the background can be thrown completely out of focus, giving a photograph which centres attention on an individual or object. Two very different end products from the same vantage point!

Taking youngsters back into their murky pasts of art lessons may remind them that **COMPOSITION** has a number of important elements. Some worth considering are:

- The overall **shape** of the object. Is it interesting? Avoid rows of objects, and images where one part of the subject becomes muddled with another. Triangular shapes are one powerful option.
- **Tone and texture.** This is important, if you wish to photograph natural scenes, trees, the sea, etc..
- **Size.** Too many photographs are taken of ant-like people in the middle distance. Most cameras will focus as close as five feet. Some can be used as close as two feet from the subject. Think big, it gives interesting, vivid results.
- **Lighting.** The beginning and the end of the day produce the most interesting natural lighting and strong images. Noon, despite the intensity of light, produces generally bleached results which are flat and lacking in any dynamism.

The use of different lenses and filters can offer a range of unusual results, many of which add a very professional element to the work.

Planning a photography course

Through experience, we have found that it is best to have prepared a fairly comprehensive set of notes on using camera equipment, a darkroom and the related issues of composition, lighting etc.. Use as many illustrations as possible and try to strike a balance between 'doing' and 'explaining'. Your ability to take good photos will not be enough, unless you can actually teach in a simple way, which makes photography come alive. Try, if possible to avoid too much 'classroom teaching'.

Because of the time-consuming nature of colour darkroom work and the fumes, and type of chemicals used, we have based the considerable darkroom emphasis of courses on black and white photography. When talking about the taking of photos, both out of doors and indoors, some of the requirements of using colour can be introduced. The use of cheap processing for colour prints has now made it much cheaper to have colour prints commercially processed than home producing black and white pictures. It's all to do with the economics of large scale production.

The rest of this section is intended to fill the gaps about photography which we would wish to see plugged. Our emphasis in planning a sequence with kids is to give them a range of photographic experiences. The sort of balance we might be suggesting would be:

- Introductory, 'Instant Photography Session' as described.
- Two Outdoor Sessions, for instance on a beach and at a motorcycle meeting.

- One Indoor Session using flash and photoflood lighting.
- Two or three Darkroom Sessions.

Photo tips

Before launching into an explanation of how to use a darkroom imaginatively, here are a few tips from our experience.

BULK FILM. If you buy a canister of 30 metres of black and white film, it saves a lot of money over purchasing individual films. To load films into empty 35 mm cartridges, you can either use a bulk loader, or it can be cut into length in a **totally** dark room and then taped onto the inner spool of the cartridge. It's especially useful if you want to use a short length of film and do not want to waste the remainder.

CAMERA METERS. Using the meters on many cameras today offers aperture or speed priority. These terms indicate that you select either speed or aperture and the camera then automatically adjust the other variable to the correct light setting. Many cameras have a needle which reacts to both variables being adjusted, and the user makes the best compromise to suit the subject being photographed.

LOADING THE DEVELOPING TANK. If youngsters are going to develop their own film, practice sessions feeding a piece of useless, exposed film into the tank spiral in total darkness are necessary. When finishing a film in a camera, try to rewind it back into the cassette, leaving the end tab of the film showing. Then, prior to loading, take the tab, pull it and cut off the narrow section. The first one and a half inches or thereabouts of film are already exposed, so you can safely thread this section onto the spiral before finishing the threading process in total darkness.

DIFFERENT LENSES. If money or available resources permit, the use of different lenses gives greater flexibility. The next diagrams help to explain the different sort of results you can expect from using different size lenses:

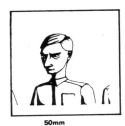    

| 50mm | 35mm | 200mm | 500mm | 20mm |

FILM SPEED. For most purposes the film speed required will be in the 100-200 ASA range. A slow speed of film indicates that the silver oxide coating of the film is very slow to react to light, therefore it is unsuitable for use in poor light conditions. It does give very high quality prints. A slow speed is about 50 ASA. Medium speed film, which we recommend using (100-200 ASA) is good for most situations and will produce good results up to about 10 x 8 inch size. Fast film, in the region of 400 ASA, is essential for use in poor light conditions, or where high grain effect is required. It is useful for shooting fast moving subjects. The quality of film coatings have progressively improved and some fast film is now almost as good as slow or medium speed film was ten years ago.

PAPERS. Printing paper is available in a variety of grades, depending upon the manufacturer's scale. The lowest numbers offer the least contrast. Higher contrast is obtained by using the harder paper. This sort of paper is particularly useful when negatives are very grey coloured overall. A short exposure coupled with hard paper will normally give a balanced print. With resin-coated papers, the surface to which the print eventually dries can be chosen in advance. Glossy is the best high-quality surface; matt and semi-matt are popular for exhibition work where reflections can ruin the impact of a strong image. Grade 3 Ilfospeed glossy or Jessop's grade 2, are good all-round papers for use in the darkroom. The size of paper you choose depends on the use to which it is to be put and the cost. You may need a couple of boxes of different size (and grade, perhaps) paper.

FILTERS. Below is a chart of filter effects on different colours using black and white film. Filters are especially useful to heighten the effects of clouds, seascapes, etc.. In contre-jour shots (into the sun) filters can accentuate the silhouette. The use of filters restricts the amount of light entering the lens and this must be compensated for by allowing a greater exposure.

FILTER	RED	BLUE	GREEN
RED	LIGHT	DARK	LIGHT
GREEN	DARK	DARK	LIGHT
BLUE	DARK	LIGHT	DARK
YELLOW	LIGHT	DARK	SAME

A contre-jour design!

USE OF LIGHTING. In the course of a series of lessons, you may, if you have the equipment, wish to consider using both flash and photo-floodlighting with the group. Photoflood bulbs are expensive and do not last very long. However, they give the opportunity for planning the effect of lighting on subjects, i.e., lighting from one source at the side, underneath, behind, above. This sort of lighting is useful with the extension-release system. A flash guide to aperture settings is usually situated on the side of most flashguns. This will give an indication as to the aperture setting to be used at various distances. If there is powerful available lighting, decrease the aperture; if it is dark, or the room in which the photo is to be taken is large, increase the amount of light by opening the iris of the aperture. (smaller f-number).

IN THE DARKROOM. Producing prints is a perfect example of being able to give kids' groups almost immediate gratification. It takes a few sessions before kids are confident enough in their use of the enlarger and the chemicals to be left alone. Therefore, make sure that you are supervising, otherwise you will be confronted by large wastage of printing paper. Ideally, you will have a timer to estimate exposure times. If you don't, like us, count: "one hundred - one hundred and one - one hundred and two- etc.," to give an indication of the number of seconds an exposure lasts.

In the enlarger, there is a negative carriage. The negative strip, usually of six frames, should be placed in the carrier with the image upside down, glossy side up. Most enlargers have a red filter which allows for positioning printing paper under the image while the light is on. You can use a frame which keeps the paper flat and gives a white border to prints. However, this is not really necessary as modern printing papers lays pretty flat on the base board of the enlarger. Getting the exposure time right is a matter of practice, which can be aided by the use of a test strip.

NEW YOUTH ARTS & CRAFT

135

Use of the strip allows for experimentation, without undue paper wastage. You slide a sheet of paper over the strip of paper progressively every two seconds, so you end up with a sample of exposures of different lengths. Because of the way the lens aperture works, giving greater depth of field with a closing of the iris, it is obvious that there is more chance of obtaining a distinct image with the use of a closed down aperture. For normal use, close down about two stops from the fully open position.

The instruction for mixing chemicals both for developing and printing films are given on individual bottles. The temperature is more critical on developing films and the times should be adhered to as closely as possible. For printing, the first tray contains developer, the second tray in the sequence contains stop solution. If it is not available, ordinary water can be used, but it will only wash the developer off, it will not halt the development process. As mentioned earlier in this section, we advocate a strong solution of fixer, to speed up the process to approximately 30 seconds duration. The diluted fixer can be stored in an air-tight bottle. The use of a different pair of tongs/forceps is recommended for each tray.

OTHER TECHNIQUES. Given that producing quick photos of self and friends is fun, there will not be too much boredom in the darkroom. Having said that, there are a couple of other quick techniques which we have successfully employed with youth groups.

THE PHOTOGRAM. This is a form of simple black and white image, which can be assembled in the darkroom. Instead of projecting light through a negative, the paper is placed on a flat surface and objects are placed on top of the printing paper. This is done under a red safe light. When solid objects are on the paper they will leave a negative image on the paper. This means that white images (shapes) appear on the paper, surrounded in black after development. More varied prints can be obtained by using objects such as combs and leaves, which are translucent. Items such as feathers will leave an image which displays texture. A combination of negatives, coins, petals, leaves, screws, keys, combs, etc., can produce a very unusual photogram.

SCREENS. Enlargements can be made through some sort of screen, if a special, textured print quality is desired. Rather like using different grades of paper, i.e., grade 0, to achieve special soft and subtle effects and Grade 6 to lose halftones (the greys), the use of screens can add or detract from the contrast of a subject. Mostly, they will add texture. Screens can be bought in negative form. These are used in conjunction with the negative. Extra printing time is required, but the texture can be worth the wait. Ranging from 'stucco'; 'old master' to 'dot' screens and 'concentric circles', the right screen has to be chosen to suit the characteristics of particular photos. With old tights, tacked to a frame or muslin, etc., and the frame placed in contact with the print paper, screens can be used without the expense of using the commercial items.

Into the future

In the professional photography arena, there is now a generation of digital cameras which do away with the need for film altogether. Pictures can be viewed on computer or TV screens and prints obtained from high quality laser printers. Whether this will become the 'norm' for photography in the next few years is still open to speculation. A competitor, the film based APS-Advanced Photo System, is aimed at the amateur field. The cartridge fits only specially made cameras, and loads automatically, with the film retracting back into the cartridge after use. There are no negatives to handle – reprints are ordered from an index print of the miniature negatives retained inside the film cartridge. The main advantage of the system is that it offers three different print formats: a standard print similar to 35 mm; a panoramic view 10 x 3½ inches, and an in between size of 6½ x 3½ inches. The small size of negative makes the print quality poorer than with 35 mm film, but the format will also be compatible with the digital transfer system of the future. However, it does mean that for youth groups it could make the darkroom redundant, perhaps to be replaced by the computer on screen edit programme!

PUPPETS

Where drama and acting can be intimidating to many children, puppetry is much more like 'play' and 'fantasy'. The characters and the plots are only limited by imagination, but, and it is a big BUT, there is a lot of preparation behind any sort of puppet show. Making puppets, inventing characters and then learning to manipulate them is all part of the fun. Individual youngsters will make their own decisions as to whether they are natural puppet makers or performers; still others may enjoy preparing scenery and props for the show. The adult(s) involved should encourage young people to participate and try on the different roles, and generally act as facilitator to ensure that planning and preparation will turn a puppet performance into a success.

As far as this section is concerned, we are assuming that making puppets will be a major part of the activity. However, you may also wish to buy ready-made puppets. Large toy shops such as Hamleys in London's Regent Street have a good range to choose from. NES Arnold offer an imaginative range of finger and glove puppets, including a selection of 'family' puppets covering different racial and occupational groups and a variety of animals. Galt offer a nice range in their 'Imaginative play' section, including some nice 'creepy crawlie' hand puppets and purpose built puppet theatre. Specialist Crafts sell basic marionette figures. We particularly liked the Igel hand puppet range from Germany which are available from the Big Top in Glasgow. (see Suppliers' Section).

Glove puppets

So called because they are made to slip over the hand like a glove, enabling the fingers to operate the puppet. They are much easier to make and manipulate than the marionette type (which is operated by an arrangement of strings from a control bar). An almost infinite variety of glove puppets are simply made using materials that you can probably purloin from your Dressing Up and Scrap Boxes. Even if you have to buy materials, you won't be much out of pocket.

The message with glove puppets, is simply to think of a character and then make it, no matter how improbable! Frankenstein, Miss Piggy, Batman, Power Rangers, favourite School Teachers – all are possible, and just as easy to make as the social worker puppet we saw being so lovingly (!) fashioned in one Intermediate Treatment Centre. Needless to say, this particular artefact was put to great therapeutic use in ventilating repressed feelings about the social work/client system, particularly as it affects the teenager in the deprived urban context (and if you believe that you'll believe anything!).

Simple Puppets

Very simple glove puppets can be made quickly and easily, and are especially suited to younger groups. The basic material could be a sock, ping-pong ball or old glove which is decorated with wool, buttons, sequins, etc., to make a face.

Alternatively, simple rod puppets can be made by drawing and painting characters on pieces of card, which are then pinned on to doweling or garden canes. A sleeve puppet can easily be made, adding simple materials to a shirt or pullover sleeve. It is easy to adapt this method to arrange for a moving mouth. The sleeve puppet can be used as it is in a 'Punch and Judy' type show with the body (supposedly) out of the audience's line of sight. If you wish though, you can add a stuffed body and legs to the sleeve.

Heads

Puppet heads can be made in many different ways, one of the simplest being to use an old (but clean) sock or stocking. This is stuffed to give it shape with an old tennis ball, foam rubber chips, or fabric. Cut off the sock at the heel and tie securely before gluing it to a conical tube (made out of cardboard, for example). This serves as the neck, and also provides a hole for the operator's fingers.

The basic head shape can also be made out of foam rubber by gluing it around a cardboard tube, and adding on shaped pieces of foam to provide features. This basic shape can be covered with material (or an old sock or stocking) before being decorated.

Large head shapes (e.g. for animals) can be formed by making a cardboard 'skeleton'. Do this by cutting out a cardboard profile of the head and then gluing or slotting on ribs. More cardboard glued between the ribs will strengthen the skeleton which can now be encased with layers of thin card. If you're clever you can form the neck (and space for the operator's fingers) at this stage, but it can just as easily be glued on at the end. Finish off by covering with cloth, fur or a thin coating of plastic wood.

Fabric covered heads can be made to vaguely resemble inhabitants of the humanoid or animal species by decorating them with buttons or sequins for eyes, wool for hair, material or cardboard for hats, etc..

Large human-type heads can be modelled from polystyrene or softwood. Use a coping saw or rasp to cut the basic shape out of polystyrene and carve fine details with a craft knife. The head should now be covered by gluing on small pieces of paper or newsprint. This adds strength, provides a final opportunity for modelling and renders the head suitable for painting. It should be covered with a final coat of glue (use woodwork adhesive, as most others will dissolve polystyrene) and sanded down. The neck can be hollowed out and strengthened in a similar way, adding a cardboard extension if necessary. Egg boxes can also be adapted to make good heads, with the hinge acting as the back of the head. By punching holes in the hinge area, the operator can open and close the mouth.

Bodies

A simple glove puppet body can be made up by sewing or gluing two shaped pieces of material together. What you are making, in effect, is an elbow length glove; this should be loose fitting, especially if it is to be used by more than one person. Depending on the kind of puppet you are making, you can include arms and hands in the cut out shapes, making sure that there is enough space for the operator's thumb and finger. This gives you a basic glove which can be glued to the head and neck. The puppet is almost complete now, needing only to be dressed and have legs added. You can use slim cardboard tubes for the legs but more permanent ones can be made by firmly stuffing tubes made of fabric with foam chips and sewing or gluing them to the glove. The puppet can be dressed by gluing appropriate bits of fabric to the glove or by making up loose fitting clothes to suit.

Animal bodies can be made by decorating the glove to suit (with fur fabric for example) or by making a stuffed animal body that is sewn to the glove so that it rests on the wrist and forearm. The cardboard method of making an animal head, mentioned above, can be adapted to make complete large bodied animals like alligators, whales, hippos, etc.. If you are using this method remember to fashion a hole in the underside for the operator's hand. A small spar of wood should be fitted into the hole for the hand to grasp, as this makes it much easier to manipulate.

Using the puppets
Glove puppets are ideal for a Punch and Judy type show, although the puppets that your kids have created may well be more suited to titles like 'Sid Snot's Ravers' or 'The Merry Mutants' Dance'. Although dialogue can be improvised, it is best to at least get the main story lines of the show committed to paper. Use of the story board technique can help a lot here (see Video Section), and you may even want to make a film of your show. The young people you work with may have strong ideas about the characters of the puppets they have made. This can help in working out a storyline. So, for instance, a robot and a dog might be marooned on an alien planet after their spaceship crashes.

The physical requirements necessary to put on the show are easy to arrange. A cloth draped over the front of a table will, at the same time, give you a playing surface for the puppets and hide the operator's legs. A good backdrop simplifies the whole undertaking as it means that the operators can sit in relative comfort while manipulating the puppets. The backdrop should ideally be supported on stand, a washing-line type arrangement, or hung from the ceiling or wall. During the show, you may want to change the scenery a number of times, as in a theatrical production. Once again, planning and preparation count a lot towards accomplishing a professional puppet show.

You can have as many puppets (and operators) as you can fit into your play area, remembering that it is possible for one operator to manipulate two puppets. All that remains now is to do some quick coaching to perfect puppet-type voices. Depending on whether or not your show would be rated a U, PG, 15 or 18, certificate, you may want to try taking it on tour to local old folk's homes, nursery schools etc..

QUESTIONNAIRES

The name conjures up rather unfortunate images of hours of laborious form filling, but in practice a well designed questionnaire can be the basis for a fun activity. Really! In addition, the nature of questionnaires is close enough to the range of available puzzle books to make the task of filling one in an enjoyable, rather than daunting, experience. To start with, any adult working with a group of youngsters should have an identified aim for using a questionnaire. Is it:

- to obtain information about an individual (or group) and their attitudes?
- to introduce a particular theme, issue or activity to a group?

In the first instance, the questionnaire format can be introduced by using a non-challenging version (see below). Since children generally like talking about themselves, this can be a tool which is easy to use. Why not try a questionnaire in the form of the old, star pen profiles, much loved by the teen pop papers of the 1950s right through to the 1990s. These run along the lines of:

Name	*Town*
Colour of eyes	*Colour of Hair*
Favourite Colour	*Favourite Popstar*
Favourite Food & Drink	*Dislikes*
What work you would	*Favourite animal*
like to do when you're older	*Sport you are best at.*

The variations are limitless and it is a relaxed sort of enterprise, without the overtones of prying too deeply. For a starter, you (as the adult) could duplicate/photocopy a sample sheet. If the group get into the exercise, they should be able to design their own forms. A little gentle control may be necessary to prevent people designing forms and questions which are too threatening or awkward for their friends to fill in. For instance, some youngsters may find the question, 'which of your friends do you like most' too intimidating. With adolescent groups, this sort of questionnaire can include questions about boy/girl friends, stars you would most like to go out with, etc.. It's not very far removed from an old commercial game called 'Tell Me', which had a spinner which gave the participant a letter and they then had to say the name of a famous actor, tree, animal, etc..

Questionnaires can be used to either assess what activities young people may wish to involve themselves in, or to introduce a specific subject to a group. As with the previous activity, it is imperative that an adult, or two, get involved in the activity, rather than using it as some sort of package which can be given to a group to keep them quiet. Really engaging with young people in this kind of process can be a revelation in gaining insight to their lifestyles, attitudes and aspirations. Youth workers, through a youth council perhaps, can use questionnaires in a variety of ways. It might be a list of alternatives for a night out in the mini-bus; it could be related to the provision of facilities in the community. The 'Rights Questionnaire' shown below has been revised by Bob Stead of Lothian Region's Welfare Rights team. It is based on a questionnaire used by the Pilton Youth Programme in the 1980s.

Rights Questionnaire

1. A policeman asks you to empty your pockets. Do you say:
      a) Bugger off.
      b) Do you have a warrant?
      c) Why?

d) You've no right.
e) Say nothing and obey.

2. If searched would you allow:
a) Examination of your clothes.
b) Taking of a blood sample.
c) Taking of your fingerprints.

3. A policeman knocks on your door and arrests you. Would you:
a) Allow a search of the house without warrant.
b) Insist on a warrant.
c) Step out and close the door.

4. Police can question:
a) Suspicious persons only.
b) Witnesses only.
c) Both A and B.
d) Anybody.

5. When questioned you:
a) Must answer.
b) Must stay and listen.
c) May walk out without listening.

6. If arrested you:
a) Must answer questions.
b) Must stay in the police station.
c) Must make a statement.
d) Must agree to a search, etc..

7. While in custody you have the right:
a) To see a solicitor.
b) To visits (parents).
c) To be cautioned or charged.
d) To telephone a solicitor.
e) To bail.

8. Police have right of search for:

   a) Prohibited drugs.
   b) Firearms.
   c) Eggs of protected birds.
   d) Papers relating to terrorism.
   e) Evo-stick.

9. Police could class as an offensive weapon, a:

   a) Knife.
   b) Penny.
   c) Broken bottle.
   d) Cosh.
   e) Spanner.
   f) Contraceptive.

Rights Questionnaire (Answers)

Question 1

The police have the power to search you if they believe you are carrying an offensive weapon or any of the following: drugs, firearms, stolen goods, birds' eggs, or anything connected with terrorism. They therefore have the right to search you for many reasons, but you can still ask why. You should only be searched by someone of your own sex. Just remember that the police have a lot more power than you have, and that you won't do yourself any favours by being rude or cheeky.

Question 2

If the police want to do more than just search you, they'll probably want you to 'go to the station' with them. In this case you can either be arrested, detained (for up to six hours), or you could go of your own free will. If you go of your own free will, the police may ask you to sign a voluntary certificate as evidence that you were not forced to go. If you are not being arrested or detained you should be free to go whenever you wish, but it may mean that you are kept much longer, as the police might detain you for six hours as soon as you ask to leave. *Ask the police whether they are arresting or detaining you.*

Unless you have been charged you would only need to allow the police to examine your clothes and take your fingerprints. You should not be subjected to any physical examination unless the police have a warrant. If you are proved innocent things like photos and fingerprints should be destroyed.

Question 3

The police do not always need a warrant to arrest you, so you cannot insist they have a warrant, but if you are arrested in your home the police may search for evidence of your guilt with or without a warrant. Ask them why they're searching though, and what they're looking for. The police have the power to enter and search any time of day or night and any day in the week if they have a warrant to search.

Question 4: 'd'

Question 5: 'b'

All that the police can **demand** to know is your name and address. If you are under 16, tell the police your age as well, as you have different rights.

Question 6: 'b/d'
You don't have to say or sign anything, but don't be rude or awkward as you'll only make trouble for yourself.

Question 7: 'c/d'
If you have been arrested or detained you should be cautioned (warned that anything you say can be taken down in evidence...) as soon as possible. You have the right to have a message sent to a solicitor and to one other named person. If you are under 16 the police must inform your parents straight away, and you shouldn't be interviewed until they or another adult of the same sex gets there. Once you have been charged, the police can either keep you in custody (in which case they must bring you to court within 24 hours or 48 at weekends), or they can release you on bail. If you are released you will have to sign a pink bail form or agree to appear in court on a certain date. If you don't turn up you could be fined or imprisoned.

Question 8 : All except 'e' as stated in question 1.

Question 9 : All except 'f'

Working with questionnaires
In many cases, young people can be encouraged to design, distribute and analyse the results of questionnaires. These can be particularly useful in the context of social skills and social education work, or to complement another activity. For example, a group investigating the history of their own local area could design a number of questionnaires to suit, e.g. on lifestyles, industry, ghosts, landmark events etc..

Utilising questionnaires in this kind of investigative way is usually a fairly challenging activity, particularly when it involves the need to approach the general public 'cold' in the street. A high degree of planning, confidence and social skill is required to persuade a 'punter' to stop and complete a street questionnaire. In using questionnaires to introduce a subject area to a group, we are pleased to offer examples of forms designed by Simon Jacquet, now of Youth Clubs Scotland, plus lots of bits from Alan and Howie! They were used as part of a loose course on **music**. The sessions involved learning to play instruments, listening to records and going to see live performances.

The purpose of the questionnaires was to broaden out the areas of music which youngsters were prepared to listen to. Records from the 1950s, 1960s and 1970s were played, and Simon himself taught riffs in a variety of music styles. Often, the members of the group, which met at Canongate Youth Project in Edinburgh in the 1980s, could relate the 1950s and 1960s lists to music their parents played at home. As this new version of the Youth Arts and Crafts Book is being published in the 1990s, we have complemented Simon's lists with ones from the 1980s and 1990s.

Perhaps, in all, a marginally devious way of introducing new music to a new generation of young people, but certainly a successful and entertaining way of doing it!

HIT RECORDS OF THE 1950s

Name ....

Here are some of the greatest rock 'n' roll songs of the fifties. Put a (✓) beside your 10 favourite records. If one of your top 10 is not there, add it to the end of the list.

Rock around the Clock, Bill Haley and the Comets	Smoke gets in your eyes, The Platters
See you later Alligator, Bill Haley and the Comets	Dream Lover, Bobby Darin
Shake, Rattle and Roll, Bill Haley and the Comets	Here Comes Summer, Jerry Keller
Putting on the Style, Lonnie Donegan	Good Golly Miss Molly, Little Richard
Rock Island Line, Lonnie Donegan	Tutti Frutti, Little Richard
Singing the Blues, Guy Mitchell	Johnny B. Goode, Chuck Berry
Sixteen Tons, Tennessee Ernie Ford	Blueberry Hill, Fats Domino
Just Walkin' in the Rain, Johnny Ray	Oh Carol! Neil Sedaka
Diana, Paul Anka	Bo Diddley, Bo Diddley
Great Balls of Fire, Jerry Lee Lewis	Not fade away, Buddy Holly
Whole Lotta Shakin', Jerry Lee Lewis	Be Bop A Lula, Gene Vincent
Chantilly Lace, The Big Bopper	Hound Dog, Elvis Presley
Dream, Everly Brothers	
Bye Bye Love, Everly Brothers	
Cathy's Clown, Everly Brothers	

HIT RECORDS OF THE 1960s

Name ....

Here are some of the greatest rock 'n' pop songs of the sixties. Put a (✓) beside your 10 favourite records. If one of your top 10 is not there, add it to the end of the list.

Lay, Lady Lay, Bob Dylan	Honky Tonk Woman, Rolling Stones
I'm Free, The Cream	As Tears go by, Marianne Faithful
All Along the Watchtower, Jimi Hendrix	Whiter Shade of Pale, Procul Harum
She Loves You, The Beatles	Tired of Waiting for You, Kinks
Hey Jude, The Beatles	House of the Rising Sun, Animals
Strawberry Fields, The Beatles	My Generation, The Who
Get Back, The Beatles	I'm a Boy, The Who
Watcha gonna do about it, Small Faces	Walking Back to Happiness, Helen Shapiro
Light my Fire, The Doors	Sound of Silence, Simon and Garfunkel
Ferry Across the Mersey, Gerry and the Pacemakers	She's not There, Zombies
Fire!, Crazy World of Arthur Brown	The Mother people, Frank Zappa
24 hours to Tulsa, Gene Pitney	A World Without Love, Peter and Gordon
Sunshine Superman, Donovan	Sunny Afternoon, The Kinks
White Rabbit, Jefferson Airplane	I'm a Believer, The Monkees
Anyone who had a Heart, Cilla Black	
Satisfaction (I can't get it), Rolling Stones	

HIT RECORDS OF THE 1970s

Name ....

Here are some of the greatest rock songs of the seventies. Put a (✓) beside your 10 favourite records. If one of your top 10 is not there, add it to the end of the list.

Stairway to Heaven, Led Zeppelin	Anarchy in the UK, The Sex Pistols
Sailing, Rod Stewart	Roxanne, The Police
Brown Sugar, The Rolling Stones	Message in a Bottle, The Police
Watching the Detectives, Elvis Costello	Heart of Glass, Blondie
Mull of Kintyre, Wings	Your Song, Elton John
Dancing Queen, Abba	Stayin' Alive, Bee Gees
London Calling, The Clash	Baker Street, Gerry Rafferty
Jean Genie, David Bowie	All Right Now, Free
Rhiannon, Fleetwood Mac	Imagine, John Lennon
My Sweet Lord, George Harrison	Message to Rudi, The Specials
Hot Love, T Rex	No More Heroes, The Stranglers
Down Down, Status Quo	Bye Bye Baby, The Bay City Rollers
Casey Jones, Grateful Dead	Virginia Plain, Roxy Music
I'm not in Love, 10 c.c.	
When I Need You, Leo Sayer	

HIT RECORDS OF THE 1980s

Name ....

Here are some of the greatest rock 'n' pop records of the eighties. Put a tick (✓) beside your favourite 10 records. If one of your top 10 is not listed, add it to the end.

Brass in the Pocket, The Pretenders	You can't Hurry Love, Phil Collins
Atomic, Blondie	Billie Jean, Michael Jackson
Geno, Dexy's Midnight Runners	Let's Dance, David Bowie
Don't Stand so Close to me, The Police	Uptown Girl, Billy Joel
This ole House, Shakin' Stevens	99 Red Balloons, Nena
Stand and Deliver, Adam and the Ants	Wake me up before you Go-Go, Wham!
Tainted Love , Soft Cell	19, Paul Hardcastle
Under Pressure, Queen and David Bowie	Into the Groove, Madonna
Don't you Want me?, Human League	Dancing in the Street, David Bowie and Mick Jagger
Land of Make Believe, Buck's Fizz	Rock me Amadeus, Falco
House of Fun, Madness	Don't Leave me this Way, Communards
Fame, Irene Cara	Nothing's gonna Stop us Now, Starship
Come on Eileen, Dexy's Midnight Runners	La Bamba, Los Lobos
Eye of the Tiger, Survivor	Pump up the Volume, M/A/R/R/S
Pass the Dutchie, Musical Youth	

HIT RECORDS OF THE 1990s

Name..

Here are some of the most popular records of the nineties. Put a (✓) beside your 10 favourite records. If one of your top 10 is not there, add it at the end of the list.

Feel like Making Love, Pauline Henry
Echo Beach, Martha and the Muffins
Shimmer, Trans Global Underground
Justified and Ancient, KLF
What time is Love? KLF
About a girl, Nirvana
All that She Wants, Ace of Base
Phorever People, Shamen
Hope Street, The Levellers
No Limit, 2 Unlimited
Little Fluffy Clouds, The Orb
What's the Frequency, Kenneth?, REM
She Bangs the Drums, Stone Roses

The Universal, Blur
Movin' on Up, Primal Scream
Wonderwall, Oasis
It's oh so Quiet, Björk
Love Rendezvous, M People
Mile End, Pulp
Changingman, Paul Weller
Cigarettes and Alcohol, Oasis
Protection, Massive Attack
Stay Together, Suede
Life is Sweet, Chemical Brothers

And for our next question.............

RUBBINGS

Well, if you thought the only thing that could be rubbed was church brasses, you can think again! Virtually anything can be rubbed, from coins to manhole covers, signs to machine parts, bones and stones.

The basic technique will be familiar to most of us, who will at some time or another have done coin rubbings using paper and soft pencil, viz:

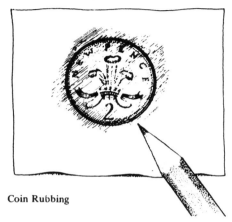

Coin Rubbing

It only takes a little 'brainstorming' and an imaginative attitude to materials to come up with interesting rubbings of a wide range of subjects. Try walls, pavements, metal plaques, decorative door handles and plates, wood, shells, fish, fencing, bark, tools, leaves, flowers, seed pots, etc..

Various kinds of paper and rubbing materials can be used. The general rule of thumb about paper is to use thin paper when a faint image is to be rubbed. Consider using different coloured papers, or newsprint and don't forget about Dayglow for mind-boggling effects! Rubbing materials like crayon, graphite stick, charcoal, tailor's chalk, Dayglow crayon and heel-ball, and Cirencester sticks (available from Specialist Crafts), especially made for brass rubbing, can be used to good effect. Half the fun is in experimenting to find the best combination of materials, e.g. white tailor's chalk on black paper.Special black and white brass rubbling paper is also manufactured to ensure the highest definition for rubbings that are important.

Project work can combine rubbings with other visual materials to form a collage. Or, young people can combine different elements together to form a 'picture' to be rubbed. The following list of materials and the rubbing method are for brass rubbings, but can easily be adapted for other purposes.

Materials

- Paper (white) – decorators lining paper is cheap and useful for practice purposes. It tears easily though, and yellows with age. Architect's detail paper is best for most purposes, bought by the roll. This is a 'rag' type paper. You'll need scissors for cutting the paper in lengths.
- Heel-ball/Cirencester sticks – these are the special wax sticks used for rubbing, made from bees-wax, tallow and lamp black.
- Brushes – two kinds. A fairly soft bristle or nylon brush for cleaning

the surface. A toothbrush to remove grit from the incised lines of the brass. Brushing the brass in this way, and freeing it of particles of grit, greatly reduces the chances of the paper tearing.

- Dusters – to remove final traces of grit after brushing.
- White cloths – one to be used before rubbing to press the paper into the incised lines of the brass – helps to get a sharper contrast between the black and white areas and gives you the **outline** of the figure – don't rub beyond that. The other cloth is used to wipe over the finished rubbing to give it a good polish.
- Masking tape – to secure the paper to the stone, wall or mounting. If the stone is in poor condition, the tape may not stick – weights can be used instead.

Method
1. Clean the brass and surrounding area thoroughly with brushes and duster to remove all traces of grit.
2. Unroll enough paper to cover the brass – cut the required length from the roll and fix it to the surrounding stone with masking tape.
3. With a clean cloth, press round the outline of the brass, and into the incised lines – this helps give a good impression and prevents you rubbing over the edge of the outline.
4. Begin your rubbing, using a blunt piece of heel-ball. It doesn't really matter where you start rubbing – it is usual to do it from the bottom up. Use firm strokes of even pressure to obtain even contrast. If your heel-ball and paper are good quality, you shouldn't have to rub too hard. When the rubbing is finished, rub it over with the second cloth to give it a good polish.

Storage
Rubbings can be sprayed with a clear plastic fixative to prevent damage. Large rubbings must be rolled (unless mounted) to store. All rubbings are affected by moisture – crayon and heel-ball can be damaged by high temperatures. If desired, rubbings can be mounted onto board for display purposes.

Although brass rubbing is rather specialised, ordinary everyday objects can be rubbed without using highly specialised materials. The technique provides a good introduction to understanding the basic print process and can be used in combination with drawing and painting to produce unusual collages.

SCRAPERBOARD
High contrast drawings and illustrations can be produced quite simply using cutting tools on scraperboard. The techniques can take a little bit of practice to learn, so it is usually best introduced to young people who can already draw reasonably successfully with a pen/pencil, AND can be trusted to work safely with the relatively sharp cutting tools!

Usually scraperboard comes in sheets of white card onto which two surfaces have been added. Underneath is a white chalk base, over which is added a thinner film of dense black ink. There are also white, silver and copper versions available, which, when cut into expose the different colours underneath. Some youngsters can also enjoy experimenting with coloured inks or coloured permanent markers. Used on top of white areas, the colours can enhance the starkness of the black and white image, but remember that this will prevent the image being photocopied, if that is the intention.

To create a scraperboard picture, cutting tools are used to lightly scrape/cut the surface thereby removing lines and small portions of the black surface. The contrasting images exposed are very striking. The cutting instruments are like old fashioned pen nibs and holders. Most manufacturers make four different nib types, which offer different thicknesses and styles of cut. Even simple results can be very powerful, providing a range of images and textures, and it is a useful medium for posters, greetings cards and book illustrations.

Scraperboard images can be designed freehand, as with Alan's little cartoon of Howie, or a tracing can be used. Chalk is spread on the reverse of a sheet of tracing paper and when a pencil is used on the top surface, the chalk lines are transferred to the scraperboard, ready for cutting.

The subjects you suggest for youthful artists will make the scraperboard work easier or harder. Copying simple designs and decorations, drawing flowers, animals, simple scenes, Christmas images – all are possible to achieve without too much practice. Usually it is quite difficult to correct mistakes once they've been made, but as long as it isn't necessary to re-cut any area, a fine line, black felt marker can be used to cover up unwanted white lines.

This is not a technique for young groups, but scraperboard is a useful medium with adolescent groups. The tools are cheap to buy; the scraperboard is a bit expensive, but relatively small pieces can be cut out for each artist.

Two final tips:
1.	Attach pieces of scraperboard to a firm surface using masking tape. This ensures that it doesn't move while the drawing is being completed.
2.	Scraperboard marks very easily and sweaty fingers leave greasy marks. So, when a piece is being worked on, place a sheet of paper under the hand to protect the artwork.

SCREEN PRINTING

This technique has more to do with inks and inspiration than with Bogart, Stone, Willis and other big screen stars! The screen referred to is a fine piece of cotton organdie (transparent muslin) which is stretched down tight over a wooden frame. By fixing a stencil to the underside of the screen, ink can be squeezed through the top of the screen to form an image on paper or fabric according to the design of the stencil.

This method of printing is a versatile one and can be used for posters, cards, T-shirts, carrier bags and signs. There is great potential, therefore, for club or group designs and motifs. In fact, groups who become proficient often find that they can earn some spare cash by printing small poster runs to order e.g. for Community Centres, local groups, discos, etc.. It is also possible to make Christmas or New Year cards with the same equipment that you use to make posters or T-shirts. Screen printing can be used to make very effective designs on fabric (e.g. for curtains or a wall hanging). This is done by repeatedly screening a design (or designs) on to the fabric until you achieve the desired effect.

This section will deal with making a basic screen and stencil and the printing process. For more detail on the extremely wide range of potential materials available, we suggest that you refer to the Specialist Crafts and NES Arnold catalogues.

The Screen

You can buy screens in various sizes (or adjustable ones) relatively cheaply, but they are quite easy to make if you want to save money. Use ordinary planed softwood (2 inch x 1 inch) to make a frame 17 inches x 15 inches – this will be suitable for most purposes. The corners must be square and can simply be butt-jointed and reinforced with metal fasteners or flat angle brackets. Make sure that the frame lies perfectly flat. It must now be treated with two coats of polyurethane varnish to prevent it twisting and warping when it is being cleaned.

The next step is to fix the fabric tightly over the frame. Cotton organdie is best, but you can also use terylene voile, polyester mono or multi filament fabric, or very high quality nylon gauze. Cut the fabric with a big enough overlap to turn it over the edges of the frame. Now staple (with a staple gun) or pin it tightly, once, in the middle of each side. Carry on stretching and stapling the fabric working from the centre out and stapling opposite sides at the same rate (if you do one side at a time the fabric will be too slack). When you get to the corners bunch the fabric up and pull it very tightly before stapling. Now make an ink reservoir by masking the edges of the fabric on both sides of the screen to a depth of 2 inches minimum, with a waterproof cloth tape or masking tape. (If you are only doing a short run, simple gummed paper tape will suffice, but cloth tape is advisable for long runs). This is done to provide space for the ink. The unmasked area formed is your maximum print area for this size of screen (15 inches x 13 inches approximately). Congratulations! – you now have a completed screen. With most materials you will need to degrease the surface using a special paste of crystals. Pre-prepared screens are usually already degreased.

A 'squeegee' is used to draw the ink across the stencil. This is simply a long rubber blade with a wooden handle. The squeegee can be exactly the same width as the print area of the screen (in this case 13 inches approximately) or smaller, in which case you will have to make two sweeps with it to fully cover the print area. They can be purchased in a variety of sizes.

Apart from ink and a stencil, this is all you need to do simple prints on paper, card or fabric.

Suitable inks are, for paper and card: Hunt Acrylic, Coates Ecoject, Specialist Colours or NES Arnold own make. For fabric: Sericol Texiscreen, Rowney's Fabric Dyes or Hunt's Textile ink. We are grateful to Specialist Crafts (DRYAD) for permission to reproduce their charts on screen meshes and inks – these are shown at the end of the section and offer options in greater detail.

Tursub can be used for thinning paper inks, Universal Screenwash for cleaning screens and squeegees, and Actisol to free clogged screens or after a break in printing. Ink Retarder can also be used to prevent clogging.

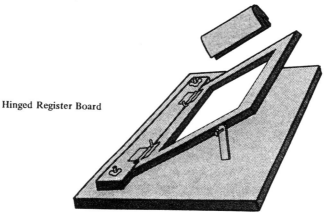

Hinged Register Board

If you intend doing two-colour prints (easy enough to do) you should prepare a hinged register board for your screen (see diagram). The hinged screen arrangement is very useful and is recommended as it keeps the screen supported in the 'up' position between prints.

The Stencil

A simple stencil can be made from paper. You can cut out letters to make a name or slogan, or cut out a design. When printed, this will give you a negative image, as the ink will pass through all areas of the screen **except** your design or slogan – this will therefore appear as white (or whatever the colour the paper is that you are printing on). A positive image can be achieved by cutting out letters or a design from a large (screen-sized) piece of paper. In this case, ink will only pass through your lettering or design, leaving the rest of the print area blank.

Paper stencils must be made from newsprint or a similar lightweight paper. They are very fragile as stencils go, and will only last for a dozen or so prints. However, they have two major advantages over all other types of stencils – they are very easy to make (and cheap!), and they do not clog up the screen (e.g. as Profilm does). This means that you can use the same screen up to about 10 times with different paper stencils, as long as the screen is carefully cleaned after each print run.

A paper stencil is fixed to the screen with ink. First lay out a couple of old newspapers as padding with a piece of paper on top. Now arrange your stencil on the piece of paper in exactly the position you want it to print. Carefully place the screen centrally on top of the stencil and paper, and have someone hold it steady. Now ladle some ink into the top reservoir (it should be the consistency of thick cream) and distribute it evenly with the squeegee. Holding the squeegee at an angle of 45-60 degrees, place it behind the ink and pull the ink down across the screen with a smooth, steady motion. If you are using a small squeegee do this twice or until the whole screen area has been covered with ink. Now repeat. Carefully lift the screen up and you will find that the stencil has stuck to it. You are now ready to make your first print.

Another method of making stencils suitable for short runs is to use French chalk or talcum powder. This should be sieved evenly onto a dark piece of paper. It can now be drawn on with fingers, needles, feathers etc. to create a pattern or lettering. Carefully lower the screen onto the chalk, ink it and squeegee (as above). Now carefully lift up the screen and you will find that the chalk has stuck to it to form a stencil. About 15 prints can be made with this method.

A longer lasting, traditional method of making a stencil is to paint out the areas through which you do not want ink to pass with Shellac varnish (you can also use stencil medium, glue or lacquer) on the underside of the screen.

If you draw your design or lettering with Shellac, a negative image will be produced when it is printed. However, you can make a positive image by painting your design or lettering onto the screen with wax or ink and then painting the whole screen with Shellac or filler. The Shellac will block all of the screen, except the image drawn in the oily ink or wax. When the Shellac or filler is dry, the ink or wax can be removed with white spirit. A positive image can now be printed.

Detailed stencils can be cut from Profilm or Stenplex. This is a layer of Shellac mounted on transparent backing paper. The design should be cut through the Shellac layer, but not the backing paper (this may take a bit of practice), and the parts to be printed removed. The stencil should now be placed, glossy side down, onto the underside of the frame and ironed through the paper at a low heat. This will fuse the stencil to the screen, and the backing paper can then be peeled off. Although it is possible to remove this kind of stencil from the screen after use with white sprit, it is a long and tedious process, likely to dispirit the keenest youngster (not to mention youth leader!) There is also the probability that the Shellac will not be completely removed, and that the next print run will suffer. On balance it is probably best to discard the screen material along with the stencil and to make up a new screen.

Photo-Stencils

High quality results can be achieved from a variety of image sources (including photographic negatives) using this method. It involves making a stencil by shining UV (ultra violet) light through the artwork onto Polycron, which is a light sensitive stencil film. The process is quite simple but you will have to get hold of a couple of UV lights and mount them in a frame above a baseboard. The positive from which the stencil is cut can be hand made by arranging anything opaque (e.g. black paper, doylies, gaskets, cut out shapes etc.) on a sheet of clear acetate. This can also be drawn on with opaque paint, ink, Letraset or Rotring pen. Super prep green film, red Sellotape can also be used to mask out large areas. Photographic effects can be obtained by using an enlarger loaded with a negative to make a positive on special photographic film; this is then used with UV light to cut the stencil onto the Polycron. You may find a print workshop locally which will provide this service.

The process is as follows:

1.   Switch on UV lights to heat up.
2.   Place Polycron shiny side up.

3. Lay artwork face down on top of Polycron and cover with a sheet of glass to hold the acetate firmly in contact with the stencil.
4. Expose for ten minutes.
5. Switch off lights.
6. Put Polycron shiny side down in a tray of hydrogen peroxide and water (1:4 solution) for one-and-a-half minutes.
7. Remove from tray and leave for one minute.
8. Wash with hot water.
9. Put stencil face down onto screen and leave to adhere.
10. Peel off plastic backing.
11. Tape the remainder of the screen (with paper or cloth covered tape depending on the length of the print run).

The key advantage of photo stencils is that you can produce a large number of prints from a stencil. A number of other photo stencil methods are available, which use, for instance, fluorescent or mercury lights. Your choice of a particular system will depend on the material you intend printing on, and the number of prints your require from each stencil. The cost of these systems varies and we recommend that you contact a specialist supplier such as Specialist Crafts to discuss your specific needs.

An alternative method is achieved by using the Hunt Speedball Easylight stencil emulsion, which is sensitive to an ordinary 150 or preferably 250 watt light bulb. Trial size quantities and full 'group' size bottles are available. Basically the technique involves mixing the emulsion with a sensitizer and then applying a positive stencil onto the squeegee side of the frame. The surface is exposed for between 10 and 15 minutes and this will produce a quality print screen. The sensitizer is a strong chemical and must be handled carefully. This process will produce around 50 prints from a single stencil.

Printing

The printing process itself can be quite messy, especially if oil-based inks are used, as they can only be cleaned with a spirit cleaner (water-based inks can easily be cleaned with water). So... have plenty of rags handy for cleaning. The provision of disposable rubber gloves, aprons and sleeve guards is highly recommended – not only does it make everyone look weird, but it obviates the need to spend half the session cleaning yourself up. You'll need a large table for printing on, and a big basin or sink with plenty of hot water on tap. You'll also need a line with bulldog clips (or clothes pegs) to hang prints up to dry.

It will be clear from the above that the printing process needs to be closely supervised and should be limited to two or three people at a time (unless you have more than one screen). However, others can be involved in designing and preparing stencils, or drying prints (with hair-drier or fan heater).

Place the piece of paper to be printed on the table and centre the screen and stencil on top. Now ladle some ink into the reservoir at the top of the screen (it should be the consistency of thick cream) and distribute it evenly across the top of the screen with the squeegee. With someone holding the screen to steady it, place the squeegee behind the ink and pull it firmly across the screen once or twice. With any luck you should now have an immaculate screen print. Remember to draw the spare ink back across the screen to the reservoir after each pull. The squeegee should always be pulled at an angle of 45-60 degrees and should be sharpened every now and again with fine sandpaper to achieve crisp prints.

Check the quality of the print and work out how many pulls are necessary for the best quality (most prints can be made with one or two pulls, although fabric may need more). When printing T-shirts or fabric always do a test print on a piece of paper. Insert a piece of card between the front and back of the shirt to prevent ink passing through, and pad underneath with newspaper for good contact with the screen. For fabric inks, follow the manufacturer's instructions – most have to be ironed for a few minutes with a hot iron through a thin cloth. Lettering stencils can be used to quickly produce printed slogans.

A separate stencil is needed for each colour if you intend doing multi-colour prints, and a hinged register board is essential for correct positioning. The process involves making prints in the first colour; allowing them to dry; cleaning the screen; changing the stencil and then overprinting with the second colour and so on. This is a time-consuming process, and it makes sense to attempt to get by with the minimum number of stencils. You can also use coloured paper. For example, with two stencils this could give a three-colour print. The register board is used by positioning the first piece of paper to be printed centrally on the board and marking the position with a piece of masking tape along each edge. Subsequent prints can therefore be easily positioned using the register marks.

Tiles

It is possible to print your own designs onto plain tiles using the screen printing method. Obviously a smaller screen is necessary for this, but otherwise the process is identical to that described above. 'End-runs' of tiles can often be obtained from manufacturers at little or no cost.

Screen printing is a relatively inexpensive craft, the major cost being that of the Polycron sheeting if you choose to use photostencils. For good results, a reasonable amount of care has to be taken at most stages in the process and it is therefore difficult to 'do' a screenprint quickly. The best way of tackling it if you have limited time (or young people with a limited concentration span) is to prepare stencils in one session, and spend the next session printing them. However, we have found that most youth groups can produce good quality results quite quickly. Happy printing – squeegees rule OK!

Screen Printing Meshes

Type of Mesh	N221 Organdie 100 TPI	P725 Nylon Screen Mesh 100 TPI	P238 Multi-filament Polyester 80 TPI	P073 Mono-filament Polyester 122 TPI	P072 Mono-filament Polyester 196 TPI
Screen Preparation	Use degreasing crystals (P075A).	Initial preparation with No. 23 degrease abrade paste (P066). Thereafter degrease crystals (P057A).	Use degrease crystals (P057A).	Initial preparation with No. 23 degrease abrade paste (P066). Thereafter degrease crystals (P057A).	Initial preparation with No. 23 degrease abrade paste (P066). Thereafter degrease crystals (P057A).
Stencil Use	Any – Profilm, direct emulsions, indirect film.	Any – Profilm, direct emulsions, indirect film.	Most – direct emulsions, indirect film. Not for use with Profilm.	Most – direct emulsions, indirect film. Not for use with Profilm.	Most – direct emulsions, indirect film. Not for use with Profilm.
Ink Usage	Reeves screen printing water colour, Coates watercolour, Hunts textile inks.	Any inks.	Any inks.	Any inks.	Any inks.
Results	Best results on fabrics. Not for fine detailed work.	Will produce basic prints on fabric. paper and card.	Will produce detailed work on fabric. Also suitable for paper & board.	Will produce fine detailed work on fabric, paper & card.	Produces extra fine detailed work. Excellent for multicolour graphs, printing on paper, card, board and fabrics.
Screen cleaning	Ink – universal screenwash (P053). Stencil – dependant on stencil used.	Ink – universal screenwash (P053). Stencil – dependant on stencil used.	Ink – universal screenwash (P053). Stencil – dependant on stencil used.	Ink – universal screenwash (P053). Stencil – dependant on stencil used.	Ink – universal screenwash (P053). Stencil – dependant on stencil used.

Screen Printing Inks

This chart contains information and suggested usage procedures for a range of inks.

Inks	Specialist Colours Screen Printing Water Colour	Printex Fabric Colour	Pearlised Screen Colour	Specialist Colours Water-Based Inks	Hunt Textile Ink	Hunt Acrylic Screen Printing Ink	Water-Based Paper & Board Ink	Coates Ecoject Spirit Based Inks
Materials used on	Paper & board Fabrics (limited fixability)	Most fabrics	Paper & board Fabrics (limited fixability)	Fabrics (cotton, polyester, poly/cotton, acrylic, felt etc.)	All fabrics	Paper, board, wood, plastic, metal (limited fabrics)	Paper & board, some grades of PVC	Paper & board
Kind of Stencil	Paper or card	Paper, card and most water resistant stencils	Paper & card	Paper, card and all water resistant films & emulsions	Water resistant films & emulsions	Water resistant films & emulsions	Use with water resistant films & emulsions P550, P987, P963	Spirit resistant film & emulsions
Mesh Type	All types	All types	All types	All types	All types	All types. Best with multi-filament & mono-filament polyester	All types and grades. For best results mono-filament polyester	All types Best with mono-filament polyester
Thin with	Water	Water	Water	Water or water based retarder P056	Retarder P962	Water or retarder P962	Water & retarder P995	Spirit thinner (P051B) & spirit retarder (P052)
Clean with	Soap & water	Soap & water	Soap & water	Soap & water or universal screen wash (P053)	Soap & water	Soap & water or universal screen wash (P053)	Spray with activator (P996) then rinse with water	Spirit thinner (P051B) and universal screen wash (P053)
Washing instructions	Not washable or dry cleanable	Washable and dry cleanable	Not washable or dry cleanable	Washable and dry cleanable	Washable and dry cleanable	Not washable or dry cleanable	Not washable or dry cleanable	Not washable or dry cleanable
Drying Instructions	Air dry within 12 hours	Air dry within 4 hours	Approximately 30 minutes	Cure dry 5 mins 140°C oven. Air dry 2 hours	Air dry within 4 hours	Air dry 20 mins. Heat dry 5 mins 275°F	Air dry 20-30 mins. Heat dry at 50°C for 15 seconds	Air dry 15 mins. 20 seconds using hot blower (hair-drier)
Indoor/ Outdoor Use	Indoor only	Both	Indoor only	Both	Both	Both	Indoor, limited outdoor	Indoor, limited outdoor
Colours in Range	10 colours	8 colours & binder	6 colours	22 colours & base (inc. fluorescents & process colours)	12 colours and base	14 colours and base	11 colours and base	12 colours and base

We gratefully acknowledge permission from Specialist Crafts (Dryad) to reproduce the two charts on screen meshes and inks.

STAINED GLASS

Traditional methods of making stained glass panels are beyond the scope of this book (though not beyond the scope of the determined youth group we suspect!) Here, we offer short-cut options for achieving the distinctive effect of stained glass using very simple materials, which are easy for young people to use.

The method, called cloisonné, involves using a pewter-coloured stained glass relief divider (which comes in handy tubes) together with stained glass paints to create the pattern of your choice on a piece of glass. There are a number of manufacturers including Cern Coleurs, Marabu and Specialist Crafts. It is also possible to add self adhesive lead strip to glass, which can be flattened using a roller. This creates very authentic looking lattice type windows and is ideal for work on terrariums.

To create stained glass type effects you will need:

- Tubes of stained glass relief divider.
- Solvent based glass paint plus stained glass varnish, or colourless medium to lighten and increase the transparency of the colours (colours may be mixed and diluted with alcohol or white spirit) OR water-based stained glass paint plus neutral cutting fluid to lighten the colours (dilute with water). Makes include Vitrail, Marabu-Decorglass and Specialist Crafts glass paints and cold enamels.
- Paint brushes.
- Tracing paper and pencils.
- Pieces of glass from your craft supplier, or other surfaces like glasses, jugs, bottles, acrylics, PVC sheets, plastic or metal foil.
- Methylated spirit to clean the glass.

Method
1. Either create, or trace a suitable pattern (e.g. from a stained glass pattern book) onto paper.
2. Clean your piece of glass with meths and place it over the pattern.
3. Trace out the pattern on the glass with the squeezed out relief divider. You should really leave it for a couple of hours before applying the paint, but if you work carefully, we haven't really found this necessary.
4. Now apply the paint by 'flowing' it with a brush inside the cloisonnés. The edges of the paint will round off by themselves. The thicker the coat, the denser the colour you'll get. For pastel shades, lighten the paint with neutral cutting fluid or varnish, as appropriate.
5. Allow to dry.
6. Some paints require a further coat of hardener.

Both small scale and large scale glass panels can be tackled using this method, and used to good decorative effect in school, youth club or home.

STONE PAINTING
We're sure that you've seen these rather quaint painted stones, which both young and old seem to enjoy turning into odd animals, birds and the like. Once painted, the finished objet d'art can be used as a paperweight, doorstop, ornament, but preferably not Lethal Weapon 5! Painted stone throwing is not to be encouraged!

With younger groups it is a good idea to use water-based paints – they are easier to remove from hair, hands and clothes. Older young people can experiment with a variety of paint mediums such as:
> oil paints; gauche, acrylics, enamels, nail varnishes and Posca pens, which are instant paint pens. Permanent felt pens can also be used effectively.

In preparation for a stone painting session, you need to co-ordinate a stone-collecting session. If you have a nearby beach, this can be turned into a fun activity in itself, or the search can be combined with a beach expedition. Before painting, it is useful to wash the stones in tap water and then thoroughly dry them. To enable drawing rough shapes onto the stones it is easier to use light coloured stones. It is easiest if only the top half is painted. The adult facilitator should encourage everyone to draw out the basic pattern on the stone before beginning painting.

For instance:

pencil lines

It can be useful to suggest some ideas for subjects in a stone painting session.
Invite the young people to try to turn a stone into a:

- cat
- dog
- rabbit
- clown

- butterfly
- frog
- hedgehog

The organiser should tell all the participants to keep their designs simple. As with any art project it is well worth encouraging individual expression. Stone painting has often been used successfully in art therapy sessions and because it lends itself to imaginative interpretation, it works particularly well with young groups and with people who may in other circumstances exhibit learning difficulties. Many of the most colourful and unusual painted stones are often produced by people who would normally not be viewed as 'artistic'.

When the stones are finished, it is well worth varnishing them with polyurethane yacht varnish or similar. Do not allow stone painters to stir the varnish too thoroughly, as this causes bubbles to form which may ruin the finished stone. Rather obviously, brushes will need to be cleaned well, after being use. Use white spirit for varnish or oil based paints, and running water to remove water-based paint from brushes.

If stones are to be placed on wooden tables or scratchable surfaces, it is a good idea to get some pieces of felt, which, once cut to size, can be stuck with PVA glue or similar to underside of the stone.

In all, you will or may need:

- at least one stone for each group member
- paints
- paint and varnish brushes
- pencils
- coloured paint pens
- varnish

- scissors
- glue
- felt
- paper towels/newspaper
- white spirit.

STORYTELLING

It is only a few hundred years since storytelling was the main mechanism for relaying news and current affairs information from community to community. It also acts as a transmitter of culture and tradition down the generations.

Nowadays, culture and information is likely to be recorded on newsprint, books, audio and video tape – and increasingly on CD Rom and computer disks. In many ways this can be seen as an advantage as a permanent record exists, but it can be argued that these media are essentially 'dead' or 'wooden'. For example, there is usually no comparison between a recorded musical work and a live version. Similarly, a book or poem comes to life if it is read out loud by the author or a skilled reader.

Although we are not suggesting a return to the days of oral information sharing and tradition, there is much to be said for the atmosphere and 'engagement' which is created by a skilled storyteller. We should recognise that people (and young people especially) love a good story and try to find ways in which we can re-create this lost art.

At a very basic level, groups of young people can be entertained through the reading of short stories. While this will not suit all groups there will be times, e.g. Halloween when most group will be open to a topical story. Of course, it is essential that the person reading the story has an expressive style – otherwise the story will not 'live' and individuals will rapidly become inattentive and bored.

We recommend that you look at the 'New Youth Games Book' as there are a few techniques in the relationship games sections which can be used to assist a group of young people to create their own stories. A simple technique which works well is for each person in the group to contribute a few sentences to a story as it goes round the group. Although this may sound banal in the extreme, it usually proves to be popular and quite often someone will come out with a punch line or contribution which is side-splittingly funny. It is also worth encouraging young people to work in small groups to create their own stories or 'yarns' – this provides pee support both in the creation and telling of the stories.

Children and young people *are* essentially creative, and if adults encourage this, some amazing results can be had. If an adult is prepared to make up and tell a story, then a challenge can be offered to one or two young people to create their own one for next week's session . Often, the results can be surprisingly good.

Finally, we leave you with **another technique** and a reminder of one of our games which ca be used to good effect in honing storytelling skills.

Put a number of objects in a box – at least one for each person who is participating. These objects can be anything at all – household items, holiday mementoes, bits 'n' bobs etc..

Invite each person to choose an object and then ask everyone to wander around the room thinking about something to transform their object into. For example, if you've picked up a book you might decide to transform it into a pot of gold. Encourage people to attach a little history to their transformed object – so the pot of gold could have been created by Merlin the magician just before he died in the Scottish Borders.

Now tell the group to stop and swap their object with the person nearest to them – along with its complete history. Continue in this fashion for another two or three swaps and then invite the group to sit in a circle and tell the stories attached to each of the objects they now have. This is a painless way of encouraging people to be inventive and demonstrates how stories can be built-up bit by bit. The technique also shows that no matter how strange or ludicrous, a story always has some information or entertainment value.

The **Telephone Game** can be quite a challenge but you'll find that if you have an extrovert or chatterbox in your group, they will usually jump at the chance of giving it a try. First of all you need to come up with a few punch lines. These could be something like: "I told you the guy next door was a policeman", or , "And there is absolutely no way I am going to do that", or , "I am a born extrovert".

A volunteer is needed who selects one of the punch lines (which have been written on cards) and sits in the middle of the group. The volunteer is challenged to invent a telephone conversation with an imaginary person and must finish the conversation with the selected punch line. It's important that you don't push young people into trying this technique, as it can be very difficult for some. When run on this kind of voluntary basis, you'll find that the natural actors and storytellers will come to the fore and that the results can be absolutely hilarious.

TIE-DYE AND FABRIC PAINTING

This method of producing fabric designs was thought of long before the Hippies 're-invented' it in the 1960s. As far back as the 6th century AD, tie-dyed silks and cottons were popular in India, China and Japan. The basic technique is very simple, ideal for work in youth groups, and involves knotting, folding or pleating the material before tying it tightly with thread or string and dyeing it. Obviously, as the dye cannot enter the tied-up areas, a pattern is produced. To a certain extent, the way the fabric is tied will determine the pattern, but there is always an element of uncertainty which adds to this craft's appeal.

Good results can be obtained very quickly with a minimum of effort which makes tie-dyeing suitable for work with most groups of young people. The equipment needed is neither complicated nor expensive and is easily obtained. You'll need a large metal tub or pot to use as a 'dye-bath' – plastic will do if you are using cold water dyes only. Apart from this, you'll need the dyes, something to stir with, rubber gloves (unless multi-coloured hands take your kids' fancy!) some string and the fabric to be dyed.

Tie-dye can be used to pattern any kind of material, including clothes. Think about tie-dyeing T-shirts, skirts, shirts, scarves, sheets, curtains etc.. Natural fabrics like linen and cotton should be dyed with colourfast cold water dyes, while synthetic fabrics are best treated with hot water dyes (not as colourfast as cold water types).
Dylon provide one of the largest ranges of different dyes currently available. NES Arnold sell Handcraft Craft Dyes, which are water based and fixed with a special F15/6 fixer. Specialist Crafts stock a new product, which is **tie-dye string**. Available in nine colours, these cut out the usual more complicated process. To use requires only about half a dozen of the strings to be tied to a T-shirt, or whatever, then the garment is boiled for 30 minutes. Adding salt fixes the colours permanently.

The usual tie and dye method
This involves thoroughly wetting the fabric before dyeing to produce the best contrast in the pattern. Although a good pattern can be produced with just one dye, it is possible to use several different colours to create intricate designs; remember though, that where two dye colours mix, a third colour will be produced! The fabric can be subjected to second and subsequent dyes either before or after the ties have been removed – or the original ties can be left intact and extra ones added. Retaining the ties intact means that some of the material will remain undyed in its original colour.

Fabric can be tied in several different ways to create markedly different patterns - a graded pattern can be made by tying the fabric in thick bunches as this affects the penetration of the dye. Try the suggestions given in the following diagram which can produce some interesting and attractive designs:

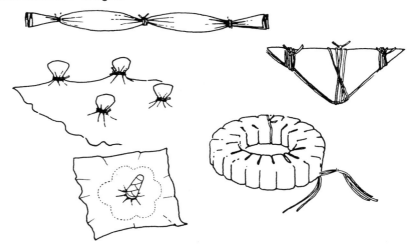

Stripes: Pleat lengthways for vertical stripes, diagonally for diagonal ones, and horizontally for horizontal stripes. The folds can be ironed to make them crisp, and should be tied at regular intervals. If more than one dye is being used, the ties can be positioned for good effect - add the new ties first before removing the old ones, so that the pleating is undisturbed.

Triangles: Pleat the fabric lengthways into four then fold it back on itself into a series of triangles, concertina-style. Bind the ends and the centre with string.

Circles: Dried beans, marbles or stones can be tied into the fabric to create a pattern of small circles. If more than one dye is to be used, the beans should be tied in different places when the process is repeated.

Sunbursts: These bigger circles can be varied depending on the number and position of the string bindings. Arrange the fabric to form a peak and bind it at various distances from the peak to produce concentric circles.

Ruching: Lay out the fabric with a length of double string across one corner. Roll the fabric diagonally around the string before forming it into a circle, ruching it tightly along the string and tying the ends.

Stitching: This can be used for initials, names and motifs. The design should first of all be pencilled onto the fabric, either freehand or with the aid of stencils. Strong thread (knotted at the end) can then be sewn over the outlines with small tacking stitches. The fabric should then be ruched tightly along the stitches and secured with a knot.

Finally, for the best results, remember to follow the dye manufacturer's instructions about fabric preparation, washing and rinsing.

Fabric Painting

A whole host of new dyes and pens for working on silk and cotton have been developed. We have experimented with Marabu-Silk, which can be applied with a brush, or washed in using the tie and tie method. Deka Silk, Elbéfix and Elbesoie are other similar product ranges. Some require fixing with a hot iron, others require steam fixing.

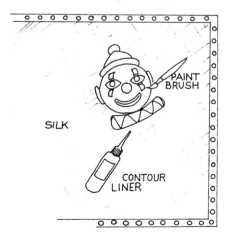

To use the Marabu-Silk method utilising a brush, the silk is stretched and tacked on to a frame. Then the contour lines for a design are painted in from a jar or squeezed from a tube with a fine nozzle. This provides frame-lines, rather like the leading on stained glass work. The contour lines can dry colourless or to a colour such as black, white, gold or silver. Then the silk dye is applied, being careful not to go over the lines. Once the dye is dry, the paintwork can be permanently fixed to the silk by applying an iron to the underside of the fabric for two minutes, with the iron on the cotton setting.

The same company manufactures some rather wonderful fabric paints called Marabu-Textil. These can be applied to virtually any smooth fabric using methods such as:
● print blocks ● stencils ● airbrush ● screen printing.
Once the paints are dry they can be made coloufast up to 40° C using an iron. They are pretty easy to use and the Marabu leaflets give precise details on paint dilutions.

Also available are a wide range of fabric paint pens and paints which can be applied with a brush. Some are specifically designed for working on silk, others will work on virtually any fabric. Galt offer fabric fun pens, metallic and glitter paints and Multicrom, which is available in a variety of colours and works on almost any surface. Javana silk paint pens and marbling inks are available from NES Arnold. Specialist Crafts can supply textile markers which are permanent and do not require ironing to fix.

VIDEO FILM MAKING

This is your chance to hit the big-time – to propel your youth group into the mysterious world of Video, Digital Cameras, the Jump Cut and the Big Close Up! Making a film can be a very rewarding activity for groups of young people, as the medium itself – film or video – has a definite glamour associated with it that creates interest and excitement and helps boost the self-image of those taking part. It is also a co-operative activity which encourages teamwork and clear communication.

Film or video can be used as a very powerful tool in work with kids. If you are trying for example, to make initial contact with young people in a particular neighbourhood, you could do worse than simply set up your equipment in an accessible location. You'll find that 'streetwise' kids will rapidly latch on to you (and to your equipment!). This kind of informal introduction to making videos can lead young people to use the equipment to explore and investigate issues that are of concern and interest to them (don't ask us what they are – ask the kids!). The medium can be particularly potent when used to represent young people's views to adults and can act as a lever in, for example, promoting the need for specific youth facilities.

The instant replay capacity of video creates the potential for a different kind of film making which has increasingly been used by youth groups. 'Social Skills' work can range from simply reflecting on how individuals and groups are perceived by the objective television eye in real life situations, to more sophisticated role play exercises which may be designed to encourage good interview skills, personal presentation, clear communication etc..

Choice of format

The choice of formats has changed dramatically since the first edition of this book when 'Super 8' was a moderately priced option for the aspiring *film* maker. Video systems have continued to reduce in price and size while becoming increasingly sophisticated. Compact cartridge formats and batteries have become the norm, making some new systems virtually pocket size. Traditional celluloid film making has become an expensive professional option – with the advent of cheap video mixing desks, video systems now reign supreme.

The newest technology to impact on 'home' movie making is the digital imaging capacity of modern computers and software. This enables images from a digital camera – still or video – to be 'downloaded' directly into a computer without the use of film or videotape. The stored image can be replayed on the computer screen or incorporated in 'multimedia' documents. Images can be cleaned up, enhanced, edited, distorted or otherwise manipulated.

Needless to say, this is immensely powerful technology which is impacting on all areas of visual communication – television companies have been using ENG (Electronic News Gathering) cameras for some years. In early 1996 a black and white digital video camera was available for little over £100. The 'QuickCam' records at 15 frames per second and gives a 160 X 120 pixel image. It produces quality black and white images and has a built in microphone.

The main drawback of digital video cameras is the small image produced on screen – it takes an awful lot of computer processing power to make moving images! Many state of the art multimedia computers can already support full screen 'real time' video images – in a couple of years, entry level computers will undoubtedly be capable of similar performance.

When buying your Camcorder the current choice is between VHS and 8mm *video*. In terms of quality there is not much to choose from, but the 8mm machines are typically more compact, as the tape size is much smaller.

With the VHS system you can buy a standard domestic sized video cartridge adapter – you simply slot your small VHS tape cartridge into this and you can then playback on any domestic VHS player. The 8mm system is different as the tape size is not compatible with domestic players.

However, the wonders of modern technology come to our rescue once more and you can in fact connect the 8mm Camcorder directly to the television or video player and playback from the 8mm machine itself. If you want a permanent domestic version of your 8mm tape you simply record from the 8 mm machine directly to a VHS tape in your domestic recorder. Thereafter you can play the VHS tape without linking up the 8mm machine.

If you have access to the funds, we recommend that you buy a video mixing desk because of the editing capability this gives you. These are available at High Street shops for between £50 and £100. The more expensive ones offer additional facilities such as titling, date recording etc..

A complete **portable video system** comprises:

- Camcorder (camera and recorder in one)
- Microphone
- Power pack and rechargeable batteries
- Tripod
- Blank video tapes/cassettes
- 'Monitor' or television
- Video light(s)

The instant replay facility of video systems makes it the ideal medium for training and social skills work.

The notes that follow are suitable for both video and film making. Although purists will cringe, we use the term *film* as a generic one encompassing the use of videotape and digital cameras.

The Type of Film to be made

It is important that the young people are involved in choosing the kind of film they want to make, and have an investment in. With luck and practice they will be creating a unique work of art! Most groups will want to make 'horror movies,' 'gangster films' or a documentary about 'our neighbourhood,' and should be encouraged to overcome some of the consequent difficulties (like learning to make someone up like Frankenstein, or getting hold of a suitable representation of a Capone-type sub-machine gun).

There are other kinds of film which you can choose to make, each requiring a different blend of production, camera, wardrobe, make-up and scripting skills. A necessary first step is to break down the chosen film type into skill areas, and to allocate roles and resources as appropriate.

The following list of film types should give you some ideas:

1. **News Film:** This is a record of events which is recorded factually using a news-programme style. It uses a 'presenter' or news reader and may incoroporate film shot on location and added into the newsroom footage. Obviously, the interest value of this type of film depends totally on what you choose to include. As long as you have interesting, exciting, or funny events to 'shoot,' then the film will be successful. This is one of the easiest

kinds of film to make – you don't need special effects, wardrobes or sophisticated camera work. Just ideas, an interviewer and a camera crew!

2.   **Documentary:** The difference between documentary and news film lies in the interpretation of events; statements are being made about the events which reflect the feelings and attitude of people making the film. It requires more planning and editing to present a coherent, balanced, or polemical point of view.

3.   **Concept:** The aim here is to convey some king of concept, mood or impression. For example, you choose a pop song or poem and film images to go along with it of a complementary or contrasting nature. You can easily work out how to convey a particular mood by carefully selecting subject matter, lighting and the 'pace' of the images you use.

4.   **Instructional:** This kind of film either conveys information, or shows you how to make or do something. The essence of the information type of film is in selecting the most important aspects or facts that you want to get across. The 'How-to-do-it' type of film needs very careful preparation in that skills and techniques needed (e.g. how to make a go-kart) must be broken down and arranged in a logical step by step progression, ready for filming.

5.   **Fiction:** This is your actual storytelling type of stuff! Essential to this kind of undertaking is the ability to devise a plot, establish a setting and develop character through the medium of film. There are several categories of fictional film, like drama, comedy, fantasy, satire and tragedy; and each of these can be set within different genres, e.g. mystery, romance, western or science fiction. Obviously, careful preparation is a key element in making a fictional film – the basic 'story board' technique outlined in a later section will be useful. As experience in film making is gained, increasing attention can be paid to the use of techniques like repetition, symbolism and the juxtaposition of shots to create special effects.

6.   **Animated (Cartoon):** Some video cameras ofer a single frame facility (being able to film one frame at a time). This can be used to make cartoons. The technique, although tedious is very simple. Indeed we have found that two or three young people will often work together happily for a long time to produce their own cartoon. The production of animated films is a fascinating process which can easily tap young people's creative potential. See later section for further details.

7.   **Experimental:** Young people often like to try out unusual effects and techniques. Indeed this is how film makers are created. Shooting through filters; panning through 360 degrees; filming at extreme angles or even upside down; filming very short, almost subliminal shots can all be tried, along with any other ideas your youth group has.

Film Jargon

This section will clue you in to some of the jargon beloved of film makers, e.g. 'cue the shot,' 'give me a BCU,' 'roll em,' 'scene 37, take 1335,' 'give me a nice long shot,' etc.. Seriously, though, the language of film making is important – much of it is a sort of technical shorthand which speeds up and clarifies communication between, for example, the director of the film and the camera crew and actors. Young people are inveterate users of slang and easily pick up film jargon.

Frame: A single image on a length of film or video.

Shot: A number of consecutive frames which have been filmed in one continuous running of the camera. There is no standard length of shot, although a short one will usually last for just a few seconds while a long one will run for maybe 10-15 seconds.

Sequence: A number of shots which develop one particular idea. This is the key unit to use when working with young people. If you consider your film as being made up of a number of scenes, each containing several sequences, then preparation and filming should be relatively straight forward. The concept of sequences can be easily understood by referring to comic strips, as they are invariably structured in this way. They can also be used to illustrate other terms used below (LS, MS, BCU, etc.).

Long Shot (LS): A shot which is taken with the camera a long way away from the subject **or** a shot where the camera **appears** to have been a long way away (e.g. by using the zoom lens).

Medium Shot (MS): A shot which is taken close to the subject, but which includes some of the surrounding as well, e.g. a shot being taken from the waist up.

Medium Close Up (MCU): Usually of a person, showing the upper half of the torso.

Close Up (CU): Where the camera is, or seems to be, very close to the object being filmed, e.g. a shot where a person's face completely fills the frame.

Big Close Up (BCU or XCU): The camera is, or seems to be, extremely close to the subject, with one feature (e.g. a person's nose) completely filling the frame.

Pan: The camera follows a moving subject horizontally, or moves across a stationary subject.

Zip-Pan: A fast horizontal rotation of the camera across the subject which produces a blurred effect.

Track The camera actually moves towards or away from a stationary subject, or follows a moving one.

Zoom: The camera appears to be moving towards, away from, or following the subject, but the effect is produced by using the zoom facility on the stationary camera. Zooming in towards a subject is often referred to as 'tightening the shot.'

Camera Angles: Normal (where the camera is level with the subject), high or low. Referred to as NA, HA, LA.

Common Problems (and how to solve them)

Reversal: This arises when separate, consecutive shots are taken in front of and then behind the subject. In the second shot the subject will appear to have reversed position or direction. In essence, the camera cannot be moved through more than 180 degrees when filming a stationary subject without creating a reversal problem.

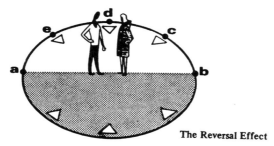

The Reversal Effect

Look at the diagram, if the camera starts off at point **a**, it can be moved as far as point **b** (or as near as dammit!) within the shaded section without reversal cropping up. If, however, the camera were to be moved as far as point **c, d** or **e**, the resulting film would show the subjects suddenly changing position. The only solution is to either avoid traversing more than 180 degrees or to show that you actually have gone behind the subject by keeping the camera running while you track around.

In some cases you may decide you actually do want a reversal effect.

The Jump cut: This is probably the most common difficulty you'll have to cope with. It arises mainly when two separate consecutive shots are taken of the same subject, and the subject (or the camera) has moved slightly between shots – the effect is that of a 'jump' or 'jerk' in the film. For all the technical prowess of our television companies, jump cuts can still be seen on the small screen now and again – watch out for them! If used sparingly, the jump can impart a shock effect to the audience if desired.

A 'Cutaway': This shot can be used to solve the jump cut problem. This involves taking a shot of the main subject, then a shot of another person or object before taking the second shot of the main subject. This is a useful technique to master as it is obvious that, say, in filming a long interview, you may want to take it in stages and therefore stop the camera several times. Cutaways can be inserted at the editing stage, in which case you need to make sure that you have a good selection of cutaway shots to use (e.g. interiors, clocks, passing traffic, etc.).

Another solution is to 'tighten the shot' (i.e. zoom in a bit) each time the camera is re-started. This will lessen the jump cut effect. Finally, you can if you wish change the camera angle or position by more than 45 degrees, as a **substantial** change will suggest to the audience that some time has elapsed, and this may solve the problem. (If changing the camera position, take care not to move it so much that you get a reversal effect).

Special Effects
Some, but by no means all video cameras offer the opportunity to experiment with special effects, such as:

Slow Motion: As normal operating speed is 18 frames per second, you will have to film at 32 f.p.s. or higher to get a good slow motion effect on playback.

Fast Motion: Film at 12 f.p.s. or slower.

Fade: Some video cameras have a special button for 'fade in' and 'fade out' effects. However, if you have a manual exposure control on the camera which can over-ride the automatic system, you will have no difficulty in achieving this effect. **To fade out:** set up your shot with the camera adjusted for manual exposure control. Use the exposure setting, if you have one, e.g. f8 which is indicated by the automatic system, and begin taking your shot. As you near the end of the shot, slowly move the exposure dial up the scale as far as it will go (i.e. towards f16 or f22). This will darken the picture. **To fade in:** set the camera to the highest exposure setting and begin shooting; gradually move the exposure control down the scale until you get to the correct setting (f8 in this case).

Appearance/Disappearance: The effect of a person or object appearing or disappearing 'on screen' is startling, but easy to arrange. The technique simply involves stopping the camera during a shot and making the appropriate change in the subject. It is crucial that the camera is firmly set on a tripod and a remote control cable should be used if possible – the camera and its settings must not be disturbed. If actors are involved in the scene, they must 'freeze' while the changes are made. Filming can now recommence, and the camera should be run for a minimum of 5 seconds after the changes have been made.

Diffusion/Distortion: These effects are obtained by filming through material which alters the image seen by the camera. Filming through a piece of glass lightly smeared with vaseline will give you a soft, diffuse effect, while fog or mist can by simulated by the use of a white or light coloured nylon stocking. Bottles, patterned glass or prisms will produce various distorted effects.

Editing the Film
Whichever way you choose to make your film, you will probably want to have a go at editing, as it greatly improves the quality of the final product. If you are using the 'film as you go' method, you may get away with using editing simply to cut out any 'duff' bits of the film. The professional method involves making up the film at the editing stage by piecing together the various scenes you have shot.

Editing can also be used to tidy up the film generally to achieve a really professional looking product. You can, for example, insert cutaway shots to get rid of jump cuts, or insert long shots to set the scene. The editing process itself can greatly affect the overall impact of the film – the use of brief shots will give it pace, emphasising any desired impression of excitement, violence, gaiety, speed, etc., lengthy shots may suggest sadness, relaxation or contentment.

Editing can therefore be a very powerful and creative part of the film making process and should never be undervalued.

Time spent at the editing stage will **always** pay dividends. Of course, persuading young people that this is the case is an altogether different story, but why not arrange a trip to your local film of television studio to watch the professionals at work? This is guaranteed to produce some budding Oliver Stone or Steven Spielberg!

Story boards and Scripting

The planning and filming process has several different stages, and there is therefore plenty of opportunity for a division of responsibility amongst those involved. Using the professional method, the stages are roughly as follows:

- pick your subject
- define the film's purpose and the audience
- write an outline of the action
- expand this to include instructions on visuals and sound (if any)
- plan out any dialogue
- write out detailed planning cards
- arrange cards in shooting order
- shoot the film
- view the film
- arrange it in scenes
- edit the scenes and put back into story order
- record and add any additional soundtracks required.

It is important to organise this material into a format that will enable you to go ahead and shoot the film easily, and story boards can help you to do this. They can be used at several stages of the planning process, and in their simplest form, aim to gather together ideas for different scenes on planning cards which are then arranged in chronological order. Index cards are suitable and can be easily pinned on to a story board, e.g.

SCENE 1	ACTION	SCENE 2	ACTION
Outside the youth club- a number of young people are gathering.	General messing about, some of it on roller-skates.	Inside the youth club two workers are talking.	Animated discussion about the kids out-side- wondering why they won't come in to play table-tennis and football.

When you begin to discuss the detailed planning cards you get involved in the nitty gritty aspects like the kind of shot required, camera angles, props, etc.. There are further possibilities here for division of responsibility as a full film crew can comprise scriptwriter, director, camera person, sound person (if needed), editor and actors, and they can begin to psyche themselves into the skills or roles they will be using.

Detailed planning cards should contain all the information you need to proceed to the filming stage, e.g.

SHOT	DESCRIPTION	CAMERA POSITION	CAMERA ANGLE	DIALOGUE
1	Outside the youth club- half a dozen young people messing about- 2 of them on roller skates.	L.S. (long shot)	N.A. (normal angle)	Yells, screams, grunts, etc.

SHOT	DESCRIPTION	CAMERA POSITION	CAMERA ANGLE	DIALOGUE
2	Jim and Alec on roller skates begin to harrass the others by running rings round them.	M.S. (medium shot)	H.A. (high angle)	Yells, screams

Once completed, detailed planning cards can be arranged on the board in either chronological or shooting order, depending on the method of filming being used.

If you wish to use a script, (i.e. if you have a keen typist!), the headings on the detailed planning cards can be used, with the scenes and shots arranged in shooting order.

Producer's check list
Denis Mooney of Scottish Television gave us some helpful hints to make sure any video project runs smoothly.

Cost: Make sure you know *exactly* how much you have to spend on your project, and produce a budget for it.

Context: Decide *before* you start what the film is going to be about.

Presentation: With most films of a news, documentary or instructional nature, you really need to spell out your intentions to the viewers. You can do this easily by structuring your films like this:

- tell them what you're going to tell them
- tell them
- tell them what you've just told them.

This may seem very crude, but it's how the TV professionals do it, and it's the best way of making sure that you really get your message across.

Closing: Always make sure you've got a strong closing quote to finish with.

Timetable: Draw up a timetable for shooting your material. If location filming or interviewing is involved, leave plenty of time for setting up and travelling between locations (it always takes longer than you think).

Locations: Make sure you have permission to film on locations – don't assume it. If people do give you access, drop them a note of thanks – it works wonders when you want to use the same location again.

Editing: Make sure to leave enough time for editing before you plan to show the film, as editing is always very time-consuming. You can use an ordinary tape recorder to help you edit. If you record your video sound track onto audio tape, you can then get it typed up. From this typescript you can then decide which piece of video goes where; this cuts out the time-consuming process of watching the whole video through several times. Using this method also helps cut down the amount of time you have to spend in an editing suite.

Voice-overs : Remember that you can use 'voice-overs' to add to a 'head shot' or landscape etc..

Interviewer's Check List

Bob Tomlinson of Scottish Television recommends a few simple techniques to make sure that interviews work well.

- Make sure that the interviewees know why they are involved in the film.
- Tell them what you expect so that they have time to prepare.
- Don't keep them hanging around, e.g. when the equipment is being set up.
- Remember that to do a five minute interview on location will probably take at least half an hour (allowing for adjusting equipment, several 'takes' etc.)
- Make a point of seeing the interviewees and talking to them (on the phone if need be) before you do the shot. This gives them a chance to get to know you and find out why you are making the film.
- Ask the interviewee what they want to say and try to incorporate their comments.
- Always use strong eye contact when interviewing to stop folk gazing into the camera lens.
- Never switch the camera off at the end of the interview. Keep it running and ask if there's anything else they'd like to be asked, any comment they want to make, or anything they think has been missed. Check this out with the camera crew as well.You'll usually find that some of the best material is recorded at this point, after the 'official' interview has finished.

Filming

It's important that at least one person in the crew is completely conversant with all the equipment that is to be used and knows how to set it up. While this is likely to be an adult to begin with, every opportunity should be taken to enable the young people themselves to gain competence in using the various bits of hardware. This applies, also, to the planning process where their involvement is crucial in making sure that both adults and young people are committed to a particular project. Although workers do have a responsibility for creative input (especially with under-stimulated children whose ideas may be few and far between) most young people can come up with good ideas given encouragement.

Although in danger of stating the obvious, here are a few simple hints to help you on you way.

- Unless using a digital camera, always have plenty of spare videotape (and batteries) to hand.
- Always use a tripod when filming.
- Use titles and credits liberally as they make for polished production. Young people love to see their names in lights anyway!
- Experiment with different ways of making captions – e.g. by using film animation techniques you can make words appear one letter at a time.
- Simple computer graphics can be used to produce interesting titles and captions. More sophisticated effects, including digital still/video images, can be fully incorporated in the film using current technology.
- Never shoot into the light – always have the light source behind the camera, or to the side.
- Always set the scene by using a long shot of the place where the action happens, e.g. the outside of a building, the seaside, etc..

Film Animation (Cartoons)

Cartoon making, or film animation as it is more correctly called, is a fascinating aspect of the film medium. The authors have seen some really stroppy young people working in close harmony to produce their version of 'Popeye'! Although essentially a repetitive activity, the creative aspect of being able to make your own cartoon seems to exert a considerable fascination on young people. So much so that they are often prepared to spend quite long periods of time concentrating on the single frame filming that is necessary to produce good results. You'll probably find film animation best suited to work with small groups of two or three young people – one to work the camera and one or two to manipulate the objects being filmed.

In most cases, film animation requires that the camera is pointing down at the floor – the 'rostrum camera' position. It is relatively easy to build a wooden frame to support the camera in this position, and photoflood bulbs for illumination can be fixed to this as well. Underneath this, within the limits of the camera's viewfinder, you need to place a 'register board'. This can simply be a wooden batten fixed to the floor with a sheet of glass placed hard against it. Each time a change is made to the cartoon background or to the cut outs (e.g. of cartoon characters) which are placed on top of it, the sheet of glass is used to hold it flat and secure. A simple way to prepare a background for a story is to draw or paint it on a long roll of cartridge paper – and when a change of scene is needed the paper is simply moved along a bit.

Having said all this, workers in Dundee use an even simpler method which has been well tested with groups of young people.

For this you will need a:

- Camera capable of making single frame exposures.
- Cable release (remote control device for single frame exposure).
- Tripod.
- Simple floodlight (e.g. ES socket and lamp mounted on a pole or tripod).

Set the camera on the tripod and aim it down at the floor as near to vertical as the tripod will allow. Fix a piece of poster paper to the floor with drawing pins to create your picture area. Illuminate this with your photoflood lamp making certain that it is firmly fixed – any movement will create annoying changes in light intensity visible in the finished cartoon. Using the cable release take two or three frames for each segment of the animation.

This kind of set up can be used for animations like:
- A white sheet of paper upon which a picture gradually draws itself.
- A collage background to which cut-out figures with speech bubbles are added.
- Toys, dolls, tools, etc. in motion (e.g. scissors having a conversation).
- Patterns drawn in spilt salt.
- Card figures with jointed limbs moving around.
- Plasticine figures and objects.
- Liquorice Allsorts vs Smarties war.

It is also possible to film '3-D' animations from the side by setting them up on a table top. The same set-up should be used with tripod, cable release and photoflood. You may also want to hang up a large cloth or blanket as a background. With this arrangement you could have Lego structures building themselves, Bendy toys in action, a pool game playing away by itself or toy cars zooming around. The key to effective animation work is to let your imagination run riot.

SUPPLIERS' GUIDE

In compiling the *New Youth Arts and Crafts* book we have contacted over fifty suppliers across the UK. We have mostly met with courtesy and assistance and in a number of cases, literally hours of advice. Because we are keen that youth organisations should support local arts and crafts suppliers as well as national specialists, we would recommend that you try to visit your local shops and see what is available. Having said that, firms like Specialist Crafts can supply the materials and equipment for the majority of the activities listed in this book. A number of the national firms offer discounts for educational and youth groups, and may have special 'sampler' packs for the various crafts available.

General suppliers

Specialist Crafts Ltd (Dryad), PO Box 247, Leicester LE1 9QS. Tel. 0116 251 0405. *Arguably the biggest range of arts and crafts supplies in the UK. Happy to offer advice and assistance as well as selling their products.*

NES Arnold Ltd, Ludlow Hill Road, West Bridgford, Nottingham NG2 6HD. Tel. 0115 945 2200. *A specialist educational supplier whose catalogue range includes arts and crafts supplies for the whole school age range.*

Galt, Culvert Street, Oldham, Lancs. OL4 2ST. Tel. 0161 627 5086. *An educational supplier, with an educational games specialism. Their catalogue includes an art section.*

Fred Aldous, PO Box 135, 35 Lever Street, Manchester 1 M60 1UX. Tel. 0161 236 2477. *A craft supplier who covers many of the crafts in this book, plus traditional crafts such as embroidery, basket making and marquetry.*

Specialist suppliers

Badge making
London Emblem PLC, Emblem House, Blenheim Road, Longmead Industrial Estate, Epsom, Surrey KT19 9AP. Tel. 01372 745433. *We use their machines for metal button badge making and can vouchsafe their reliability.*

Enterprise Products, 36 Ridgeway Road, Redhill, Surrey EH1 6PH. Tel. 01737 772185. *A similar type of range to London Emblem.*

Circus and juggling skills
Jugglemania, 119 Chiltern Drive, Surbiton, Surrey KT5 8LS. Tel. 0181 390 6855. *An interesting array of circus, juggling and magic products, including books.*

The Big Top, 45-49 King Street, Glasgow G1 5RA. Tel. 0141 552 7763. *Special friends to youth and playworkers. They stock a good range of circus, juggling and playwork equipment including face paints from Grimas.*

The Boggle Brothers, 3 Jubilee Cottages, Herrington, Bath. *Circus and juggling skill tutors and performers.*

Design and Technology supplies
Trylon Ltd, Wollaston, Northants NN29 7QJ. Tel. 01933 664275. *Suppliers of candle making materials and many other CDT materials. A co-operative who want to help!*

Dyes
Dylon International, Worsley Bridge Road, Lower Sydenham, London SE26 5HD. Tel. 0181 663 4801. *The UK's main supplier of dyes for use on all sorts materials.*

Fabric and glass paints
Marabu, through Edding Ltd, Edding House, Merlin Centre, Acrewood Way, St Albans, Herts AL4 0JY. Tel. 01727 846688. *Includes Marabu silk, decorglass and textile ranges of paints and dyes, plus the Edding pen selection.*

Jewellery suppliers
Manchester Minerals, Rooth Street, Heaton Norris, Stockport, Cheshire SK4 1DJ. Tel. 0161 477 0435. *One of the best ranges of supplies for jewellery making.*

H.S. Walsh, 243 Beckenham Road, Beckenham, Kent BR3 4TS. Tel. 0181 778 7061. *Highly specialist suppliers of clock making, silversmithing and casting.*

Fimo, through Inscribe Ltd, Woolmer Industrial Estate, Bordon, Hants GU35 9QE. Tel. 01420 475747. *Suppliers of the Fimo range of modelling and jewellery making materials.*

Modelling, carving and sculpting
Alec Tiranti Ltd, 70 High Street, Theale, Reading, Berks RG7 5AR. Tel. 01734 302775. *A substantial catalogue of specialist resources, including how-to-do-it books on various aspects of carving and moulding.*

Leatherwork
Le Prevo Leathers, Blackfriars, Stowell Street, Newcastle upon Tyne NE1 4XN. Tel. 0191 232 4179. *Extremely helpful specialist leather suppliers.*

S. Glassner, 476 Kingston Road, Raynes Park, London SW20 8DX. Tel. 0181 543 1666. *A good range of special leather working supplies.*

Pyrography
Janik Enterprises Ltd, Brickfield Lane, Ruthin, Clwyd LL15 2TN. Tel. 01824 702096.*Specialist suppliers of pyrography materials and equipment plus wooden and leather products*

BIBLIOGRAPHY

This bibliography is a fair indication of some of the books and resources which we have used to inform and improve our own arts and crafts work. The age of some of the books (and their likely availability) are indicative of the number of years we have been working with young people! We do not know the date of publication of a few of the books – sorry! In addition to the books listed in this section, we would strongly recommend readers to get hold of current catalogues and resource books produced by suppliers such as Specialist Crafts, Galt, NES Arnold, Le Prevo Leathers, London Emblem and others listed in the Suppliers' section.

GENERAL GUIDES
Anderson, Enid, 'Crafts and the Disabled', Batsford, 1982
Caket, Colin, 'Infant Crafts', Blandford Press, 1983
Harlow Eve, 'The Book of Handicrafts', Sundial Books, 1975
Hawes, Sonia, 'Simply Art', NAYC Publications, 1981
Jenkins and Morris, 'Crafts from your microwave', Quintet Publishing, 1994
Make It Easy Cards, Hamlyn Publishing Group, 1978
NES Arnold, 'Introducing Art' series (includes drawing, painting, printing, clay and 3-D construction) NES Arnold, 1996
NFPA/Play Train, 'Play Ideas Bank', Play-Train, Birmingham, undated
Paget, Dawn, 'The Art of Craft', Cassell, 1990
Park, Louise, 'Art Attack', Ashton Scholastic
Readers Digest Manual of Handicrafts, Readers Digest, 1980
Simmons, Rosemary, 'Printmaking in Easy Steps', Cassell and Collier Macmillan, 1977
Specialist Crafts, '500 series' Arts booklets (16 page booklets – a variety of titles on enamelling through to braid weaving)

AIRBRUSHING
Breckon, Brett, 'Airbrushing and photo-retouching', Apple Press, 1987
Leek, Michael, 'Encyclopedia of Airbrush techniques', Headline, 1995
Tombs Curtis and Hunt, 'The Airbrush Book', Orbis, 1980

CALLIGRAPHY
Goffe and Ravenscroft, ' Calligraphy step-by-step', Harper Collins, 1994
Martin, Judy, 'The Complete Guide to Calligraphy', Phaidon, 1984
Pearce, Charles, 'Little Manual of Calligraphy', Harper Collins, 1982
Thomson, George, 'The Art of Calligraphy', Treasure Press, 1985

CANDLE MAKING
Carey, Mary,'Candle Making', Evans Brothers Ltd, 1974
Millington, Deborah, 'Traditional Candlemaking: simple methods of manufacture', Intermediate Technology Publications, 1992
Strose, Susanne, 'Candle Making', Sterling Publishing Co Inc, 1968

COLLAGE
Beaney, Jan, 'Fun with Collage', Kaye and Ward, 1979
Cooper, Graham & Sargent, Douglas, 'Painting the Town', Phaidon, 1979
Korstad, Mueller Mar, 'Murals: Creating an Environment', Davis Publications Inc, 1979
Nuttall, Prudence, 'Make a Collage', Evans, 1974
Pluckrose, Henry, 'Collage Ideas', Evans, 1979
Steele, Philip 'Collage', Kingfisher Books, 1993

COOKING AND BAKING

Coles, Angela, 'The Reluctant Cook', Whittet Books Ltd, 1980

Holloway, Malcolm ,'The "How to" Book of Bread and Bread making', Blandford Press, 1981

McCallum, Cass, 'The Real Food Guide: Pulses, Seeds and Grains', Richard Drew Publishing, 1981

NPFA, in 'Towards a Safer Adventure Playground', NPFA, 1985

Pay, Joanna, 'Cooking for kids the healthy way', Dunitz, 1986

Queen's College Glasgow, 'The Glasgow Cookery Book', John Smith & Son, 1975

Richardson, Rosamund, 'Vegetarian cooking for children', Piatkus, 1986

COSTUMES AND DRESSING UP

Asher, Jane, 'Jane Asher's Fancy Dress', Pelham, 1983

Beaton, Claire et al, 'Let's Dress Up', Merehurst, 1995

Caudron, C, 'Usborne Book of Dressing-up' Usborne, 1993

CYCLING

Ballantine, Richard, 'Richard's New Bicycle Book', Pan, 1989

Plas, Rob vander, 'The Mountain Bike Book', San Francisco Bicycle Books, 1993

DÉCOUPAGE

Anaya Publishers, 'Creative Papercrafts', Anaya, 1994

Moxley, Juliet, 'Découpage', Letts

Thomas and Fox, 'Practical Découpage', Anaya, 1993

ENAMELLING

McGrath, Jinks, 'First Steps in Enamelling', Apple Publishing, 1994

Untracht, Oppi, 'Enamelling on Metal', Pitman, 1977

FACE PAINTING AND MAKE-UP

Alkema, Chester J, 'Mask-Making', Oak Tree Press, 1976

Beaton, Clare, 'Face painting', Kingfisher, 1990

Grimas, Face Painting for professional and hobby', Grimas, 1992

Quant, Mary, 'Mary Quant on Make-Up', Century Hutchins, 1986

Snazaroo, 'Fantastic Faces', 'First Faces' and 'Five minute faces'. Snazaroo, various dates

FLOWERCRAFT

Berry et al, 'Flowercraft', Collins and Brown, 1995

Westland, Pamela, 'Glorious Flowercraft', Apple Press

JEWELLERY MAKING

Bagley, Peter, 'The Encyclopedia of Jewellery Techniques', B.T. Batsford, 1986

Bagley, Peter, 'Making Silver Jewellery', B.T. Batsford, 1982

Budwig and Coles, 'Book of Beads'

Case, Barbara, 'World of Beads', David and Charles, 1995

Hutton, Helen, 'Practical Gemstone Craft', Studio Vista, 1972

Wicks, Sally, 'Jewellery Making Manual'

KITES

Denyer, Miles, 'Making Kites', Apple Publishing, 1993

Gallot, Phillipe, 'Making and Flying Fighting Kites', Batsford, 1990

Pelham, David, 'The Penguin Book of Kites', Penguin, 1976

Lloyd, Ambrose et al, 'Making and Flying Kites', Hamlyn, 1977

LEATHERWORK
Cope, A and J, 'Leatherwork', Pan
Grainger, Sylvia, 'Leatherwork', Kestrel Books, 1978
Hayes and Vincent, 'Making it in Leather', David and Charles, 1973
Michael, Valerie, 'Leatherworking Handbook', Cassell, 1994

LINO PRINTING
Palmer, Frederick, 'Monoprint Techniques', Batsford, 1975
Simmons, Rosemary, 'Printmaking in Easy Steps', Cassell and Collier, Macmillan, 1977

MAGAZINES AND NEWSPAPERS
Bjelland, Harley, 'Create your own Desktop Publishing System', Windcrest, 1994
InterAction, 'Make-it-Yourself Handbook', InterAction, 1982
Parker, Roger C, 'Desktop Publishing and Design for Dummies', IDG Books, 1995
Zeitlyn, Jonathan, 'Print: how you can do it yourself', InterAction, 1980

MASKS
Baranski, Matthew, 'Mask Making', Worcester, 1972
Peters, J, 'Make a Mask', Batsford
Wright, Lyndie, 'Masks', Franklin Watts, 1991

MOBILES
Mytton-Davis, Peter, 'Mobiles', Ward Lock, 1971
Pointney, Kate, 'Make a Mobile', Faber and Faber, 1974

MURALS
Bamett, Alan W, 'Community Murals', Cornwall Books, 1984
Directory of Social Change, 'The Mural Kit', undated
Mueller, Mary Korstad, 'Murals', Davis Publications, 1979
Pavey, Don, 'Art-based Games', Methuen, 1979

PAINTING, DRAWING AND VARIATIONS
Edwards, Betty, 'Drawing on the Right Side of the Brain', Souvenir Press, 1979
Miura, Einen, 'The art of marbled paper', Zaehnsdorf, 1990

PAPIER MÂCHÉ
Anaya Publishers, 'Creative Papercrafts', Anaya, 1994
Elliot, Marion, 'Papier Mâché Project Book
Robins, Deri, 'Papier Mâché', Kingfisher Books, 1993
Usborne How to make series, 'Papier Mâché', Usborne, 1993

PEBBLE POLISHING
'How to Polish Gemstones', available through Manchester Minerals
Fletcher, Edward, 'Pebble Polishing', Blandford Press, 1972
Jarrard, Reginald Arthur, 'The Amateur Lapidary', Barton, 1969

PERFORMANCE ARTS
Bolton, Reg, 'Circus in a Suitcase', New Plays Incorporated, 1982
Finnegan, Dave, 'The Complete Juggler', Butterfingers, 1982

Kostelanetz, Richard, 'The Theatre of Mixed Means', Pitman, 1970

PHOTOGRAPHY
Ilford Book of Classroom Photography, Ilford
Davenport, David, 'A Practical Guide to prize winning photography', Oxford Illustrated Press, 1987
Peach and Butterfield, 'Photography', Usborne Guide, 1987
Pickering, John, 'Photography for Children', Batsford, 1976

PUPPETS
Currell, David, 'Puppet Making'
Fraser, Peter, 'Puppets and Puppetry', Batsford, 1980

PYROGRAPHY
Grainger, Stuart, 'An Introduction to Pyrography'
Havez, Bernard, 'Pyrography', Evans Brothers, 1978

RUBBINGS
Busby, Richard J, 'Beginners Guide to Brass Rubbing', Pelman Books, 1969
Bodor, John J, 'Rubbings and Textures: A Graphic Technique', Chapman Reinhold, 1968

SCREEN PRINTING
Bristow, Nicholas, 'Screenprinting', Batsford, 1990
Hollebone, Sarah, 'Screen Printing: The Beginners Guide', A & C Black Ltd, 1980
Kinsey, Anthony, 'The Art of Screen Printing', Batsford, 1979
Stellabrass, Anne, 'Fabric Screeprinting'
Treweek and Zeitlyn, 'Alternative Printing Book', Penguin 1983

SPRAY CAN ART
Chalfont and Prigoff, 'Spraycan Art', Thames and Hudson, 1987

STAINED GLASS
Bier, Barry, 'The Art of Stained Glass',
Metcalf, Robert, 'Making Stained Glass', David and Charles, 1972
Shedenhelm, W, 'Stained Glass', Tab Books, 1987

TIE DYE AND FABRIC PRINTING
Ball, Kazz, 'Learn Fabric Painting', Harper Collins, 1989
Buckanan, Celia, 'Tie-Dyeing'
Campbell, Joy, 'Batik', Apple Publishing, 1994
Meilach, Dona, 'Contemporary Batik and Tie-dye', Allen and Unwin, 1973
Williams, Melanie, 'Fabric Painting

VIDEO FILM MAKING
Dowmunt, Terry, 'Video with Young People', InterAction, 1980
Hannen, Foss, 'How to Make your own Video Programmes', Elm Tree Books, 1982
Hedgecoe, John, 'Complete Guide to Video', Collins and Brown, 1992
Lewis, Roland, 'Video Maker's Handbook', Macmillan, new edition, 1995

A classic for all ages: over 37,000 copies sold!

"...quite irresistible" was heard from the Groupvine.
"Excellent. There is only one other book to compare with it," is the word from Scripture Union.
'A compendium resource of the first order,' say Young People Now.

THE NEW YOUTH GAMES BOOK

By Alan Dearling and Howie Armstrong
Humorous illustrations and cartoons by Jerry Neville

Bright and breezy, this is the **biggest collection of practical games and activities for working with young people ever compiled**. It includes: Relationship games; Puzzles and 2-player games; Icebreakers; Games using darts, pool, cards, coins, marbles and dominoes; Mini-bus games; New games; Activity group games; Games for younger groups; Commercial games; and simulations.

There is something for all ages! It encourages interaction between adults and young people to: have fun; develop positive relationships with peers and adults; learn literacy and numeracy skills; increase creativity and imagination; improve communication skills; cope with tension and stressful situations; break down barriers and ease the getting-to-know new people process; identify problems and help find solutions; build trust, sensitivity and understanding; develop self-awareness; improve social skills; and build confidence.

For everyone who works with young people, this book is bursting with games and sequences for use in a range of informal and social education settings. How long games last and what sort of situations they might be used in....How to give the dartboard and pool table a new lease of life....Additional ways to utilise the badminton or recreation hall.....Simulations for senior member or staff training.....Relationship games and icebreakers for in more structured group situations...for all ages and every situation, you will find ideas and solutions based on the authors combined 50 years' experience working in youth and community centres, youth social work, I.T. and schools. Make your life and the lives the young people you are working with just a little bit richer and more fulfilling. Order a copy today!

Over 200 games   124 drawings   232 pages   Paperback   1-898924-00-7   Available now   £9.95

CREATIVE OUTDOOR WORK WITH YOUNG PEOPLE

Written and illustrated by Alan Smith

"...wonderfully imaginative, inspiring, and practical..." Scottish Child. *"...page after page of games, activities and words of wisdom, all designed with safety codes of practice in mind."* Right Angle. *"...full of excellent ideas..."* Youthwork. *"...light-hearted but immensely practical...(these activities) promote independence, challenge and imagination as well as teamwork and co-operation."* Times Educational Supplement

Everyone working, or wanting to work out of doors with young people – especially youth leaders, teachers and instructors – can use this book for residential work, a training course lasting several weeks, or a 'one-off' day trip...whether to Scotland or following an urban trail. Here are **95 activities and games**, covering: finding the way, orienteering, camp activities, problem solving, studying the environment, canoe games and 'other outdoor activities' (everything from off-road motor-cycling to fishing). Plus sections on: Planning and safety; Choosing and using accommodation; the National Curriculum. The activities have been successfully used with a broad range of young people between the ages of 8 and 18, as well as in a variety of training courses, such as 'Training the Trainer'. **You can easily adapt or modify the ideas and material** to suit the experience of the young people involved, the resources available, and the outdoor conditions.

Alan Smith teaches Geography and Outdoor Education in a Nottingham comprehensive school and has wide experience of teaching out of doors. His **lively drawings and engaging sense of humour** help to make outdoor activities more accessible and appealing to the young people involved.

Large format paperback   Illustrated   176 pages   1-898924-25-2   Available now   £10.95